TEACHER'S PLANNING GUIDE

Project-Based Inquiry Science

EVER-CHANGING EARTH

NSF

IT's ABOUT TIME ®
HERFF JONES EDUCATION DIVISION

IT's ABOUT TIME®

HERFF JONES EDUCATION DIVISION

84 Business Park Drive, Armonk, NY 10504
Phone (914) 273-2233 Fax (914) 273-2227
www.its-about-time.com

Program Components

Student Edition	**Durable Equipment Kit**
Teacher's Planning Guide	**Consumable Equipment Kit**
Teacher's Resources Guide	**Multimedia**
	— *My World* Software
	— *Earth Science Content DVD*

ISBN 978-1-58591-629-0
1 2 3 4 5 CRS 12 11 10 09

This project was supported, in part, by the **National Science Foundation**
under grant nos. 0137807, 0527341, and 0639978.
Opinions expressed are those of the authors and not necessarily
those of the National Science Foundation.

Principal Investigators

Janet L. Kolodner is a Regents' Professor in the School of Interactive Computing in the Georgia Institute of Technology's College of Computing. Since 1978, her research has focused on learning from experience, both in computers and in people. She pioneered the Artificial Intelligence method called *case-based reasoning*, providing a way for computers to solve new problems based on their past experiences. Her book, *Case-Based Reasoning*, synthesizes work across the case-based reasoning research community from its inception to 1993.

Since 1994, Dr. Kolodner has focused on the applications and implications of case-based reasoning for education. In her approach to science education, called Learning by Design™ (LBD), students learn science while pursuing design challenges. Dr. Kolodner has investigated how to create a culture of collaboration and rigorous science talk in classrooms, how to use a project challenge to promote focus on science content, and how students learn and develop when classrooms function as learning communities. Currently, Dr. Kolodner is investigating how to help young people come to think of themselves as scientific reasoners. Dr. Kolodner's research results have been widely published, including in *Cognitive Science, Design Studies,* and the *Journal of the Learning Sciences.*

Dr. Kolodner was founding Director of Georgia Tech's EduTech Institute, served as coordinator of Georgia Tech's Cognitive Science program for many years, and is founding Editor in Chief of the *Journal of the Learning Sciences*. She is a founder of the International Society for the Learning Sciences, and she served as its first Executive Officer. She is a fellow of the American Association of Artificial Intelligence.

Joseph S. Krajcik is a Professor of Science Education and Associate Dean for Research in the School of Education at the University of Michigan. He works with teachers in science classrooms to bring about sustained change by creating classroom environments in which students find solutions to important intellectual questions that subsume essential curriculum standards and use learning technologies as productivity tools. He seeks to discover what students learn in such environments, as well as to explore and find solutions to challenges that teachers face in enacting such complex instruction.

Dr. Krajcik has authored and co-authored over 100 manuscripts and makes frequent presentations at international, national, and regional conferences that focus on his research, as well as presentations that translate research findings into classroom practice. He is a fellow of the American Association for the Advancement of Science and served as president of the National Association for Research in Science Teaching. Dr. Krajcik co-directs the Center for Highly Interactive Classrooms, Curriculum and Computing in Education at the University of Michigan and is a co-principal investigator in the Center for Curriculum Materials in Science and The National Center for Learning and Teaching Nanoscale Science and Engineering. In 2002, Dr. Krajcik was honored to receive a Guest Professorship from Beijing Normal University in Beijing, China. In winter 2005, he was the Weston Visiting Professor of Science Education at the Weizmann Institute of Science in Rehovot, Israel.

Daniel C. Edelson is Vice President for Education and Children's Programs at the National Geographic Society. Previously, he was the director of the Geographic Data in Education (GEODE) Initiative at Northwestern University, where he led the development of Planetary Forecaster and Earth Systems and Processes. Since 1992, Dr. Edelson has directed a series of projects exploring the use of technology as a catalyst for reform in science education and has led the development of a number of software environments for education. These include My World GIS, a geographic information system for inquiry-based learning, and WorldWatcher, a data visualization and analysis system for gridded geographic data. Dr. Edelson is the author of the high school environmental science text, *Investigations in Environmental Science: A Case-Based Approach to the Study of Environmental Systems.* His research has been widely published, including in the *Journal of the Learning Sciences,* the *Journal of Research on Science Teaching, Science Educator*, and *Science Teacher*.

Brian J. Reiser is a Professor of Learning Sciences in the School of Education and Social Policy at Northwestern University. Professor Reiser served as chair of Northwestern's Learning Sciences Ph.D. program from 1993, shortly after its inception, until 2001. His research focuses on the design and enactment of learning environments that support students' inquiry in science, including both science curriculum materials and scaffolded software tools. His research investigates the design of learning environments that scaffold scientific practices, including investigation, argumentation, and explanation; design principles for technology-infused curricula that engage students in inquiry projects; and the teaching practices that support student inquiry. Professor Reiser also directed BGuILE (Biology Guided Inquiry Learning Environments) to develop software tools for supporting middle school and high school students in analyzing data and constructing explanations with biological data. Reiser is a co-principal investigator in the NSF Center for Curriculum Materials in Science. He served as a member of the NRC panel authoring the report Taking Science to School.

Mary L. Starr is a Research Specialist in Science Education in the School of Education at the University of Michigan. She collaborates with teachers and students in elementary and middle school science classrooms around the United States who are implementing *Project-Based Inquiry Science*. Before joining the PBIS team, Dr. Starr created professional learning experiences in science, math, and technology, designed to assist teachers in successfully changing their classroom practices to promote student learning from coherent inquiry experiences. She has developed instructional materials in several STEM areas, including nanoscale science education, has presented at national and regional teacher education and educational research meetings, and has served in a leadership role in the Michigan Science Education Leadership Association. Dr. Starr has authored articles and book chapters, and has worked to improve elementary science teacher preparation through teaching science courses for pre-service teachers and acting as a consultant in elementary science teacher preparation. As part of the PBIS team, Dr. Starr has played a lead role in making units cohere as a curriculum, in developing the framework for PBIS Teacher's Planning Guides, and in developing teacher professional development experiences and materials.

Acknowledgements

Three research teams contributed to the development of *Project-Based Inquiry Science* (PBIS): a team at the Georgia Institute of Technology headed by Janet L. Kolodner, a team at Northwestern University headed by Daniel Edelson and Brian Reiser, and a team at the University of Michigan headed by Joseph Krajcik and Ron Marx. Each of the PBIS units was originally developed by one of these teams and then later revised and edited to be a part of the full three-year middle-school curriculum that became PBIS.

PBIS has its roots in two educational approaches, Project-Based Science and Learning by Design™. Project-Based Science suggests that students should learn science through engaging in the same kinds of inquiry practices scientists use, in the context of scientific problems relevant to their lives and using tools authentic to science. Project-Based Science was originally conceived in the hi-ce Center at the University of Michigan, with funding from the National Science Foundation. Learning by Design™ derives from Problem-Based Learning and suggests sequencing, social practices, and reflective activities for promoting learning. It engages students in design practices, including the use of iteration and deliberate reflection. LBD was conceived at the Georgia Institute of Technology, with funding from the National Science Foundation, DARPA, and the McDonnell Foundation.

The development of the integrated PBIS curriculum was supported by the National Science Foundation under grants no. 0137807, 0527341, and 0639978. Any opinions, findings and conclusions, or recommendations expressed in this material are those of the authors and do not necessarily reflect the views of the National Science Foundation.

PBIS Team

Principal Investigator
Janet L. Kolodner

Co-Principal Investigators
Daniel C. Edelson
Joseph S. Krajcik
Brian J. Reiser

NSF Program Officer
Gerhard Salinger

Curriculum Developers
Michael T. Ryan
Mary L. Starr

Teacher's Planning Guide Developers
Rebecca M. Schneider
Mary L. Starr

Literacy Specialist
LeeAnn M. Sutherland

NSF Program Reviewer
Arthur Eisenkraft

Project Coordinator
Juliana Lancaster

External Evaluators
The Learning Partnership
Steven M. McGee
Jennifer Witers

The Georgia Institute of Technology Team

Project Director:
Janet L. Kolodner

Development of PBIS units at the Georgia Institute of Technology was conducted in conjunction with the Learning by Design™ Research group (LBD), Janet L. Kolodner, PI.

Lead Developers, Physical Science:
David Crismond
Michael T. Ryan

Lead Developer, Earth Science:
Paul J. Camp

Assessment and Evaluation:
Barbara Fasse
Daniel Hickey
Jackie Gray
Laura Vandewiele
Jennifer Holbrook

Project Pioneers:
JoAnne Collins
David Crismond
Joanna Fox
Alice Gertzman
Mark Guzdial
Cindy Hmelo-Silver
Douglas Holton
Roland Hubscher
N. Hari Narayanan
Wendy Newstetter
Valery Petrushin
Kathy Politis
Sadhana Puntambekar
David Rector
Janice Young

The Northwestern University Team

Project Directors:
Daniel Edelson
Brian Reiser

Lead Developer, Biology:
David Kanter

Lead Developers, Earth Science:
Jennifer Mundt Leimberer
Darlene Slusher

Development of PBIS units at Northwestern was conducted in conjunction with:

The Center for Learning Technologies in Urban Schools (LeTUS) at Northwestern, and the Chicago Public Schools
Louis Gomez, PI;
Clifton Burgess, PI
for Chicago Public Schools.

The BioQ Collaborative
David Kanter, PI.

The Biology Guided Inquiry Learning Environments (BGuILE) Project
Brian Reiser, PI.

The Geographic Data in Education (GEODE) Initiative
Daniel Edelson, Director

The Center for Curriculum Materials in Science at Northwestern
Brian Reiser,
Daniel Edelson,
Bruce Sherin, PIs.

The University of Michigan Team

Project Directors:
Joseph Krajcik
Ron Marx

Literacy Specialist:
LeeAnn M. Sutherland

Project Coordinator:
Mary L. Starr

Development of PBIS units at the University of Michigan was conducted in conjunction with:

The Center for Learning Technologies in Urban Schools (LeTUS)
Ron Marx, Phyllis Blumenfeld,
Barry Fishman,
Joseph Krajcik,
Elliot Soloway, PIs.

The Detroit Public Schools
Juanita Clay-Chambers
Deborah Peek-Brown

The Center for Highly Interactive Computing in Education (hi-ce)
Ron Marx,
Phyllis Blumenfeld,
Barry Fishman,
Joseph Krajcik,
Elliot Soloway,
Elizabeth Moje,
LeeAnn Sutherland, PIs.

Project-Based Inquiry Science

Field-Test Teachers

National Field Test

Tamica Andrew
Leslie Baker
Jeanne Bayer
Gretchen Bryant
Boris Consuegra
Daun D'Aversa
Candi DiMauro
Kristie L. Divinski
Donna M. Dowd
Jason Fiorito
Lara Fish
Christine Gleason
Christine Hallerman
Terri L. Hart-Parker
Jennifer Hunn
Rhonda K. Hunter
Jessica Jones
Dawn Kuppersmith
Anthony F. Lawrence
Ann Novak
Rise Orsini
Tracy E. Parham
Cheryl Sgro-Ellis
Debra Tenenbaum
Sarah B. Topper
Becky Watts
Debra A. Williams
Ingrid M. Woolfolk
Ping-Jade Yang

New York City Field Test

*Several sequences of PBIS
units have been field- tested
in New York City under the
leadership of Whitney Lukens,
Staff Developer for Region 9,
and Greg Borman, Science
Instructional Specialist,
New York City Department of
Education*

6th Grade

Norman Agard
Tazinmudin Ali
Heather Guthartz Aniba
Asher Arzonane
Asli Aydin
Shareese Blakely
John J. Blaylock
Joshua Blum
Tsedey Bogale
Filomena Borrero

Zachary Brachio
Thelma Brown
Alicia Browne-Jones
Scott Bullis
Maximo Cabral
Lionel Callender
Matthew Carpenter
Ana Maria Castro
Diane Castro
Anne Chan
Ligia Chiorean
Boris Consuegra
Careen Halton Cooper
Cinnamon Czarnecki
Kristin Decker
Nancy Dejean
Gina DiCicco
Donna Dowd
Lizanne Espina
Joan Ferrato
Matt Finnerty
Jacqueline Flicker
Helen Fludd
Leigh Summers Frey
Helene Friedman-Hager
Diana Gering
Matthew Giles
Lucy Gill
Steven Gladden
Greg Grambo
Carrie Grodin-Vehling
Stephan Joanides
Kathryn Kadei
Paraskevi Karangunis
Cynthia Kerns
Martine Lalanne
Erin Lalor
Jennifer Lerman
Sara Lugert
Whitney Lukens
Dana Martorella
Christine Mazurek
Janine McGeown
Chevelle McKeever
Kevin Meyer
Jennifer Miller
Nicholas Miller
Diana Neligan
Caitlin Van Ness
Marlyn Orque
Eloisa Gelo Ortiz
Gina Papadopoulos
Tim Perez
Albertha Petrochilos
Christopher Poli
Kristina Rodriguez

Nadiesta Sanchez
Annette Schavez
Hilary Sedgwitch
Elissa Seto
Laura Shectman
Audrey Shmuel
Katherine Silva
Ragini Singhal
C. Nicole Smith
Gitangali Sohit
Justin Stein
Thomas Tapia
Eilish Walsh-Lennon
Lisa Wong
Brian Yanek
Cesar Yarleque
David Zaretsky
Colleen Zarinsky

7th Grade

Mayra Amaro
Emmanuel Anastasiou
Cheryl Barnhill
Bryce Cahn
Ligia Chiorean
Ben Colella
Boris Consuegra
Careen Halton Cooper
Elizabeth Derse
Urmilla Dhanraj
Gina DiCicco
Lydia Doubleday
Lizanne Espina
Matt Finnerty
Steven Gladden
Stephanie Goldberg
Nicholas Graham
Robert Hunter
Charlene Joseph
Ketlynne Joseph
Kimberly Kavazanjian
Christine Kennedy
Bakwah Kotung
Lisa Kraker
Anthony Lett
Herb Lippe
Jennifer Lopez
Jill Mastromarino
Kerry McKie
Christie Morgado
Patrick O'Connor
Agnes Ochiagha
Tim Perez
Nadia Piltser
Chris Poli

Carmelo Ruiz
Kim Sanders
Leslie Schiavone
Ileana Solla
Jacqueline Taylor
Purvi Vora
Ester Wiltz
Carla Yuille
Marcy Sexauer Zacchea
Lidan Zhou

8th Grade

Emmanuel Anastasio
Jennifer Applebaum
Marsha Armstrong
Jenine Barunas
Vito Cipolla
Kathy Critharis
Patrecia Davis
Alison Earle
Lizanne Espina
Matt Finnerty
Ursula Fokine
Kirsis Genao
Steven Gladden
Stephanie Goldberg
Peter Gooding
Matthew Herschfeld
Mike Horowitz
Charlene Jenkins
Ruben Jimenez
Ketlynne Joseph
Kimberly Kavazanjian
Lisa Kraker
Dora Kravitz
Anthony Lett
Emilie Lubis
George McCarthy
David Mckinney
Michael McMahon
Paul Melhado
Jen Miller
Christie Morgado
Ms. Oporto
Maria Jenny Pineda
Anastasia Plaunova
Carmelo Ruiz
Riza Sanchez
Kim Sanders
Maureen Stefanides
Dave Thompson
Matthew Ulmann
Maria Verosa
Tony Yaskulski

EVER-CHANGING EARTH

Ever-Changing Earth is based on a unit *Earth Structures and Processes* developed by the Geographic Data in Education (GEODE) Initiative and the Center for Learning Technologies in Urban Schools (LeTUS) at Northwestern University. *Ever-Changing Earth* was developed by the *Project-Based Inquiry Science* project in conjunction with the Center for Curriculum Materials in Science at Northwestern University (Brian Reiser, Daniel Edelson, Bruce Sherin, PIs).

Ever-Changing Earth
Developers
Edward Denecke
Jennifer Mundt Leimberer
Janet L. Kolodner
Mary L. Starr

Project Consultant
Daniel Edelson

Contributing Field-Test Teachers
Bryce Cahn
Tara O'Neill
Christopher Poli
Carmelo Ruiz
Purvi Vora
Ester Wiltz

Earth Structures and Processes
Project Director
Daniel Edelson

Lead Developers
Jennifer Mundt Leimberer
Josh Radinsky

Other Developer
Mary Pat Pardo

Contributors
Lindsey Own
Ben Loh
Matthew Rossi
David Smith
Darlene Slusher

Consultants
LeeAnn Sutherland
Rebecca Schneider
Colleen Riley

Pilot Teachers
Joan Billingham
Jean Bramelette
Lou Ellen Finn
Sonia Flores
Jennifer Mundt Leimberer
Kathleen North-Tomcyzk
Jennifer Olson
Mary Pat Pardo
Thea Raedeke
Carlos Rodriguez
Sandi Terry
Judith Lachance-Whitcomb

Production Assistants
Samuel Hong
Elizabeth Van Buren
Andrew Watson
Jean Sutow

The development of *Ever-Changing Earth* was supported by the National Science Foundation under grant nos. 0137807, 0527341, and 0639978. The development of *Earth Structures and Processes* was supported by the National Science Foundation under grants no. ESI-0352478, REC-9720377, REC-9720383, REC-0337598. Any opinions, findings, and conclusions or recommendations expressed in this material are those of the authors and do not necessarily reflect the views of the National Science Foundation.

Ever-Changing Earth Teacher's Planning Guide

Learning Set 1
How Can My Region Be Described?

Science Concepts: *Topography, elevation, depth, sea level, maps, shaded-relief maps, satellite imaging, topographic maps, contour lines, using visualization tools, organizing data, sharing data.*

Learning Set 2

What Is the Structure of Earth?

Science Concepts: *Plates, plate tectonics, structure of Earth, crust, mantle, core, seismic waves, seismology, density, magma, lithosphere, asthenosphere, inner core, outer core, Earth systems, atmosphere, biosphere, hydrosphere, geosphere, plate boundaries, faulting, folding, oceanic and continental crust, understanding models, making observations and inferences, organizing data, sharing data, using evidence to explain.*

Learning Set 3
What Happens at Plate Boundaries?

Science Concepts: *Plate boundaries, earthquakes, tsunamis, focus, epicenter, body waves, surface waves, P waves, S waves, transverse waves, seismograph, magnitude, Richter Scale, intensity, Modified Mercalli Intensity Scale, earthquake safety, finding the epicenter, locating plate boundaries, using visualization tools, working with maps, reading and analyzing data, using evidence to explain, sharing data.*

Learning Set 6

*What Geologic Activity
Happens at Plate Boundaries?*

Science Concepts: *Plate interactions, convergent
boundaries, subduction zones, buckling zones,
divergent boundaries, rift zones, transform
boundaries, trenches, basaltic magma, andesitic
magma, using visualization tools, organizing data,
using evidence to explain, sharing data.*

Answer the Big Question

*What Processes Within
Earth Cause Geologic Activity?*

Welcome to Project-Based Inquiry Science!

Welcome to Project-Based Inquiry Science (PBIS): A Middle-School Science Curriculum!

This year, your students will be learning the way scientists learn, exploring interesting questions and challenges, reading about what other scientists have discovered, investigating, experimenting, gathering evidence, and forming explanations. They will learn to collaborate with others to find answers and to share their learning in a variety of ways. In the process, they will come to see science in a whole new, exciting way that will motivate them throughout their educational experiences and beyond.

What is PBIS?

In project-based inquiry learning, students investigate scientific content and learn science practices in the context of attempting to address challenges in or answer questions about the world around them. Early activities introducing students to a challenge help them to generate issues that need to be investigated, making inquiry a student-driven endeavor. Students investigate as scientists would, through observations, designing and running experiments, designing, building, and running models, reading written material, and so on, as appropriate. Throughout each project, students might make use of technology and computer tools that support their efforts in observation, experimentation, modeling, analysis, and reflection. Teachers support and guide the student inquiries by framing the guiding challenge or question, presenting crucial lessons, managing the sequencing of activities, and

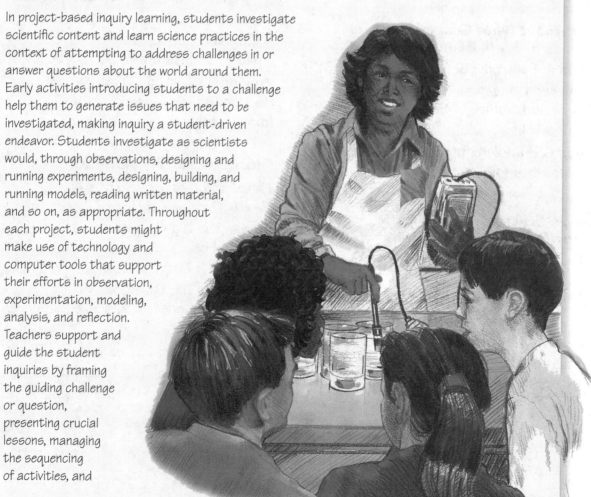

eliciting and steering discussion and collaboration among the students. At the completion of a project, students publicly exhibit what they have learned along with their solutions to the specific challenge. Personal reflection to help students learn from the experience is embedded in student activities, as are opportunities for assessment.

The curriculum will provide three years of piloted project-based inquiry materials for middle-school science. Individual curriculum units have been defined that cover the scope of the national content and process standards for the middle-school grades. Each Unit focuses on helping students acquire qualitative understanding of targeted science principles and move toward quantitative understanding, is infused with technology, and provides a foundation in reasoning skills, science content, and science process that will ready them for more advanced science. The curriculum as a whole introduces students to a wide range of investigative approaches in science (e.g., experimentation, modeling) and is designed to help them develop scientific reasoning skills that span those investigative approaches.

Technology can be used in project-based inquiry to make available to students some of the same kinds of tools and aids used by scientists in the field. These range from pencil-and-paper tools for organized data recording, collection, and management to software tools for analysis, simulation, modeling, and other tasks. Such infusion provides a platform for providing prompts, hints, examples, and other kinds of aids to students as they are engaging in scientific reasoning. The learning technologies and tools that are integrated into the curriculum offer essential scaffolding to students as they are developing their scientific reasoning skills, and are seamlessly infused into the overall completion of project activities and investigations.

Standards-Based Development

Development of each curriculum Unit begins by identifying the specific relevant national standards to be addressed. Each Unit has been designed to cover a specific portion of the national standards. This phase of development also includes an analysis of curriculum requirements across multiple states. Our intent is to deliver a product that will provide coverage of the content deemed essential on the widest practical scope and that will be easily adaptable to the needs of teachers across the country.

Once the appropriate standards have been identified, the development team works to define specific learning goals built from those standards, and takes into account conceptions and misunderstandings common among middle-school students. An orienting design challenge or driving question for investigation is chosen that motivates achieving those learning goals, and the team then sequences activities and the presentation of specific concepts so that students can construct an accurate understanding of the subject matter.

Inquiry-Based Design

The individual curriculum Units present two types of projects: engineering-design challenges and driving-question investigations. Design-challenge Units begin by presenting students with a scenario and problem and challenging them to design a device or plan that will solve the problem. Driving-question investigations begin by presenting students with a complex question with real-world implications. Students are challenged to develop answers to the questions. The scenario and problem in the design Units and the driving question in the investigation Units are carefully selected to lead the students into investigation of specific science concepts, and the solution processes are carefully structured to require use of specific scientific reasoning skills.

Pedagogical Rationale

Research shows that individual project-based learning units promote excitement and deep learning of the targeted concepts. However, achieving deep, flexible, transferable learning of cross-disciplinary content (e.g., the notion of a model, time scale, variable, experiment) and science practice requires a learning environment that consistently, persistently, and pervasively encourages the use of such content and practices over an extended period of time. By developing project-based inquiry materials that cover the spectrum of middle-school science content in a coherent framework, we provide this extended exposure to the type of learning environment most likely to produce competent scientific thinkers who are well grounded in their understanding of both basic science concepts and the standards and practices of science in general.

Evidence of Effectiveness

There is compelling evidence showing that a project-based inquiry approach meets this goal. Working at Georgia Tech, the University of Michigan, and Northwestern University, we have developed, piloted, and/or field-tested many individual project-based units. Our evaluation evidence shows that these materials engage students well and are manageable by teachers, and that students learn both content and process skills. In every summative evaluation, student performance on post-tests improved significantly from pretest performance (Krajcik, et al., 2000; Holbrook, et al., 2001; Gray et. al. 2001). For example, in the second year in a project-based classroom in Detroit, the average student at post-test scored at about the 95th percentile of the pre-test distribution. Further, we have repeatedly documented significant gains in content knowledge relative to other inquiry-based (but not project-based) instructional methods. In one set of results, performance by a project-based class

in Atlanta doubled on the content test while the matched comparison class (with an excellent teacher) experienced only a 20% gain (significance p < .001). Other comparisons have shown more modest differences, but project-based students consistently perform better than their comparisons. Most exciting about the Atlanta results is that results from performance assessments show that, within comparable student populations, project-based students score higher on all categories of problem-solving and analysis and are more sophisticated at science practice and managing a collaborative scientific investigation. Indeed, the performance of average-ability project-based students is often statistically indistinguishable from or better than performance of comparison honors students learning in an inquiry-oriented but not project-based classroom. The Chicago group also has documented significant change in process skills in project-based classrooms. Students become more effective in constructing and critiquing scientific arguments (Sandoval, 1998) and in constructing scientific explanations using discipline-specific knowledge, such as evolutionary explanations for animal behavior (Smith & Reiser, 1998).

Researchers at Northwestern have also investigated the changes in classroom practices that are elicited by project-based units. Analyses of the artifacts students produce indicate that students are engaging in ambitious learning practices, requiring weighing and synthesizing many results from complex analyses of data, and constructing scientific arguments that require synthesizing results from multiple complex analyses of data (Edelson et al, 1998; Reiser et al, 2001). Students are engaged in planning, performing, monitoring and revising their investigations, and reporting on their investigation processes as well as their results (Loh et al, 1998). In general, the classrooms engaging in project-based activities reveal substantial moves toward a scientific discourse community in which students focus on arguing from evidence, critiquing ideas, and conjecturing, rather than simply reporting on what they have read or been told (Tabak & Reiser, 1997).

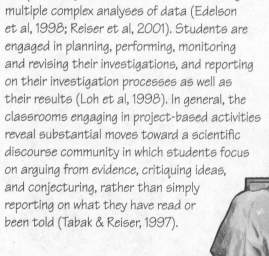

Introducing PBIS

What Do Scientists Do?

1) Scientists...address big challenges and big questions.

Students will find many different kinds of *Big Challenges* and *Questions* in *PBIS* Units. Some ask them to think about why something is a certain way. Some ask them to think about what causes something to change. Some challenge them to design a solution to a problem. Most are about things that can and do happen in the real world.

Understand the Big Challenge or Question

As students get started with each Unit, they will do activities that help them understand the *Big Question* or *Challenge* for that Unit. They will think about what they already know that might help them, and they will identify some of the new things they will need to learn.

Project Board

The *Project Board* helps you and your students keep track of their learning. For each challenge or question, they will use a *Project Board* to keep track of what they know, what they need to learn, and what they are learning. As they learn and gather evidence, they will record that on the *Project Board*. After they have answered each small question or challenge, they will return to the *Project Board* to record how what they have learned helps them answer the *Big Question* or *Challenge*.

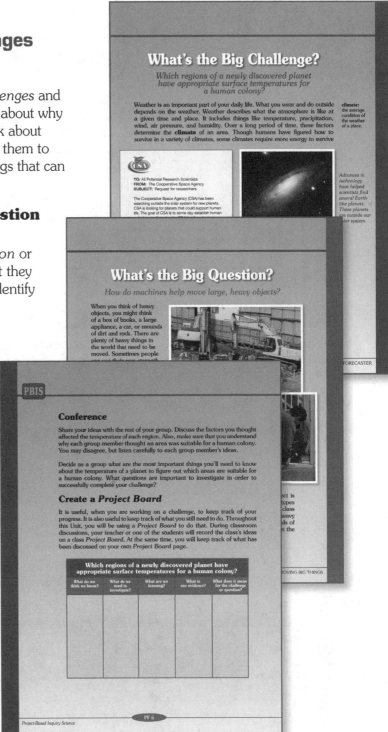

Learning Set 1

How Do Flowing Water and Land Interact in a Community?

The big question for this unit is *How does water quality affect the ecology of a community?* So far you have considered what you already know about what water quality is. Now you may be wondering where the water you use comes from. If you live in a city or town, the water you use may come from a river. You would want to know the quality of the water you are using. To do so, it is important to know how the water gets into the river. You also need to know what happens to the water as the river flows across the land.

You may have seen rivers or other water bodies near your home, your school, or in your city. Think about the river closest to where you live. Consider from where the water in the river comes. If you have traveled along the river, think about what the land around the river looks like. Try to figure out what human activities occur in the area. Speculate as to whether these activities affect the quality of water in the river.

To answer the big question, you need to break it down into smaller questions. In this *Learning Set*, you will investigate two smaller questions. As you will discover, these questions are very closely related and very hard to separate. The smaller questions are *How does water affect the land as it moves through the community?* and *How does land use affect water*

Address the Big Challenge

How Do Scientists Work Together to Solve Problems?

You began this unit with the question, *how do scientists work together to solve problems?* You did several small challenges. As you worked on those challenges you learned about how scientists solve problems. You will now watch a video about real-life designers. You will see what the people in the video are doing that is like what you have been doing. Then you will think about all the different things you have been doing during this unit. Lastly, you will write about what you have learned about doing science and being a scientist.

Watch

IDEO Video

The video you will watch follows a group of designers at IDEO. IDEO is an innovation and design firm. In the video, they face the challenge of designing and building a new kind of shopping cart. These designers are doing many of the same things that you did. They also use other practices that you did not use. As you watch the video, record the interesting things you see.

After watching the video, answer the questions on the next page. You might want to look at them before you watch the video. Answering these questions should help you answer the big question of this unit: *How do scientists work together to solve problems?*

100

Learning Sets

Each Unit is composed of a group of *Learning Sets*, one for each of the smaller questions that needs to be answered to address the *Big Question* or *Challenge*. In each *Learning Set*, students will investigate and read to find answers to the *Learning Set's* question. They will also have a chance to share the results of their investigations with their classmates and work together to make sense of what they are learning. As students come to understand answers to the questions on the *Project Board*, you will record those answers and the evidence they collected. At the end of each *Learning Set*, they will apply their knowledge to the *Big Question* or *Challenge*.

Answer the Big Question/ Address the Big Challenge

At the end of each Unit, students will put everything they have learned together to tackle the *Big Question* or *Challenge*.

2) Scientists...address smaller questions and challenges.

What Students Do in a Learning Set

Understanding the Question or Challenge

At the start of each *Learning Set*, students will usually do activities that will help them understand the *Learning Set's* question or challenge and recognize what they already know that can help them answer the question or achieve the challenge. Usually, they will visit the *Project Board* after these activities and record on it the even smaller questions that they need to investigate to answer a *Learning Set's* question.

Investigate/Explore

There are many different kinds of investigations students might do to find answers to questions. In the *Learning Sets,* they might

- design and run experiments;
- design and run simulations;
- design and build models;
- examine large sets of data.

Don't worry if your students haven't done these things before. The text will provide them with lots of help in designing their investigations and in analyzing thier data.

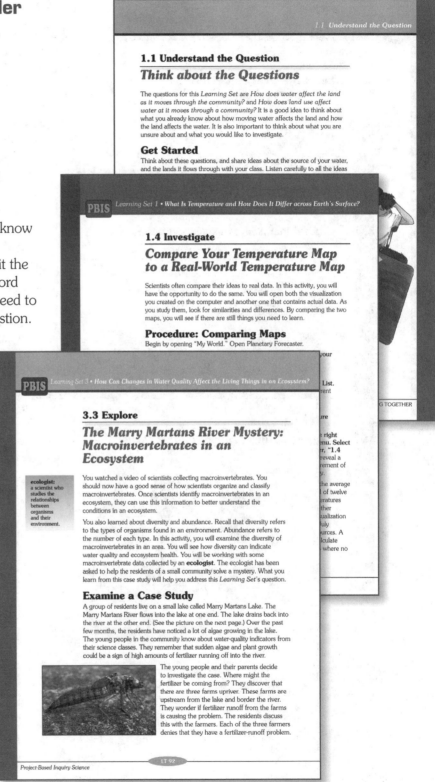

1.1 Understand the Question

Think about the Questions

The questions for this *Learning Set* are *How does water affect the land as it moves through the community?* and *How does land use affect water at it moves through a community?* It is a good idea to think about what you already know about how moving water affects the land and how the land affects the water. It is also important to think about what you are unsure about and what you would like to investigate.

Get Started

Think about these questions, and share ideas about the source of your water, and the lands it flows through with your class. Listen carefully to all the ideas

---

PBIS *Learning Set 1 • What Is Temperature and How Does It Differ across Earth's Surface?*

1.4 Investigate

Compare Your Temperature Map to a Real-World Temperature Map

Scientists often compare their ideas to real data. In this activity, you will have the opportunity to do the same. You will open both the visualization you created on the computer and another one that contains actual data. As you study them, look for similarities and differences. By comparing the two maps, you will see if there are still things you need to learn.

Procedure: Comparing Maps
Begin by opening "My World." Open Planetary Forecaster.

PBIS *Learning Set 3 • How Can Changes in Water Quality Affect the Living Things in an Ecosystem?*

3.3 Explore

The Marry Martans River Mystery: Macroinvertebrates in an Ecosystem

ecologist: a scientist who studies the relationships between organisms and their environment.

You watched a video of scientists collecting macroinvertebrates. You should now have a good sense of how scientists organize and classify macroinvertebrates. Once scientists identify macroinvertebrates in an ecosystem, they can use this information to better understand the conditions in an ecosystem.

You also learned about diversity and abundance. Recall that diversity refers to the types of organisms found in an environment. Abundance refers to the number of each type. In this activity, you will examine the diversity of macroinvertebrates in an area. You will see how diversity can indicate water quality and ecosystem health. You will be working with some macroinvertebrate data collected by an **ecologist**. The ecologist has been asked to help the residents of a small community solve a mystery. What you learn from this case study will help you address this *Learning Set's* question.

Examine a Case Study
A group of residents live on a small lake called Marry Martans Lake. The Marry Martans River flows into the lake at one end. The lake drains back into the river at the other end. (See the picture on the next page.) Over the past few months, the residents have noticed a lot of algae growing in the lake. The young people in the community know about water-quality indicators from their science classes. They remember that sudden algae and plant growth could be a sign of high amounts of fertilizer running off into the river.

The young people and their parents decide to investigate the case. Where might the fertilizer be coming from? They discover that there are three farms upriver. These farms are upstream from the lake and border the river. They wonder if fertilizer runoff from the farms is causing the problem. The residents discuss this with the farmers. Each of the three farmers denies that they have a fertilizer-runoff problem.

Project-Based Inquiry Science   LT 92

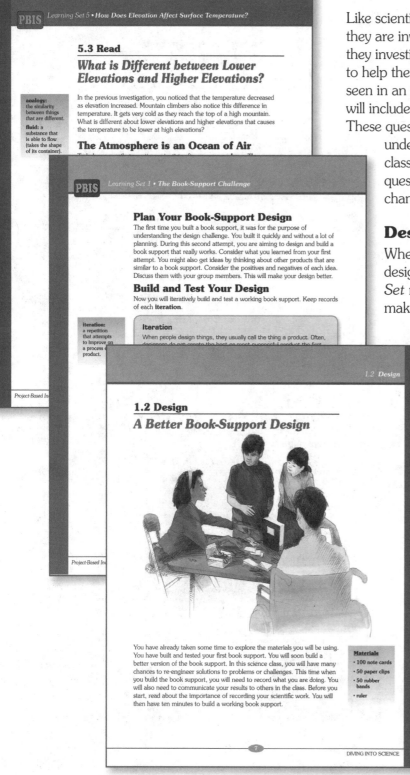

5.3 Read

What is Different between Lower Elevations and Higher Elevations?

analogy: the similarity between things that are different.

fluid: a substance that is able to flow (takes the shape of its container).

In the previous investigation, you noticed that the temperature decreased as elevation increased. Mountain climbers also notice this difference in temperature. It gets very cold as they reach the top of a high mountain. What is different about lower elevations and higher elevations that causes the temperature to be lower at high elevations?

The Atmosphere is an Ocean of Air

Plan Your Book-Support Design

The first time you built a book support, it was for the purpose of understanding the design challenge. You built it quickly and without a lot of planning. During this second attempt, you are aiming to design and build a book support that really works. Consider what you learned from your first attempt. You might also get ideas by thinking about other products that are similar to a book support. Consider the positives and negatives of each idea. Discuss them with your group members. This will make your design better.

Build and Test Your Design

Now you will iteratively build and test a working book support. Keep records of each **Iteration**.

iteration: a repetition that attempts to improve on a process product.

Iteration

When people design things, they usually call the thing a product. Often, designers do not create the best or most successful product the first

1.2 Design

1.2 Design

A Better Book-Support Design

You have already taken some time to explore the materials you will be using. You have built and tested your first book support. You will soon build a better version of the book support. In this science class, you will have many chances to re-engineer solutions to problems or challenges. This time when you build the book support, you will need to record what you are doing. You will also need to communicate your results to others in the class. Before you start, read about the importance of recording your scientific work. You will then have ten minutes to build a working book support.

Materials
• 100 note cards
• 50 paper clips
• 50 rubber bands
• ruler

Read

Like scientists, students will also read about the science they are investigating. They will read a little bit before they investigate, but most of the reading they do will be to help them understand what they have experienced or seen in an investigation. Each time they read, the text will include *Stop and Think* questions after the reading. These questions will help students gauge how well they understand what they have read. Usually, the class will discuss the answers to *Stop and Think* questions before going on so that everybody has a chance to make sense of the reading.

Design and Build

When the *Big Challenge* for a Unit asks them to design something, the challenge in a *Learning Set* might also ask them to design something and make it work. Often students will design a part of the thing they will design and build for the *Big Challenge*. When a *Learning Set* challenges students to design and build something, they will do several things:

- identify what questions they need to answer to be successful

- investigate to find answers to those questions

- use those answers to plan a good design solution

- build and test their design

Because designs don't always work the way one wants them to, students will usually do a design challenge more than once. Each time through, they will test their design. If their design doesn't work as well as they would like, they will determine why it is not working and identify other things they need to investigate to make it work better. Then, they will learn those things and try again.

Explain and Recommend

A big part of what scientists do is explain, or try to make sense of why things happen the way they do. An explanation describes why something is the way it is or behaves the way it does. An explanation is a statement one makes built from claims (what you think you know), evidence (from an investigation) that supports the claim, and science knowledge. As they learn, scientists get better at explaining. You will see that students get better, too, as they work through the *Learning Sets*.

A recommendation is a special kind of claim—one where you advise somebody about what to do. Students will make recommendations and support them with evidence, science knowledge, and explanations.

3.5 Explain

Create an Explanation

After scientists get results from an investigation, they try to make a claim. They base their claim on what their evidence shows. They also use what they already know to make their claim. They explain why their claim is valid. The purpose of a science explanation is to help others understand the following:

* what was learned from a set of investigations
* why the scientists reached this conclusion

Later, other scientists will use these explanations to help them explain other phenomena. The explanations will also help them predict what will happen in other situations.

You will do the same thing now. Your claim will be the trend you found in your experiment. You will use data you collected and science knowledge you have read to create a good explanation. This will help you decide whether your claim is valid. You will be reporting the results of the investigation to your classmates. With a good explanation that matches your claim, you can convince them that your claim is valid.

Because your understanding of the science of forces is not complete, you may not be able to fully explain your results. But you will use what you have read to come up with your best explanation. Scientists finding out about new things do the same thing. When they only partly understand something, it is impossible for them to form a "perfect" explanation. They do the best they can based on what they understand. As they learn more, they make their explanations better. This is what you will do now and what you will be doing throughout PBIS. You will explain your results the best you can based

4.3 Explain and Recommend

Explanations and Recommendations about Parachutes

As you did after your whirligig experiments, you will spend some time now explaining your results. You will also try to come up with recommendations. Remember that explanations include your claims, the evidence for your claims, and the science you know that can help you understand the claim. A recommendation is a statement about what someone should do. The best recommendations also have evidence, science, and an explanation associated with them. In the *Whirligig Challenge*, you created explanations and recommendations separately from each other. This time you will work on both at the same time.

Create and Share Your Recommendation and Explanation

Work with your group. Use the hints on the *Create Your Explanation* pages to make your first attempt at explaining your results. You'll read about parachute science later. After that, you will probably want to revise your explanations. Right now, use the science you learned during the *Whirligig Challenge* for your first attempt.

Write your recommendation. It should be about designing a slow-falling parachute. Remember that it should be written so that it will help someone else. They should be able to apply what you have learned about the effects of your variable. If you are having trouble, review the example in *Learning Set 3*.

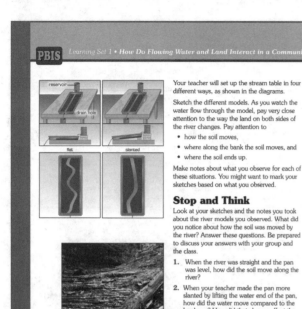

3) Scientists...reflect in many different ways.

PBIS provides guidance to help students think about what they are doing and to recognize what they are learning. Doing this often as they are working will help students be successful student scientists.

Tools for Making Sense

Stop and Think

Stop and Think sections help students make sense of what they have been doing in the section they are working on. *Stop and Think* sections include a set of questions to help students understand what they have just read or done. Sometimes the questions will remind them of something they need to pay more attention to. Sometimes they will help students connect what they have just read to things they already know. When there is a *Stop and Think* in the text, students will work individually or with a partner to answer the questions, and then the whole class will discuss the answers.

Reflect

Reflect sections help students connect what they have just done with other things they have read or done earlier in the Unit (or in another Unit). When there is a *Reflect* in the text, students will work individually or with a partner or small group to answer the questions. Then, the whole class will discuss the answers. You may want to ask students to answer *Reflect* questions for homework.

Analyze Your Data

Whenever students have to analyze data, the text will provide hints about how to do that and what to look for.

Mess About

"Messing about" is a term that comes from design. It means exploring the materials to be used for designing or building something or examining something that works like what is to be designed. Messing about helps students discover new ideas—and it can be a lot of fun. The text will usually give them ideas about things to notice as they are messing about.

What's the Point?

At the end of each *Learning Set*, students will find a summary, called *What's the Point?*, of the important information from the *Learning Set*. These summaries can help students remember how what they did and learned is connected to the *Big Question* or *Challenge* they are working on.

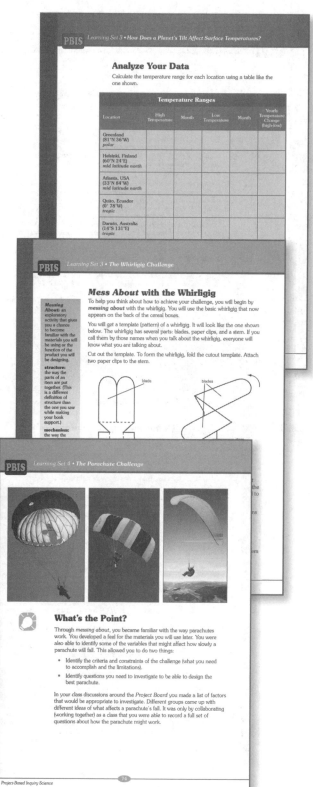

3.3 Explore

The Marry Martans River Mystery: Macroinvertebrates in an Ecosystem

ecologist: a scientist who studies the relationships between organisms and their environment.

You watched a video of scientists collecting macroinvertebrates. You should now have a good sense of how scientists organize and classify macroinvertebrates. Once scientists identify macroinvertebrates in an ecosystem, they can use this information to better understand the conditions in an ecosystem.

You also learned about diversity and abundance. Recall that diversity refers to the types of organisms found in an environment. Abundance refers to the number of each type. In this activity, you will examine the diversity of macroinvertebrates in an area. You will see how diversity can indicate water quality and ecosystem health. You will be working with some macroinvertebrate data collected by an **ecologist**. The ecologist has been asked to help the residents of a small community solve a mystery. What you learn from this case study will help you address this *Learning Set*'s question.

Examine a Case Study

A group of residents live on a small lake called Marry Martans Lake. The Marry Martans River flows into the lake at one end. The lake drains back into the river at the other end. (See the picture on the next page.) Over the past few months, the residents have noticed a lot of algae growing in the lake. The young people in the community know about water-quality indicators from their science classes. They remember that sudden algae and plant growth could be a sign of high amounts of fertilizer running off into the river.

The young people and their parents decide to investigate the case. Where might the fertilizer be coming from? They discover that there are three farms upriver. These farms are upstream from the lake and border the river.

Communicate Your Results

Investigation Expo

Scientists always share their understandings with each other. Presenting their results to others is one of the most important things that scientists do. You will share what you have found in an *Investigation Expo*. To prepare for this, you will use an overhead transparency.

Trace the diagram that you drew of your model onto an overhead transparency. Be ready to describe your investigation and clearly detail all your results. The answers to the following questions will be very helpful in preparing your presentation.

- Describe how the water moved in the model. (What patterns did you see?)
- Describe why you think your prediction was accurate or inaccurate.
- How did the outcome compare to your prediction?
- Where did the water flow more quickly? How was the flow different from what you predicted?
- Where did the water pool?

As you look at the overheads presented by other students, make sure you can answer these questions. Ask questions that you need answered to understand the results and the explanations others have made.

What's the Point?

In this section, you built a model to simulate how water flows across a landscape when it rains. Placing different-sized objects under the paper created the higher and lower elevations. You also drew a sketch of the model, and predicted how water will run over the paper. When you ran the simulation you probably noticed that the water always moved from areas of high elevation to areas of lower elevation. Water cannot move uphill. You also noticed that water flowed and created puddles in several places as it flowed. These puddles represent lakes or ponds in the real world.

Water on land works that way too. If you watch where rain falls in one rainstorm, you will be able to predict the path water will take in the next rainstorm. This is the case as long as the land stays the same from the first rainstorm to the next. You will need to consider how new construction in Wamego might change the land and affect how water flows.

4) Scientists...collaborate.

Scientists never do all their work alone. They work with other scientists (collaborate) and share their knowledge. *PBIS* helps students by giving them lots of opportunities for sharing their findings, ideas, and discoveries with others (the way scientists do). Students will work together in small groups to investigate, design, explain, and do other science activities. Sometimes they will work in pairs to figure out things together. They will also have lots of opportunities to share their findings with the rest of their classmates and make sense together of what they are learning.

Investigation Expo

In an *Investigation Expo*, small groups report to the class about an investigation they've done. For each *Investigation Expo*, students will make a poster detailing what they were trying to learn from their investigation, what they did, their data, and their interpretation of the data. The text gives them hints about what to present and what to look for in other groups' presentations. *Investigation Expos* are always followed by discussions about the investigations and about how to do science well. You may want to ask students to write a lab report following an investigation.

Plan Briefing/Solution Briefing/ Idea Briefing

Briefings are presentations of work in progress. They give students a chance to get advice from their classmates that can help them move forward. During a *Plan Briefing*, students present their plans to the class. They might be plans for an experiment for solving a problem or achieving a challenge. During a *Solution Briefing*, students present their solutions in progress and ask the class to help them make their solutions better. During an *Idea Briefing*, students present their ideas, including their evidence in support of their plans, solutions, or ideas. Often, they will prepare posters to help them make their presentation. Briefings are almost always followed by discussions of their investigations and how they will move forward.

Solution Showcase

Solution Showcases usually happen near the end of a Unit. During a *Solution Showcase*, students show their classmates their finished products—either their answer to a question or solution to a challenge. Students will also tell the class why they think it is a good answer or solution, what evidence and science they used to get to their solution, and what they tried along the way before getting to their answers or solutions. Sometimes a *Solution Showcase* is followed by a competition. It is almost always followed by a discussion comparing and contrasting the different answers and solutions groups have come up with. You may want to ask students to write a report or paper following a *Solution Showcase*.

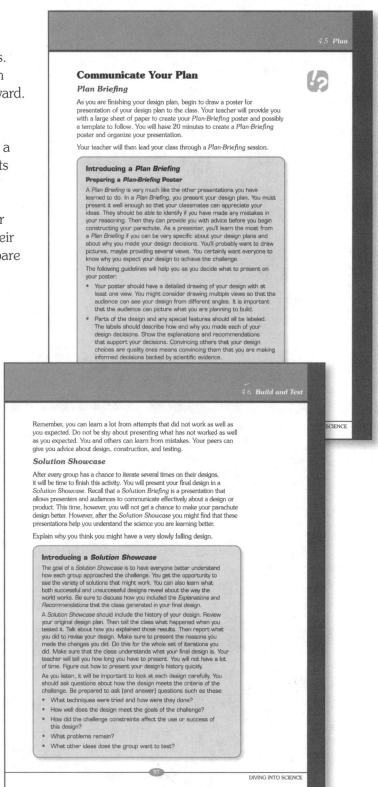

First, develop your own questions. When you have completed your two questions, take the questions back to your small group. Share all the questions with one another. Carefully consider each question and decide if it meets the criteria for a good question. With your group, refine the questions that do not meet the criteria. Choose the two most interesting questions to share now with the class. Give your teacher the rest of the questions so they might be used later.

Update the *Project Board*

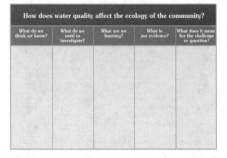

How does water quality affect the ecology of the community?				
What do we think we know?	What do we need to investigate?	What are we learning?	What is our evidence?	What does it mean for the challenge or question?

You will now share your group's two questions with your class. Be prepared to support your questions with the criteria you used. Your teacher will help you with the criteria if needed. Then your teacher will add your questions to the *Project Board*. Throughout this *Learning Set*, you will work to answer some of these questions.

Later in this *Learning Set*, you will conduct some investigations and use models to understand how water moves through the land, and how it affects the land it flows through. The investigations will require you to make careful

Conference

Teams of scientists often work together to solve problems. They hold group discussions. That is what you are going to do. During your discussion, you can present questions that you have. Sometimes if you do not have an answer, someone else might. You might also present a question that no one else had thought of. This can start your group thinking in a new direction.

Discuss your map with a partner and then with your group. Listen and observe as others present their maps to the group. As you present your prediction map, include answers to these questions:

- How did you decide what temperatures to use to color each area?
- How did you decide where to start and where to go to next?
- In which parts of the world do you feel very confident about your predictions, and which parts do you feel unsure about?

After everyone has presented their maps, take note of where there was agreement and where there were differences. Later on you will compare your predictions to a real surface-temperature map.

You have compared your temperature predictions for Earth with those of others in your group. Now, work again with your partner to create a prediction map based on discussions you've just had. Begin with a...group were in agreement...is disagreement...few minutes to...or evidence...something, t...

Update the *Project Board*

Remember that the *Project Board* is designed to help the class keep track of what they are learning and their progress toward a Unit's *Big Question* or *Challenge*. At the beginning of each Unit, the class creates a *Project Board*, and together records what students think they know about answering the *Big Question* or addressing the *Big Challenge* and what they think they need to investigate further. Near the beginning of each *Learning Set*, the class revisits the *Project Board* and adds new questions and information they think they know to the *Project Board*. At the end of each *Learning Set*, the class again revisits the *Project Board*. This time, they record what they have learned, the evidence they have collected, and recommendations they can make about answering the *Big Question* or achieving the *Big Challenge*.

Conference

A *Conference* is a short discussion among a small group of students before a more formal whole-class discussion. Students might discuss predictions and observations, they might try to explain together, they might consult on what they think they know, and so on. Usually, a *Conference* is followed by a discussion around the *Project Board*. In these small group discussions, everybody gets a chance to participate.

 What's the Point? Students review what they have learned in each *Learning Set*.

 Stop and Think Student answer questions that help them understand what they have done in a section.

 **Communicate** Students share their ideas and results with their classmates.

Record Students record their data as they gather it.

NOTES

NOTES

EVER-CHANGING EARTH

As a Student Scientist, you will...

Ask QUESTIONS

Pursue **ANSWERS**

APPLY MEANING

Make MEANING

Share **ANSWERS**

Ever-Changing Earth

Content

Students begin to answer the *Big Question* of the Unit *What processes within Earth cause geologic activity?* by familiarizing themselves with a specific Earth structure that represents one or more of the constructive forces of different Earth processes. Students build their knowledge about Earth and the processes that shape it through models, data collection, analysis, and information sharing throughout the Unit. They look at earthquake and volcano data in real time, using the Internet and firsthand descriptions of the events. They observe and describe multiple years of data, and data using the visualization tool *My World.* Pairs use this data to explain the processes making the plates move and changing Earth's crust. They find patterns in the earthquake and volcano data and identify the plates and the ways they are moving. They think about how these movements lead to different kinds of changes to the crust, how earthquakes happen in different places, how volcanoes are shaped in different ways, and how the topography of the land is different. By connecting all of the information gathered through readings, investigations, and information sharing, students are able to ultimately create an explanation for the changes happening in the region of their Earth structures.

Investigations

Students begin by investigating different mapping techniques to visualize the Earth structure they have been assigned. They use topographic maps and Earth-imaging software to explore the regions of their Earth structures. They use computer-generated data maps from *My World* to explore their region and to compare and contrast their Earth structure to others. Students read about and explore different models of Earth to compare its layers. They evaluate these models and use observations of how liquids of different densities interact to infer the role of density in the formation of the lithosphere. In *Learning Set 3,* students model plate interactions with clay and interpret their observations, preparing them to make inferences between the relationship of plate movements and earthquakes. They analyze real-time earthquake data to find patterns. They make these observations using data covering different time intervals, building the knowledge base needed until they have enough data to identify the plate boundaries in their Earth structure region. *Learning Set 4* takes them through the process used by scientists to observe and measure earthquakes. Students focus on why Earth's crustal plates move. Students

$43\frac{1}{4}$ *class periods*

A class period is considered to be one 40 to 50 minute class.

observe a demonstration of convection currents created by density differences in water, and apply this concept to Earth's mantle. This demonstration helps them to begin to understand what drives the entire process of plate movement. In *Learning Set 5,* students collect volcano data using *My World* to identify and describe different kinds and patterns of volcanic activity in the region of their Earth structure. From the data and models, students begin to describe and explain the processes changing the crust in their region. They make connections between all that they have observed and learned about earthquakes and volcanoes in *Learning Set 6.* They refine their descriptions as they look at patterns in earthquake, volcano, and topographic data. They use this to finalize their explanation for the processes causing geologic activity in the region of their Earth structure and globally.

Nature of Science

Students engage in the behavior and habits of scientists as each pair goes through an iterative process to build and refine their plate boundary inferences. They share new information they obtain about their Earth structure and the plate boundaries in their region with neighboring regions. Through information sharing and collaboration, students are able to build on each other's ideas, refine their ideas, and build a complete map of the plates that make up Earth's crust.

Artifacts

Throughout *Ever-Changing Earth,* students develop artifacts of their learning. The *Project Board* is one example of a class artifact that is displayed and changed as students add questions they need to answer, concepts they are learning, and the evidence that supports those concepts. Students create and add to a *Picture Map* throughout the Unit. Each pair annotates several maps of their Earth structure, including those in *My World, Three-page Maps,* and several other data maps. Each pair maintains a *Region Project Board,* where they keep track of the observations they are making about their Earth structure and their evolving explanations of each observation. As they come to understand their own Earth structures and those in regions close to their own, each pair contributes to the *Big World Map* that will eventually include an overlay outlining Earth's plates. Students create a file of work containing their prediction maps, along with each explanation they create throughout the process. The final product is a presentation of their explanation, which includes a display of all their maps, models, and other select works.

LOOKING AHEAD

Students should work in pairs throughout the Unit. Each group will be assigned an Earth structure and region to work on. There are eight Earth structures to work on. If your class is small and you will not be able to assign all Earth structures to pairs, try to pick neighboring Earth structures so groups can share their data and make sense of a region. When selecting pairs consider the goals for each student, how the material will challenge them, how they will challenge each other, and how they will share the workload.

Students will need to use *My World* on computers during this Unit. It would be best to have one computer available per pair of students. If this is not possible, consider how you will efficiently set up computer usage.

Student groups should also have a folder to hold their collective work during the Unit. This folder should stay in the classroom in case of student absences.

Targeted Concepts, Skills, and Nature of Science	Section
Scientists often work together and then share their findings. Sharing findings makes new information available and helps scientists refine their ideas and build on others' ideas. When another person's or group's idea is used, credit needs to be given.	Intro, LS 1, LS 2, LS 3, LS 4, LS 5, LS 6
Scientists must keep clear, accurate, and descriptive records of what they do so they can share their work with others and consider what they did, why they did it, and what they want to do next.	Intro, LS 1, LS 2, LS 3, LS 4, LS 5, LS 6
Identifying factors that could affect the phenomenon you are investigating is an important part of planning scientific research.	Intro
Scientists make claims (conclusions) based on evidence obtained (trends in data) from reliable investigations.	LS 2, LS 3, LS 4, LS 5, LS 6
Explanations are claims supported by evidence, accepted ideas, and facts.	LS 2, LS 3, LS 4, LS 5, LS 6
Graphs and tables are an effective way to analyze and communicate results of scientific investigation.	LS 1, LS 2, LS 3, LS 4, LS 5, LS 6
Scientists use models and tools, such as Geographic Information Systems, and a variety of maps to develop claims and explanations from evidence in the data.	LS 1, LS 2, LS 3, LS 4, LS 5, LS 6
Earthquake activity, volcanic activity, and topography are all evidence that Earth's crust is moving and changing.	LS 2, LS 3, LS 4, LS 5, LS 6
Interactions between Earth's crustal plates can result in mountain building, rift valleys, and geologic activity such as earthquakes and volcanoes. Underwater volcanic activity may form underwater mountains, which can thrust above the ocean's surface to become islands.	LS 2, LS 3, LS 5, LS 6

Targeted Concepts, Skills, and Nature of Science	Section
Earth is a system made up of different layers, each with a distinctive composition and set of characteristics. These layers interact, driving the processes that shape Earth.	LS 2, LS 4, LS 6
The way in which plates collide depends on the density of the interacting plates. Continental crust is less dense than oceanic crust and, therefore, has greater buoyancy. This causes continental crust to float over the denser oceanic crust when these plates converge.	LS 6
New crust is formed at the mid-ocean ridge where the plates move apart. Oceanic crust is destroyed when it collides with continental crust and is subducted. In this way, Earth's crust is recycled.	LS 5, LS 6
Plate interactions may be classified into zones, including rift zones, subduction zones, buckling zones, and transform zones. Patterns in earthquake and volcano data help scientists identify these zones.	LS 6
Earth's crust is constantly changing. These changes are usually a very slow process that is not immediately observable. Some changes are very rapid and are observable.	LS 2, LS 5
The hot core of Earth drives the processes that bring about changes in the crust by creating convection currents in the mantle material. These convection currents drive plate motion.	LS 4
Scientists measure and record earthquake activity using the Richter Scale and the Modified Mercalli Intensity Scale. The Richter Scale is used for measuring the magnitude of an Earthquake. The Mercalli Scale is used to measure the intensity.	LS 3
Measuring instruments are important in scientific inquiry for accurately comparing the volumes and weights of substances.	LS 2
Scientific investigations and measurements are considered reliable if the results are repeatable by other scientists using the same procedures.	LS 1, LS 3

Unit Materials List

Quantities based on groups of 4-6 students.		
Unit Durable Classroom Items	**Section**	**Quantity**
Metric ruler	1.2, 2.3, 3.4, 4.2	1
Plexiglass piece, 8 in. x 10 in.	1.2	1
Transparent oblong tub	1.2	1
Transparencies	1.2, 3.6, 6.3	1
Plastic beaker, 1 L	1.2	1
Graduated cylinder, 100 mL, PMP	2.4	1
Clear plastic cup, 10 oz	2.4	4
Modeling clay, 1 lb	3.1	2
Drawing compass	3.4	1
Blue marker	3.5	4
3-oz plastic cup	4.2	1
Big Data Map, laminated	3.6	1

NOTES

Quantities for 5 classes of 8 groups.

Unit Durable Classroom Items	Section	Quantity
Learning Cycle Action Posters, Set of 5	All	1
Big World Map, laminated	Intro, 3.2, 3.5, 5.1, 5.2, 5.4, 6.3, 6.BBQ, ABQ	1
Project Board, laminated	Intro, 1.BBQ, 2.1, 2.BBQ, 3.2, 3.5, 3.6, 3.7, 3.BBQ, 4.1, 4.2, 4.BBQ, 5.1, 5.2, 5.4, 5.BBQ, 6.1, 6.BBQ, ABQ	5
Project Board transparency	Intro, 1.BBQ, 2.1, 2.BBQ, 3.2, 3.5, 3.6, 3.7, 3.BBQ, 4.1, 4.2, 4.BBQ, 5.1, 5.2, 5.4, 5.BBQ, 6.1, 6.BBQ, ABQ	1
Push pins, pkg. of 100	Intro	1
My World Software	1.1, 3.6, 3.7 5.1, 6.3	1
Electronic scale - 0.01g Readability, 0-200 g	2.3	1
Coiled spring toy	3.2	1
Ribbon, 12 in., varying widths	3.2	1
Earth Science Content DVD	4.2	1

Unit Materials List

Quantities for 5 classes of 8 groups.		
Unit Durable Group Items	**Section**	**Quantity**
Black permanent marker	1.2	1
Wax paper roll	3.1	2
Transparency marker set	3.6, 6.3	1
Aluminum foil, 15 cm x 15 cm square	4.2	1

Quantities for classes of 8 groups.		
Unit Consumable Classroom Items	**Section**	**Quantity**
Masking tape	1.2, 3.6	6
Colored pencils	Intro, 1.BBQ, 2.1, 2.4, 2.5, 3.5, 4.2, 5.4, 6.1, 6.2	6
Restickable easel pad	Intro, 1.BBQ, 2.1, 2.5, 4.2, 5.4, 6.2, 6.BBQ	7
Unlined index cards, 3 in. x 5 in., pkg. of 100	1.BBQ, 2.BBQ, 3.BBQ, 4.BBQ, 5.BBQ, 6.BBQ	20
Disposable beral pipettes, 3-mL bulb draw, pkg. of 10	2.4	20
Markers, set of 8	3.5, 3.6, 3.7, 5.1, 5.2	6
Lightweight non-corrugated cardboard, 1 cm x 1cm squares	4.2	2
Food coloring (red, blue, green, yellow)	2.4,4.2	2
Rubber bands, size #33, 1 lb	4.2	1

Additional Items Needed Not Supplied	Section	Quantity
Computer with Internet connection	1.2, 3.5	1 per classroom
Earth-imaging software	1.2	1 per classroom
Three-dimensional object, not to exceed 6 in. x 9 in. x 4 in.	1.2	1 per group
Hard-boiled egg	2.2	1 per pair
Mystery box	2.3	1 per group
Dishwashing soap, baby oil, water, and glycerine, 10 mL each	2.4	1 set per group
World map	3.2	1 per classroom
Yellow marker	3.6	1 per student
DVD player with monitor or television	4.2	1 per classroom
Access to hot and cold water	4.2	1 per classroom
2-L plastic bottle, cut off just above the label (remove the label after cutting)	4.2	1 per group
Long wooden pencil (sharpened)	4.2	2 per group

NOTES

....

....

....

....

....

NOTES

What's the Big Question?

What Processes Within Earth Cause Geologic Activity?

◀ *2 class periods*

A class period is considered to be one 40 to 50 minute class.

Overview

Students are introduced to the *Big Question, What processes within Earth cause geologic activity?* They read letters describing the regions and the Earth structures they will analyze throughout the Unit. Students work in pairs to research the regions described in the pen pal letters. Each pair will study a different region. Then, each pair works with a larger group of students who studied the same region to select observations and facts from their pen pal letter that demonstrate the geologic activity in their region. Groups present this information to the class and use latitude and longitude to describe where their region is on the map. They discuss similarities and differences in the regions they have read about and what they need to learn more about. The class creates a *Project Board,* listing what they think they know about their Earth structures and what they will need to investigate to answer the *Big Question.*

Targeted Concepts, Skills, and Nature of Science	Performance Expectations
Scientists often work together and then share their findings. Sharing findings makes new information available and helps scientists refine their ideas and build on others' ideas. When another person's or group's idea is used, credit needs to be given.	Students should share their individual ideas with their group and groups should share their ideas with the class as they consider what they think they know about the Earth structures they are studying and what they need to investigate.
Scientists must keep clear, accurate, and descriptive records of what they do so they can share their work with others and consider what they did, why they did it, and what they want to do next.	Students should keep detailed records of their initial ideas as they begin their class *Project Board* for the Unit.
Identifying factors that could affect the phenomenon being investigated is an important part of planning scientific research.	Students may identify some factors that they think might cause change in their Earth structure.

Materials	
1 per class	*Big World Map* Class *Project Board* *Ever-Changing Earth Teacher Notes and Suggested Data* table
1 per student	*Project Board* page
1 box per class	Pushpins

Activity Setup and Preparation

Students will be working in pairs. Each pair will study an Earth structure.

To select pairs, use the table below as a guideline. The table gives an idea of difficulty of data interpretation and analysis. When selecting pairs, consider the goals for each student, how the material will challenge them, how they will challenge each other, and how they will share the workload.

Group Assignments

Earth Structures	Notes to Teacher
Java Trench (Example for teacher use)	Moderately easy observation, easy explanation
Baja Peninsula	Moderately difficult observation and explanation
Hawaiian Islands	Easy observation, moderately easy explanation
Iceland	Moderately difficult observation and explanation
Mount Aconcagua	Easy observation and explanation
Mount Everest	Easy observation and explanation
Mount Fuji	Easy observation and explanation
Mount Kilimanjaro	Moderately difficult observation and explanation
Mount Popo	Moderately difficult observation and explanation
Mount St. Helens	Moderately difficult observation and explanation

Review the *Ever-Changing Earth Teacher Notes* and *Suggested Data* table in the Appendix to get an overview of what groups are expected to be able to describe about their Earth structure throughout the Unit.

Homework Options

Reflection

- **Science Content:** Describe some features of the Earth structure you were assigned. What other places on Earth do you know of that have a similar structure? *(Students should describe the land features, location, and the type of structure, e.g., fault line, volcano, etc.)*

NOTES

....

....

....

....

....

....

....

....

....

....

NOTES

What's the Big Question?

What Processes Within Earth Cause Geologic Activity?

The ground is shaking and **volcanoes** are erupting in regions around the world. Powerful events, such as **earthquakes** and volcanic eruptions, reshape Earth's surface. They also take lives and change survivors forever.

In 1989, an earthquake in the San Francisco Bay area killed 63 people and caused nearly $6 billion in damage. In 2008, a huge earthquake in China killed almost 70,000 people and left about 5 million people without homes. Volcanic eruptions have the power to level the land around them. However, while many volcanoes are destructive, others form new mountains and more land. Volcanic activity in the Hawaiian Islands has added acres of new land along with many new islands. In this Unit, you will identify the causes of these kinds of **geologic** activity and how processes deep within Earth make them happen.

volcano: a vent in the surface of Earth through which magma and associated gases and ash erupt.

earthquake: a sudden motion or trembling in Earth caused by the abrupt release of slowly accumulated strain.

geology (geologic): the study of planet Earth: the materials of which it is made, the processes that act on these materials, the products formed, and the history of the planet and all its forms since its origin.

The 2008 earthquake in China devastated the Sichuan province.

Think about the pictures on the following pages. Each one shows a place in the world where earthquakes or volcanic eruptions are reshaping Earth's surface. This Unit will help you understand why geologic activity happens in these places.

EE 3

EVER-CHANGING EARTH

What's the Big Question?

What Processes Within Earth Cause Geologic Activity?

15 min

The class is introduced to the Unit's Big Question.

○ Engage

Begin by discussing the geologic events described in the student text— the San Francisco earthquake of 1989 and the earthquake in China in 2008. Emphasize that these events can permanently change the landscape and the communities of the affected regions and can kill thousands of people. Elicit students' ideas about what causes such powerful events. Ask students what is happening to the ground under their feet. Are different things happening to the ground in different places?

*A class period is considered to be one 40 to 50 minute class.

"Please stand up. What do you think is happening right now in the ground under us? Is it moving? Is it solid? Is it sturdy?"

Record students' ideas. Some students may have heard that plates in the Earth cause earthquakes. Tell them that they will learn more about this.

META NOTES

By eliciting students' initial ideas, you prepare students to begin thinking about the concepts that will be introduced. When students consider their ideas before being introduced to new ideas, they are more inclined to change or add on to their ideas.

Knowledge of students' initial ideas will help you guide students to a deeper understanding.

NOTES

PBIS

Mt. Katmai, one of Alaska's Aleutian arc of volcanoes, exploded in 1912 in the largest eruption in the twentieth century. This 4000-mile island chain is home to ten percent of the world's active volcanoes. About 170 eruptions have taken place in this region over the last 100 years.

200 FT. FROM KATMAI VOLCANO IN ERUPTION, ALASKA. © M.HORNER. 1913

Mt. Katmai Volcano

METERS ABOVE SEA LEVEL	FEET ABOVE SEA LEVEL
Over 3000	Over 10,000
1500 to 3000	5000 to 10,000
600 to 1500	2000 to 5000
300 to 600	1000 to 2000
150 to 300	500 to 1000
0 to 150	0 to 500

Arctic Ocean

ARCTIC CIRCLE 66°N

ALASKA

Fairbanks

Anchorage

Bering Sea

Mt. Katmai

Juneau

Aleutian Islands

Pacific Ocean

EE 4

Project-Based Inquiry Science

△ Guide

Ask students to describe what they see in each of the pictures in the student text. Tell them that these formations were caused by geologic events. The captions to the photographs give some information about the events. Point out the photograph of Mt. Katmai erupting. The volcano and the formations in the student text are Earth structures. Explain to students that an Earth structure is a shape formed by geologic activity.

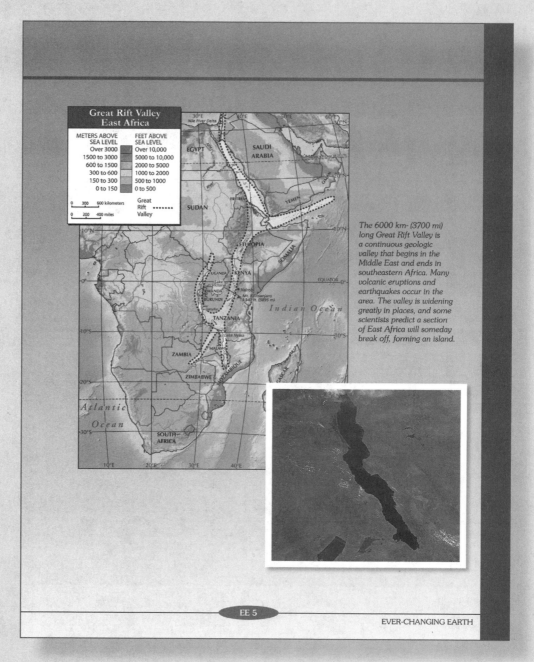

The 6000 km- (3700 mi) long Great Rift Valley is a continuous geologic valley that begins in the Middle East and ends in southeastern Africa. Many volcanic eruptions and earthquakes occur in the area. The valley is widening greatly in places, and some scientists predict a section of East Africa will someday break off, forming an island.

Let students know they will study some very large and important Earth structures. They will work in pairs, and each group will study an Earth structure. A pen pal who lives near the Earth structure they are studying will help them by providing information. As groups learn about their Earth structures, they will share what they learn with the class.

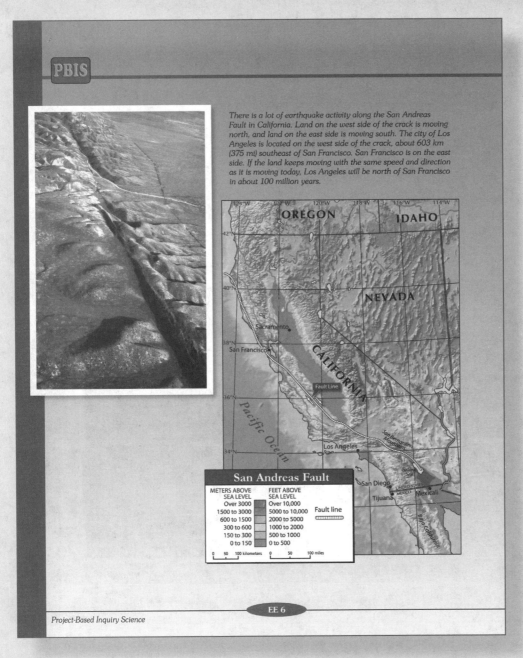

There is a lot of earthquake activity along the San Andreas Fault in California. Land on the west side of the crack is moving north, and land on the east side is moving south. The city of Los Angeles is located on the west side of the crack, about 603 km (375 mi) southeast of San Francisco. San Francisco is on the east side. If the land keeps moving with the same speed and direction as it is moving today, Los Angeles will be north of San Francisco in about 100 million years.

San Andreas Fault

METERS ABOVE SEA LEVEL	FEET ABOVE SEA LEVEL
Over 3000	Over 10,000
1500 to 3000	5000 to 10,000
600 to 1500	2000 to 5000
300 to 600	1000 to 2000
150 to 300	500 to 1000
0 to 150	0 to 500

Fault line

EE 6

Project-Based Inquiry Science

Tell students that the *Big Question* of this Unit is *What processes in Earth cause geologic activity?* Emphasize that the class's investigations into Earth structures will allow students to answer this question, and that the class is depending on each pair to contribute their findings. Also emphasize that students should keep this question in mind as they study their Earth structures and as they discuss what other groups have learned about their Earth structures.

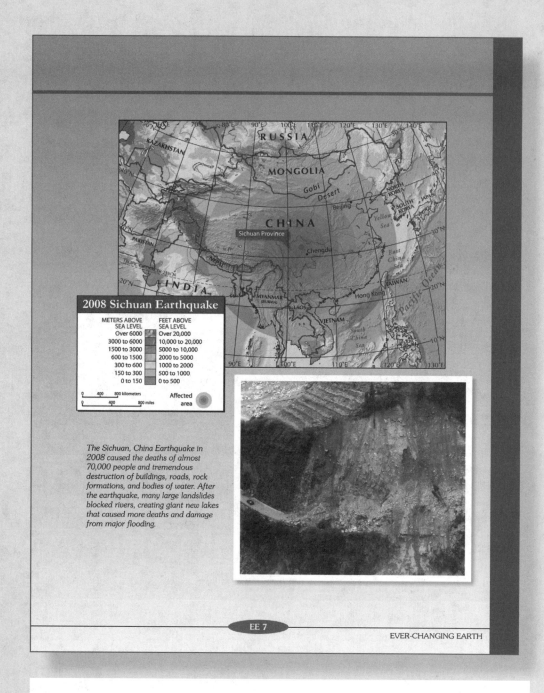

2008 Sichuan Earthquake

METERS ABOVE SEA LEVEL	FEET ABOVE SEA LEVEL
Over 6000	Over 20,000
3000 to 6000	10,000 to 20,000
1500 to 3000	5000 to 10,000
600 to 1500	2000 to 5000
300 to 600	1000 to 2000
150 to 300	500 to 1000
0 to 150	0 to 500

Affected area

The Sichuan, China Earthquake in 2008 caused the deaths of almost 70,000 people and tremendous destruction of buildings, roads, rock formations, and bodies of water. After the earthquake, many large landslides blocked rivers, creating giant new lakes that caused more deaths and damage from major flooding.

EE 7

EVER-CHANGING EARTH

NOTES

....

....

....

PBIS

Earth structure: a definable shape formed by geologic activity.

The Big Question for this Unit is *What processes within Earth cause geologic activity?* To answer this question, your class will investigate eight regions of the world where geologic activity, past and present, affects the land and, perhaps, the people living there. Within each region, an interesting **Earth structure**, formed as a result of the geologic activity, will serve as the focus of your investigation. As you work through this Unit, a pen pal who lives near the Earth structure in your region will help you. Working with your partner, you will explain the geologic activity in your region and how this activity resulted in the formation of your Earth structure. The class will also work together to develop an understanding of processes deep within Earth that drive geologic activities.

The *Big Question* has been divided into several smaller questions to help you answer it. As you answer these smaller questions, you will become an expert about your Earth structure and its surrounding region. Answering the *Big Question* will require knowledge about many different regions, so you will need to do what scientists do—share information, teach others about your region, and listen to and learn from others. As you and your classmates answer the smaller questions, you will be solving pieces of the puzzle to help you answer the *Big Question*. You will also use many of the science practices you have heard about and used in other Units.

Welcome to Ever-Changing Earth.
Enjoy your journey as a student scientist.

EE 8

Project-Based Inquiry Science

NOTES

....

....

....

Think About the Big Question

5 min

Students discuss what they will be doing during the Unit to answer the Big Question.

Think About the *Big Question*

The *Big Question* for this Unit is *What processes within Earth cause geologic activity?* As in other Units, you will answer this *Big Question* by answering several smaller questions. In doing so, you will learn many things about the structure of Earth and the processes at work within Earth. Using some of the same tools as scientists, you will become an expert on the geologic activity in the region assigned to you.

First, you and your partner will get to know your Earth structure and the region in which it is located. Your pen pal lives near the Earth structure and has written a letter that includes helpful information. This letter describes the region where the Earth structure is located, the kind of geologic activity in the region, and special features of the Earth structure or changes happening there. You will refer to your pen pal letter throughout this Unit.

Get Started

With your partner, carefully read the letter from your pen pal and observe the photo of the Earth structure you will be investigating. There is a lot of information in the letter. Read the letter all the way through the first time, and then read it again, looking for important facts that will help you learn about the region. To help you find these facts, use the following questions as a guide.

- Where is the Earth structure located?

- What is the general shape of the Earth structure and surrounding land?

- What geologic activity has occurred in the past or is occurring now in the region? What facts in the letter describe earthquake activity in this region? What facts describe volcanic activity in the region?

- How does this region compare to where you live?

- What kind of additional information do you need to explain how your Earth structure developed? How do you think a scientist would learn more about it?

EE 9

EVER-CHANGING EARTH

△ Guide

Let students know that they will answer the *Big Question* by answering smaller questions. First they will familiarize themselves with their assigned Earth structure and the surrounding region by reading letters from their pen pals. These letters will describe the region where the Earth structure is located and will give helpful information about geologic activity in the region and special features or changes of the region.

"In other Units, you have answered *Big Questions* by first answering smaller questions. That is what you will do here. The first step is to get a general idea about the Earth structure you are studying. You'll want to know where it is, what the region is like, and what the structure is. You are going to read a letter from your pen pal, who lives in the region where your Earth structure is. The letter will tell you about the region and the structure."

△ Guide

Tell students they should read the letter from their pen pal twice. The first time, they will simply get acquainted with their pen pal and their assigned region. The second time, they should use the bulleted questions in the student text to guide their reading.

"When you get your assignment, you'll read the letter from your pen pal twice. The first time, just read it and note anything that interests you. The second time you, look for specific things. The questions in your texts will guide you."

⬡ Get Going

Assign a pen pal letter to each pair and give students a timeframe to read the letters.

As students read the letters, circulate among the classroom and ask pairs if they can describe their region. Ask if they can explain why the Earth structure is there and what information could help them explain the Earth structure.

Get Started

10 min

Groups are assigned a letter and then read their assigned letters.

NOTES

....

....

....

Selamat Pagi, Friends!

My name is Benny, and I'm writing to you from Bandung, a city of almost 2 million people on the island of Java. I heard you want to learn more about our country and the Java Trench, so I'm sending you some facts. I want to tell you a few things about my homeland.

Some people here still have unusual ideas about our volcanoes. When a scientist came to study one of the volcanoes, he found a small bundle of folded leaves in one of his boxes. One of our geologists said it was a coin left by an old woman who wanted to wish him luck studying the volcano. Later, he found out the truth. The woman was not wishing him luck; she had come to make sure his equipment would not affect the eruptions. She and others here believe that volcanoes erupt for a reason. Some people here believe that eruptions bring justice and revenge to the world.

If you came to visit, I would take you to many geological sites, but first I would take you to the local wildlife preserve. There you could see the Komodo dragon. It is the world's largest lizard and can grow to more than 3 m (almost 10 ft) in length! I bet you don't have lizards that size in your country.

You will have a great time learning about Indonesia and exploring the Java Trench. Many people call it the shadow of Indonesia. If you came to visit, I would show you many important geological sites. In case you ever can come to Java, here are your first two Indonesian words—Selamat Pagi and Salemat Tinggal—the first means hello and the second means good-bye.

Selemat Tinggal!

Your friend,
Benny Makmur
Bandung, Java, Indonesia

ES 10

NOTES

....

....

....

Fact sheet:
Java Trench

Location:
10°S 110°E

The Java Trench is located in Indonesia about 305 km (190 mi) off the southwestern coasts of the islands of Sumatra and Java.

Geological Activity:
Indonesia has 76 active volcanoes, more than any other country in the world. It is known for powerful earthquakes and explosive volcanoes. In 1883, an island called Krakatoa, off the west coast of Java in the Sunda Strait, had three active volcanoes. Small eruptions and a large earthquake occurred beginning in May of that year. By August, all three volcanoes were spitting out ash and steam. On August 26, the island exploded and the next morning, most of the island was gone. Rocks and lava continued to shoot into the sky. The entire mountain, all 790 m (2600 ft) was gone. The eruptions triggered tsunamis (giant ocean waves) which battered the coastal towns on the islands of Java and Sumatra. The waves reached heights up to 40 m (130 ft) and were powerful enough to fling ashore coral blocks that weighed up to 272 kg (600 lbs). More than 36,000 residents of the towns died by the time all the waves had stopped.

Physical Description:
The Java Trench is a deep valley that runs along the islands of Sumatra and Java. It is the deepest part of the Indian Ocean—7450 m (24,442 ft) below sea level. The islands in this region are largely the steep tops of volcanic mountains.

Interesting Things:
After the huge explosion of Krakatoa, only about one—fifth of the original island remained above water. A short distance away, a small new island was forming. It was called Anak Krakatau (meaning Child of Krakatoa) and it surfaced in 1959. Since then, it has been very active and has been growing in size and height with every small eruption. Many people say that Anak Krakatau will one day experience an explosion similar to that of Krakatoa.

ES 11

NOTES

....

....

....

Hola Amigos y Amigas!

My name is Salvador, and I want to tell you about my home in Mexico. I'm sending you a fact sheet about the geology of our region. I was born and have lived all my life in Baja California, Mexico. My family owns a small hotel in Loreto, a town of more than 10,000 people in north central Baja. If you look on a map, you'll see that Baja looks like it is separating from the rest of Mexico. Some people call it a heel that is breaking off from a woman's shoe.

We have lots of earthquakes here. There is a Mexican legend about the god, El Diablo, who made giant rips in the ground so he and his people didn't have to walk the long way around whenever they wanted to start some mischief on Earth.

If you ever visit this area, bring plenty of bottled water. It is very hot and dry. My hometown didn't receive a single drop of rain last year! But not all of Baja is desert. If you head down toward my sister's house in Cabo San Lucas, on the southern tip of the peninsula, you will see crops such as cotton, sugar cane, and olives. Some of the southern mountains also have forests that are used for our local economy.

Think about visiting us! I hope you have fun learning about Baja.

Su amigo,
Salvador Cabrera
Baja California, Mexicoa

NOTES

....

....

....

Fact Sheet:
Baja Peninsula

Location:
28°N 113°W
The northernmost state of Mexico, a peninsula that is bounded by the United States to the north, the Pacific Ocean to the west, and the Sea of Cortez to the east.

Geological Activity:
Many different volcanoes can be found around the Baja Peninsula, but eruptions have not been common recently. Many were active in the past 10,000 years but not in recent history. One active volcano is Tres Virgenes, which means Three Virgins. It is located in central Baja, not too far from Loreto. It has not erupted since the late 1700s and is surrounded by lava flows. Earthquakes are common, and many occur under the water in the Sea of Cortez.

Physical Description:
Baja California is very different from other landforms. It is a long, narrow peninsula 1,288 km (800 mi) long. There are barren, rugged mountains, such as the Sierra de la Victoria and the Sierra de la Laguna mountain ranges, in the south. These are much steeper than the Sierra Juarez and Sierra San Pedro mountain ranges in the north, which slope gently toward the Pacific coast. There are also islands with mountains, such as Cedros Island, off the coast of Baja. Mountains cover only about a quarter of the land. The rest of the area is made up of a lot of flat desert. Northern Baja is extremely hot and dry. Nearly 1,550 km² (600 mi²) are desert. But even the desert land is rich and valuable for the many forms of cacti and other rare plant life. The rich volcanic soil around the volcano is good for many plants, such as majestic elephant trees.

The mountains are not very tall, or as jagged and rough as some other mountain chains. The highest peak on Baja California is Cerro de la Encantada in northern Baja. It is more than 3,080 m (10,105 ft) above sea level. That isn't very high for a mountain.

Interesting Things:
The Baja Peninsula looks like it is breaking off from the mainland of Mexico. The Baja Peninsula appears to be moving north at a rate of about 6 cm (2.5 in.) every year. Some people think that someday the Baja Peninsula and coastal California will become an island.

EE 13

NOTES

....

....

....

Aloha Everyone!

My name is Keona, and I'm so glad to be a part of the team! My family and I are excited to help you in your investigation of Hawaii. Please look at the fact sheet I made for you.

Our small town of Kea'au, on the Big Island, is close to Kilauea Volcano. My grandfather once told me the story of this volcano. A long time ago, a man named Kamehameha led an army to attack a place called Pau. When the men gathered to defend Pau, Kilauea began rumbling. It sent a dark cloud into the air. Thunder and lightning started. The cloud rose and grew and covered the whole area in darkness, blocking out the Sun. Then Kilauea erupted, throwing up sand and burning rock, killing most of the men, even though they were far away from the mountain. The few survivors returned home, but they didn't stand a chance against Kamehameha's army. With the eruption of Kilauea, Kamehameha had been shown that Pele, goddess of fire, favored him over all other leaders. This helped him conquer and unite the islands, and he became the ruler of Hawaii. With stories like this one about the dangers of Kilauea, it may seem strange that so many people come to visit the volcano. But most of the time, Hawaiian volcanoes are not dangerous.

If you ever get here to see the volcano for yourself, you should take some time off and enjoy the Sun and beaches. I can show you Hawaii's famous black sand beaches. I hope the information I sent helps in your investigation!

Your friend,
Keona Kawens
Kea'au, Hawaii, U.S.A. (The Big Island)

Project-Based Inquiry Science

EE 14

NOTES

Fact Sheet:
Hawaiian Islands, USA

Location:
19°N 155°W
The state of Hawaii, located in the Pacific Ocean, has eight main islands, from east to west: Hawaii, Kahoolawe, Maui, Lanai, Molokai, Oahu, Kauai, and Niihau. The complete island chain includes almost 20 spread out in a line. It looks like a necklace of shells stretching northwest from the main island (Hawaii), and it is easy to imagine they are all a string of mountains connected under the water. The Big Island is the newest and the largest. As the islands get farther from the Big Island, they get smaller.

Geological Activity:
The island of Hawaii is made up of five volcanoes, two of which are the most active in the world, Kilauea and Mauna Loa. The most recent eruption of Kilauea started in 1983. Since then, lava flows covering more than 100 km^2 (39 mi^2) have destroyed nearly 200 houses and added new coastline to the island. About 90 percent of the surface of the volcano is less than 1100 years old and 70 percent is younger than 600 years. That is very young for Earth. Mauna Loa has erupted more than 35 times since the island was first visited by Westerners in the 1800s. The last eruption of Mauna Loa started on March 25, 1984. The eruption followed a three-year period of slowly increasing earthquake activity and a 6.6 Richter Scale magnitude earthquake. The volcanoes of Hawaii are some of the best places on Earth to view lava flows. Lava quietly flows out of lava tubes or spits out like a fountain. Thin pahoehoe lava flows can move as fast as 56 km per hour (35 mph) creating a shining smooth black surface. Thicker a'a lava flows more slowly and forms rocky, rough surfaces when it cools. Ground surfaces formed from a'a lava can be sharp and painful to walk across.

Physical Description:
Hawaii is a chain of 20 volcanic islands. The largest of these islands is Hawaii, also called The Big Island. This island consists of five volcanoes, two of which are Mauna Loa and Kilauea. Mauna Loa is the largest volcano on Earth and rises gradually from the ocean floor to 4 km (25 mi) above sea level. Its summit is about 17 km (56,000 ft) above its base on the ocean floor. This enormous volcano covers half the island of Hawaii and, on its own, equals about 85 percent of all the other Hawaiian Islands combined.

Interesting Things:
The Hawaiian island chain grows and changes every day. When hot lava runs in the cool sea, new land is created. About 20 hectares (50 acres) of new land are created every year. New land is also being created deep under the sea. A diving team is exploring a new volcano off the coast of Hawaii. It may be a new landmass forming on the ocean floor. One day, probably many years from now, it will be high enough to form a new island.

EE 15

NOTES

Greetings Friends!

My name is Suna. I have been asked to tell you more about Iceland. I'm writing this letter to you at 11 PM from a park near my house. I live in the town of Akureyri, in northern Iceland, where the Sun sets at 1 AM in the summertime! It rises only an hour later. Isn't that amazing? You in the United States spell our country's name as Iceland, here we spell it Island. It means the same thing to us.

There are only 15,000 people living in Akureyri, which may seem like a small town compared to most American cities. However, it is the second largest city in Iceland after Reykjavik, the capital. Akureyri is only a few miles from the Arctic Circle and is one of the northernmost cities in the world. Just because we're so far north doesn't mean we don't grow crops. We have many kilometers of rich farmland, especially in the southern and southwestern regions. Also, all children growing up in Iceland become very good at fishing.

The ancient people of my country thought that volcanoes were the entrance to the underworld, the home of the Prince of Darkness, Hekla. When the fires burned, souls were being dragged down. When the fires cooled, Hekla would be throwing souls from the embers into the snow and ice to cool them off, so they wouldn't become too used to the fires.

If you ever come to Iceland, don't forget your camera, because you'll see some of the most beautiful natural scenery anywhere. I hope all this information helps you.

Your pal,
Suna Ericsson
Akureyri, Island (Iceland)

ÍSLAND

75

Project-Based Inquiry Science

EE 16

NOTES

....

....

....

Fact Sheet:
Iceland

Location:
65°N 21°W
The second largest island in Europe. Iceland is in the north Atlantic Ocean.
close to the Arctic Circle. about midway between New York and Moscow.

Geological Activity:
Iceland has as many as 34 volcanoes. Some are currently active and some are
not. About one volcanic eruption happens every five years. Iceland is covered
with glaciers. The fire and ice make a spectacular combination. Geysers. volcanic
lava fountains. and hot springs are common in Iceland. Lava fields cover almost
11 percent of the country, and glaciers cover almost 12 percent. Earthquakes are
also frequent here. Some of these earthquakes go unnoticed. The volcanoes
are frequent here but also diverse. Eruptions sometimes happen along fissures
and craters. and others occur deep on the ocean floor. Some eruptions
are explosive and occur at the tops of high mountains. Still others bubble quietly
and ooze lava from small. flat volcanoes.

Physical Description:
Iceland is a large island in the middle of the Atlantic Ocean. The island
consists of a central volcanic plateau with elevations from about 700 to 800 m
(2300 to 2600 ft) ringed by mountains with elevations as high as 2119 m (6952 ft).

Interesting Things:
New islands are born around Iceland. Near the island is a large group of
submarine (underwater) volcanic islands. In 1963, one of these submarine
volcanoes started erupting. For three-and-a-half years. lava flows built up to
form the new island of Surtsey. Iceland's smallest volcano system is Lysuholl.
made up of a chain of small cinder cone volcanoes. The people of Iceland often
must deal with volcanoes. For example. in 1973, a huge explosion on the island of
Heimaey threatened a nearby town. The town's 5000 residents were forced to
evacuate. and some of the town was destroyed by the lava flows. In an effort
to save other homes and businesses. sea water was sprayed on the lava flow.
This action slowed and moved the flow and saved the town's harbor. The
eruption lasted about six months. When it was all over. about 229 cubic
meters (300 million cubic yards) of material was ejected during the eruption.
The island had expanded. and it had a new volcanic cinder cone that was over
100 m (350 ft) above sea level.

EE 17

NOTES

....

....

....

Greetings!

My name is Tenzing. I live in Nepal and have been asked to give you some information about the Himalayan Mountains and Mount Everest. I am happy to help with your investigation. My family and I live in a village near the border with Tibet.

These mountains have a rich history, especially Mount Everest, the highest mountain in the world. The famous Sherpa, Tenzing Norgay (my namesake) accompanied Sir Edmund Hillary of New Zealand, in 1953, as the first climbers on record to reach the top of Mount Everest. The Sherpas are a group of people in this area who are famous for being expert guides on mountain-climbing expeditions. Since 1953, more than 500 people, including many Sherpa guides, from 20 different countries, have successfully climbed to the top of Mount Everest. Sadly, many people have died trying to climb the peaks of Everest and K2 (the second-highest mountain). Some hazards, such as thundering avalanches, flash storms, and hidden crevasses, are beyond a climber's control. Though Mount Everest is taller, K2 is more dangerous and more difficult to climb, or summit. In 1954, two Italian climbers reached the top of K2 after many attempts by others.

We also have many volcanoes and earthquakes. Can you imagine volcanoes in a snow-filled place? Maybe you can visit one day and see for yourself. My people have a very old culture, and we have many legends about the earthquakes. One is that there is a cavern beneath Earth, the home of the Nagas, where serpents with 1000 heads, dressed in purple, shake their heads and cause Earth to shake. Enjoy learning more about our land and our famous Mount Everest.

Your pal,
Tenzing Sharwa
Namche Bazaar, Nepal

EE 18

Project-Based Inquiry Science

NOTES

....

....

....

Fact Sheet:
Mount Everest

Location:
28°N 87°E
Mount Everest is part of the Great Himalayan Mountain Range that stretches across northern India and makes a border between India and the rest of Asia.

Geological Activity:
Earthquakes and avalanches are common occurrences and make the Himalayas dangerous, especially to those unfamiliar with the area. Volcanoes are scattered throughout the area. The mountain range grows about 3 cm (1.2 in.) each year. Forces from the surrounding area push these mountains upward. However, the ground erodes away almost as fast, so the mountain range stays about the same height.

Physical Description:
A large number of the world's highest peaks are located in the Himalayas. Mount Everest is the tallest peak in the world at 8850 m (29,035 ft) and K2 is the second-tallest peak at 8611 m (28,250 ft). The Himalayas make a "wall" between India and the rest of Asia, which results in two very different climates in the region and many different ecosystems. The mountains block the warm, moist Indian monsoon winds, so the plateau of Tibet is one of the driest and coolest places on Earth. In contrast, these monsoon winds heap heavy rainfall on India. The variety of elevations and range of rainfall create a number of different forest and desert ecosystems.

Interesting Things:
The highest peaks on Earth are still getting higher. The Himalayan Mountain Range grows about 3 cm (1.2 in.) every year.

At the summit of Mount Everest, scientists have found fossils of ancient sea cucumbers and plants, showing that the highest peak in the world today was once at the bottom of a deep ocean.

EE 19

NOTES

....

....

....

Konichiwa, Friends!

My name is Kazuo and I just said *"Hello"* to you in Japanese. My cousin, Saburo, and I will be your personal advisors as you learn about Japan! You have probably heard of sushi, sumo wrestlers, and video games that come from our country. But there is another side to Japan that we will be exploring. Please take time to look at the fact sheet I sent. My cousin and I both live in Odawara. It is a coastal city of about 200,000 people. It is about 50 km (31 mi) from the capital city of Tokyo, and less than 32 km (20 mi) from our most famous mountain, Mount Fuji.

I hope you like this Japanese earthquake legend. A giant catfish lived in mud beneath Earth. It liked to play pranks and would be still only for the god Kashima, who protected the people from earthquakes. When Kashima kept a mighty rock with magical powers over the catfish, Earth was still. When he relaxed his guard, the catfish thrashed about, causing earthquakes.

Japan is a very beautiful country. If you ever visit, I'm sure we can give you a boat tour of the area around our hometown. I hope all this helps, and I hope to hear from you soon.

Your friends,
Kazuo Matsuyama and
Saburo Matsuyama
Odawara, Japan

EE 20

NOTES

....

....

....

Fact Sheet:
Mount Fuji

Location:
35oN 139oE
Mount Fuji is on the island of Honshu, one of the several thousand islands of Japan.

Geological Activity:
Mount Fuji is one of 265 volcanoes and 20 active volcanoes in Japan. Mount Fuji last erupted in 1707, but the region experiences frequent volcanic activity and earthquakes. An earthquake is recorded every hour in Japan. In 1923, a huge 8.0 magnitude earthquake on the Richter Scale and the fire that followed killed about 143,000 people and destroyed over 300,000 buildings. These events change the shape of land and can be devastating to Japan's large population. Japan is roughly the size of California but has a population that is nearly four times larger. Japan is also known for its unusually explosive volcanoes. It leads the world with 41 large eruptions during the past 2000 years.

Japan also faces disaster from offshore. Seismic activity under the ocean creates tsunamis that can rise to over 30 m (almost 100 ft). These high waves can cause destruction and severe erosion when they hit low-lying coastal areas.

Physical Description:
The Japanese islands are the tops of very large mountains. These mountains are steep and rugged. Mount Fuji is the highest peak of the many peaks among these mountains with an elevation of 3776 m (12,388 ft). Mount Fuji is a steep-sided cone-shaped volcano. Its image is common in Japanese art. East of the islands is a series of deep submarine trenches. One is the Japan Trench with the deepest point being 8513 m (27,929 ft) below sea level. That is almost five miles below sea level.

Interesting Things:
The region of the Japanese Islands has one of the largest concentrations of submarine (underwater) volcanoes. These submarine volcanoes sometimes erupt and become new islands. Fukutoku-Okanoba is one of these massive volcanoes. Large clouds of sulfur discolor the water, and rock builds up to form new land that eventually emerges from the sea. In 1986, Fukutoku-Okanoba did just that and then a few months later the peak collapsed, so the mountain was below the sea again.

EE 21

NOTES

....

....

....

Hello, Friends!

My name is Pablo. I want to tell you about the Andes Mountains, the longest mountain chain in the world. My family has lived in the steep Andes Mountains for many generations. I included a fact sheet containing many interesting things. I hope you learn a lot from it.

We live in the town of Mendoza, Argentina, near Mount Aconcagua, the highest mountain peak in the Western Hemisphere. During the summer, my brother Raul leads climbing groups to the top of Mount Aconcagua. A few mules carry most of the gear up the steep slopes, but it still takes several days to reach the 6960 m (22,835 ft) tall top of this mountain. We have lots of earthquakes here. The ancient Peruvians, who also lived in the Andes, believed that whenever their god visited Earth to count how many people there were, his footsteps caused earthquakes. To shorten his task, the people ran out of their houses to shout, "I'm here, I'm here!"

If you ever decide to visit the mountains, you will have to bring lots of different types of clothing because you will go through all kinds of climates. And don't forget your camera. One of the greatest sights here is the sunset from the top of Mount Aconcagua. As the Sun dips down toward the west, all the mountain peaks turn a copper-brown shade. It reminds us of all the minerals mined here in the Andes, such as copper, gold, tin, platinum, lead, and zinc. The word Andes means copper color in the Peruvian Indian language.

Good luck studying our beautiful Andes!

Sincerely,
Pablo Fuentes
Mendoza, Argentina

Project-Based Inquiry Science

EE 22

NOTES

....

....

....

Fact Sheet:
Mount Aconcagua

Location:
33°S 70°W
Mount Aconcagua is in the southern part of the Andes Mountain range, located in South America. The Andes is the longest mountain range in the world. It runs north to south along the western coast of South America, from the hot tropical rain forests of Venezuela in the north to the cold tip of Patagonia in the south. It is 7250 km (4500 mi) long.

Geological Activity:
Mount Aconcagua is not a volcano, but there are 204 active volcanoes in the Andes. The volcanoes are quite beautiful to look at, but the ash clouds that pour out of them create hazards for airplanes and for people on the ground. Many homes are destroyed by mudflows. Mudflows occur when volcanic waste mixes with water. The mudflows go down steep mountain slopes at great speeds and destroy everything in the way. Earthquakes happen all the time—small ones and big ones. The biggest earthquake ever recorded in history (8.5 on the Richter Scale) occurred in the Andes in 1960. Thousands of people were killed and millions of homes were destroyed. The intense shaking caused by earthquakes causes landslides that can injure residents. The shaking also creates tsunamis, giant ocean waves, that can affect places as far away as Australia.

Physical Description:
The Andes is a narrow range of steep mountains that runs the length of South America. These steep mountains rise quickly from sea level. A deep trench runs parallel to the mountains next to the continent under the Pacific Ocean. The depths of the trench plunge to more than 5000 m (16,404 ft) below sea level. Wide ranges of elevations and the length of the Andes create a wide range of ecosystems—deserts, rain forests, sandy beaches next to steep cliffs, and fast-moving rivers that carry water from the mountain tops to the ocean.

Interesting Things:
The Andes Mountain Range grows in elevation about 3 cm (1.2 in.) per year. The mountains are also home to the world's highest volcano with a recorded eruption, and the volcano with the highest summit. Both of these volcanoes are in Chile. The Andes experience some of the largest and most frequent earthquakes in the world.

EE 23

NOTES

Hola, Norté Americanos,

On behalf of my family, I'd like to welcome you to Mexico. My name is Consuela and I live in the city of Puebla.

Puebla is southeast of Mexico City, the second biggest metropolitan area in the world. More than 20 million people live there. Our city of Puebla is also pretty large with more than a million people. Mount Popocatépetl, "Mount Popo" we call it, is only 40 km (25 mi) southeast of our town. This volcano is part of a range of volcanoes in Southern Mexico that line up from east to west. You can see Mt. Popo from far away because it is snow-capped and its peak is 5000 m (16,400 ft) above sea level.

An ancient Mexican people, the Aztecs, tell of a beloved princess who fell in love with a military captain. When the princess thought her love had been killed in battle, she became very ill and died of grief. The captain returned and carried the princess out of the city, where he also died of grief. The gods were sad at the death of the two young people and turned their bodies into great volcanoes, the biggest of which is Popocatépetl, the Captain, who throws out smoke to show he still watches over his beloved princess.

I've included a fact sheet so you can learn a lot about Mount Popo. Adios!

Buena Suerte,
Consuela Sanchez
Puebla, Mexico

EE 24

NOTES

....

....

....

Fact Sheet:
Mount Popocatépetl (or Mount Popo)

Location:
19°N 98°W
Mount Popocatépetl is part of the Trans-Mexican Volcanic Belt
that extends 900 km (560 mi) from east to west across central
southern Mexico.

Geological Activity:
An active volcano, formally called Mount Popocatépetl is 40 km
(25 mi) away from Puebla. Mount Popocatépetl was named by the
ancient Aztecs. Translated literally, it means "Smoking Mountain".
They called it this because steam and volcanic gases were constantly
pouring out of its large crater. Small columns of steam have been
observed coming out of the crater even in recent years. The gigantic
crater is 612 m (2008 ft) across; that's almost seven entire
football fields. In December of 1994, ash began to rain down, and
there was a series of earthquakes. The volcano had numerous minor
eruptions, frightening the townspeople, so the government moved
everyone farther from the volcano.

Geologists from around the world met to predict what the mountain
was going to do, but there was no huge explosion. The major eruptions
took place more than 10,000 years ago. The last serious eruption
occurred around the ninth century. About 20 minor eruptions have
been recorded since then.

Physical Description:
Mount Popocatépetl is a symmetrical volcanic cone and is
North America's fifth-highest peak. The base of the volcano is
covered in trees of oak and pine, and the top is covered in snow.

Interesting Things:
Many vulcanologists have studied "Popo" because most volcanoes
tend to have future eruptions that are very like their earlier ones.
They also study it because of the 20 million people who live close
enough to be threatened by its eruptions.

EE 25

NOTES

....

....

....

Jambo, Friends!

My name is Akili, and I just said "Hello" in Swahili, the native language of my country of Tanzania. You must excuse me because I am quite tired from my most recent trip. I just came back from climbing the great Mount Kilimanjaro. I can't wait to tell you all about Tanzania, my homeland and birthplace. My family lives in the town of Tanga. We are located in northern Tanzania. With a population of more than 200,000, our city is one of the largest in the country.

I can't wait to get my pictures developed from my trip up to the top of Kibo, which is the name of Mount Kilimanjaro's highest peak. From Kibo, there are great views of the grasslands of Tanzania. Once you reach Kibo, there is an icy crater, almost a mile wide, surrounded by steam. The whole place smells like rotten eggs from the sulfur. You definitely need to see the pictures. If you ever decide to visit, be sure to brush up on some Swahili phrases and get ready to see one of the tallest mountains in the world—and perhaps the location of the world's next ocean!

Ashanti native legends tell of a bull that tried to move a great rock buried in the plains. When it crashed into the rock at full speed, the rock split apart and flew in all directions, making the mountains of Africa. I hope you can use my information and the fact sheet. So, I will now say Jambo! (It also means "good-bye.")

Sincerely,
Akili Ngwonko
Tanga, Tanzania

Project-Based Inquiry Science

EE 26

NOTES

....

....

....

Fact Sheet:
Mount Kilimanjaro

Location:
3°S 37°E Mount Kilimanjaro lies on the border of Tanzania and Kenya, just south of the Equator. It is part of the Great African Rift Valley.

Geological Activity:
Mount Kilimanjaro is one of 20 volcanoes in the southern end of the Great African Rift valley. Its highest and youngest volcanic cone is named Kibo. Kibo has not been active in modern times, but steam and sulfur are still emitted from a 2.4 km (1.5 mi) crater at its summit. Many of the volcanoes in this region have erupted as recently as 1996, while others are considered extinct. This region is also home to the "Land of the Giant Craters". Some of these craters are 23 km (14 mi) across. They become this wide because the floor of the volcano sinks. These craters often fill with water. The water is warm, salty, and smells of sulfur (like rotten eggs) from the geological activity under the ground. All of this shifting leads to frequent earthquakes.

Physical Description:
Mount Kilimanjaro rises from the grasslands of the Great African Rift Valley as the tallest free-standing mountain in the world. The highest peak, Kibo, is 5895 m (19,335 ft) tall. Kilimanjaro is also considered one of the easiest mountains to climb. You can see the gradual slopes in the picture. If you are in good health and take one of the safe routes, you can reach the top even if you have no mountain-climbing experience. Climbers start their journey in the diverse grasslands and lakes of the flat valley. At the base of the mountain is a misty jungle. During the climb, the temperature drops and plant life changes. The higher elevations are covered in snow, even though this region is near the Equator.

Interesting Things:
The rock material coming from the volcanoes is similar to the rock material that comes out of volcanoes on the ocean floors. Scientists think that in thousands of years this region will eventually drop below sea level and the ocean will fill this valley with water.

EE 27

NOTES

....

....

....

Conference

5 min

Groups prepare presentations.

Conference

latitude: a north-south measure of a point on Earth's surface relative to the Equator. The latitude is measured in degrees (0° to 180°) north or south from the Equator.

longitude: the east-west position of a point on Earth's surface, relative to the Prime Meridian, an imaginary line chosen on Earth's surface that stretches from the North Pole to the South Pole and passes through Greenwich, England. The longitude is measured in degrees (0° to 180°) east or west from the arbitrary line.

You will need to know about many different regions to answer the *Big Question*, so you will be sharing information about your region with the class throughout this Unit. During this first presentation, you will communicate what you learned from your pen pal letter about the geologic activity in your region and your Earth structure.

There may be several pairs of students assigned to the same Earth structure. Meet with everyone who is assigned to your Earth structure, and prepare a presentation for the class. Prepare to present everything you learned from your pen pal letter about your Earth structure and the geologic activity in your region.

Be prepared to show where in the world your Earth structure is located. Using the latitude and longitude provided by your pen pal, locate your Earth structure on the *Big World Map* and mark it with a pushpin. The *Big World Map* shows the continent outlines and the lines of **latitude** and **longitude**. It is one type of map you will use to collect and analyze data throughout this Unit.

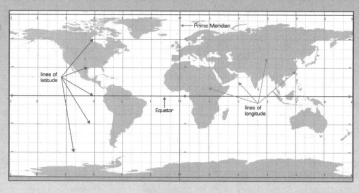

The Big World Map

EE 28

Project-Based Inquiry Science

△ Guide

Once students have read the letters from their pen pals, let them know they will share what they learned with the class. Tell the class that each Earth structure has been assigned to at least one pair. Pairs will share their data and ideas throughout this Unit so that they can understand all of Earth's structures and the processes that create them. To prepare their presentations, they should meet with any other pairs that were assigned the same Earth structure.

When students assigned to the same Earth structure have met, distribute pushpins. Have each group put a pushpin in the *Big World Map* to show where their Earth structure is. Then have them begin preparing their presentations. This would be a good time to introduce latitude and longitude, using the *Latitude and Longitude* textbox in the student text.

Emphasize that groups' presentations must include what the group considers the most important facts and observations about their Earth structure, explanations that they have for the movements and changes that occur in the region, a map of their region, a picture of the region, and their pen pal letter.

☐ Assess

Monitor groups and note ideas they do not fully agree on. These ideas should be turned into investigative questions for the *Project Board*.

NOTES

Latitude and Longitude

5 min

Students are introduced to longitude and latitude.

Latitude and Longitude

One way to identify locations on Earth is by using latitude and longitude. Latitude is a north-south measure of position on Earth. It is defined by the angle measured from the **Equator**, an imaginary line around the middle of Earth that is an equal distance from the North and South Poles. Because the Equator is midway between the North and South Poles, its latitude is 0°. Latitude is measured starting from the Equator and moving north or south.

To measure distance east or west, scientists use longitude lines. Longitude is an east-west measure of position on Earth. Longitude is shown as imaginary lines that run north to south from pole to pole. The starting point for measuring longitude is called the **Prime Meridian**. It goes through Greenwich, England. Similar to the Equator, its longitude is 0°. Longitude lines run between the geographic North and South Poles.

To describe the position of a place on Earth, you would use both latitude and longitude. By locating where a location's latitude and longitude intersect, you can easily find it on a map. Both latitude and longitude are measured in degrees. These degrees are different than the degrees used to measure temperature.

Equator: an imaginary line around the middle of Earth that is an equal distance from the North and South Poles.

Prime Meridian: an imaginary line chosen on Earth's surface that stretches from the North Pole to the South Pole and passes through Greenwich, England.

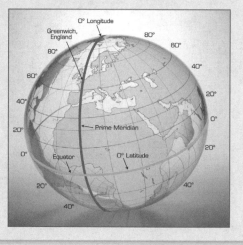

EE 29

EVER-CHANGING EARTH

△ Guide

Begin by explaining that latitude is used to describe how far north or south a location is. Longitude is used to describe how far east or west a location is. Both longitude and latitude measure the distance from a single, fixed line on the globe. Longitude measures the distance from Prime Meridian, a line that runs through Greenwich, England, the North Pole and the South Pole. Latitude measures the distance from the Equator, a line that is equally distant from the North and South Poles.

Communicate

When you present, begin by sharing the name of your Earth structure and pointing to its location on the *Big World Map.* Follow this with a description of your region based on your pen pal letter. Be sure to include any geologic activity and changes that have occurred there.

While other groups are presenting, identify Earth structures that are similar to yours. Listen for descriptions of geologic activity similar to what is happening in your region. Ask questions if you do not understand what has been happening in a region. Some of the information other groups present may help you identify things you would like to learn more about.

Reflect

1. Which regions have Earth structures similar to yours? How are they similar? How are they different?

2. How does the geologic activity occurring in the region of your Earth structure compare with that occurring in other regions? Describe any similarities, as well as any differences.

3. What do you need to learn more about to understand the geologic activity in your region?

Create a *Project Board*

When you work on a project to answer a *Big Question,* you need to keep track of your progress and what you still need to do. A useful way to do this is with a *Project Board.* The *Project Board* helps you to organize questions, investigations, results, and conclusions. It can also help you decide what to do next. During classroom discussions, the class's ideas will be recorded on a class *Project Board.*

EE 30

Project-Based Inquiry Science

Communicate

15 min

Groups present their Earth structure and have a class discussion on it.

META NOTES

It is important for students to learn about all the Earth structures being studied by the class. They will be using information and data from the Earth structures during the Unit to find patterns in volcanic and earthquake activity that will lead them to define the tectonic plates.

△ Guide

Let students know that when they present, they should point out where their region is on the *Big World Map* and they should describe their Earth structure and region to the class.

Let the class know it is important that they listen for interesting observations, explanations, and questions. Emphasize that they should pay particular attention to the details of Earth structures that may be similar to theirs. Point out that the information about similar Earth structures may help students think of new ideas or questions.

Have each group present their Earth structure to the class. Encourage students to ask questions and participate in a class discussion.

Model how to ask questions for students, for example: "That wasn't clear to me, could you say that another way?"

Reflect

10 min

Students discuss the Reflect *questions with their groups, and lead a class discussion of their responses.*

may help you identify things you would like to learn more about.

Reflect

1. Which regions have Earth structures similar to yours? How are they similar? How are they different?

2. How does the geologic activity occurring in the region of your Earth structure compare with that occurring in other regions? Describe any similarities, as well as any differences.

3. What do you need to learn more about to understand the geologic activity in your region?

Create a Project Board

⬡ Get Going

After groups have presented their Earth structures, have students discuss the *Reflect* questions with their partners. Let them know they will share their answers with the class.

☐ Assess and Guide

As pairs discuss the *Reflect* questions, ask them which Earth structures presented by their classmates they have discussed, and what similarities those Earth structures have to their Earth structure. Note any differences in the ways groups compare the Earth structures that were presented. These differences can be discussed later.

△ Guide

Lead a class discussion of the *Reflect* questions. Encourage students to give reasons why their Earth structure is or is not similar to another Earth structure. They should also explain how the geologic activity in a region is similar to geologic activity in their region. Encourage students to suggest things that would be helpful to know about other groups' regions.

J. What do you need to learn more about to understand the geologic activity in your region?

Create a *Project Board*

When you work on a project to answer a *Big Question*, you need to keep track of your progress and what you still need to do. A useful way to do this is with a *Project Board*. The *Project Board* helps you to organize questions, investigations, results, and conclusions. It can also help you decide what to do next. During classroom discussions, the class's ideas will be recorded on a class *Project Board*.

Create a *Project Board*

5 min

The class creates a Project Board.

△ Guide

As students discuss their regions and what they would like to learn more about, tell them that they will keep track of their progress and what they still have to learn using a *Project Board*. As in previous Units, students will update the *Project Board* as they proceed until they gather enough information from everyone's Earth structures to explain the changes happening in the regions around the Earth structures.

Record the *Big Question, What processes within Earth cause geologic activity?*, at the top of their *Project Board* and have students record it at the top of their *Project Board* pages.

TEACHER TALK

"Now that we have learned something about all of the Earth structures and the surrounding regions, we can start to think about how we're making progress towards answering the *Big Question: What processes within the Earth cause geologic activity?* You may already have some ideas about what causes geologic activity in your region. To keep track of what we are learning, we need to record our ideas of what we think we know, and what we need to investigate. We have used a *Project Board* before. We'll use a *Project Board* to keep track of this information in this Unit.**"**

Remind students what the five columns of the *Project Board* are: *What do we think we know? What do we need to investigate? What are we learning? What is our evidence?* and *What does it mean for the challenge or question?* Have students write the *Big Question* in the top part of their *Project Board*.

The *Project Board* has space for answering five guiding questions:

- What do we think we know?
- What do we need to investigate?
- What are we learning?
- What is our evidence?
- What does it mean for the challenge or question?

What processes within Earth cause geologic activity?				
What do we think we know?	What do we need to investigate?	What are we learning?	What is our evidence?	What does it mean for the challenge or question?

To get started, identify the important questions you need to answer. In this Unit, the *Big Question* is *What processes within Earth cause geologic activity?*

NOTES

....

....

....

....

PBIS

Project Board

The pen pal letter you received helped you to identify features in the region of your Earth structure, as well as some of the geologic activity that has happened or is happening now. The letter also helped you think about what you do not yet understand well. For example, you do not know why earthquakes and volcanic eruptions occur. Record the *Big Question* at the top of the *Project Board.* In the first two columns of the *Project Board,* you will record what you think you know and what you need to learn more about to address the *Big Question.*

What do we think we know?

In this column of the *Project Board,* record what you think you know about processes within Earth that cause geologic activity such as earthquakes and volcanic eruptions. Discuss and record what you think you know about earthquakes and volcanic eruptions and where they occur. You may have studied earthquakes and volcanoes before and already have some knowledge about them. Talk about all the facts and ideas you have, big and small.

What do we need to investigate?

In this column of the *Project Board,* record the things you need to learn more about to explain the geologic activity occurring in your region and how it helped form your Earth structure. During your group and class discussions of the *Big Question,* you may have found that you disagreed with some of the ideas of others. This column is designed to help you keep track of things that are debatable, unknown, and need to be investigated.

Later in this Unit, you will return to the *Project Board* many times. For now, work as a class and begin filling in the first two columns of the *Project Board.*

Project-Based Inquiry Science

Project Board

10 min

Students record their progress on the Project Board.

△ Guide

Ask students what they think they know about the changes and movements that occur in certain areas of Earth. Ask them what they know about volcanoes and earthquakes and where they occur. Record students' responses in the first column and have students write them in their own *Project Boards.* There are some facts within the pen pal letters that students may list.

Some examples of what students might list as what they think they know are listed below:

- Earthquakes are common and become more frequent before a volcanic eruption.

- Volcanoes can occur above ground and under water.

- Earthquakes can occur above ground and under water.

- Volcanoes can cause landslides.

Finally, ask students what they need to investigate further to be able to answer the *Big Question*. In this column, students should suggest what they are not sure of or any ideas under dispute. Record their questions in the *What do we need to investigate?* column, and have students write them on their own *Project Board* pages. Some examples of what students might list as what they need to investigate are listed below:

- How do Earth structures form?

- Are all mountains caused by volcanoes? What else could cause a mountain to form?

- What kinds of Earth structures are there?

- How does volcanic activity form structures?

- Are there a lot of earthquakes? Why?

- Are there a lot of volcanoes? Why?

- Did volcanoes help form our Earth structure?

◇ Evaluate

The second column of the *Project Board* should contain generalized *how* and *why* questions similar to the examples provided above.

NOTES

....

....

....

....

Assessment Options

Targeted Concepts, Skills, and Nature of Science	How do I know if students got it?
Scientists often work together and then share their findings. Sharing findings makes new information available and helps scientists refine their ideas and build on others' ideas. When another person's or group's idea is used, credit needs to be given.	**ASK:** What did you learn from other groups' presentations? **LISTEN:** Students should list information on the *Project Board* that they learned from other groups' presentations.
Scientists must keep clear, accurate, and descriptive records of what they do so they can share their work with others and consider what they did, why they did it, and what they want to do next.	**ASK:** Why is it helpful to record your ideas on the *Project Board?* **LISTEN:** Students should recognize that recording their ideas on the *Project Board* will allow them to see what they have learned and what they still need to learn.
Identifying factors that could affect the phenomenon being investigated is an important part of planning scientific research.	**ASK:** Why is it important to learn about the geologic activity and the region around your Earth structure? **LISTEN:** Students should understand it is important to learn about things that could affect their Earth structure.

NOTES

....

....

EVER-CHANGING EARTH

Teacher Reflection Questions

- What misconceptions about Earth structures do students have? What ideas do you have to address these during the Unit?

- The *Unit Introduction* introduced the *Big Question*. How could you tell if students were motivated by this question? What ideas do you have to foster their motivation and application of ideas?

- What management issues came up while groups were working on their pen pal letters?

NOTES

LEARNING SET 1 INTRODUCTION

Learning Set 1

How Can My Region Be Described?

◄ $4\frac{1}{2}$ *class periods*

A class period is considered to be one 40 to 50 minute class.

Students investigate their Earth structures and regions using color maps and other visualization tools.

Overview

Students begin exploring their Earth structures by considering its topography. They use color maps and other visualization tools to identify significant features of their Earth structures and their regions. By doing this, they learn to interpret patterns in the information provided by the visualization tools. Then they use Earth-imaging software to further explore their Earth structures and regions. They synthesize everything they have learned from using different visualization tools by drawing a picture of their Earth structure. In a list below the drawing, they include important information they learned about the Earth structures, as well as where they learned it. By recording where they have learned the listed information and the information in their drawing, they track what they are learning, how they are learning it, and how they are using it. Students present what they have learned about their Earth structure and its region to the class, allowing students to compare their Earth structures, their use of the visualization tools, and their interpretations of data to their classmates. These early modeling and sharing activities prepare students to think about complex data as they learn more about their Earth structures.

Targeted Concepts, Skills, and Nature of Science	Section
Scientists must keep clear, accurate, and descriptive records of what they do so they can share their work with others and consider what they did, why they did it, and what they want to do next.	1.1, 1.2, 1.BBQ
Graphs and tables are an effective way to analyze and communicate results of scientific investigation.	1.1, 1.BBQ

EVER-CHANGING EARTH

Targeted Concepts, Skills, and Nature of Science	Section
Scientists use models and tools, such as Geographic Information Systems, and a variety of maps to develop claims and explanations from evidence in the data.	1.1, 1.2, 1.BBQ
Scientists often work together and then share their findings. Sharing findings makes new information available and helps scientists refine their ideas and build on others' ideas. When another person's or group's idea is used, credit needs to be given.	1.BBQ

Activity Setup and Preparation

Students will use the *My World* software to investigate the Earth structures in their region during this *Learning Set*. You will need to demonstrate how to use the software. Take some time before class to familiarize yourself with *My World's* interface. When the software loads, you will find a *Library* dropdown in the leftmost section (make sure that the *Construct* tab is selected). Use the dropdown to select *Earth Structures & Processes*. Then double click on *EarthstructuresIntro.m3vz* in the pane below the dropdown. The *Visualize* tab should automatically be selected when the project loads. In the right pane, you should see a map of the world, and a toolbox above the map. The *Pointer Tool* allows you to retrieve data on any location on the map. The hand tool allows you to move the map within the viewer.

The rightmost tool, which has a line graph for an icon, is the *Create Vertical Profile* tool. Select this tool. In the pop-up dialogue box, set the sample rate to *every 10 km* and click *OK*. Draw a line on the map by clicking where you want one endpoint of the line, and then double click where you want the other endpoint. The software will generate a graph showing the elevation or depth of Earth's surface along the line that you drew.

In the left pane, you will see a list of layers. Each layer can be turned on or off by toggling the eye icon next to the layer's name. Try turning the different layers on and off to see what they do.

Use the *Map View* dropdown at the top right of the viewer to select different Earth structures to view.

Students will also need to use Earth-imaging software. Make sure you know how to navigate the globe using the software before class. You should be able to find street addresses on the globe and locations using its latitude and longitude. In the Earth-imaging software, you can enter a street address in the *Fly to* field to navigate there. You can also enter latitude and longitude in the *Fly to* field to find a location. Type the latitude first, then the longitude, separated by commas. For example, to find the Java Trench into the Earth-imaging software, type *10°S, 110°E* in the *Fly to* field.

Learning Set 1

How Can My Region Be Described?

To understand geologic activity in a region, scientists first learn all they can about the region. They want to know where the region is located and what it looks like, including its size and shape and any Earth structures located there. Knowing the history of any geologic activity in the region is also important. You will gather the same information about your region. In this *Learning Set*, you will learn how to do this by answering a smaller question: *How can my region be described?*

Geologists are people who are trained in and work in any of the geologic sciences. To gather information about a region, they use a variety of different tools to see, or visualize, Earth's surface. These visualization tools help them determine the locations and shapes of Earth regions and structures and to observe where and when geologic activity is happening. Geologists can then look for connections between geologic activity and the appearance of the region.

geologist: a person who is trained in and works in any of the geologic sciences.

You will be working as geologists do when they investigate a region of Earth. Some of the visualization tools you will use to examine the surface of your region and your Earth structure will be similar to those that geologists use. Others have been designed so that anyone with an interest in geography or geology can use them to explore.

EE 33

EVER-CHANGING EARTH

Learning Set 1

How Can My Region Be Described?

5 min

Students are introduced to the question of the Learning Set.

◯ Engage

Begin by asking students to describe the Earth structure in their region. Ask if they can describe what the structure looks like.

Emphasize that being able to describe how something looks and to visualize it can help to learn about it.

*A class period is considered to be one 40 to 50 minute class.

△ Guide

Tell students that they will use visualization tools to see what their regions and Earth structures look like. Emphasize that geologists regularly use visualization tools to see Earth's surface.

TEACHER TALK

"Geologists, the scientists who study the structures and processes of the Earth, use visualization tools to see the surface of the Earth. In order to answer the question of the *Learning Set, How Can My Region Be Described?* you will use visualization tools, just as geologists do."

NOTES

1.1 Understand the Question

Thinking About How My Region Can Be Described

◀ *2 class periods*

A class period is considered to be one 40 to 50 minute class.

Overview

Students investigate the topographic features of their regions using color maps. They are introduced to some basic concepts of topography that will help them understand and describe their regions. Then they use a visualization software tool, *My World,* to explore color maps of regions of Earth. Using these maps, they identify significant features of their regions and develop an understanding of how these features can be used to describe a region. They create vertical profiles of their Earth structures, using graphs of elevation and depth to interpret the topographic data in the color map. By comparing the information from their color maps with the descriptions from their pen pal letters, they analyze the strengths and limitations of visualization tools.

Targeted Concepts, Skills, and Nature of Science	Performance Expectations
Scientists must keep clear, accurate, and descriptive records of what they do so they can share their work with others and consider what they did, why they did it, and what they want to do next.	Students should keep clear, accurate, and descriptive records of the topography of their Earth structure and their comparisons with other Earth structures.
Graphs and tables are an effective way to analyze and communicate results of scientific investigation.	Students should recognize that a graph of elevations and depths can help them interpret their data.
Scientists use models and tools, such as Geographic Information Systems, and a variety of maps to develop claims and explanations from evidence in the data.	Students should be able to describe the topography of their Earth structure using their three-dimensional models.

Materials	
1 per student	Group's pen pal letter *My Profile Grid* page *My World Region Map* page
1 per class	Computer with *My World*
1 per class (optional)	Color map

Activity Setup and Preparation

Before class, arrange to have computers available for students. Make sure that *My World* is installed on these computers. Also make sure that you have a computer available to use for demonstration. If you have a projector for the demonstration computer, get it ready before class. Ensure that you are comfortable with the software before giving the demonstration.

Homework Options

Reflection

- **Science Content:** What ideas do you have about how the shape of an Earth structure could provide information on the processes that cause change in Earth structures? *(Students should begin to construct ideas about how the shapes of Earth structures correlate to the processes that formed them.)*

Preparation for 1.2

- **Science Content:** Describe the prominent features of your Earth structure that people would notice if they were viewing it from a helicopter. *(Students' descriptions should include the prominent features and describe how these would appear from above.)*

SECTION 1.1 IMPLEMENTATION

1.1 Understand the Question

Thinking About How My Region Can Be Described

Your pen pal letter gave you some information about your region and Earth structure, but it did not provide everything you will need to know. To gain a better understanding of your region and Earth structure, you need to collect more data about its shape and geologic activity.

In this *Learning Set,* you will use several different visualization tools. Each one will enable you to learn more about the **topography**—the general arrangement of a land surface, including its relief (height and slope) and the position of its natural and human-made features—of your region and your Earth structure. The topography of a region can give clues about the geologic activity occurring there and what is causing it. Different visualization tools can help you identify different topographic features of your region. Topographic features are the detailed characteristics of the topography of a region. They might include the locations, heights, and slopes of mountains, and the locations and depths of valleys and rivers.

topography: the general arrangement of a land surface, including its relief (height and slope) and the position of its natural and human-made features.

The topographic features of this region include mountains, valleys, and rivers.

EE 34

Project-Based Inquiry Science

1.1 Understand the Question

Thinking About How My Region Can Be Described

5 min

Students are introduced to the activity.

△ Guide

Begin by pointing out the photograph in the student text. Ask students how they would describe the landscape in the photograph. Students should say that there are mountains in the landscape. Students may also say that there are valleys and bodies of water.

Tell students that the mountains, valleys, and lakes are physical features, or topography, of the region. Let them know they will study the topography of their regions in this section. Emphasize that the topography of the region may give them clues about the geologic activity happening there.

TEACHER TALK

❝How would you describe the landscape in the picture? What physical features do you see?

These physical features are important, because they can give you clues about the geological activity happening in a region. We call the physical features of a region its topography.❞

NOTES

_____

_____

_____

_____

_____

_____

_____

_____

_____

_____

_____

1.1 Understand the Question

Get Started

Scientists use several kinds of images and maps to visualize different topographic features of a region. One important feature of a region is its **elevation** or **depth**. Elevation is the vertical distance (height) from **sea level** (the average height of the surface of the oceans) to a point on Earth's surface. Depth is the distance below sea level of a point on Earth's surface. To find this information, a scientist might use a **color map**. Color maps use different colors to represent changes in the elevation and depth of Earth's surface. You will be using color maps in a computer program called *My World* to examine the topography of your region and Earth structure.

You will be introduced to *My World* by working with your class, using *My World* to answer questions about Earth's topography. You will then work with your partner, using *My World* to investigate your region and Earth structure in detail.

elevation: the vertical distance (height) from sea level to a point on Earth's surface.

depth: distance below sea level of a point on Earth's surface.

sea level: the average height of the surface of the oceans; it is used as a reference point for the measurement of elevation and depth.

color map: a map that uses color to show changes in the elevation and depth of Earth's surface.

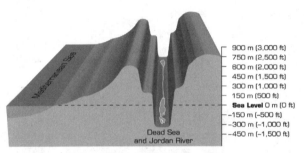

- 900 m (3,000 ft)
- 750 m (2,500 ft)
- 600 m (2,000 ft)
- 450 m (1,500 ft)
- 300 m (1,000 ft)
- 150 m (500 ft)
- **Sea Level** 0 m (0 ft)
- −150 m (−500 ft)
- −300 m (−1,000 ft)
- −450 m (−1,500 ft)

Mediterranean Sea

Dead Sea and Jordan River

The Dead Sea is a hypersaline (very salty) lake bounded by Israel and the West Bank on the west, and Jordan on the east. It is 420 m (1378 ft) below sea level, and its shores are the lowest point on the surface of Earth on dry land. At 380 m (1247 ft) deep, the Dead Sea is the deepest salt lake in the world.

EE 35

EVER-CHANGING EARTH

△ Guide

Tell students that scientists use maps to see the physical features of regions. One important physical feature of a region often shown on maps is elevation or depth. The student text defines these terms, but make sure students understand them. Elevation refers to how far above sea level a point on Earth's surface is, and depth refers to how far below sea level a point on Earth's surface is.

Get Started

10 min

Students are introduced to color maps.

"The elevation of a location is how far above sea level a location is. Sea level is the level of the surface of the ocean. Most places on land are higher than sea level. The depth of a location is how far below sea level a location is. Locations at the bottom of the sea are below sea level and have depth.**"**

Try to show students an example of a color map. Explain that the different colors on the map represent different elevations or depths. Let students know they will use similar maps in this section.

NOTES

_____

_____

_____

_____

_____

_____

_____

_____

_____

_____

_____

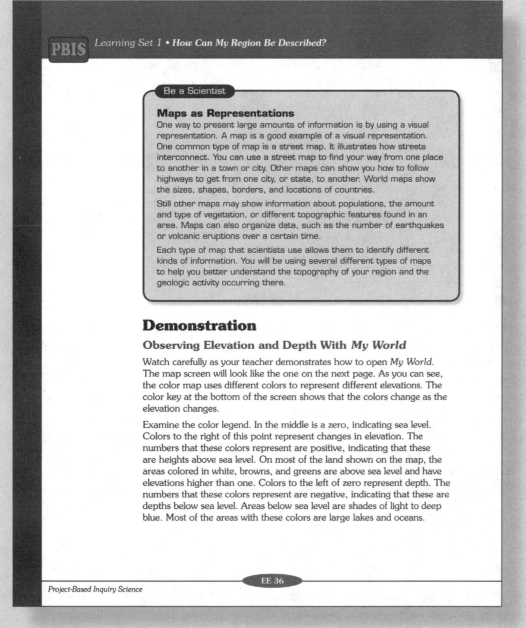

Be a Scientist

Maps as Representations

One way to present large amounts of information is by using a visual representation. A map is a good example of a visual representation. One common type of map is a street map. It illustrates how streets interconnect. You can use a street map to find your way from one place to another in a town or city. Other maps can show you how to follow highways to get from one city, or state, to another. World maps show the sizes, shapes, borders, and locations of countries.

Still other maps may show information about populations, the amount and type of vegetation, or different topographic features found in an area. Maps can also organize data, such as the number of earthquakes or volcanic eruptions over a certain time.

Each type of map that scientists use allows them to identify different kinds of information. You will be using several different types of maps to help you better understand the topography of your region and the geologic activity occurring there.

Demonstration

Observing Elevation and Depth With *My World*

Watch carefully as your teacher demonstrates how to open *My World*. The map screen will look like the one on the next page. As you can see, the color map uses different colors to represent different elevations. The color key at the bottom of the screen shows that the colors change as the elevation changes.

Examine the color legend. In the middle is a zero, indicating sea level. Colors to the right of this point represent changes in elevation. The numbers that these colors represent are positive, indicating that these are heights above sea level. On most of the land shown on the map, the areas colored in white, browns, and greens are above sea level and have elevations higher than one. Colors to the left of zero represent depth. The numbers that these colors represent are negative, indicating that these are depths below sea level. Areas below sea level are shades of light to deep blue. Most of the areas with these colors are large lakes and oceans.

EE 36

Project-Based Inquiry Science

Be a Scientist: Maps as Representations

5 min

The class discusses what kinds of information they can get from maps.

⚠ Guide

Emphasize that there are many different kinds of maps, and that maps can represent all kinds of information about places. Ask students what kinds of maps they have seen. They have probably seen street maps before. Point out that street maps represent how streets interconnect (information that is useful for drivers), but do not show elevations and depths.

Emphasize that maps can also show political boundaries, the populations of different places, the vegetation, and different topographic features. Let students know they will use several different kinds of maps.

Demonstration: Observing Elevation and Depth with *My World*

20 min

Students watch a demonstration of how to use My World.

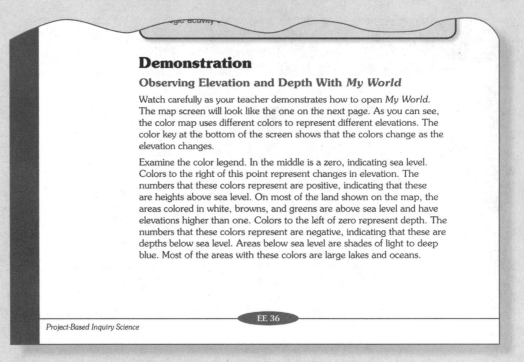

Demonstration

Observing Elevation and Depth With *My World*

Watch carefully as your teacher demonstrates how to open *My World*. The map screen will look like the one on the next page. As you can see, the color map uses different colors to represent different elevations. The color key at the bottom of the screen shows that the colors change as the elevation changes.

Examine the color legend. In the middle is a zero, indicating sea level. Colors to the right of this point represent changes in elevation. The numbers that these colors represent are positive, indicating that these are heights above sea level. On most of the land shown on the map, the areas colored in white, browns, and greens are above sea level and have elevations higher than one. Colors to the left of zero represent depth. The numbers that these colors represent are negative, indicating that these are depths below sea level. Areas below sea level are shades of light to deep blue. Most of the areas with these colors are large lakes and oceans.

EE 36

Project-Based Inquiry Science

△ Guide

Start *My World* and point out the parts of *My World's* interface described earlier in the *Activity Setup and Preparation*. Select *Earth Structures & Processes* from the *Library* dropdown. Then double click *EarthstructuresIntro.m3vz* in the pane below the dropdown. The viewer will automatically switch to the *Visualize* tab. This tab shows a color map of the world. Point out the legend at the bottom of the screen. The key shows what the colors on the map represent. Dark blues represent depths of around -5000 m (-16,404 ft). Greens show elevations near sea level, and Earth tones to white represent higher elevations.

TEACHER TALK

❝Notice this key at the bottom. It says *Elevation & Depth.* See how it goes from dark blue to light blue, then from dark green to white and the numbers go from -5750 to 0, and then from 0 to 5750? On the map, places that are dark blue have depths of around -5000 m (-16,404 ft). Places that are light blue have depths close to sea level. If you waded out into the sea, you would be standing on ground that would be light blue on the map. Places that are dark green on the map have a very low elevation, close to sea level. If you stood on the beach, you would be standing on ground that would be dark green on the map. The highest elevations are represented by these shades of white at the right of the key. High mountains would be white on the map.❞

The *Pointer Tool* is used to find the elevation or depth of a particular location. When you select the *Pointer Tool* on the toolbar, move and click the arrow over a location on the map, and a number will appear on the screen. This number indicates how many meters the location is above or below sea level.

You can also see the longitude and latitude by moving the arrow over the location. As you move the arrow over a location, its longitude and latitude appear at the bottom of the screen. Recall that longitude is the distance east or west of the Prime Meridian, measured in degrees. Latitude is the distance north or south of the Equator, and it is also measured in degrees.

The color changes on the map provide a lot of information. When large areas of the map are shaded with the same color, there is little or no change in elevation. When an area has several colors or shades of colors, the elevation is changing. If the colors on the map change a lot over a short distance, the elevation is changing quickly. This might indicate a hilly or mountainous area if the elevation is a positive number, or a deep trench in the ocean if the number is negative.

META NOTES

You can change the colors in the color key. To do this, double click the *Elevation & Depth* layer in the *Layer List* on the left side of the screen. In the window that pops up, you can set the colors of the elevations individually or you can select a new color scheme. A continuous color scheme such as *Grayscale* may help students understand relief maps.

Show students how they can use the *Pointer Tool* to display a numeric elevation or depth of any location on the map. Clicking any location on the map with the *Pointer Tool* will put a marker on the depth or elevation of that location with a numerical reading on the key at the bottom of the screen. Point out how the latitude and longitude of locations appear at the bottom of the screen as you move the arrow over locations.

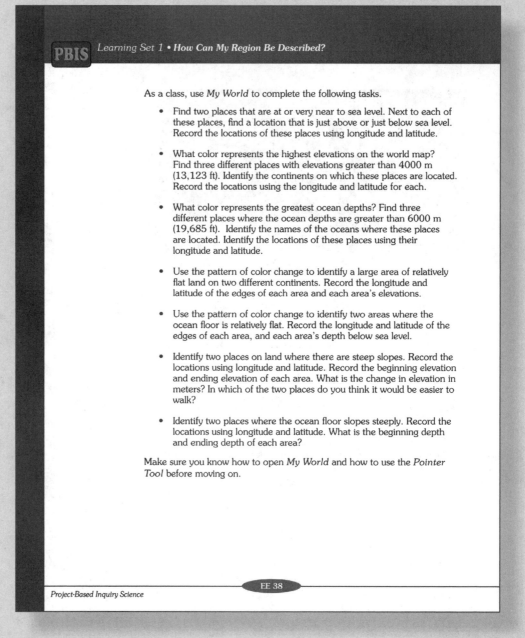

As a class, use *My World* to complete the following tasks.

- Find two places that are at or very near to sea level. Next to each of these places, find a location that is just above or just below sea level. Record the locations of these places using longitude and latitude.

- What color represents the highest elevations on the world map? Find three different places with elevations greater than 4000 m (13,123 ft). Identify the continents on which these places are located. Record the locations using the longitude and latitude for each.

- What color represents the greatest ocean depths? Find three different places where the ocean depths are greater than 6000 m (19,685 ft). Identify the names of the oceans where these places are located. Identify the locations of these places using their longitude and latitude.

- Use the pattern of color change to identify a large area of relatively flat land on two different continents. Record the longitude and latitude of the edges of each area and each area's elevations.

- Use the pattern of color change to identify two areas where the ocean floor is relatively flat. Record the longitude and latitude of the edges of each area, and each area's depth below sea level.

- Identify two places on land where there are steep slopes. Record the locations using longitude and latitude. Record the beginning elevation and ending elevation of each area. What is the change in elevation in meters? In which of the two places do you think it would be easier to walk?

- Identify two places where the ocean floor slopes steeply. Record the locations using longitude and latitude. What is the beginning depth and ending depth of each area?

Make sure you know how to open *My World* and how to use the *Pointer Tool* before moving on.

EE 38

Project-Based Inquiry Science

Read the bulleted questions in the student text to the class, and have the class answer each question. Use the following guidelines.

- You may want to zoom in on a continent. You could, for instance, zoom in on North America. Students should look for regions that are dark green or very light blue. The dark green and light blue regions will be found next to each other at coastlines. The southeastern part of North America has a lot of area near sea level. Be sure to select the *Pointer Tool* after you have adjusted the map so that you can get data on locations.

- To determine which color represents the highest elevations, students can simply refer to the color legend at the bottom of the map. They should look for places on the map with this color. They might identify the Andes in South America, the Himalayas in Asia, or the Sentinel Mountains in Antarctica. Each of these covers large areas, so they may select different points with different elevations within these areas.

- To determine which color represents the greatest depths, students can refer to the color legend at the bottom of the map. Students should look for places on the map with this color. They might identify the deep region about 250 mi (402 km) east of Japan (144°E, 38°N), or they might identify places within the Java Trench. There are also places in the bottom of the Atlantic Ocean that are more than -6000 m (19,685 ft) deep and can be found by dragging the *Pointer Tool* around the dark blue regions.

- The criterion for flat regions identified by students is that they should be large regions with fairly uniform color. Northern Russia, for instance, contains large regions that have elevations below 180 m (591 ft). In some places, this may be hard to judge. With the default color scheme, the color variation within the Himalayas is slight, but the variation of elevations can be greater than 1000 m (3281 ft).

- Students should use color to find flat regions on the sea floor, and check their choices with the arrow. They might identify the region around the Northern Sea Route to the north of Russia, which has depths between -310 m to -190 m (-1017 ft to 623 ft). There are relatively flat regions in the northern Pacific Ocean and to the south of the Horn of Africa that students might identify. The criterion for flat regions identified by students is that they should have fairly uniform color and have relatively narrow ranges of depths as revealed by the *Pointer Tool*.

- Students should identify places on land where there are great differences in elevation in small areas.

- Students should identify places on the seafloor where there are great differences in elevation in small areas.

Examine a Region in *My World*

10 min

Students examine their regions in My World.

Examine a Region in *My World*

Now you will work with the class to use *My World* to examine the topography of a particular region—the area around the Java Trench in Indonesia. Notice how your teacher uses the *Pointer Tool* and *My World*'s commands to zoom in on an area and see it in more detail. As a class, use the *My World* map and the following questions, to gather information about the region's topography.

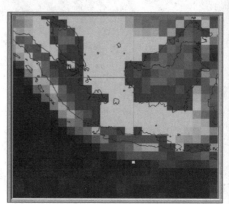

The Java Trench region in My World.

- Search around this region. Where is the highest elevation? What is the elevation of the highest point near its Earth structure?

- Where are the lowest elevations in the region around this Earth structure? What is the elevation of the lowest point?

- Where does the land have the steepest slopes? Describe how the colors change when the slope is steep.

- Find a place where the land is more gently sloped. Describe how the colors change when Earth's surface is flatter.

Stop and Think

1. The colors on the color map indicate the elevation and depth of places on Earth. Changes in the colors show the changes in the elevation or depth. How can you tell when Earth's surface slopes steeply? How can you tell when Earth's surface has a gentle slope?

2. Describe the color pattern you would see for a mountain with very steep sides. What color pattern would you see for a very flat area?

3. Describe the color pattern you would see if the ocean floor had a gentle slope. What color pattern would you see if there was a deep valley on the ocean floor?

4. How would you be able to tell where shorelines are located?

EE 39

EVER-CHANGING EARTH

△ Guide

Have students start *My World* on their computers if they have not already. Once they have loaded the *Earth Structures* project, show the class how to zoom in on the Java Trench. Let them know that they will answer questions about the Java Trench using *My World,* so they will need to be able to view it correctly.

○ Get Going

Ask the class where the highest elevation in the region of the Java Trench is. What is the highest elevation near the Earth structure? Students may look on the Island of Java. Using the *Pointer Tool*, you can find places on Java with an elevation of 900 m (2952 ft). In the immediate vicinity of the Earth structure on the ocean floor you can find places with depths of only about -2300 m (-7546 ft).

Ask the class what the lowest point in the Java Trench is. Students should be able to find places with depths around -6000 m (-19,685 ft).

Ask the class where the steepest slopes around the Java Trench are. The steepest slopes appear to be on the seafloor, on the northern side of the trench. The color here changes from dark blue to light blue in a small area. This is equivalent to a change of about 4000 m (13,123 ft) elevation in about 100,000 m (328,084 ft) laterally.

Ask students to identify gentle slopes. How do the colors change on gentle slopes? There are gentle slopes near the coasts of Java and Sumatra, and on the land. Students should observe that the colors change less dramatically when the slopes are gentle.

◇ Evaluate

Before going on to the *Stop and Think* questions, make sure that students have found and zoomed in on the Java Trench in *My World*.

NOTES

....

....

....

....

....

....

META NOTES

As with any map, the *My World* map has limited resolution. The precise summits of mountains do not appear on the map. Instead, the elevation of a mountain's summit will be included in the range of elevations within a small area. For this reason, students may find several coordinates for roughly the same location that have the same elevation or depth.

META NOTES

Note that in the default color scheme, the elevations just under 350 m are green and elevations just over 350 m are yellow. This qualitative change may be confusing for students. On a continuous color scheme, the change in shade between 100 m and 600 m will be slight.

Stop and Think

10 min

Students answer the questions with their partners.

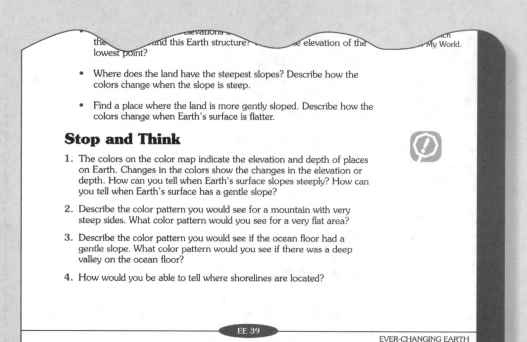

the _____ and this Earth structure? _____ e elevation of the _____ My World. lowest point?

- Where does the land have the steepest slopes? Describe how the colors change when the slope is steep.

- Find a place where the land is more gently sloped. Describe how the colors change when Earth's surface is flatter.

Stop and Think

1. The colors on the color map indicate the elevation and depth of places on Earth. Changes in the colors show the changes in the elevation or depth. How can you tell when Earth's surface slopes steeply? How can you tell when Earth's surface has a gentle slope?

2. Describe the color pattern you would see for a mountain with very steep sides. What color pattern would you see for a very flat area?

3. Describe the color pattern you would see if the ocean floor had a gentle slope. What color pattern would you see if there was a deep valley on the ocean floor?

4. How would you be able to tell where shorelines are located?

EE 39

EVER-CHANGING EARTH

△ Guide

After the class has discussed the topography of the Java Trench, tell them they will use what they have learned to answer the *Stop and Think* questions. Have them discuss the questions with their partners.

☐ Assess

As students discuss the *Stop and Think* questions, ask pairs what ideas they have discussed. The answers to some of these should have already come up in the class discussion. However, the second question requires students to imagine a mountainside, where the ground slopes steeply. They should recognize that the colors on a mountainside will change dramatically. The fourth question requires students to think about the color pattern at a shoreline. In the default color scheme, shorelines are clearly visible, since points that are just below sea level have a light blue color and points that are just above sea level are dark green. Note that in a continuous color scheme, such as *Grayscale*, shorelines are more difficult to see.

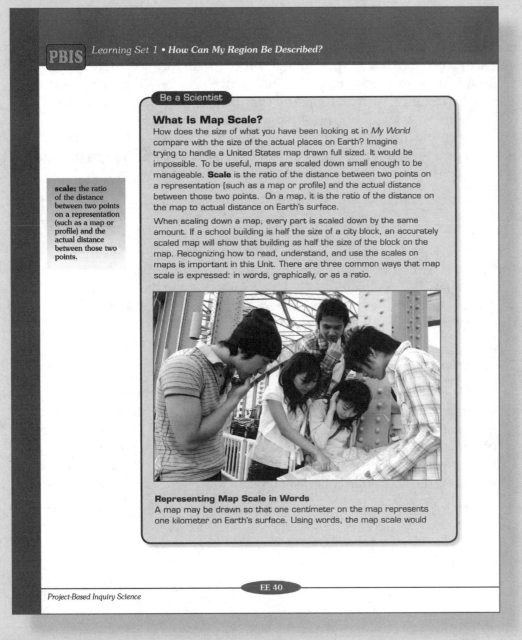

PBIS *Learning Set 1 • How Can My Region Be Described?*

Be a Scientist

What Is Map Scale?

How does the size of what you have been looking at in *My World* compare with the size of the actual places on Earth? Imagine trying to handle a United States map drawn full sized. It would be impossible. To be useful, maps are scaled down small enough to be manageable. **Scale** is the ratio of the distance between two points on a representation (such as a map or profile) and the actual distance between those two points. On a map, it is the ratio of the distance on the map to actual distance on Earth's surface.

When scaling down a map, every part is scaled down by the same amount. If a school building is half the size of a city block, an accurately scaled map will show that building as half the size of the block on the map. Recognizing how to read, understand, and use the scales on maps is important in this Unit. There are three common ways that map scale is expressed: in words, graphically, or as a ratio.

scale: the ratio of the distance between two points on a representation (such as a map or profile) and the actual distance between those two points.

Representing Map Scale in Words
A map may be drawn so that one centimeter on the map represents one kilometer on Earth's surface. Using words, the map scale would

EE 40

Project-Based Inquiry Science

Be a Scientist: What Is Map Scale?

5 min

Students read how to represent map scale.

⬡ Get Going

Explain scale to the class. Point out that maps cannot be as large as the areas they represent, and are usually much smaller. The scale of a map is the ratio of sizes or distances on the map to sizes or distances on Earth's surface. Tell students that scale can be represented in three different ways. It can be expressed verbally, graphically, and as a ratio.

TEACHER TALK

"A street map that was as large as the city it represented would not be useful. You need a map that is much smaller than the city it represents. To do this, a map represents a given distance such as 1 km with a much smaller distance, such as 1 cm. You can then tell how far apart any locations are using the scale of the map. The scale is the relationship between the distances on the map to the distances on Earth's surface. If 1 cm on the map represents 1 km on Earth's surface, two towns that are 3 cm apart on the map must be 3 km apart on Earth's surface.

Scale can be expressed in words, as a ratio, or graphically."

Discuss how scale can be expressed verbally. The student text uses the example of a map in which 1 cm represents 1 km. Verbally, this can be expressed as "1 cm equals 1 km." This can be written 1 cm = 1 km. To find the actual distance between two places, you would measure the distance on the map and use the scale to calculate the actual distance.

TEACHER TALK

"Scale is often expressed in words. For instance, if 1 cm represents 1 km on a map, this can be expressed as "1 cm equals 1 km." If you wanted to find an actual distance using this map, you would measure the distance on the map and use the scale to calculate the actual distance. If you measured a distance of 10 cm on the map, you would calculate 10 cm = 10 km, so the actual distance would be 10 km."

NOTES

....

....

....

....

1.1 Understand the Question

be expressed with the words *one centimeter equals one kilometer*, or it could be written as *1 cm = 1 km*. To find the actual distance between two places, you would measure the distance between the two places on the map (in centimeters) and then follow the directions in the words to calculate the actual distance (in kilometers).

Representing Map Scale Graphically

A graphic map scale shows scale by using a line with smaller intersecting lines. It looks like a ruler. The long line represents distance on the map and is marked with the corresponding distance on the ground. To find the distance between two places, mark off the distance between the two places on the map and compare that to the graphic scale.

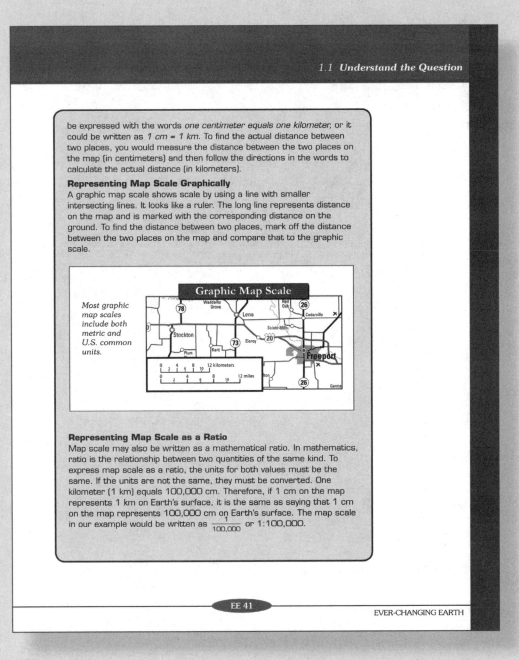

Most graphic map scales include both metric and U.S. common units.

Representing Map Scale as a Ratio

Map scale may also be written as a mathematical ratio. In mathematics, ratio is the relationship between two quantities of the same kind. To express map scale as a ratio, the units for both values must be the same. If the units are not the same, they must be converted. One kilometer (1 km) equals 100,000 cm. Therefore, if 1 cm on the map represents 1 km on Earth's surface, it is the same as saying that 1 cm on the map represents 100,000 cm on Earth's surface. The map scale in our example would be written as $\frac{1}{100,000}$ or 1:100,000.

Discuss how scale can be represented graphically. Graphically, 1 cm represents 1 km can be expressed by a line on which each centimeter is marked as a kilometer. To find the actual distance between two places, you mark off the distance on the map and measure it with the graphic map scale.

"Scale can also be expressed visually, with a line marked like a ruler. The marks represent units of distance on the ground. If a kilometer on the ground is represented by a centimeter on the map, a graphic map scale would have marks a centimeter apart, labeled "1 km, 2 km, ..." and so on.**"**

Discuss how scale can be expressed as a ratio. Since there are 100,000 cm in 1 km, 1 cm represents 1 km can be expressed as the ratio 1:100,000, which can also be written as 1/100,000.

"To express the scale as a ratio, you have to find the ratio of the units. There are 100,000 cm in 1 km. The ratio of distances on the map to distances on Earth is 1 cm to 1 km, or 1:100,000.**"**

NOTES

Observe the Topography of Your Region Using *My World*

Working with your partner, you will now use the color maps found in *My World* to better understand the topography of your region. Pay attention to how the colors change, indicating changes in elevation and depth. If you need more information about using *My World*, look in the *Using My World* section near the back of the book.

Procedure

1. Prepare an elevation and depth map of your region by following these instructions.

   a) **Open** *My World.* From the *Data Library*, select *Earth Structures & Processes.*

   b) **Open the** *EarthstructuresIntro* **file.** The latitude and longitude, continents, countries, lakes, rivers, and elevation and depth data are available in this file.

   c) **In the** *Construct* **layer, select** *Earth Structures* from the *Layer List.* You will see a yellow box around the layer, and the layer will turn from gray to white. Click on the *Show/Hide* layer button to the right to activate this layer.

   d) **Select** *Earth Structure* **boxes.** In the *Layer List,* find the layer titled *Earth Structure boxes.* Click on the *Show/Hide* layer button to the right to activate this layer.

   e) **Center the map on your Earth structure** and zoom in so that your region fills the screen. Or choose your area from the *Map View* menu. If any layers are removed when you do this, be sure to turn them back on.

   f) **Select** *Elevation & Depth* in the *Layer List* **and turn it on.** Turn on this layer by clicking the *Show/Hide* layer button to reveal the eye icon.

2. Examine the topography of your Earth structure in *My World.* Remember to use the *Pointer Tool* to find the elevation and depth of

Materials
- *My World Region Map* page
- colored pencils or crayons

EE 42

Project-Based Inquiry Science

Observe the Topography of Your Region Using *My World*

10 min

Students run the procedure in My World.

META NOTES

Students may need guidance as they examine the slopes of the land. Because of the great size of the geographic regions students are studying, and because of the scale of the map, they should examine the slope of the land over distances of at least 200 km. While students may know of places within a city where the land slopes steeply, this will not be apparent on the map unless the average slope over a distance of at least 100 km is steep.

△ Guide

Begin by letting students know that they will now use *My World* to investigate their regions. Have students start *My World* and load the *Earth Structures & Processes* project if they have not already. Have them turn the *Earth Structure* and *Elevation Depth* layers on and center their screens on their Earth structure. Distribute *My World Region Map* pages.

Have students take a moment to examine the topography of their Earth structure using the *Pointer Tool* to find depths and elevations. Have them fill in their *My World Region Map* pages with their answers to each of the questions in the second part of the procedure.

any point on the map. Answer the questions on the next page. Record your answers on a *My World Region Map* page. As you answer the questions, color each area you identify according to the colors on the *My World* map.

- Identify the highest elevations in your region. Mark these locations on your *My World Region Map* page with their longitude and latitude, and record their elevations.

- Identify the lowest elevations or depths in your region. Mark these locations on your map with their longitude and latitude, and record their elevations.

- In the area around your Earth structure, identify the deepest parts of the ocean. How deep are they? Mark the deepest parts of the ocean on your map using longitude and latitude. Record the depths.

- In the area around your Earth structure, identify where the land is steeply sloped. How can you tell? Mark these areas on your map with arrows pointing to the steep slopes, and record the elevations.

- In the area around your Earth structure, where is the land more gently sloped? How can you tell? Mark these areas on your map with arrows pointing to the gently-sloped and flat parts of the land. Record the elevations.

Reflect

Answer these questions and be prepared to share your answers with the class.

1. How does the information on your maps compare with the description written by your pen pal?

2. What are the strengths and weaknesses of *My World* representations?

3. What else do you think you need to know about the topography of your region and Earth structure to be able to compare it to other regions?

EVER-CHANGING EARTH

☐ Assess

As students use *My World* to answer the questions, ask pairs how they are finding answers to the bulleted questions. If you think that students are misidentifying the highest and lowest points or areas with steep slopes, ask them what color in their region represents the highest point and what color represents the lowest point. Students may need guidance for the second and third bullets; the second bullet refers to the lowest elevations or depths of places on land within the regions.

△ Guide

Have students discuss the *Reflect* questions with their partners. Emphasize that they should be prepared to share their answers with the class.

☐ Assess

As student pairs discuss the *Reflect* questions, ask them how their maps compare to what they learned from their pen pal letters. What were the strengths and weaknesses of *My World?* Listen for the following in students' discussions:

1. Students should be able to find most of the significant features of their Earth structure and region on the map. However, they should recognize where the map does not allow them to see some details. For instance, Mt. Everest reaches an elevation of 8611 m, but the average elevation of the smallest area calculated by *My World* is only 5731 m. This is not an inaccuracy, it is simply an effect of the scale of the map.

2. Students should fairly evaluate what they were able to do and what they were not able to do with *My World*. If they discovered that some of the things described in their pen pal letters could not be found on their maps, they should identify this as a weakness.

3. This question is meant to engage students in thinking about what they need to learn. If students have difficulty with this question, you might ask them what comparisons they can now make. If they have trouble making comparisons, ask why.

NOTES

....

....

....

....

....

Reflect

10 min

Students answer the Reflect *questions.*

Create a Vertical Profile of Earth's Surface in Your Region

10 min

Students create vertical profiles of Earth's surface.

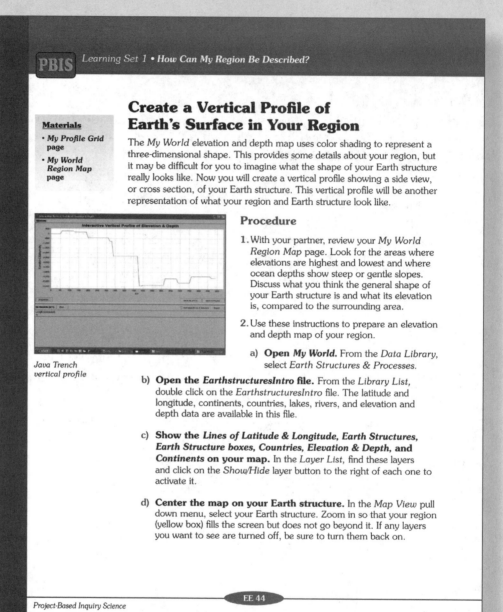

Create a Vertical Profile of Earth's Surface in Your Region

The *My World* elevation and depth map uses color shading to represent a three-dimensional shape. This provides some details about your region, but it may be difficult for you to imagine what the shape of your Earth structure really looks like. Now you will create a vertical profile showing a side view, or cross section, of your Earth structure. This vertical profile will be another representation of what your region and Earth structure look like.

Materials
- *My Profile Grid* page
- *My World Region Map* page

Java Trench vertical profile

Procedure

1. With your partner, review your *My World Region Map* page. Look for the areas where elevations are highest and lowest and where ocean depths show steep or gentle slopes. Discuss what you think the general shape of your Earth structure is and what its elevation is, compared to the surrounding area.

2. Use these instructions to prepare an elevation and depth map of your region.

   a) **Open *My World.*** From the *Data Library,* select *Earth Structures & Processes.*

   b) **Open the *EarthstructuresIntro* file.** From the *Library List,* double click on the *EarthstructuresIntro* file. The latitude and longitude, continents, countries, lakes, rivers, and elevation and depth data are available in this file.

   c) **Show the *Lines of Latitude & Longitude, Earth Structures, Earth Structure boxes, Countries, Elevation & Depth,* and *Continents* on your map.** In the *Layer List,* find these layers and click on the *Show/Hide* layer button to the right of each one to activate it.

   d) **Center the map on your Earth structure.** In the *Map View* pull down menu, select your Earth structure. Zoom in so that your region (yellow box) fills the screen but does not go beyond it. If any layers you want to see are turned off, be sure to turn them back on.

EE 44

Project-Based Inquiry Science

△ Guide

Begin by having students review the *My World Region Maps* with their partners. Emphasize that they should use their observations of their region from *My World* and their maps to develop ideas about what their Earth structure looks like.

When students have had a few minutes to discuss their Earth structures, distribute *My Profile Grid* pages and have them start *My World* if necessary. Have them load the *Earth Structures* project following the steps in this segment. Have each pair view their Earth structure by selecting it in the *Map View* pull-down menu. Students should have the following layers turned on in their *Layers List: Lines of Latitude & Longitude, Earth Structures, Countries, Elevation & Depth,* and *Continents.*

Once students have *My World* set to show their Earth structure properly, go over the instructions for creating a vertical profile. These are listed in the third step. They will first need to select the *Create Vertical Profile* tool (the rightmost tool on the toolbar). Then a dialogue box, *Vertical Profile of,* will come up. They should set *Sample Every* to *10 km.* They can then use their cursors to draw a line across the map, clicking once to create one endpoint and then double clicking to create the other endpoint. They should draw their line horizontally across their region. This will give them a graph resembling a cross section of Earth's surface along the line they draw. They should draw the graph on their *My Profile Grid* pages and shade everything below the line of the graph to show what it would look like if they cut into Earth along their line. They should then repeat the procedure with a vertical line.

NOTES

....

....

....

....

....

....

....

3. Create a vertical profile of your Earth Structure.

a) **Select the *Create Vertical Profile Tool*.**
Click on the *Create Vertical Profile Tool* in the map tool bar. A dialogue box will open that states: *Create Vertical Profile of:* Elevation & Depth, *Profile Field:* Elevation & Bathymetry, and *Sample Every:* 60 miles.

b) **Change the *Sample Every:* distance.**
Change the default distance between samples from 60 mi to 10 km. Once you have changed the *Sample Every:* distance, click OK.

c) **Draw a line along which to view a vertical profile.** Start by drawing an east-west (horizontal) line across the width of the yellow *Earth Structure box* so it passes through the green square marking your Earth Structure. Move your cursor to where you would like to start the line and click once, then drag your cursor to draw the line. Click once to add a new segment to the profile line, or double click to stop drawing the line and show the profile graph.

d) **Sketch the vertical profile.** Examine the vertical profile graph on the screen. On a *My Profile Grid* page, label the horizontal and vertical axes to match those in the vertical profile and sketch the profile line. The red profile line in *My World* represents Earth's surface. Color the area below the line brown to represent the surface. Draw a horizontal line across the graph to represent sea level. Color the area between sea level and the profile line blue to represent water. You now have a side view, or cross-section, of your Earth structure. After sketching an east-west profile, repeat the procedure to create a north-south profile.

Reflect

Study the vertical profile. It shows a side view, or cross section, of Earth's surface along a line passing through your Earth structure. Use the profile to answer the following questions.

EVER-CHANGING EARTH

Give students some time to study their vertical profiles. Emphasize that their vertical profiles do not preserve the ratio of vertical scale to horizontal scale.

☐ Assess

As students study their vertical profiles, ask pairs to describe the surface of their Earth structure. They should be able to use their profiles to describe the slopes, high points, and low points of their Earth structure.

Check students' sketches. Ask them to describe what their sketches represent. They should understand that the shaded regions of their sketches represent Earth.

1. How accurately do you think your vertical profile represents the shape of Earth's surface in your region?

2. How would you describe the shape of Earth's surface in your region? For example, is it mountainous or flat? Does it have deep valleys on land or beneath the ocean? Are there islands?

3. Describe the strengths and weaknesses of your vertical profile. How accurately do you think it represents your Earth structure?

4. What information would help you improve your vertical profile?

Create a Region Project Board

You are already familiar with using a class *Project Board* to keep track of your progress toward answering the *Big Question* of the Unit. In this Unit, you are investigating your own Earth structure and region in addition to answering the *Big Question*. You will use a *Region Project Board* to help you keep track of what you are learning about your region and what you still need to investigate. The question for your *Region Project Board* is *What do I know about my region?*

Record what you have learned about your region in the *What are we learning?* column of the *Region Project Board*. Make sure to record evidence in the *What is our evidence?* column. Next to each entry in the *What is our evidence?* column, record the tool you used to gather your information. You may have come up with questions about your region, or about how you can use *My World* to learn more about your region. Record these questions in the *What do we need to investigate?* column.

What's the Point?

To study changes in Earth and Earth structures, you need to use the tools used by scientists and the data available from these tools. Many visualization tools enable you to learn about the topography, or physical features, of a region.

Each type of visualization tool allows you to visualize different features, so you may need to use several different visualization tools to fully understand a region's topography. You used two types of tools in *My World*, a color map that used different colors to help you visualize the elevation and depth of your region, and a vertical profile tool that allowed you to visualize a cross section of your Earth structure.

EE 46

Reflect

10 min

Students answer and discuss the Reflect *questions.*

⬡ Get Going

Have students discuss the *Reflect* questions with their partners.

☐ Assess

You can lead a class discussion to find out what observations students made about vertical profiles, or you can ask pairs about their answers to the *Reflect* questions.

Look for the following in students' responses:

1. Students should consider how the landscape appears in their maps, and how it is described in their pen pal letters. They may find that their vertical profile misses significant features of their Earth structure, misrepresenting the region.

2. Students should compare the elevations at the highest points in their regions to other regions on Earth's surface to help them judge whether the region is mountainous. Relying on the vertical profile alone may be misleading, since the vertical profile can exaggerate slopes. They may also need to verify that areas at or below sea level are covered in water. Further, they should consider whether their profiles capture all of the important formations in their region.

3. Students should be aware of the vertical scale distortion of the vertical profiles. They should also be aware that a cross section represents only a very small portion of the surface and may miss important formations.

4. Students should consider what extra information they need to describe Earth's surface in the area shown in their vertical profile. This might include information about bodies of water and relative elevations and depths.

NOTES

_____

_____

_____

_____

_____

_____

_____

_____

Create a Region Project Board

You are already familiar with using a class *Project Board* to keep track of your progress toward answering the *Big Question* of the Unit. In this Unit, you are investigating your own Earth structure and region in addition to answering the *Big Question*. You will use a *Region Project Board* to help you keep track of what you are learning about your region and what you still need to investigate. The question for your *Region Project Board* is *What do I know about my region?*

Record what you have learned about your region in the *What are we learning?* column of the *Region Project Board*. Make sure to record evidence in the *What is our evidence?* column. Next to each entry in the *What is our evidence?* column, record the tool you used to gather your information. You may have come up with questions about your region, or about how you can use *My World* to learn more about your region. Record these questions in the *What do we need to investigate?* column.

Create a Region Project Board

5 min

Students create their Region Project Boards.

△ Guide

Introduce students to the *Region Project Board* by reminding them of the class *Project Board* they created earlier. They should record the question *What do I know about my region?* at the top of their *Region Project Board*. Have them record what they have learned about their regions in the *What are we learning?* column. Students should include information about the greatest elevations and depths in their region, as well as the slopes and overall shape of the region's Earth structures. Have them record questions about their regions in the *What do we need to investigate?* column. Students should have questions about what geologic processes led to the specific topographic features they observed in their Earth structure and region. For instance, they should plan to investigate steep slopes, or great elevations and depths.

NOTES

Assessment Options

Targeted Concepts, Skills, and Nature of Science	How do I know if students got it?
Scientists often work together and then share their findings. Sharing findings makes new information available and helps scientists refine their ideas and build on others' ideas. When another person's or group's idea is used, credit needs to be given.	**ASK:** How did working together and discussing ideas in a group and with the class help you? **LISTEN:** Students should describe how working together and discussions helped them to formulate their ideas.
Identifying factors that lead to variation is an important part of scientific investigation.	**ASK:** What factors do you think lead to changes in your Earth structure? Why is it important to identify these? **LISTEN:** Students should identify possible causes for the formation of their Earth structure and changes that occur with it. They should be able to describe that it is important to know what causes change to understand what affects the Earth structure of a region.

NOTES

....

....

....

....

Targeted Concepts, Skills, and Nature of Science	How do I know if students got it?
Scientific investigations and measurements are considered reliable if the results are repeatable by other scientists using the same procedures.	**ASK:** How do you know if your claims seem reliable? **LISTEN:** Students should state that correlations between similar Earth structures support their early claims about how their Earth structure formed.
Scientists use models to simulate processes that happen too fast, too slow, on a scale that cannot be observed directly (either too small or too large), or that are too dangerous.	**ASK:** What models did we use in class today? Why did we use them? **LISTEN:** Students should be able to describe both the color maps and the vertical profiles as models. These models are scaled down to represent something that is otherwise too large to observe easily.
Scientists use models and tools, such as Geographic Information Systems, and a variety of maps to develop claims and explanations from evidence in the data.	**ASK:** How did the color maps and the vertical profiles you constructed help you to make claims about the processes that shape Earth? **LISTEN:** Students should be able to describe that the maps help them understand the shape of their Earth structure and that the shape is related to the processes that formed it.

Teacher Reflection Questions

- How did students' understanding of the topographies of their regions evolve as they explored them through visualizations?

- Describe how the visualization tools (color maps and vertical profiles) helped students' understanding of their Earth structure.

- What management issues came up while students were using *My World?* What ideas do you have for next time?

NOTES

1.2 Investigate

How Can My Earth Structure Be Described?

◄ $1\frac{1}{4}$ *class periods*

A class period is considered to be one 40 to 50 minute class.

Overview

Students are introduced to Earth-imaging software, learning how to navigate the surface of Earth in detailed satellite photographs. They use the Earth-imaging software to explore the neighborhood around their school and around their homes to develop a sense of what kinds of information they can get from satellite photographs. Then they use the Earth-imaging software to explore their regions and Earth structures, building on what they learned using color maps and analyzing how each of these tools help them obtain and interpret information. They create topographic maps with contour lines of a three-dimensional structure. From this, they gain an understanding of how contour lines represent elevations and slopes. By the end of the section, they are able to analyze and evaluate how the visualization tools they have used give them information and help them interpret it.

Targeted Concepts, Skills, and Nature of Science	Performance Expectations
Scientists must keep clear, accurate, and descriptive records of what they do so they can share their work with others and consider what they did, why they did it, and what they want to do next.	Students should keep descriptive, accurate, and well-documented responses to the questions in the investigative procedure.
Graphs and tables are an effective way to analyze and communicate results of scientific investigation.	The class should use the *Project Board* to help communicate and keep track of their ideas and what they need to investigate. They should annotate maps and create tables to communicate what they have found from their investigation of Earth structures.
Scientists use models and tools, such as Geographic Information Systems, and a variety of maps to develop claims and explanations from evidence in the data.	Students should use models (color maps, three-dimensional maps, and computer-generated maps) to help them understand their Earth structure.

Materials	
1 per student	*Three-page Map* Tracing paper *Region Project Board* page
1 per group	Computer with Internet access Metric ruler Three-dimensional structure Plastic beaker Clear plastic box Waterproof marker Plexiglass piece Erasable marker Black permanent marker Transparency
2-6 cups per group, as needed	Water

Activity Setup and Preparation

Students will need access to the Internet in this section.

In the *More to Learn* segment, students will need three-dimensional structures such as stones, or other structures with irregular surfaces. Make sure to have these ready and available for this segment.

Homework Options

Reflection

- **Science Content:** Describe a topographic map and what it tells you about your Earth structure. *(Students should be able to describe that a topographic map shows how the elevation of an Earth structure varies, define contour lines, and describe what it tells them about their Earth structure in terms of how steep the land is.)*

SECTION 1.2 IMPLEMENTATION

1.2 Investigate

How Can My Earth Structure Be Described?

Geographic Information Systems (GIS) are computer programs that make it possible for you to observe regions of the world in three dimensions. This technology begins with photographs taken by **satellites** orbiting Earth. Satellites are placed in Earth's orbit by humans to communicate signals, or to obtain and send scientific data. Satellite photographs show land features such as mountains, valleys, rivers, and lakes. They also show vegetation, ice, snow, and human-made structures such as buildings and roads. When seamlessly assembled by a computer program, these photographs provide a three-dimensional view of the world. GIS programs provide detailed information about each location that allows you to identify an area's elevation and depth and where land features are located.

In this section, you will use an Earth-imaging program to examine satellite images of your region and Earth structure. Before looking at your region, you will be able to familiarize yourself with this program by using it to explore your own neighborhood or other places on Earth that interest you. The program enables you to look at features of the land as if you are far above Earth. Using the navigation tools, you can circle up steep mountainsides or soar into low valleys. You can follow rivers and other bodies of water wherever they go, and then you can travel to your region and observe actual views of your Earth structure.

You will begin your exploration of the data by focusing on the area where you live. The questions provided in the procedure will help you identify specific topographic details of this area. You will then use the program to investigate the region where your pen pal lives.

satellite: in this case, an object orbiting Earth, placed there by humans to communicate signals or to collect and send scientific data.

Materials
- computer with Internet connection
- metric ruler
- *Three-page Map*
- *Region Project Board* page

Examine Earth's Topography Near Your School and Home

Procedure

1. Open the Earth-imaging program.

EE 47

EVER-CHANGING EARTH

1.2 Investigate

How Can My Earth Structure Be Described?

5 min

Students are introduced to Earth-imaging software.

△ Guide

Begin by introducing Earth-imaging software. Tell students that this technology joins photographs of the Earth's surface taken by satellites to show details of Earth's surface including cities, geologic features, vegetation, and even snow on the ground. Let students know that they will use this technology to describe their Earth structures and regions, but first they will look at the topography around their school and homes.

*A class period is considered to be one 40 to 50 minute class.

Examine Earth's Topography Near Your School and Home

10 min

Students examine the topography around their school and home using Earth-imaging software.

2. Using the navigation tool provided, type in your school's address and hit <Go> or <Enter>.

3. Use the navigation tools to zoom in as far as you can on your location. If possible, notice the season when the image was taken. What details of the photographs help you identify the time of day or year?

4. Zoom back out from your school. Use the tools to move around in the image. Look for locations or landmarks that are familiar to you. Use them to locate your home.

   • What clues in the image did you use to find your home?

   • What is the latitude and longitude for your home?

   • Move over the image and locate a friend's home or favorite place in town. What details can you see there?

   If the program you are using has a *pushpin* feature or other location marker, select it from the menu, and then click on your home to mark it in the software.

5. Center your school in the image and zoom out again until the altitude is about 40 km (25 mi) above Earth's surface.

   • Describe the topography of this area. Look for mountains, hills, and flat areas. Include water features such as lakes, rivers, streams, and oceans. Where is each land feature located in the image you are looking at? Use the ruler tool to measure the distance, in kilometers, from each of these land features to your school.

   • Is the area where you live a large city, a small city, or in the countryside? How do the images indicate that?

   • Green areas show vegetation—grass, plants, and trees. Is more land taken up by buildings or vegetation?

   • Select a favorite spot in your neighborhood. Identify its elevation. The elevation is usually shown at the bottom of the window. Look for a place that has higher elevation.

   • What is the highest elevation in the region you are investigating? What is its elevation? What is its longitude and latitude?

◯ Get Going

Have students start the Earth-imaging software on their computers. Briefly point out the navigation tools they will use. In this program, they can find a location field (using the *Fly to* tool) where they can type an address, or the latitude and longitude of a location. Point out the zoom controls located on the right side of the viewer.

Have students enter the address of their school in the location field. If they have entered the address correctly, the software should give them a bird's-eye view of the school. Have them zoom in to get as close a look as possible. Ask them what kinds of details they see. Do they recognize features of their school?

Have students zoom out from their school and use familiar landmarks to find their home in the satellite images. They should move the images to center in on their home. Ask them what details they can see. Can they find the home of a friend? Have them mark their homes with location markers if their software has them (there is usually a *Pushpin Tool* for this).

Have students center the satellite images on their school again and zoom out to an altitude of about 40 km (25 mi). Their software should display both the elevation of the location they are looking at and the altitude of their view. In some Earth-imaging software, the latter is called *Eye alt* and is displayed at the bottom right side of the viewer. Ask them what the features of the region are. How would they describe the topography? Would they describe their home area as a city or as a rural area? Is there a lot of vegetation around their home, or is it mostly buildings? Have them identify a place they know near their home and find its elevation in the viewer. Also have them identify the highest and lowest points in the region of their home. Is their region hilly or flat? How can they tell?

NOTES

Stop and Think

10 min

Students answer the questions with their partners.

- What is the lowest elevation in the region you are investigating? What is its elevation or depth? What is its longitude and latitude?

- Is the land around you flat, hilly, or mountainous? How do the images indicate that?

Stop and Think

Think about your experience using the Earth-imaging program. Recall what you observed in the region where you live as you answer these questions. Be prepared to discuss the answers with the class.

1. What topographic features in your neighborhood or surrounding area did you see that you did not know about? What features surprised you?

2. How did the Earth-imaging program show elevation and depth? How did it show steep or gentle slopes?

3. What have you learned about using an Earth-imaging program that you think the rest of the class should know as they continue using it to explore Earth's topography?

Investigate the Region of Your Earth Structure

Procedure

1. Open the Earth-imaging program. Using the navigation tool provided, enter the location of your Earth structure by typing in its longitude and latitude. Type these numbers very carefully.

2. Using the navigation tools, explore the region. Zoom in on your Earth structure and fly over the surrounding region. Record your observations.

3. Use the *pushpin* feature or other location marker on the toolbar to mark the location of your Earth structure.

4. Zoom out from your Earth structure until the area you are looking at is about 300 km (186 mi) wide.

   - Describe the topography of this area. Look for mountains, hills, and flat areas. Include water features such as lakes, rivers, streams, and oceans. Where is each land feature located in this image? How close are these land features to your Earth structure?

EE 49

EVER-CHANGING EARTH

△ Guide

Have students discuss the *Stop and Think* questions with their partners. If you have time, you might want to lead a class discussion of these questions.

Use the following guidelines when discussing students' ideas:

1. This question is meant to help students reflect on what they learned and on what topographic features are easily studied with Earth-imaging software.

2. Students should notice that for many parts of the United States, the variations in elevation and depth may be too slight to see how they are represented. In the Earth-imaging software, elevations, depths, and slopes are shown using distortions in the surface of the map. At high elevations, the distance between two points is exaggerated; where the land slopes steeply, lines of latitude and longitude skew away from each other. The Himalayas provide a good example of this. Note that in the Earth-imaging software the degree of exaggeration can be changed in the *Preferences* menu.

3. This question is meant to engage students in collaborating and sharing their knowledge.

△ Guide

Go over the procedure in the student text with the class. Students should begin by typing the coordinates for their Earth structure into the location field in their Earth-imaging software. The coordinates for Mount Everest would be entered as *28°N, 87°E*. Once their Earth structure is in the field of view, they should explore the region and put a location marker on their Earth structure.

Students should zoom out until they are looking at an area that is about 300 km (186 mi) wide. Using this wider view, they should describe the topography of the region. They should identify major features of the topography, such as hills, mountains, valleys, rivers, and lakes. They should identify and describe cities in the region. As with their home area, students should describe how much of the region is covered in vegetation and how much is covered in buildings. They should identify the highest and lowest points in the region and record their elevations or depths. Then they should describe the features of the Earth structure. Is the land around the Earth structure steeply sloped? What are the highest and lowest points in the Earth structure?

Finally, students should outline their regions on their *Three-page Maps* and mark the location of their Earth structure in the region.

⬡ Get Going

Distribute the *Three-page Maps* and have students get started.

Investigate the Region of Your Earth Structure

15 min

Students examine their regions and Earth structures using the Earth-imaging software.

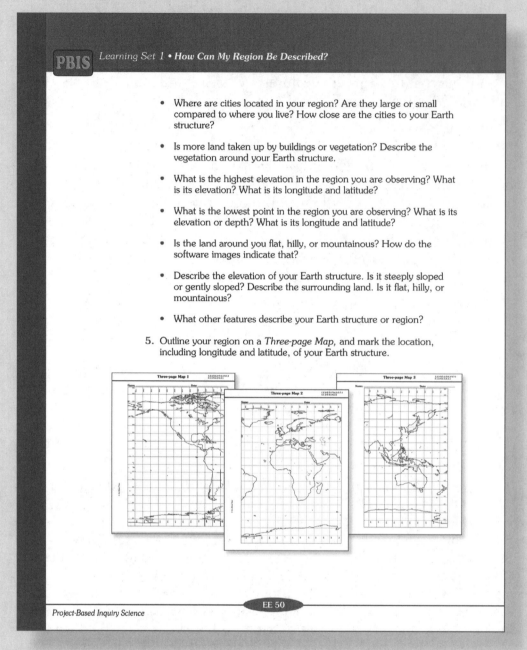

- Where are cities located in your region? Are they large or small compared to where you live? How close are the cities to your Earth structure?

- Is more land taken up by buildings or vegetation? Describe the vegetation around your Earth structure.

- What is the highest elevation in the region you are observing? What is its elevation? What is its longitude and latitude?

- What is the lowest point in the region you are observing? What is its elevation or depth? What is its longitude and latitude?

- Is the land around you flat, hilly, or mountainous? How do the software images indicate that?

- Describe the elevation of your Earth structure. Is it steeply sloped or gently sloped? Describe the surrounding land. Is it flat, hilly, or mountainous?

- What other features describe your Earth structure or region?

5. Outline your region on a *Three-page Map,* and mark the location, including longitude and latitude, of your Earth structure.

EE 50

Project-Based Inquiry Science

△ Guide and Assess

As students explore their Earth structures and regions, ask them what features they have identified. Help them with any difficulties they are having using the Earth-imaging software. If you think they have missed important features or misidentified features, ask them questions about the features to help them see their mistake. If you find that several students share any misconceptions about interpreting the topographic features, take a moment to address the misconceptions with the class.

Students' *Three-page Maps* should indicate latitude and longitude. Students should outline their regions on the maps.

1.2 Investigate

Update Your *Region Project Board*

In this *Learning Set,* you are gathering information about your region in different ways. Add what you have learned so far about your region to the *What are we learning?* column of your *Region Project Board.* Make sure to record the evidence for this information in the *What is our evidence?* column.

Next to each entry in the *What is our evidence?* column, record the tool you used to gather that evidence. You may also have some ideas about what is causing the geologic activity in your region. Record those ideas in the *What do we think we know?* column. In the *What do we need to investigate?* column, record new questions you have about your Earth structure or region.

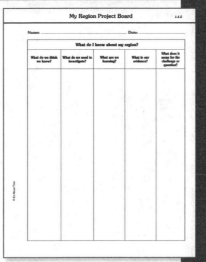

My Region Project Board

Name: _____ Date: _____

What do I know about my region?

What do we think we know?	What do we need to investigate?	What are we learning?	What is our evidence?	What does it mean for the challenge or question?

Reflect

1. What did you learn about your region using satellite images that you could not observe using other representations?

2. Why is it useful to examine several different representations to learn about a region's topography?

What's the Point?

Geologists use many different data sources when they are gathering information about a region. Firsthand accounts, like those in your pen pal letters, give them an idea of the major geologic events that are happening. These events are easy to observe without any special tools. Looking at a well-drawn representation allows you to see a lot of information at once. Geologists also use a variety of visualization tools that indicate different features of the region. Using multiple representations, you can gather more data about the topography of a place than with just one representation.

An Earth-imaging program can help you visualize an area in three dimensions and get details about the region at the same time. However, with these representations, you cannot examine large areas and compare them to one another very easily.

EE 51

EVER-CHANGING EARTH

Update Your *Region Project Board*

10 min.

Students record what they have learned in their Region Project Boards.

△ Guide

Have students record everything they have learned about their regions on their *Region Project Board.* They should also record their evidence for everything they have learned and, in the same column, what tool they used to learn it.

As students record what they have learned on their *Region Project Board,* guide them to recognize the kinds of things they should record by asking them about specific questions about what you heard them discuss or have seen on their *Three-page Maps.* Make sure they record these things.

More to Learn: How Do Topographic Maps Represent Earth's Surface?

5 min

Students create topographic maps.

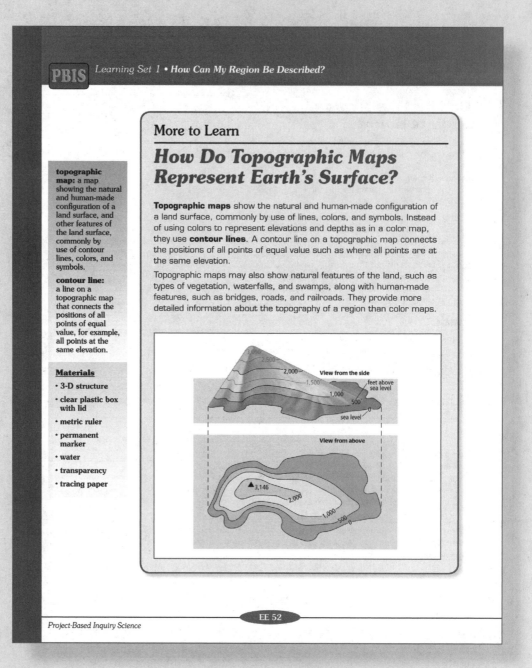

More to Learn

How Do Topographic Maps Represent Earth's Surface?

Topographic maps show the natural and human-made configuration of a land surface, commonly by use of lines, colors, and symbols. Instead of using colors to represent elevations and depths as in a color map, they use **contour lines**. A contour line on a topographic map connects the positions of all points of equal value such as where all points are at the same elevation.

Topographic maps may also show natural features of the land, such as types of vegetation, waterfalls, and swamps, along with human-made features, such as bridges, roads, and railroads. They provide more detailed information about the topography of a region than color maps.

topographic map: a map showing the natural and human-made configuration of a land surface, and other features of the land surface, commonly by use of contour lines, colors, and symbols.

contour line: a line on a topographic map that connects the positions of all points of equal value, for example, all points at the same elevation.

Materials
- 3-D structure
- clear plastic box with lid
- metric ruler
- permanent marker
- water
- transparency
- tracing paper

View from the side

feet above sea level

3,000
2,500
2,000
1,500
1,000
500
0

sea level

View from above

▲ 3,146
2,000
1,000
500
0

EE 52

Project-Based Inquiry Science

△ Guide

You will need suitable three-dimensional structures to make maps with for this section. These might include dioramas, stones, and other structures with irregular surfaces.

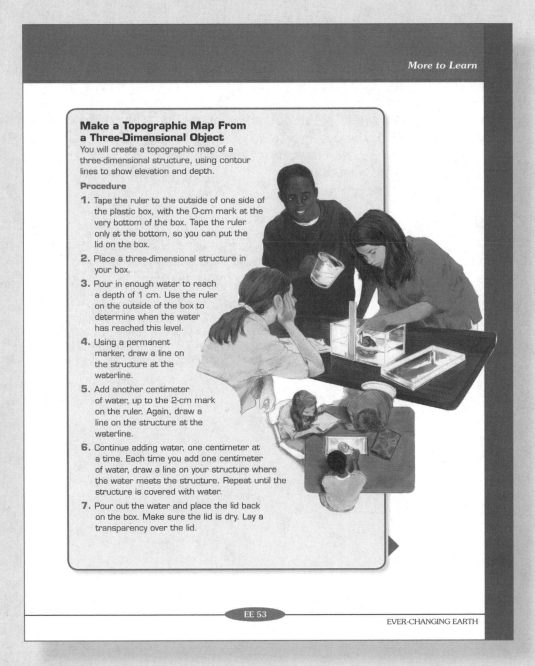

More to Learn

Make a Topographic Map From a Three-Dimensional Object

You will create a topographic map of a three-dimensional structure, using contour lines to show elevation and depth.

Procedure

1. Tape the ruler to the outside of one side of the plastic box, with the O-cm mark at the very bottom of the box. Tape the ruler only at the bottom, so you can put the lid on the box.

2. Place a three-dimensional structure in your box.

3. Pour in enough water to reach a depth of 1 cm. Use the ruler on the outside of the box to determine when the water has reached this level.

4. Using a permanent marker, draw a line on the structure at the waterline.

5. Add another centimeter of water, up to the 2-cm mark on the ruler. Again, draw a line on the structure at the waterline.

6. Continue adding water, one centimeter at a time. Each time you add one centimeter of water, draw a line on your structure where the water meets the structure. Repeat until the structure is covered with water.

7. Pour out the water and place the lid back on the box. Make sure the lid is dry. Lay a transparency over the lid.

EE 53

EVER-CHANGING EARTH

Make a Topographic Map From a Three-Dimensional Object

10 min

Students create topographic maps of three-dimensional structures.

△ Guide

Begin by drawing students' attention to the map in the student text. Point out the contour lines on the map, and ask them how they can tell how elevations change on the map. Can they tell where the land slopes steeply? How?

Let them know they will make topographic maps. Show them how they will set up the materials for making topographic maps. Tape a ruler to the inside of a clear box so that the 0-cm mark is flush with the base of the box.

Then put a three-dimensional structure like the one students will use into the box. Show students how they will pour 1 cm of water into the box and trace the waterline on the three-dimensional structure with a waterproof marker. Tell them they will continue adding water, 1 cm at a time, until the three-dimensional structure is submerged. Show them how they will place the transparency over the lid of the box. Then show the students how they can see the lines on the three-dimensional object through the top of the box and how they will trace these lines onto the transparency. Let them know that tracing these onto a sheet of paper will give them a topographic map of the three-dimensional structure.

⬡ Get Going

Distribute the materials, including the three-dimensional structures, plastic boxes, rulers, markers, water, transparencies, and tracing paper. Have students work with their groups to create topographic maps.

As groups work on creating topographic maps, monitor their progress. Make sure they focus on the task and help them with any difficulties that arise.

Be sure that water spills are promptly cleaned up and do not present hazards.

NOTES

8. Through the top of the box, you will see the lines you drew on the structure. Trace each of these lines on the transparency. These are the contour lines.

9. Put a sheet of tracing paper over the transparency. Trace the contour lines onto the paper to make a topographic map of the structure.

Stop and Think

1. Each side of your structure was shaped differently. Find a place where the structure's shape seemed to change quickly. How did the contour lines show this steep area of the structure? What would the contour lines show in a less-steep area?

2. Find a feature of your structure that was not shown in your topographic map. Why do you think it is not clear in your map?

3. What could be done to make the contour map a better representation of the structure?

Reflect

1. Imagine a topographic map of Earth. Draw the pattern of contour lines that would represent a hill. A valley. A flat plain.

2. What are the advantages of using a topographic map compared to the other visualization tools you have used? What are the disadvantages?

3. In what ways are contour lines similar to the colors used on *My World*'s color maps?

Topographic maps can help people prepare for a hike. By reading the map, you can tell if you will be hiking on very steep- or gently-sloped land. You will also know if you need to wear boots to hike through watery areas such as streams or swamps.

EE 54

Stop and Think

5 min

Students answer questions with their groups.

◯ Get Going

When students have finished creating topographic maps, have them discuss the *Stop and Think* questions with their groups.

◇ Evaluate

After students have had a few minutes to discuss these questions, lead a brief class discussion of the answers. Make sure they understand that the closer together the contour lines are on the topographic map, the steeper the represented slope is.

Reflect

5 min

Students answer the Reflect *questions.*

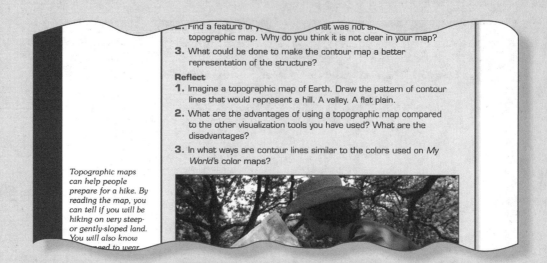

2. Find a feature of y_____ ____ was not sh_____ topographic map. Why do you think it is not clear in your map?

3. What could be done to make the contour map a better representation of the structure?

Reflect

1. Imagine a topographic map of Earth. Draw the pattern of contour lines that would represent a hill. A valley. A flat plain.

2. What are the advantages of using a topographic map compared to the other visualization tools you have used? What are the disadvantages?

3. In what ways are contour lines similar to the colors used on *My World*'s color maps?

Topographic maps can help people prepare for a hike. By reading the map, you can tell if you will be hiking on very steep- or gently-sloped land. You will also know ___ ___ed to wear.

△ Guide and Assess

Have students answer the *Reflect* questions with their groups. They should draw topographic maps of land with hills, valleys, and plains. Check their drawings to make sure they understand how to use contour lines. If you see any misconceptions in their work, take a moment to address these with the class.

If there is time, consider leading a brief class discussion of the last two *Reflect* questions. Students should compare the kinds of information they were able to get from different visualizations and evaluate how easily they could interpret the information using the different visualizations.

Teacher Reflection Questions

- How were you able to help students identify topographical features in the satellite photographs?

- What evidence do you have that students understand the strengths and limitations of the visualization tools they are using?

- How did you keep students focused on the task as they explored satellite photographs and created topographic maps?

Back to the Big Question

What Processes Within Earth Cause Geologic Activity?

◀ $1\frac{1}{4}$ *class periods*

A class period is considered to be one 40 to 50 minute class.

Students describe and compare their Earth structures, and consider what they still need to learn about their Earth structures.

Overview

Students list the geologic terms they have learned, make sketches to show the defining features of each geologic term, and record connections between the terms, synthesizing the geologic ideas they have learned. They synthesize what they have learned about their Earth structures by creating drawings of them. They analyze how they used observations from the visualization tools to learn about the Earth structures and evaluate each of the visualization tools. Then they present their drawings to the class, and look for similarities and differences in the Earth structures presented. Finally, they record what they have learned and what they need to investigate in order to better describe and compare their Earth structures on the *Project Board.*

Targeted Concepts, Skills, and Nature of Science	Performance Expectations
Scientists often work together and then share their findings. Sharing findings makes new information available and helps scientists refine their ideas and build on others' ideas. When another person's or group's idea is used, credit needs to be given.	Students should work together in small groups to describe their regions and Earth structures. Groups should then share their descriptions with the class.
Scientists must keep clear, accurate, and descriptive records of what they do so they can share their work with others and consider what they did, why they did it, and what they want to do next.	Students should keep clear, accurate, and descriptive records of what the topography of their Earth structure and their comparisons with other Earth structures.

Targeted Concepts, Skills, and Nature of Science	Performance Expectations
Graphs and tables are an effective way to analyze and communicate results of scientific investigation.	Students should use the *Project Board* and possibly other tables to organize information. This assists in analyzing the information and sharing it with others.
Scientists use models and tools, such as Geographic Information Systems, and a variety of maps to develop claims and explanations from evidence in the data.	Students should be able to describe the topography of their Earth structure using observations from the visualization tools they have used.

Materials	
100 per group	Index cards
1 per group	Poster sheets
1 per class	Class *Project Board* *Ever-Changing Earth Teacher Notes and Suggested Data* table

Homework Options

Reflection

- **Science Process:** Which of the visualization tools would you use to navigate the land if you were on an expedition to explore your Earth structure on foot? Which of the visualization tools would you use to navigate the land if you were trying to estimate the amount of land that could be used for agriculture in your region? Why? *(Students should use their experiences with the visualization tools to evaluate which would be better for each task.)*

Preparation for Learning Set 2

- **Science Process:** What can you learn about geologic activity in your region by studying the features of your Earth structure? *(This question is meant to engage students in thinking about how the features of their Earth structure provide clues to the geologic activity there.)*

Learning Set 1

Back to the Big Question

What Processes Within Earth Cause Geologic Activity?

You took an important step toward answering the *Big Question* for this Unit when you identified and described your region of the world to answer the smaller question: *How can my region be described?* In the process, you learned to use several different tools scientists use when answering that type of question. By combining what you could observe using each representation, you developed a good description of the topography of your region.

Build a *Picture Map*

While you began to answer the *Big Question*, you learned these geologic terms: *topographic features, topography, elevation, depth, sea level, longitude, latitude, satellites, topographic maps,* and *contour lines.* You also used some of the different representations scientists use to investigate the characteristics of your region—*color maps* and *satellite images.*

Record each of the italicized terms on a separate index card, using large letters so that others can see. On the back of each card, draw a picture to represent its geologic term. Make your picture as accurate as possible. Be sure to include features that would help someone else understand the geologic term.

When you have completed each card, share them with your group. Listen carefully as someone in your group describes each geologic term. Offer your ideas for how the description of each of the geologic terms might be improved. Then, lay the cards on the table to show how the ideas connect.

EE 55

EVER-CHANGING EARTH

Learning Set 1

Back to the Big Question

< 5 min

Students review the Big Question.

△ Guide

Remind students of the *Big Question, What processes within Earth cause geologic activity?* Emphasize that they have made progress toward answering the *Big Question* by identifying their regions and important features of their Earth structures. This activity will help them make further progress toward answering the *Big Question.*

*A class period is considered to be one 40 to 50 minute class.

Build a Picture Map

15 min

Students record and illustrate the geologic ideas they have learned and their connections to each other on index cards.

process, you ...ed to use several different tools scientists use when answering that type of question. By combining what you could observe using each representation, you developed a good description of the topography of your region.

Build a *Picture Map*

While you began to answer the *Big Question,* you learned these geologic terms: *topographic features, topography, elevation, depth, sea level, longitude, latitude, satellites, topographic maps,* and *contour lines.* You also used some of the different representations scientists use to investigate the characteristics of your region—*color maps* and *satellite images.*

Record each of the italicized terms on a separate index card, using large letters so that others can see. On the back of each card, draw a picture to represent its geologic term. Make your picture as accurate as possible. Be sure to include features that would help someone else understand the geologic term.

When you have completed each card, share them with your group. Listen carefully as someone in your group describes each geologic term. Offer your ideas for how the description of each of the geologic terms might be improved. Then, lay the cards on the table to show how the ideas connect.

△ Guide

Begin by telling students that they will now develop descriptions of their Earth structures, including the features they have observed, using the geologic ideas they have learned. As a first step to developing the descriptions, students will make maps showing how the geologic ideas connect to each other. To do this, they will record each of the geologic terms they have learned on an index card. On the back of each card, they will draw a picture that represents the term on the front of the card. They will share their cards with their partners, collaborate to improve the descriptions, and arrange the cards on the table to show how the ideas connect. Emphasize that students will share their descriptions with the class.

NOTES

....

....

....

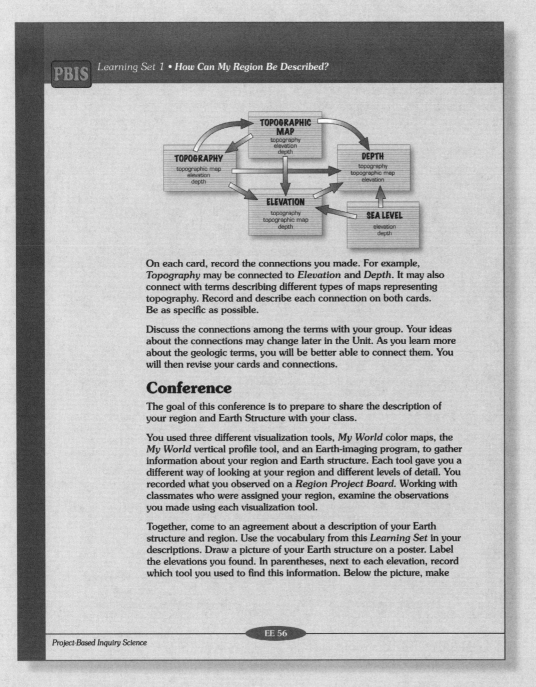

On each card, record the connections you made. For example, *Topography* may be connected to *Elevation* and *Depth*. It may also connect with terms describing different types of maps representing topography. Record and describe each connection on both cards. Be as specific as possible.

Discuss the connections among the terms with your group. Your ideas about the connections may change later in the Unit. As you learn more about the geologic terms, you will be better able to connect them. You will then revise your cards and connections.

Conference

The goal of this conference is to prepare to share the description of your region and Earth Structure with your class.

You used three different visualization tools, *My World* color maps, the *My World* vertical profile tool, and an Earth-imaging program, to gather information about your region and Earth structure. Each tool gave you a different way of looking at your region and different levels of detail. You recorded what you observed on a *Region Project Board*. Working with classmates who were assigned your region, examine the observations you made using each visualization tool.

Together, come to an agreement about a description of your Earth structure and region. Use the vocabulary from this *Learning Set* in your descriptions. Draw a picture of your Earth structure on a poster. Label the elevations you found. In parentheses, next to each elevation, record which tool you used to find this information. Below the picture, make

◯ Get Going

Distribute index cards. Emphasize that each student should create a set of cards illustrating geologic terms, and that they should share their cards with their partners when they have finished.

△ Guide and Assess

As students work on their cards, monitor their progress and assist them with any difficulties they encounter. If they need guidance as they create sketches to illustrate their geologic terms, have them imagine they are trying to explain these ideas to someone using sketches. Ask them questions about the ideas to guide them towards statements they can illustrate.

If students have difficulty arranging their cards, ask them what the most important connections between the ideas they have illustrated are. For each idea, what other ideas do they have to use in an explanation?

When they have arranged their cards on the table, they should record the connections on each card.

Conference

15 min

Students compare the tools they have used and compile everything they have learned about their Earth structures in drawings.

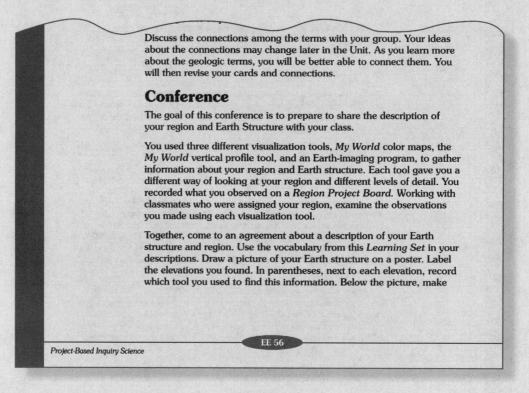

Discuss the connections among the terms with your group. Your ideas about the connections may change later in the Unit. As you learn more about the geologic terms, you will be better able to connect them. You will then revise your cards and connections.

Conference

The goal of this conference is to prepare to share the description of your region and Earth Structure with your class.

You used three different visualization tools, *My World* color maps, the *My World* vertical profile tool, and an Earth-imaging program, to gather information about your region and Earth structure. Each tool gave you a different way of looking at your region and different levels of detail. You recorded what you observed on a *Region Project Board*. Working with classmates who were assigned your region, examine the observations you made using each visualization tool.

Together, come to an agreement about a description of your Earth structure and region. Use the vocabulary from this *Learning Set* in your descriptions. Draw a picture of your Earth structure on a poster. Label the elevations you found. In parentheses, next to each elevation, record which tool you used to find this information. Below the picture, make

EE 56

Project-Based Inquiry Science

△ Guide

Remind students that their goal is to develop descriptions of their Earth structures. Now that they have mapped the connections between the geologic terms they have learned, they will combine their observations to create a picture of their Earth structure. To do this, they will first review their observations, analyzing how they obtained their observations and evaluating the visualization tools they used.

"Remember that you're working toward descriptions of your Earth structures. You have completed the first step of building a *Picture Map* of the geologic ideas you have learned. Now you're going to use the observations you made with *My World* and the Earth-imaging software to make a picture of your Earth structure. First, you are going to review your observations and compare what you have learned from each tool. Then, you will use your observations to create a picture of your Earth structure."

Have students begin by comparing the observations they made with each tool. Emphasize that this comparison should allow them to describe the strengths and limitations of each visualization tool. Have them record what each visualization tool enabled them to observe.

Have students draw a picture of their Earth structure. On their drawings, they should record the elevations and depths they observed using the visualization tools and, in parentheses, which tool they used to observe each elevation.

Below the drawing, students should list important things they learned about their region and Earth structure. The list should include topographic features they have identified. As in the drawing, they should also identify which tool they used to observe each feature in parentheses.

NOTES

....

....

....

....

....

Communicate: Share Your Data and Interpretations

15 min

Students present what they have learned about their regions and Earth structures.

a list of the important information you learned about your region and Earth structure, including details you learned from the pen pal letter. For every detail you include, document your source of information in parentheses.

Communicate

Share Your Data and Interpretations

As you present your poster to the class, describe what you now know about your region's topography. Be specific about information the different visualization tools provided. As you share details of your region, use the terms from this *Learning Set*.

As you listen, pay attention to the similarities and differences among the regions and Earth structures. When the presentations are complete, you will be asked to identify two regions similar to yours. Think about how each region is like yours. How are the regions similar in elevation and in changes in elevation? Also, pay attention to details that might show that your region is different from others. Listen to other groups' use of the geologic terms.

As always, ask questions if you think your classmates need to clarify any observations they have made. Make sure to be respectful.

The June 17, 1996 eruption of Ruapehu Volcano in New Zealand as witnessed by Thor Thordarson, an Icelandic vulcanologist (a scientist who studies volcanoes). According to his account, the eruption produced a pitch-black column about 4 km (2.5 mi) high and 10 km (6.2 mi) wide.

Reflect

1. What descriptive words did your classmates use when talking about their regions and Earth structures?

△ Guide and Assess

Once students have recorded important information about their region and Earth structure, have them present what they have learned to the class. Emphasize that their presentations need to describe the general shape of their Earth structures and to specify how they used observations from each of the visualization tools to revise what they learned from their pen pal letters.

Let students know they will identify two regions similar to theirs after presentations, so they will need to pay close attention to similarities and differences between the Earth structures.

While groups are presenting, assess their responses using the *Ever-Changing Earth Teacher Notes and Suggested Data* table in the Appendix to check students' work. Encourage students to ask questions of presenting groups. Model for students the kinds of questions they should ask. If a pair has left out important information, ask the class what other information they would like to know about the Earth structure.

○ Get Going

When groups have finished presenting their descriptions and their sketches, have students discuss the *Reflect* questions with their partners. Emphasize that they should be prepared to discuss their answers with the class.

△ Guide and Assess

As pairs discuss the *Reflect* questions, monitor their progress and ask them what ideas they have discussed. Listen for the following in students' responses.

1. This question should help students identify the most characteristic features of the regions and Earth structures their classmates described.

Reflect

5 min

Students answer the Reflect *questions with their partners.*

NOTES

2. Which regions and Earth structures presented by your classmates are most similar to yours? Describe what makes them similar. What else would you need to know about each region to better compare them to each other?

3. Choose two regions that are different from yours. Describe how the land features of these regions make them different. What else would you need to know about each region to contrast them with one another?

4. You have examined the topography of your region and Earth structure. Now think about the changes reported in your region. *What do you think might be causing those changes?* Add your ideas to the *What do we think we know?* column of your *Region Project Board.*

After you discuss the answers to these questions as a class, do your best to answer the *Big Question* together: *What processes within Earth cause geologic activity?*

Update the *Project Board*

You now know a lot about the topography of the regions your class is studying. You know that some Earth structures have higher elevations than others. You know that some regions are very similar to yours and some are very different. Think about the characteristics that make regions similar or different. Record this information in the *What are we learning?* column of the class *Project Board.* Be sure to include evidence that supports the information in the *What is our evidence?* column.

Add questions you have about the topography of the regions to the *What do we need to investigate?* column. Your questions might be about what makes regions similar or different, or about how you can better describe the regions. You might record a question about the elevation or steepness of each Earth structure, questions about the kinds of visualization tools you could use to answer your questions, or questions about the geologic activity.

Finally, you have discussed ideas with your class about the answer to the *Big Question.* Add any ideas that came up during this discussion to the *What do we think we know?* column of the *Project Board.* Add questions that came up to the *What do we need to investigate?* column.

2. Students should support their claims about which regions are most similar with specific observations. This question should also engage them in thinking about what else they need to learn.

3. Students should support their claims with specific observations and they should think about what else they need to learn to compare the regions.

△ Guide

Begin by asking the class to share their ideas about the similarities and differences they observed in the regions' topography and add this information to the *Project Board*.

Ask the class what investigative questions they have that could be put on the class *Project Board*.

◇ Evaluate

Students should ask questions that will help them understand more about their Earth structures. Look for questions like What is the lowest point in my Earth structure? and What is the elevation of the largest part of my Earth structure? They should think about information that would better help them compare their regions to other regions and representations that would help them get that information.

Students should record similarities and differences that they recognize in the *What do we think we know?* column. For instance, they should say that Hawaii and Mount Everest are very different, with very different elevations, and different topographic features such as rivers and oceans.

△ Guide

Ask students if they want to add anything to the first column. They should describe what they think they know about Earth structures and how they form.

Remind students to record the new items on the class *Project Board*, and on their individual *Project Boards*.

Update the *Project Board*

10 min

The class discusses group questions, and updates the Project Board.

META NOTES

Students will also be filling out Columns 3 and 4 (*What are we learning?* and *What is our evidence?*) of the *Project Board* during the next section. What goes into the *Project Board* should be general enough to describe the groups of landforms.

NOTES

Assessment Options

Targeted Concepts, Skills, and Nature of Science	How do I know if students got it?
Scientists must keep clear, accurate, and descriptive records of what they do so they can share their work with others and consider what they did, why they did it, and what they want to do next.	**ASK:** Why was it important to keep track of which observations you used for the information in your drawings? How can you determine what you still want to learn and how you can learn it? **LISTEN:** Students should recognize that keeping track of which observations they used helps them learn effective ways of finding the information they need. They may also recognize that knowing what information was supported with observations can help them see what supporting observations they still need.
Graphs and tables are an effective way to analyze and communicate results of scientific investigation.	**ASK:** How did organizing geologic terms by their connections with other terms help you? How did recording the things you have learned in a list with your drawing help? **LISTEN:** Students should recognize that organizing terms by their connections helped them to understand how all of these geologic terms are related and can be applied to understanding Earth structures. Making a list of the things they learned with the drawings should have helped students see how individual observations were related to their final interpretations.
Scientists use models and tools, such as Geographic Information Systems, and a variety of maps to develop claims and explanations from evidence in the data.	**ASK:** How did you use the visualization tools to develop a description of your Earth structure? **LISTEN:** Students should say that they used the visualization tools to make observations and develop interpretations of their observations.

Teacher Reflection Questions

- What evidence do you have that students have considered all of their observations in developing descriptions of their Earth structures?

- What challenges do you expect students to encounter when they learn about the structure of Earth? How can you help them with these?

- How were you able to encourage discussion during students' presentations? What can you do to encourage discussion in future presentations?

NOTES

NOTES

LEARNING SET 2 INTRODUCTION

Learning Set 2

What Is the Structure of Earth?

◀ $6\frac{1}{2}$ *class periods*

A class period is considered to be one 40 to 50 minute class.

Students explore the structure of Earth.

Overview

Students begin by investigating the effects of geologic processes on Earth's surface by examining photographs of places where earthquakes and volcanic activity have caused observable changes. They create posters summarizing the evidence they found that Earth's crust is not continuous as well as their ideas about Earth's structure and what causes the geologic activity they observed. After discussing their ideas with the class, students are introduced to a model of Earth's structure, in which the crust is broken like a cracked eggshell, and they use what they know to evaluate the model. They learn in greater detail about the layers of Earth, including information about Earth's plates and the composition, temperature, and pressure of Earth's layers. After reading about how Earth's crust floats on its mantle, they create a density column using liquids of different densities, and explore how a substance with low density will float above a substance with high density. Using the new information they have learned, they create their own models of Earth's structure and consider ways in which their new models are stronger than the first model they read about. Finally, they create *Picture Maps* of the geologic concepts in this *Learning Set,* synthesizing the information they have learned.

LOOKING AHEAD

Section 2.4 contains detailed information about the structure of Earth. It may be helpful for you to read *Section 2.4* before beginning this *Learning Set.*

Targeted Concepts, Skills, and Nature of Science	Section
Scientists often work together and then share their findings. Sharing findings makes new information available and helps scientists refine their ideas and build on others' ideas. When another person's or group's idea is used, credit needs to be given.	2.1, 2.2, 2.3, 2.5, 2.BBQ
Scientists must keep clear, accurate, and descriptive records of what they do so they can share their work with others and consider what they did, why they did it, and what they want to do next.	2.1, 2.3, 2.5, 2.BBQ
Scientists make claims (conclusions) based on evidence obtained (trends in data) from reliable investigations.	2.1, 2.3, 2.BBQ

Targeted Concepts, Skills, and Nature of Science	Section
Earthquake activity, volcanic activity, and topography are all evidence that Earth's crust is moving and changing.	2.1, 2.2, 2.BBQ
Scientists use models and tools, such as Geographic Information Systems, and a variety of maps to develop claims and explanations from evidence in the data.	2.2, 2.5
Earth's crust is constantly changing. These changes are usually a very slow process that is not immediately observable. Some changes are very rapid and are observable.	2.2
Interactions between Earth's crustal plates can result in mountain building, rift valleys, and geologic activity such as earthquakes and volcanoes. Underwater volcanic activity may form underwater mountains, which can thrust above the ocean's surface to become islands.	2.4
Earth is a system made up of different layers, each with a distinctive composition and set of characteristics. These layers interact, driving the processes that shape Earth.	2.4
Measuring instruments are important in scientific inquiry for accurately comparing the volumes and weights of substances.	2.4
Graphs and tables are an effective way to analyze and communicate results of scientific investigation.	2.BBQ
Explanations are claims supported by evidence. Evidence can be experimental results, observational data, and other accepted scientific knowledge.	2.BBQ

NOTES

....

....

....

....

Activity Setup and Preparation

In *Section 2.2,* students will be introduced to a model of Earth's structure that uses a hard-boiled egg. Prepare hard-boiled eggs for your students before going over this section. You will need one hard-boiled egg for each group.

In *Section 2.3,* students will determine what is inside a mystery box. You will need to obtain suitable boxes and objects to put inside these boxes. The objects should all be similar, but slightly different. It should be difficult for students to determine what is inside each of them, but not impossible. The boxes should be opaque and should give the objects some room to move.

In *Section 2.4,* students will create density columns using samples of liquid. You will need glycerin, baby oil, dishwashing soap, and water. You will also need small cups for the samples of these liquids. Before class, prepare 20-mL samples of each of these liquids and of water.

Students' Initial Conceptions and Capabilities	
	• Students may harbor misconceptions about the relationship between topography and Earth's structure. For instance, some students may conceive of geographic locations as flat places located on or above a spherical Earth. (Sneider and Pulos 1983; Vosniadou 1991)
	• Students may not realize Earth is continually changing. They may think that Earth has always been the same, or that there were only isolated changes in Earth's history. (Freyberg 1985)

NOTES

....

....

....

....

....

....

....

....

NOTES

LEARNING SET 2 IMPLEMENTATION

Learning Set 2

What Is the Structure of Earth?

Earthquakes and volcanoes are two of the most dramatic types of geologic activity described by the pen pals. You may be familiar with some of the effects of these geologic events. However, to answer the *Big Question*, you need to know more about Earth's internal structure.

In this *Learning Set,* you will use techniques similar to those used by Earth scientists to learn more about the structure of Earth. After you know more about the inside of Earth, you will be better able to answer the *Big Question: What processes within Earth cause geologic activity?*

Damage you can see on Earth's surface, such as this broken roadway, may lead to questions about geologic activity under the surface.

EE 59

EVER-CHANGING EARTH

Learning Set 2

What Is the Structure of Earth?

5 min

Students are introduced to the Learning Set.

○ Engage

Begin by having students look at pictures of the regions described by the pen pals. Tell them that all of these regions have been affected by geologic activity, such as earthquakes and volcanoes. Ask them if they have any ideas about what causes these geologic activities.

Tell students they will be investigating the structure of Earth's interior in this *Learning Set*. They will use techniques similar to those used by Earth scientists. Investigating the structure of Earth's interior will help them to answer the *Big Question: What processes within Earth cause geologic activity?*

*A class period is considered to be one 40 to 50 minute class.

NOTES

2.1 Understand the Question

Think About the Structure of Earth

◀ *1 class period*

A class period is considered to be one 40 to 50 minute class.

Overview

Students begin thinking about the structure of Earth by observing changes in Earth's surface during geologic events. Working with their partners, they examine photographs of places on Earth's surface that show the effects of geologic events. They identify specific changes and gather evidence that Earth's surface is not continuous. Discussing their observations with their classmates, they evaluate how evidence the class gathered can be used to support interpretations of their observations. After presenting their ideas about the structure of Earth's surface in posters, they discuss what they think they know, what they need to investigate, and update the *Project Board*.

Targeted Concepts, Skills, and Nature of Science	Performance Expectations
Scientists often work together and then share their findings. Sharing findings makes new information available and helps scientists refine their ideas and build on others' ideas. When another person's or group's idea is used, credit needs to be given.	Students should work with their partners and other groups who examined the same pictures to develop ideas about the structure of Earth's surface; then, they should present their ideas to the class and consider how to investigate the ideas discussed.
Scientists must keep clear, accurate, and descriptive records of what they do so they can share their work with others and consider what they did, why they did it, and what they want to do next.	Students should keep clear, accurate, and descriptive records of the ideas about Earth's structure that they developed in their discussions.
Scientists make claims (conclusions) based on evidence obtained (trends in data) from reliable investigations.	Students should gather evidence supporting whether the surface of Earth is continuous or broken.

Targeted Concepts, Skills, and Nature of Science	Performance Expectations
Earthquake activity, volcanic activity, and topography are all evidence that Earth's crust is moving and changing.	Students should recognize that some of their observations of changes on Earth's surface are evidence that Earth's surface is not continuous and parts of it move and change.

Materials	
1 per group	Poster sheet
1 per class	Class *Project Board*
1 per student	*Project Board* page

NOTES

Homework Options

Reflection

- **Science Content:** What kind of changes do you think have occurred around your Earth structure because of geologic activity? Would these changes be similar to the changes you observed in the photographs? How? *(Students should refer to the geologic activity described in their pen pal letters. They should identify similarities between the volcanic or seismic activity in their regions and the volcanic or seismic activity shown in the photographs.)*

- **Science Content:** What ideas did you get from discussing the photographs with your classmates? Did your conclusions about the structure of Earth's surface change? *(Students should describe how their discussions with their classmates contributed to their ideas about the structure of the Earth's surface.)*

Preparation for 2.2

- **Science Content:** Based on your observations of changes in Earth's surface due to geologic activity, do you think the interior of the Earth is completely solid? Why or why not? *(This question is meant to help students think about the question of the structure of Earth's surface and connect that to the larger question of the structure of Earth. Students may say that the presence of forces capable of causing a volcanic eruption within Earth suggests that the interior of the Earth is not all solid.)*

NOTES

....

....

....

....

....

....

NOTES

SECTION 2.1 IMPLEMENTATION

2.1 Understand the Question

Think About the Structure of Earth

When you look around you at Earth's surface, it may seem like one continuous covering. But information in your pen pal letters supports evidence of a different idea. Perhaps there are breaks in Earth's surface that allow the ground to shake and volcanoes to erupt. Exploring the characteristics of Earth's surface may provide evidence about why geologic activity occurs.

Earth's surface looks continuous. But is it?

Get Started

Photographs taken from areas affected by earthquakes or volcanic eruptions show that something has caused buildings and highways to collapse, or large areas of land to be leveled. Examining the photographs on the next two pages may give you some ideas about what is moving.

With your partner, choose one of the geologic events pictured on the next two pages. Observe the series of photographs you selected and answer the following questions:

- What changes occurred in the area you selected? Changes might be large or small. You might notice that the size, shape, or position of parts of the area may have changed. Describe each of these changes.

- What evidence do you see in the photographs that might indicate Earth's surface is not one continuous piece?

EE 60

Project-Based Inquiry Science

2.1 Understand the Question

Think About the Structure of Earth

5 min

Students start thinking about the structure of Earth's surface.

○ Engage

Begin by asking students whether they think Earth is covered by one continuous covering. Ask them what some clues to answer the question might be.

> "Do you think Earth is covered by one solid, unbroken piece, or do you think that there are breaks in the covering of Earth? What are some clues that might help you decide whether Earth's covering is broken?"

Tell students that by exploring the characteristics of Earth's surface, such as whether it is broken or unbroken, they may be able to find evidence about why geologic activity occurs.

Get Started

10 min

Groups examine photographs of the effects of geologic events.

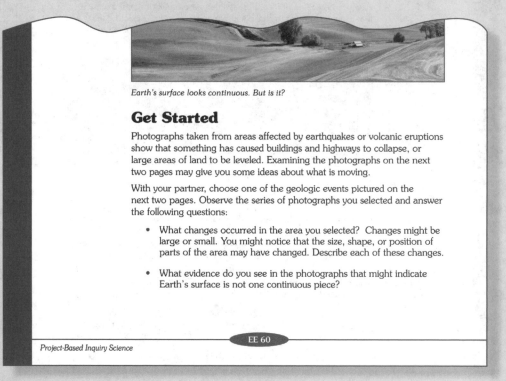

Earth's surface looks continuous. But is it?

Get Started

Photographs taken from areas affected by earthquakes or volcanic eruptions show that something has caused buildings and highways to collapse, or large areas of land to be leveled. Examining the photographs on the next two pages may give you some ideas about what is moving.

With your partner, choose one of the geologic events pictured on the next two pages. Observe the series of photographs you selected and answer the following questions:

- What changes occurred in the area you selected? Changes might be large or small. You might notice that the size, shape, or position of parts of the area may have changed. Describe each of these changes.

- What evidence do you see in the photographs that might indicate Earth's surface is not one continuous piece?

Project-Based Inquiry Science

EE 60

△ Guide

Point out the photographs in the student text. Explain that these photographs show changes in Earth's surface caused by earthquakes or volcanic eruptions. The photographs of Mount St. Helens is an example showing the area before, during, and after a geologic event. The photographs below show the before and after of a geologic event—a Guatemalan earthquake in 1976. On the following page, the formation of Surtsey Island shows another type of geologic event. Emphasize that by examining these series of photogrpahs, students may find clues to whether Earth's surface is continuous or broken. They may also be able to infer from these photographs what moves when there are earthquakes or volcanic eruptions.

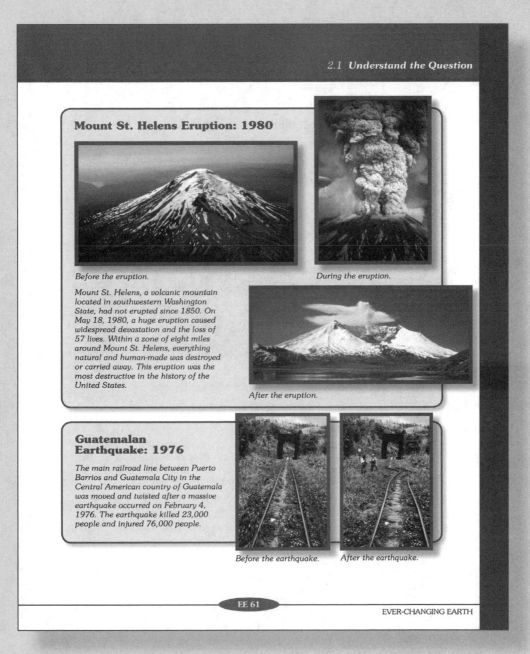

Mount St. Helens Eruption: 1980

Before the eruption.

During the eruption.

Mount St. Helens, a volcanic mountain located in southwestern Washington State, had not erupted since 1850. On May 18, 1980, a huge eruption caused widespread devastation and the loss of 57 lives. Within a zone of eight miles around Mount St. Helens, everything natural and human-made was destroyed or carried away. This eruption was the most destructive in the history of the United States.

After the eruption.

Guatemalan Earthquake: 1976

The main railroad line between Puerto Barrios and Guatemala City in the Central American country of Guatemala was moved and twisted after a massive earthquake occurred on February 4, 1976. The earthquake killed 23,000 people and injured 76,000 people.

Before the earthquake. *After the earthquake.*

EE 61

EVER-CHANGING EARTH

Tell students they will work with their partners to make observations about what has happened in these series of photographs. They will answer the questions in the student text for one series of photographs, and they will use their answers to develop ideas about Earth's surface and processes within Earth.

⬡ Get Going

Have each group choose one of the geologic events shown in the photographs. Have them work with their partners to answer the questions in the student text.

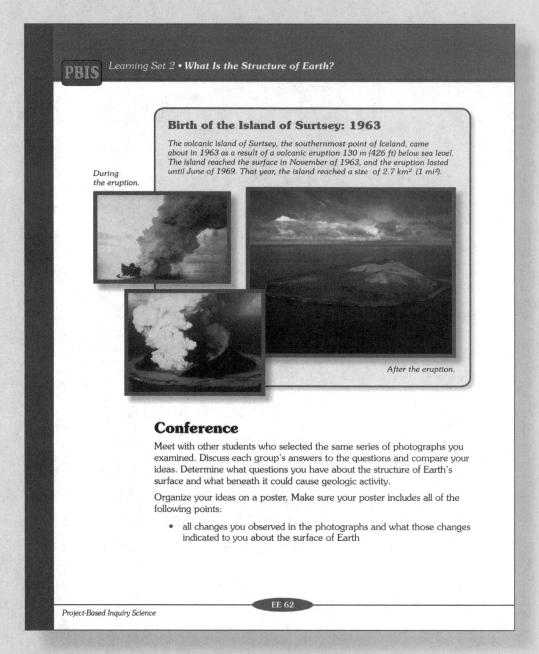

Birth of the Island of Surtsey: 1963

The volcanic island of Surtsey, the southernmost point of Iceland, came about in 1963 as a result of a volcanic eruption 130 m (426 ft) below sea level. The island reached the surface in November of 1963, and the eruption lasted until June of 1969. That year, the island reached a size of 2.7 km² (1 mi²).

During the eruption.

After the eruption.

Conference

Meet with other students who selected the same series of photographs you examined. Discuss each group's answers to the questions and compare your ideas. Determine what questions you have about the structure of Earth's surface and what beneath it could cause geologic activity.

Organize your ideas on a poster. Make sure your poster includes all of the following points:

- all changes you observed in the photographs and what those changes indicated to you about the surface of Earth

EE 62

◇ Evaluate

As groups examine the pictures, assess the observations they are making from the photographs. In the case of the volcanic eruption at Mount St. Helens, they should observe that the shape of the mountain has changed. The mountain was solid with a conical shape, but the eruption broke through the top of the mountain and changed the shape of the mountain to a bowl shape. They should also note that the eruption is evidence that there are non-solid materials within Earth, and that Earth's surface can be broken, as it was at the site of the volcano.

In the case of the Guatemalan earthquake, students should observe that the railroad tracks along the ground have been bent, suggesting that parts of Earth's surface have been dislocated in relation to the rest. They should note that this is evidence that parts of Earth's surface can move independently of other parts, which could not happen if Earth's surface was continuous.

In the case of the volcanic eruption below sea level at Surtsey Island, students should observe that the island has appeared where the eruption occurred. Students should note that this eruption is evidence that there are non-solid materials within Earth and that Earth's surface can be broken.

It is all right if some groups have not made these observations and inferences yet. They will discuss their observations with other groups and with the class, giving them a chance to learn from each other. It is important that some students in the class make these observations.

△ Guide

When students have had time to answer the questions about the photographs, have them meet with other students who examined the same geologic event. They should discuss the changes they observed and any evidence that Earth's surface is not continuous. They should determine what questions they still have about the structure of Earth's surface. Let students know they will present the ideas their group discusses to the class shortly.

⬡ Get Going

Have students work with their partners to create posters showing the ideas from their discussions. Emphasize that their posters should address the bulleted points in the student text. The posters should include the changes they observed in the photographs and their interpretations of the changes. They should include brief descriptions of their discussions. They should describe ideas about the structure of Earth's surface and what causes geologic activity along with supporting evidence from the photographs. Posters should also include questions the students want to investigate.

☐ Assess

As groups prepare posters, ask what ideas about Earth's surface they are presenting and what evidence for their ideas they are presenting. Look for ideas about whether Earth's surface is continuous. If students' ideas do not address this, ask if their discussions of the photographs gave them any new ideas about whether Earth's surface is continuous. Ask what questions they may want to investigate.

Conference
10 min

Students discuss their observations and interpretations with other students who examined the same photographs.

Communicate:
Share Your
Ideas

15 min

Groups present their ideas to the class.

- a brief description of the discussion you had with your group. Include the similarities and differences in your ideas.

- your ideas about the structure of Earth's surface and what beneath it could cause geologic activity. Include any evidence in the photographs supporting your ideas.

- any questions you want to investigate to better understand the structure of Earth

Communicate

Share Your Ideas

Groups will take turns presenting their ideas to the class. After all of the groups have presented, discuss the different ideas presented about the structure of Earth's surface. If there are disagreements, the class may want to divide into two groups: one group that supports the idea that Earth's surface is continuous and unbroken, and one that supports the idea that the surface is not continuous. Groups should provide evidence to support their opinions. If there is still disagreement about which idea the evidence supports, a question about the structure of Earth's surface should be added to the *Project Board*.

Update the *Project Board*

Record any ideas about the structure of Earth's surface and what is beneath it in the *What do we think we know?* column of the *Project Board*. You developed some questions about what you need to investigate to better answer the *Big Question*. Record your questions in the *What do we need to investigate?* column. Throughout this *Learning Set,* you will be expanding on these ideas and finding answers to your questions. This will help you answer the *Big Question* for this Unit, *What processes within Earth cause geologic activity?*

What's the Point?

Your observations may indicate that Earth's surface is one continuous piece. But further data, collected in places where there is a lot of geologic activity, provide evidence that pieces of Earth's surface are moving. If pieces of Earth's surface are moving, perhaps the crust is not one continuous piece. It may instead be broken in to pieces that each shift and move.

EE 63

EVER-CHANGING EARTH

⬡ Get Going

Have groups present their ideas and posters to the class.

☐ Assess

As groups present, assess how well students support their ideas with evidence. Listen for disagreements and take note of how students address those disagreements. Do they ask each other questions, or point out where supporting evidence is weak? Did students note the ways their interpretations were different from other students' interpretations?

Students should also briefly discuss what ideas came out of their discussions with other groups. If their observations and interpretations changed during the discussions, this should be reflected in their presentations.

△ Guide

After all groups have presented, lead a class discussion of the ideas that were presented. If groups disagree about whether Earth's surface is continuous, consider dividing the class into two groups: one to argue for a continuous surface and one to argue for a broken surface.

Emphasize that groups should provide evidence for their ideas. Students who are listening to presentations should ask the presenting group for evidence if they think an idea is not supported by evidence.

◇ Evaluate

During the presentations, groups should present questions they would like to investigate. These should include questions about the big pieces that make up Earth's surface:

- Where are they?
- Can they be seen?
- What are they made of and how deep down are they?

These should also include questions about how these pieces affect geologic processes:

- What happens when the pieces move?
- Why do they move?
- What is under the pieces?

Disagreements about interpretations of the evidence should suggest an investigative question for the *Project Board*.

△ Guide

Ask students what ideas about the structure of Earth's surface can be recorded on the *Project Board*. These ideas should go in the *What do we think we know?* column of the *Project Board*. Ask what investigative questions students can record on the *Project Board*. These should go in the *What do we need to investigate?* column. The questions that students asked during the presentations should be recorded on the *Project Board*.

Update the Project Board

15 min

Students lead a discussion of what ideas and questions to record on the Project Board.

Assessment Options

Targeted Concepts, Skills, and Nature of Science	How do I know if students got it?
Scientists often work together and then share their findings. Sharing findings makes new information available and helps scientists refine their ideas and build on others' ideas. When another person's or group's idea is used, credit needs to be given.	**ASK:** How did sharing your ideas with the class help you to improve them? **LISTEN:** Students should have used the class discussions to build on their ideas and to determine what questions they still need to investigate.
Scientists must keep clear, accurate, and descriptive records of what they do so they can share their work with others and consider what they did, why they did it, and what they want to do next.	**ASK:** Why is it important to record what you think you know and what you want to learn on the *Project Board?* **LISTEN:** Students should recognize that recording what they think they know and what they want to learn allows them to consider their progress and what they still need to do to answer the *Big Question.*
Scientists make claims (conclusions) based on evidence obtained (trends in data) from reliable investigations.	**ASK:** Why is it important to support your ideas with evidence from your observations? **LISTEN:** Students should realize they can come closer to agreement if they base their ideas upon verifiable evidence. Without evidence, students could not have a meaningful discussion about their disagreements.
Earthquake activity, volcanic activity, and topography are all evidence that Earth's crust is moving and changing.	**ASK:** What observations suggest that Earth's cover moves and changes? **LISTEN:** Students should see that the displacement of parts of Earth's surface in the photographs of an earthquake suggests that Earth's cover has moved and changed at that place.

Teacher Reflection Questions

- What difficulties did students have making inferences about the structure of Earth's surface from their observations? What difficulties do you expect them to have connecting their observations to the concepts of plate tectonics? How can you help them with this?

- How were you able to help students understand the concepts in this section, such as a continuous and discontinuous Earth surface? How can you help them in the future?

- How were you able to engage students in discussing their interpretations of their observations? What can you try next time?

NOTES

NOTES

2.2 Explore

A Model of Earth's Structure

◀ **1 class period**

A class period is considered to be one 40 to 50 minute class.

Overview

Students use what they have observed and what they know about Earth to evaluate a model of Earth's interior and crust. Reading a letter from a student in Java, they are introduced to a model that uses the cracked shell of a hard-boiled egg to represent Earth's crust. From the letter, the students learn about the movement of hot rock within Earth and are given a model that explains why earthquakes and volcanic eruptions happen. Students evaluate the strengths and weaknesses of the model and consider what information they still need to obtain to explain why earthquakes and volcanic eruptions happen.

Targeted Concepts, Skills, and Nature of Science	Performance Expectations
Scientists often work together and then share their findings. Sharing findings makes new information available and helps scientists refine their ideas and build on others' ideas. When another person's or group's idea is used, credit needs to be given.	Students should discuss the strengths and weaknesses of the hard-boiled egg model with their partners and then share their ideas with the class.
Scientists use models and tools, such as Geographic Information Systems, and a variety of maps to develop claims and explanations from evidence in the data.	Students should demonstrate understanding that models can help scientists investigate real-world phenomena. They should evaluate the hard-boiled egg as a model of Earth based on how well it represents Earth and how well it helps them investigate Earth's structure.
Earth's crust is constantly changing. These changes are usually a very slow process that is not immediately observable. Some changes are very rapid and are observable.	Students should demonstrate understanding that Benny's model predicts that the motion of hot rock in Earth's mantle will move the plates in Earth's crust.

Targeted Concepts, Skills, and Nature of Science	Performance Expectations
Earthquake activity, volcanic activity, and topography are all evidence that Earth's crust is moving and changing.	Students should begin trying to find patterns in Earth structures that may allow them to find repeatable patterns in the processes that shaped them.

Materials	
1 per group	Hard-boiled egg

Hard-boiled eggs can be scalding hot after boiling. Ensure that the eggs are cool before you or students handle them.

Activity Setup and Preparation

Before class, prepare a hard-boiled egg for each group in your class. The shell of the egg should be lightly cracked, so that the shell has several large fragments.

Homework Options

Reflection

- **Science Content:** What new information about the structure of Earth did you learn from Benny's model? What more do you need to find out to explain geologic activity? *(Students should identify information about Earth's layers, including the motion of the rock in the mantle and the plates in the crust. They should consider how this information helps them explain geologic activity and what they still need to learn to explain geologic activity.)*

Preparation for 2.3

- **Science Process:** What do you think the greatest obstacles are to learn about the structure of Earth's interior? How do you think scientists get around these obstacles? *(This question is meant to engage students in thinking about the challenges of studying Earth's structure. They should see that scientists' inability to directly observe Earth's interior is a significant obstacle.)*

SECTION 2.2 IMPLEMENTATION

2.2 Explore

A Model of Earth's Structure

model: a representation of a process, system, or object that makes it possible to examine some aspects of the process, system, or object.

Benny Makmur is from the island of Java. His island is one of many that make up the nation of Indonesia. Indonesia is one of the most volcanically active regions of the world. In his letter, Benny shares a **model** of Earth's structure that the teacher presented to his class. A model is a representation of a process, system, or object that makes it possible to examine some aspects of the process, system, or object. Benny will tell you some ways that Earth is like a cracked, hard-boiled egg. You may have a real one to examine as you read Benny's letter. If you do not have one to look at, imagine one as you read.

Be a Scientist

Models
Useful models are at a size that people can easily examine. To use a model to investigate, the model needs to be similar to the real world in ways that are important for what the scientist is investigating.

A globe is an example of a familiar model. A globe represents Earth's shape and usually some surface features. When you look at a globe, you can see that Earth is a sphere. You also see where there are continents, oceans, and mountains. A globe helps you examine Earth and the continents all at once. This would not be possible without this model.

EE 64

Project-Based Inquiry Science

2.2 Explore

A Model of Earth's Structure

5 min

Students are introduced to the activity.

△ Guide

Remind students that they have already observed changes in Earth's surface. Some students found evidence that Earth's surface was discontinuous. They will now read a letter that describes a model of Earth's structure, including the structure of its surface.

*A class period is considered to be one 40 to 50 minute class.

Be a Scientist: Models

5 min

Students discuss how scientists use models.

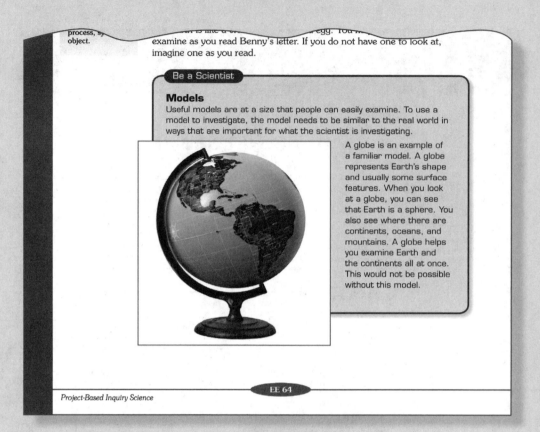

process, sy... object.

...an is like a ... egg. You... examine as you read Benny's letter. If you do not have one to look at, imagine one as you read.

Be a Scientist

Models
Useful models are at a size that people can easily examine. To use a model to investigate, the model needs to be similar to the real world in ways that are important for what the scientist is investigating.

A globe is an example of a familiar model. A globe represents Earth's shape and usually some surface features. When you look at a globe, you can see that Earth is a sphere. You also see where there are continents, oceans, and mountains. A globe helps you examine Earth and the continents all at once. This would not be possible without this model.

EE 64

Project-Based Inquiry Science

△ Guide

Before giving students hard-boiled eggs and reading the letter, discuss what models are and how they are useful for investigating objects or ideas. A globe is an example of a model. Ask students how a globe is similar to Earth. How is it different? When using models, it is important to understand how they represent real objects, and how they are different from the objects they represent.

You might also take a moment to discuss the models that students have already used. The maps and images students examined in *My World* were models. On foot, it can be very difficult to find out how distant your home is from landmarks in the neighborhood and may be impossible to find out how distant it is from landmarks in other cities, states, and countries. Using a model, such as map or globe, makes it very easy to find out how far your home is from landmarks around the world.

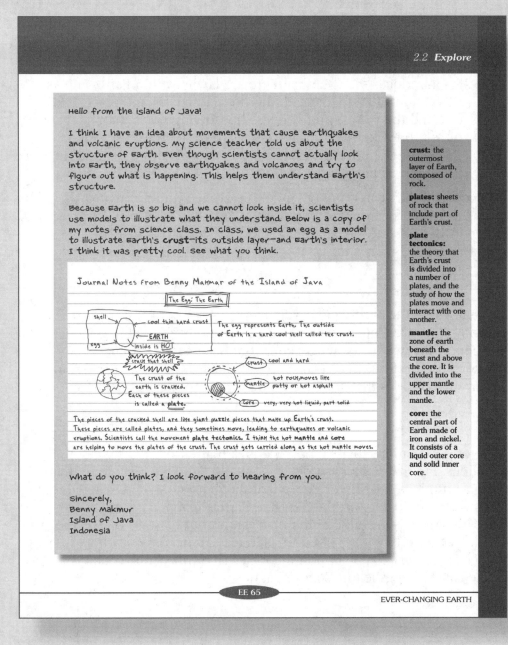

2.2 Explore

Hello from the island of Java!

I think I have an idea about movements that cause earthquakes and volcanic eruptions. My science teacher told us about the structure of Earth. Even though scientists cannot actually look into Earth, they observe earthquakes and volcanoes and try to figure out what is happening. This helps them understand Earth's structure.

Because Earth is so big and we cannot look inside it, scientists use models to illustrate what they understand. Below is a copy of my notes from science class. In class, we used an egg as a model to illustrate Earth's **crust**—its outside layer—and Earth's interior. I think it was pretty cool. See what you think.

Journal Notes from Benny Makmur of the Island of Java

The Egg: The Earth

The egg represents Earth. The outside of Earth is a hard cool shell called the crust.

The crust of the earth is cracked. Each of these pieces is called a **plate**.

The pieces of the cracked shell are like giant puzzle pieces that make up Earth's crust. These pieces are called plates, and they sometimes move, leading to earthquakes or volcanic eruptions. Scientists call the movement **plate tectonics**. I think the hot **mantle** and core are helping to move the plates of the crust. The crust gets carried along as the hot mantle moves.

What do you think? I look forward to hearing from you.

Sincerely,
Benny Makmur
Island of Java
Indonesia

crust: the outermost layer of Earth, composed of rock.

plates: sheets of rock that include part of Earth's crust.

plate tectonics: the theory that Earth's crust is divided into a number of plates, and the study of how the plates move and interact with one another.

mantle: the zone of earth beneath the crust and above the core. It is divided into the upper mantle and the lower mantle.

core: the central part of Earth made of iron and nickel. It consists of a liquid outer core and solid inner core.

EE 65

EVER-CHANGING EARTH

Letter from Benny

20 min

The students discuss the letter from Benny.

META NOTES

The hard-boiled eggs are models and should not be eaten. Monitor students to make sure they do not eat the eggs. Dropped eggs should be cleaned up promptly.

◯ Get Going

Hand out the hard-boiled eggs. Then read the letter from Benny with the class.

△ Guide

Using Benny's notes, discuss what Benny learned about the structure of Earth. Benny's notes introduce several important ideas about Earth's structure. As you discuss these, it is important to encourage students to think about how these ideas can help explain geologic activity.

Benny's model uses the cracked eggshell to represent the plates in Earth's surface. His notes say that the motion of these plates leads to earthquakes and volcanic eruptions. Ask students how they think this might happen.

Benny also introduces the idea that there are layers within Earth. Earth's crust is the outermost layer. Beneath this are the mantle and core. The crust is cool and the mantle and core are hot. Benny notes that the mantle consists of hot rock like putty or hot asphalt, and he thinks that the hot mantle and core help move the plates in the crust. The hot rock of the mantle carries the plates along as it flows.

Ask students if they can think of any observations from *My World*, the Earth-imaging software, or from the photos they examined that could be evidence to support Benny's ideas. Can they think of observations that could be evidence against Benny's ideas?

TEACHER TALK

"Think about the observations you made in *My World* and the Earth-imaging software. Could any of those observations be used as evidence to support Benny's ideas? What about your observations from the photographs of the sites of a volcano and an earthquake? Can you think of any observations that could be used as evidence against Benny's ideas?"

Listen for observations that support the idea that Earth's crust is not continuous and that Earth's interior is not solid. Students may recall that volcanic eruptions provide evidence that there are non-solid materials within Earth, which could support the idea that Earth's mantle consists of non-solid rock. They may also recall that the photograph of bent rails on the ground provide evidence that parts of Earth's surface can become dislocated relative to other parts. This could support the idea that Earth's crust contains pieces like the cracked eggshell in Benny's model.

Learning Set 2 • What Is the Structure of Earth?

Stop and Think

1. What does Benny think is moving to cause earthquakes and volcanic eruptions?

2. Use evidence from the photographs you examined earlier to identify strengths in Benny's model.

3. Use what you know about Earth and evidence from the photographs you examined earlier to identify weaknesses in Benny's model. What is missing from his model?

4. How convinced are you about Benny's model? What else would you need to know to determine the accuracy of Benny's model?

5. How do you think scientists can determine what the inside of Earth looks like beneath the crust?

What's the Point?

Scientists cannot look deep inside Earth. But by observing earthquakes and volcanoes on Earth's surface, they can get some information about the structure of Earth. Benny's letter tells you that Earth has three major layers. The outermost layer is called the crust. The crust is broken up into sections called plates. Below the crust is the mantle, Earth's middle layer. Beneath that is Earth's innermost layer, the core. The movement of plates causes earthquakes and volcanoes. The theory of plate movement is called plate tectonics.

EE 66

Project-Based Inquiry Science

Stop and Think

20 min

Students lead a class discussion of the Stop and Think *questions.*

◯ Get Going

Have students answer the *Stop and Think* questions with their partners. Let them know they will share their answers with the class.

△ Guide and Assess

When students have had time to answer the *Stop and Think* questions, guide a class discussion of their responses. Listen for the following responses:

1. Students should recall that Benny said the plates in Earth's crust were moving and causing earthquakes and volcanic eruptions. Students might also say that Benny explained that the rock in the mantle carries the plates with it as it moves.

2. Students should identify ways Benny's model could explain geologic activity they observed in the photographs and ways the model could support their conclusions. Benny's idea that Earth's crust contains moving plates suggests explanations for earthquakes—perhaps, the plates collide. The model supports the conclusion that Earth's surface is not continuous and instead, it is fractured like a cracked eggshell.

3. Students should identify ways that Benny's model does not resemble Earth. An obvious dissimilarity is that a hard-boiled egg is ovoid, while Earth is very close to a sphere in shape. Also, Benny thinks the hot rock in the mantle moves and carries the plates with it, but the model does not explain why the hot rock moves. Students may also judge that the model does not explain all of the geologic activity they have observed. More information is needed to explain why volcanoes and earthquakes occur.

4. Students should use the strengths and weaknesses they identified to evaluate the model. They should also evaluate how well the model is supported by evidence and science knowledge. Ideally, students will recognize that the only evidence they have is from observations of Earth's surface. In order to determine the accuracy of the model, students will need verifiable information about the interior of Earth. If observations cannot be made directly, they will need to obtain evidence indirectly.

5. This question is meant to engage students in thinking about how to investigate Earth's interior. Students may suggest probes, core samples, or studying materials that come from beneath Earth's surface, such as lava or oil from wells.

Assessment Options

Targeted Concepts, Skills, and Nature of Science	How do I know if students got it?
Scientists often work together and then share their findings. Sharing findings makes new information available and helps scientists refine their ideas and build on others' ideas. When another person's or group's idea is used, credit needs to be given.	**ASK:** How was it helpful to discuss the *Stop and Think* questions with your partner? What ideas came out of your discussion? **LISTEN:** Students should recognize that discussing their ideas helps them to refine those ideas.
Scientists use models and tools, such as Geographic Information Systems, and a variety of maps to develop claims and explanations from evidence in the data.	**ASK:** How is Benny's model useful? Why use a model at all? **LISTEN:** Students should recognize that models such as Benny's, allow them to investigate objects indirectly that are too large for them to investigate directly.
Earth's crust is constantly changing. These changes are usually a very slow process that is not immediately observable. Some changes are very rapid and are observable.	**ASK:** Why was it important that Benny noted in his model that the hot rock in the mantle moved? **LISTEN:** Students should understand that Benny thinks the hot rock carries the plates in the crust with it as it moves.
Earthquake activity, volcanic activity, and topography are all evidence that Earth's crust is moving and changing.	**ASK:** What evidence do you have that the plates in Earth's crust move as Benny has predicted? **LISTEN:** Students should identify observations of changes in Earth's surface.

Teacher Reflection Questions

- What misconceptions about Earth's structure do you think students have? How can you address these misconceptions?

- How were you able to engage students in evaluating Benny's model? What might you try next time?

- How were you able to keep students focused as they examined the hard-boiled eggs? How can you keep them focused in future activities?

NOTES

....

....

....

....

....

....

....

....

....

....

SECTION 2.3 INTRODUCTION

2.3 Explore

Making Observations and Inferences

◀ *1 class period*

A class period is considered to be one 40 to 50 minute class.

Overview

Students examine boxes that contain mystery objects. They observe the weight of the boxes, the sounds they make when someone shakes them, and other attributes they can observe without opening the box. They make inferences about the objects in the boxes based on their observations and their knowledge of common objects. Once everyone has made inferences about what is in the boxes, they share their observations and inferences with the class, further distinguishing between observation and inference as they gather feedback from their classmates. They consider what reasoning skills they used to infer what is in each box, and how they can use these reasoning skills to make inferences about Earth's surface around their Earth structure, the geologic activity around their Earth structure, and what is beneath Earth's surface. This allows them to gain an understanding of how scientists can make inferences about what is within Earth.

Targeted Concepts, Skills, and Nature of Science	Performance Expectations
Scientists often work together and then share their findings. Sharing findings makes new information available and helps scientists refine their ideas and build on others' ideas. When another person's or group's idea is used, credit needs to be given.	Students should work with their partners to make inferences about what is inside their mystery boxes. Then they should share their inferences with the class.
Scientists must keep clear, accurate, and descriptive records of what they do so they can share their work with others and consider what they did, why they did it, and what they want to do next.	Students should use their *Observations and Inferences* pages to keep detailed records of how they made observations and inferences.

Targeted Concepts, Skills, and Nature of Science	Performance Expectations
Scientists make claims (conclusions) based on evidence obtained (trends in data) from reliable investigations.	Students should make observations and use these observations to make inferences.

Materials	
1 per group	Mystery box *Observations and Inferences* pages

Activity Setup and Preparation

In this section, students will determine what is inside mystery boxes by shaking them, smelling them, hefting them, and making every observation possible without actually opening the box. Prepare mystery boxes by selecting a group of objects that are similar, but slightly different. These might be a set of blocks that includes a hexagonal block, a cubic block, and so forth. The boxes should be opaque and large enough to give the objects room to move around. Try your selection of objects and boxes before class to make sure that it will be difficult, but not impossible for students to determine what is inside each box.

Homework Options

Reflection

- **Science Process:** Why are inferences important for studying the structure of Earth? *(Students should realize that inferences are important because not all of Earth can be studied by direct observation and scientists must use their direct observations of Earth's surface to make inferences about what lies below the surface.)*

Preparation for 2.4

- **Science Process:** What information about Earth's surface do you think would help you infer what is under Earth's surface? *(This question is meant to engage students in thinking about what is under Earth's surface and how observations of Earth's surface can be used to make inferences.)*

SECTION 2.3 IMPLEMENTATION

◀ *1 class period* *

2.3 Explore

Making Observations and Inferences

Scientists cannot crack open Earth to determine what is happening far beneath the surface. They have tried unsuccessfully to drill through the crust to the mantle. But scientists know more than what they can observe.

To learn about Earth's interior, scientists use **observations** and measurements made at or near Earth's surface. Using these observations, they make **inferences** about what they cannot see. Observations are data gathered with one or more senses—what you can see, hear, feel, smell, or taste. Sometimes observations are made with the help of tools or instruments. Doctors use stethoscopes to better hear heartbeats. Geologists use instruments to measure temperature, movement, and other characteristics. Inferences are interpretations of observations. People make inferences by using what they know to reason about what they have observed. You will be collecting data and making inferences to answer questions on the *Project Board*. Before doing that, you need to understand what it means to make inferences based on observations.

You have already made some inferences in this *Learning Set*. You observed photographs showing that objects attached to Earth's surface had moved in interesting ways. You inferred from those observations that Earth's crust is made of pieces that move. You inferred this because an unbroken, continuous covering of rock would not allow the changes you observed.

You will practice making observations and inferences again, this time noting the ways you make inferences. You will make observations of several objects that you cannot see or touch and then make inferences about what those objects might be. You will think about how you arrived at those inferences.

observations: data that are gathered using one or more senses of sight, hearing, touch, smell, or taste, sometimes with the help of instruments.

inference: an interpretation of observations; reasoning that suggests causes or explanations of what has been observed.

Some of the deepest places scientists have access to are South African gold mines. These gold mines may extend two miles into Earth, but they are still in Earth's crust.

EE 67

EVER-CHANGING EARTH

2.3 Explore

Making Observations and Inferences

5 min

Students continue making observations and inferences.

△ Guide

Tell students that scientists cannot observe anything below Earth's crust. Ask students how they think scientists might determine what the structure of Earth's interior is. Ask them how scientists could have discovered the layers that Benny's note described. Students may suggest that scientists can use their observations of earthquakes and volcanic activity to determine what is under Earth's surface.

*A class period is considered to be one 40 to 50 minute class.

Tell students that scientists make observations at or near Earth's surface. They reason about the causes and explanations of what they observed using logic to determine what is under Earth's surface. Tell students that this kind of reasoning is called inference. Ask students what the difference between observation and inference is. They should recognize that observations are obtained directly through the senses, while inferences require interpretation of observations and reasoning.

TEACHER TALK

"You know now that reasoning about causes or explanations of what has been observed is inference. But how is an inference different from an observation? If I see that a volcano has erupted, is that an observation or an inference? (*Observation.*) If I determine that plates in Earth's surface move based on what I know about volcanoes and earthquakes, is that an observation or an inference? (*Inference.*) What is the difference?"

Point out that students have made observations and inferences in this *Learning Set*. They observed changes in Earth's surface that occurred during a geologic event. They inferred that Earth's crust is discontinuous and contains pieces that move and change. The changes students saw were observations because they were obtained directly from their senses. The latter were inferences because students used reasoning to interpret their observations.

TEACHER TALK

"When you examined pictures of geologic events, you made observations and inferences. You looked at the photographs and noted what you saw. That is observation. Then you considered what evidence you could find in the photographs that indicated that Earth's surface was not one continuous piece. That is inference."

Tell students they will practice making observations and inferences in this section.

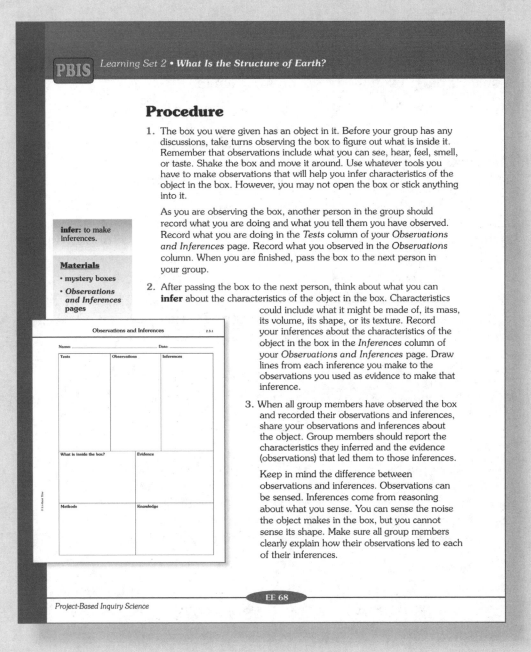

Learning Set 2 • *What Is the Structure of Earth?*

Procedure

1. The box you were given has an object in it. Before your group has any discussions, take turns observing the box to figure out what is inside it. Remember that observations include what you can see, hear, feel, smell, or taste. Shake the box and move it around. Use whatever tools you have to make observations that will help you infer characteristics of the object in the box. However, you may not open the box or stick anything into it.

   infer: to make inferences.

   As you are observing the box, another person in the group should record what you are doing and what you tell them you have observed. Record what you are doing in the *Tests* column of your *Observations and Inferences* page. Record what you observed in the *Observations* column. When you are finished, pass the box to the next person in your group.

   Materials
   • mystery boxes
   • *Observations and Inferences* pages

2. After passing the box to the next person, think about what you can **infer** about the characteristics of the object in the box. Characteristics could include what it might be made of, its mass, its volume, its shape, or its texture. Record your inferences about the characteristics of the object in the box in the *Inferences* column of your *Observations and Inferences* page. Draw lines from each inference you make to the observations you used as evidence to make that inference.

3. When all group members have observed the box and recorded their observations and inferences, share your observations and inferences about the object. Group members should report the characteristics they inferred and the evidence (observations) that led them to those inferences.

   Keep in mind the difference between observations and inferences. Observations can be sensed. Inferences come from reasoning about what you sense. You can sense the noise the object makes in the box, but you cannot sense its shape. Make sure all group members clearly explain how their observations led to each of their inferences.

EE 68

Project-Based Inquiry Science

Procedure
15 min

Students start making inferences about what is in the mystery boxes.

△ Guide

Distribute the mystery boxes and the *Observations and Inferences* pages. Tell students they are going to work with their partners to figure out what is in their box. Let students know they may shake and move their boxes, however, they may not open the box or stick anything inside it. Each student should take a turn examining their box.

As each student observes their box, another student should record what he or she is doing in the *Tests* column of the *Observations and Inferences* page. Before the student with the box passes it on, his or her observations should be recorded in the *Observations* column.

After recording observations, each student should make inferences about the characteristics of the object inside the box, such as its mass, volume, shape, texture, and composition. They should record their inferences in the *Inferences* column of the *Observations and Inferences* page and draw lines from each inference to the observation that supports it.

Once all members of a group have made observations and inferences, they should share their observations and inferences with the group. As each member of the group presents, the others should listen for how the member's observations led to his or her inferences. Encourage students to ask each other clarifying questions.

Groups should discuss what they think their object is. Someone in the group should record their ideas. They should record what they think the object is along with their evidence at the bottom of the *Observations and Inferences* page.

Finally, groups should make two lists: one of the methods they used to make observations and one of the knowledge they used to infer what was in the box.

☐ Assess

As groups examine the mystery boxes, monitor their progress and ask what observations they have made and what they have inferred from their observations. Pay attention to how students distinguish between observations and inferences. If they confuse observations and inferences, note this as something to discuss in the upcoming *Communicate* segment.

△ Guide

When groups have finished with their first mystery boxes, they should switch boxes with another group and repeat the procedure.

2.3 Explore

You might want to revise your lists of observations and inferences as you have these discussions. Make sure your list of observations includes only what you sensed.

4. Discuss your ideas about what the object is. Someone in the group should act as recorder and make a list of all of the ideas. Then, decide what you think the object is. Record what you think the object is in the *What is inside the box?* part of your *Observations and Inferences* page. Record the evidence that supports your choice on the bottom of the page. In the *Evidence* box, include the inferences you made about these observations.

5. As a group, make two lists:

   • the methods used to make observations that helped you infer what is in the box

   • the knowledge about objects that you used to infer (make inferences about) what is in the box

6. Switch boxes with another group and repeat steps 1 through 5. Use a new *Observation and Inferences* page for each box you examine.

Communicate

Share Your Ideas

Each group has now examined two mystery boxes. As your teacher holds up each box, share four things with the class:

   • observations you made about what is inside the box and how you made these observations (e.g., by shaking the box, by listening)

   • what you think the object inside the box *is like* and the knowledge you used to make these inferences

   • what you think the object *is* and the knowledge you used to make that inference

   • how confident you are of what is in the box

As you listen to your classmates, make sure they are distinguishing between observations and inferences. Again, make sure all presenters clearly explain how their observations led to each of their inferences.

EE 69

EVER-CHANGING EARTH

Communicate: Share Your Ideas

15 min

Students lead a class discussion of their mystery boxes.

△ Guide

Lead a class discussion of the mystery boxes. Hold up each mystery box and have the groups that examined that box share their observations, the methods they used to make their observations, their inferences, the knowledge they used to make their inferences, and how confident they are of their inferences.

△ Guide and Assess

If any groups are confusing observations with inferences, have the class discuss this. You may need to guide the class by asking questions about a misclassified observation or interpretation, such as:

- What was involved in making this observation?
- What did your senses tell you?
- What makes it an observation?

After students have discussed their inferences and their confidence in their inferences, open the mystery boxes. If there were any mystery boxes for which students could not make accurate inferences, ask the class if they have any ideas about what made these boxes difficult. Discuss how students were able to make accurate inferences about the other boxes. Ask them if they were able to use any knowledge they already have about objects to make inferences about those boxes. Ask them if they were able to make more observations of those boxes. This discussion should help students develop their understanding of inferences.

TEACHER TALK

"Which boxes were you able to make the most accurate inferences about? Which boxes were more difficult? What made some boxes more difficult than others? How were you able to make accurate inferences about the other boxes?"

NOTES

Be a Scientist

Making Inferences from Observations

You have just been making inferences based on observations. You made observations about the objects in each box using a variety of methods. You then used those data to infer characteristics of the object inside and used what you know about objects to infer what was in the box. This is the way scientists infer what is inside Earth. They cannot look into Earth or even drill down deep enough to study its inner layers, so they collect data by making observations. Using these data, they can make inferences about what the inner structure of Earth is like. They become more confident about their inferences as more kinds of data are collected.

Reflect

Earlier in this *Learning Set*, you observed the way objects on Earth's surface moved as a result of an earthquake or volcano. Based on these observations, you inferred that Earth's surface is not just one unbroken layer of rock but is made of separate rock pieces that move. Try making some other inferences.

1. You have read about where earthquakes and volcanoes have taken place in your region. You have also observed the topography of Earth's surface in your region. What inferences can you make about the rocks that cover Earth's surface in your region?

2. How confident are you about these inferences? What else do you think you need to observe to be more confident?

3. List two things you think scientists might need to observe to make inferences about what is beneath Earth's surface.

What's the Point?

Investigating something that you cannot directly observe requires making inferences based on observations. Information cannot be gathered about the interior of Earth through direct observation. Instead, it must be gathered through inference. Scientists use observations made at or near Earth's surface to make inferences about what lies beneath. Observations include what can be sensed—seen, heard, felt, smelled, or tasted. Inferences are made by using what is already known to reason about what has been observed.

Be a Scientist: Making Inferences from Observations

5 min

Students read more about how scientists make inferences about Earth's interior.

△ Guide

Before students answer the *Reflect* questions, emphasize that scientists make inferences about what is within Earth the same way students made inferences about what was in their mystery boxes. Students used observations and what they already know about objects to infer what was in the box. Scientists make observations of Earth's surface to make inferences about Earth's inner structure.

Reflect

10 min

Students answer the Reflect *questions with their partners.*

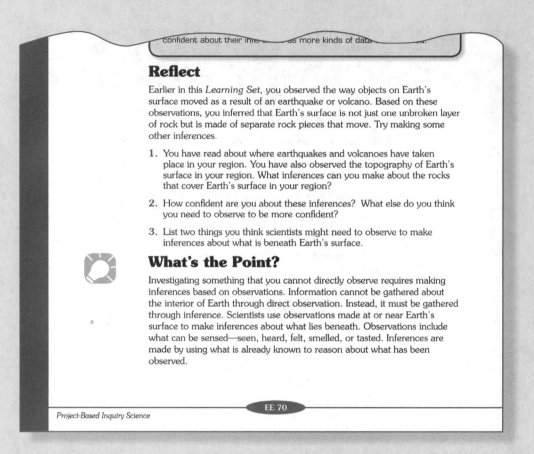

confident about their inferences as more kinds of data are gathered.

Reflect

Earlier in this *Learning Set,* you observed the way objects on Earth's surface moved as a result of an earthquake or volcano. Based on these observations, you inferred that Earth's surface is not just one unbroken layer of rock but is made of separate rock pieces that move. Try making some other inferences.

1. You have read about where earthquakes and volcanoes have taken place in your region. You have also observed the topography of Earth's surface in your region. What inferences can you make about the rocks that cover Earth's surface in your region?

2. How confident are you about these inferences? What else do you think you need to observe to be more confident?

3. List two things you think scientists might need to observe to make inferences about what is beneath Earth's surface.

What's the Point?

Investigating something that you cannot directly observe requires making inferences based on observations. Information cannot be gathered about the interior of Earth through direct observation. Instead, it must be gathered through inference. Scientists use observations made at or near Earth's surface to make inferences about what lies beneath. Observations include what can be sensed—seen, heard, felt, smelled, or tasted. Inferences are made by using what is already known to reason about what has been observed.

EE 70

Project-Based Inquiry Science

△ Guide

Have students discuss the *Reflect* questions with their partners.

1. Students should think about what could cause the earthquakes, volcanic activity, and topographic features in their region, and use their ideas to make inferences about Earth's surface there. Students should suggest ways that the earthquakes and volcanic activity can explain topographic features in their regions. For example, students studying the Java Trench might suggest that the island that has been forming is composed of rock from volcanic eruptions under the sea. They should use the example of Surtsey to support this idea.

2. Students should evaluate how well they can support their inferences with the observations and knowledge they have. They should think about what additional knowledge would help them explain their observations and to support their inferences.

3. This question is meant to engage students in thinking about what observations would help to provide evidence for explanations of the geologic activities and topographic features of Earth's surface they

have read about. Students may suggest that they would like to know more about the materials that emerge from volcanic eruptions, or global patterns of earthquakes and volcanic eruptions. It is important that students consider what information would be useful in making inferences about what is beneath Earth's surface.

Assessment Options

Targeted Concepts, Skills, and Nature of Science	How do I know if students got it?
Scientists often work together and then share their findings. Sharing findings makes new information available and helps scientists refine their ideas and build on others' ideas. When another person's or group's idea is used, credit needs to be given.	**ASK:** How did sharing your observations and inferences with the class help you? **LISTEN:** Students should have used discussions with the class to refine their reasoning about what was in the mystery boxes.
Scientists must keep clear, accurate, and descriptive records of what they do so they can share their work with others and consider what they did, why they did it, and what they want to do next.	**ASK:** Why was it important to record how you used your observations to make inferences? **LISTEN:** Students should recognize that recording their observations allowed them to share their procedures and reasoning with the class.
Scientists make claims (conclusions) based on evidence obtained (trends in data) from reliable investigations.	**ASK:** Why was it important to make observations before you made inferences about what was in the mystery box? **LISTEN:** Students should explain that inferences are based on observations, and without observations, scientists have nothing on which to base their ideas.

Teacher Reflection Questions

- What difficulties did students have understanding the distinction between observations and inferences? What can you do to help them?

- How were you able to help students see that making inferences the way they did with the mystery boxes is not different from what scientists do when they cannot observe something directly? How can you help students make this connection?

- How did you keep students focused on their task as they made observations of the mystery boxes? What might you try next time?

NOTES

2.4 Read

What Do Scientists Know About Earth's Surface and Interior?

◀ $1\frac{1}{2}$ *class periods*

A class period is considered to be one 40 to 50 minute class.

Overview

Students learn how scientists use observations and inferences to determine the structure of Earth. By reading about the composition, temperature, pressure, and motion of each layer of Earth, students develop an understanding of Earth's structure and how its structure causes geologic activity. In addition to learning about the core and mantle, students learn more about the plates of Earth's crust and how their motion causes earthquakes, volcanic eruptions, and changes in Earth's topography. After learning about the composition of Earth's crust and mantle, students investigate how substances with different densities interact. They combine liquids with different densities in a graduated cylinder and observe how the liquids sort by density. They consider how the lower density of Earth's plates allows them to float on the mantle, connecting their knowledge of Earth's crust with their observations of liquids.

Targeted Concepts, Skills, and Nature of Science	Performance Expectations
Interactions between Earth's crustal plates can result in mountain building, rift valleys, and geologic activity such as earthquakes and volcanoes. Underwater volcanic activity may form underwater mountains, which can thrust above the ocean's surface to become islands.	Students should demonstrate they understand how the topographic features they observed using Earth-imaging software and the changes to Earth's surface they observed in photographs were caused by the motion of crustal plates.
Earth is a system made up of different layers, each with a distinctive composition and set of characteristics. These layers interact, driving the processes that shape Earth.	Students should demonstrate they understand Earth's structure, including the composition, the temperature, and the pressure of its layers.

Targeted Concepts, Skills, and Nature of Science	Performance Expectations
Measuring instruments are important in scientific inquiry for accurately comparing the volumes and weights of substances.	Students should use a medicine dropper and a graduated cylinder to measure the volumes of different liquids.

Materials

1 per group	Graduated cylinder Beral Pipette
4 per group	Clear plastic cups
20 mL each per group	Water Glycerin Baby oil Dishwashing soap
1 per student	*Density Column* page
1 set per group	Colored pencils or markers

NOTES

Activity Setup and Preparation

Before class, prepare samples of liquids for students. Put 20-mL samples of baby oil, water, dishwashing soap, and glycerin in small cups. You should prepare at least one sample of each liquid for each group. It would also be a good idea to try creating a density column of your own before class.

Homework Options

Reflection

- **Science Process:** How are scientists able to use meteorites to infer the composition of Earth's mantle and core? What knowledge about Earth's origins do they use? *(Students should describe how scientists compare the composition of meteorites to the composition of Earth's crust using the knowledge that Earth formed from the same clouds of debris that the meteorites did. They should explain that scientists can conclude that the overall composition of Earth is similar to that of the meteorites. They can also conclude that elements from the meteorites that are not found in Earth's crust are probably present in Earth's mantle or core.)*

Preparation for 2.5

- **Science Content:** What did you learn in this section that surprised you? How did what you learned in this section reinforce what you have already learned? *(This question is meant to help students recognize any misconceptions they had and how they are learning.)*

NOTES

NOTES

SECTION 2.4 IMPLEMENTATION

◀ $1\frac{1}{2}$ *class periods**

2.4 Read

What Do Scientists Know About Earth's Surface and Interior?

Earth's crust is very thick, and scientists may never be able to observe Earth's interior directly by going through the crust. But when a volcano erupts, material is ejected. When scientists examine these materials, they can learn more about what materials make up the layers of Earth.

Scientists also use data collection tools to gather information about the movement of Earth's crust. Areas where earthquakes occur provide much of this data. Using all these observations, geologists have inferred a great deal about the structure and characteristics of the crust and interior layers of Earth.

You have read that Earth consists of three main layers—the crust, mantle, and core. The crust is the rocky, outermost layer. The mantle is the midsection, and the core is the center. Each layer has its own characteristics and **composition** —the parts, ingredients, or elements that form a whole. As you read this section, make note of the differences and similarities among the layers, the order of the layers, and how they might interact with one another.

> **composition:** the parts, ingredients, or elements that form a whole.

Seismologists study Earth's interior by making inferences from their observations of Earth's surface using several tools and techniques. This seismologist is checking the temperature under the surface at a volcano.

EE 71

EVER-CHANGING EARTH

2.4 Read

What Do Scientists Know About Earth's Surface and Interior?

5 min

Students read through what scientists know about Earth's structure.

△ Guide

Begin by letting students know they will now learn about the structure of Earth's interior. This will help them understand how processes within Earth cause geologic activity.

Students will also learn how scientists were able to infer the things they know about the structure of Earth's interior. Scientists cannot directly observe Earth's interior, but they can make some observations from Earth's surface. Students will learn about how scientists study Earth's interior from the surface.

*A class period is considered to be one 40 to 50 minute class.

META NOTES

In this section, students should develop an understanding of the overall structure of Earth and how this structure relates to geologic activity. It is also important for students to understand how scientists infer much of what they know about Earth. It is less important for students to memorize terms like lithosphere or geosphere.

TEACHER TALK

"You have inferred from your observations that Earth's surface is not continuous. Now you will learn what scientists have inferred about the structure of Earth's interior, and how they have made the observations that have allowed them to make these inferences."

Before discussing how scientists study Earth's interior, remind students that Earth has three main layers—the crust, the mantle, and the core. One question about Earth's interior that interests scientists is the composition of each of these layers.

NOTES

_____

_____

_____

_____

_____

_____

_____

_____

_____

_____

_____

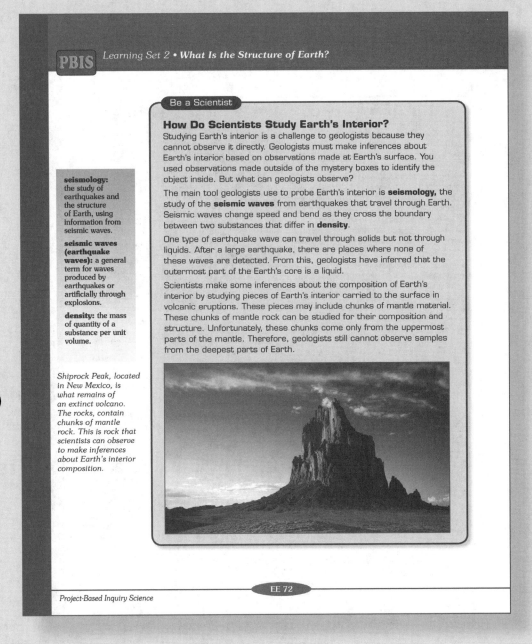

Project-Based Inquiry Science

EE 72

Be a Scientist: How Do Scientists Study Earth's Interior?

10 min

Students read about how scientists study Earth's interior.

Within the image:

Be a Scientist

How Do Scientists Study Earth's Interior?
Studying Earth's interior is a challenge to geologists because they cannot observe it directly. Geologists must make inferences about Earth's interior based on observations made at Earth's surface. You used observations made outside of the mystery boxes to identify the object inside. But what can geologists observe?

The main tool geologists use to probe Earth's interior is **seismology,** the study of the **seismic waves** from earthquakes that travel through Earth. Seismic waves change speed and bend as they cross the boundary between two substances that differ in **density**.

One type of earthquake wave can travel through solids but not through liquids. After a large earthquake, there are places where none of these waves are detected. From this, geologists have inferred that the outermost part of the Earth's core is a liquid.

Scientists make some inferences about the composition of Earth's interior by studying pieces of Earth's interior carried to the surface in volcanic eruptions. These pieces may include chunks of mantle material. These chunks of mantle rock can be studied for their composition and structure. Unfortunately, these chunks come only from the uppermost parts of the mantle. Therefore, geologists still cannot observe samples from the deepest parts of Earth.

seismology: the study of earthquakes and the structure of Earth, using information from seismic waves.

seismic waves (earthquake waves): a general term for waves produced by earthquakes or artificially through explosions.

density: the mass of quantity of a substance per unit volume.

Shiprock Peak, located in New Mexico, is what remains of an extinct volcano. The rocks, contain chunks of mantle rock. This is rock that scientists can observe to make inferences about Earth's interior composition.

Learning Set 2 • What Is the Structure of Earth?

△ Guide

Emphasize that scientists cannot directly observe Earth's interior. Instead, they use tools to make observations from the surface of Earth. Emphasize that this is similar to the way students made observations of the objects in the mystery boxes without looking directly into the boxes. As an example of the tools scientists use to make observations from Earth's surface, discuss seismology. Seismology is the study of vibrations in the Earth, especially seismic waves (the vibrations from earthquakes). Seismic waves are affected by the type of material they run through. They change as they leave one material and enter another material with a different density.

Another way scientists infer what is beneath Earth's surface is by subjecting rocks on the surface to the extremely high temperatures and pressures of Earth's interior and observing what happens. To do this, they build machines that model the high temperatures and pressures of Earth's mantle and core. Using these machines, they examine what happens to rocks under these conditions. They pass vibrations through these experimental rocks in the lab to see if the vibrations match observations of seismic waves that pass through actual rocks in the mantle and core.

Scientists also make inferences about Earth's composition based on what they know about the origin of our planet. There is much evidence that Earth formed from a cloud of debris, some of which remains in the form of **meteors** and asteroids. A meteor is a streak of light in the night sky that results when a solid object (a meteoroid) hits Earth's atmosphere. Analyzing the composition of **meteorites**, meteors that are large enough to survive passage through Earth's atmosphere and hit the ground, provides evidence of Earth's original composition. Geologists compare Earth's original composition to that of the crust and upper mantle to see what is missing. They then make inferences about what is in the lower mantle and core.

This lab is like an extreme kitchen, where furnaces and pressure vessels that simulate the temperatures and pressures of Earth's mantle are used to "cook" rocks.

meteor: a streak of light in the night sky that results when a small, solid object (a meteoroid) hits Earth's atmosphere.

meteorite: a meteor that is large enough to survive its passage through Earth's atmosphere and hit the ground.

Earth originally formed from solar system debris such as these iron and stony meteorites. Studying the composition of meteorites provides evidence of Earth's original composition.

NOTES

....

....

....

Discuss how seismic waves travel through different materials, and what scientists can infer from their observations of these waves. One type of wave only travels through solids. Scientists have observed places where these waves do not appear after earthquakes. From this, they have inferred that the outermost part of Earth's core is liquid. Emphasize that this kind of inference is similar to the inferences students made about the objects in the mystery boxes. Just as students were able to use indirect observations to infer what was in the box, scientists are able to use indirect observations to infer what is in Earth.

Discuss the methods scientists use to infer the composition of Earth's interior. Sometimes they are able to find chunks of mantle rock that were carried to the surface in volcanic eruptions. They study these rocks to get a sample of the composition of Earth's outer mantle. Scientists also make inferences about Earth's interior by subjecting rocks from Earth's surface to the temperatures and pressures of Earth's mantle and core. They pass vibrations similar to seismic waves through the molten rocks and compare their observations to observations of seismic waves in Earth.

Discuss how scientists use what they know about Earth's origins and their observations of meteorites to make inferences about the composition of Earth's interior. There is evidence that Earth formed from the same cloud of debris meteorites form from. Geologists conclude that the original composition of Earth was similar to the composition of these meteorites. By comparing the quantities of different materials in meteorites to the quantities of those materials in the crust and upper mantle of Earth, scientists can make inferences about what is in the lower mantle and core of Earth.

NOTES

....

....

....

....

....

....

....

Earth's Crust

15 min

Students read further about the layers of Earth.

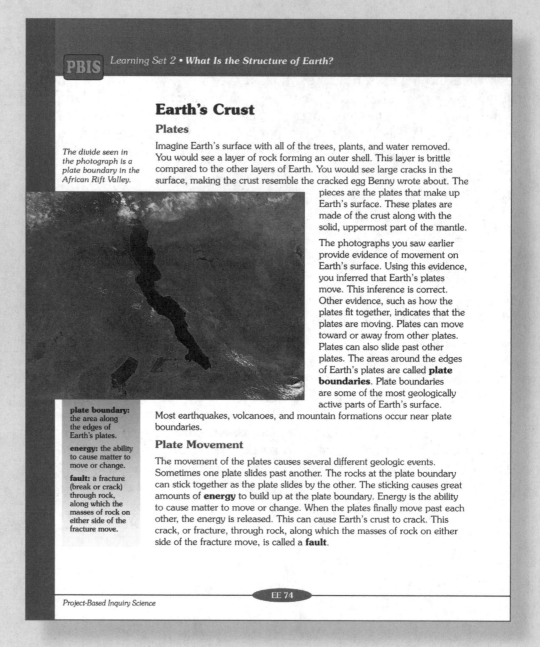

Earth's Crust

Plates

The divide seen in the photograph is a plate boundary in the African Rift Valley.

Imagine Earth's surface with all of the trees, plants, and water removed. You would see a layer of rock forming an outer shell. This layer is brittle compared to the other layers of Earth. You would see large cracks in the surface, making the crust resemble the cracked egg Benny wrote about. The pieces are the plates that make up Earth's surface. These plates are made of the crust along with the solid, uppermost part of the mantle.

The photographs you saw earlier provide evidence of movement on Earth's surface. Using this evidence, you inferred that Earth's plates move. This inference is correct. Other evidence, such as how the plates fit together, indicates that the plates are moving. Plates can move toward or away from other plates. Plates can also slide past other plates. The areas around the edges of Earth's plates are called **plate boundaries**. Plate boundaries are some of the most geologically active parts of Earth's surface.

Most earthquakes, volcanoes, and mountain formations occur near plate boundaries.

plate boundary: the area along the edges of Earth's plates.

energy: the ability to cause matter to move or change.

fault: a fracture (break or crack) through rock, along which the masses of rock on either side of the fracture move.

Plate Movement

The movement of the plates causes several different geologic events. Sometimes one plate slides past another. The rocks at the plate boundary can stick together as the plate slides by the other. The sticking causes great amounts of **energy** to build up at the plate boundary. Energy is the ability to cause matter to move or change. When the plates finally move past each other, the energy is released. This can cause Earth's crust to crack. This crack, or fracture, through rock, along which the masses of rock on either side of the fracture move, is called a **fault**.

EE 74

Project-Based Inquiry Science

△ Guide

Describe the plates that make up Earth's surface. Earth's surface is a relatively brittle layer of rock that is fragmented. The fragments are the large plates that were discussed before. The places where they meet are called plate boundaries. Together, with the solid, uppermost part of the mantle, the plates make up the lithosphere.

Ask students where on Earth's surface they would expect to find evidence that Earth's plates move. Ask them if they think the photographs they examined earlier were of places on plate boundaries or places on the solid parts of plates. Remind them that they inferred that the changes they observed were due to plates moving. Tell them that the plates move toward each other and away from each other, and they also slide past each other. This leads to a lot of change at plate boundaries, such as the changes they observed in the photographs. Emphasize that most earthquakes, volcanoes, and mountain formations occur near plate boundaries.

NOTES

_____

_____

_____

_____

_____

_____

_____

_____

_____

_____

_____

When two plates move toward each other, they can collide. This also results in the release of a lot of energy. Imagine the tremendous force resulting from two large sections of Earth's crust colliding. This force puts strain on the rocks, and friction between the two plates results in high heat that may melt the rocks. Over a very long time, this movement, friction, and strain can cause Earth's crust to form **folds,** or bends. These folds are one kind of mountain. Whether or not this happens depends on the temperature, amount of force and strain, and the type of rock. The Appalachian Mountains resulted from many folds forming in Earth's crust. This mountain range extends 2400 km (1500 mi) through the eastern United States, north to Canada.

fold: a bend in rocks.

fault-block mountains: mountains that form when one side of a fault is lifted above the other side.

You can see the bends, or folds, in the rock that makes up the Appalachian Mountains.

Sometimes the changes that result from moving plates are very complicated. For example, mountains may form along faults. When one side of a fault is lifted above the other side, **fault-block mountains** may form. Slowly, over millions of years, the uplifted side may rise miles above the other side. One example of fault-block mountains is the Grand Teton Mountain Range, part of the Rocky Mountains. This mountain range extends 65 km (40 mi) along the western border of Wyoming.

EVER-CHANGING EARTH

Describe how the motion of plates can lead to geologic activity. One important situation in which the motion of plates can cause geologic activity happens when two plates moving past each other become locked in place and build up energy. When they slip, the energy released can crack Earth's crust, causing a fault. Plates can also collide. Over time this can cause the rock to fold into mountains. Mountains can also form when one side of a fault is lifted over the other side. Such mountains are called fault-block mountains.

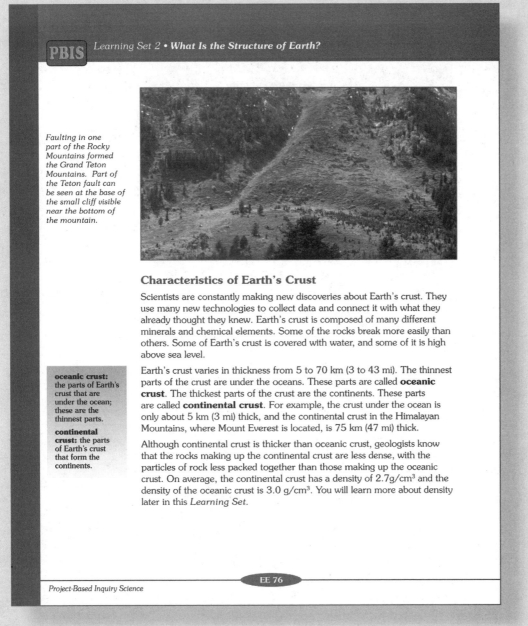

Faulting in one part of the Rocky Mountains formed the Grand Teton Mountains. Part of the Teton fault can be seen at the base of the small cliff visible near the bottom of the mountain.

Characteristics of Earth's Crust

Scientists are constantly making new discoveries about Earth's crust. They use many new technologies to collect data and connect it with what they already thought they knew. Earth's crust is composed of many different minerals and chemical elements. Some of the rocks break more easily than others. Some of Earth's crust is covered with water, and some of it is high above sea level.

oceanic crust: the parts of Earth's crust that are under the ocean; these are the thinnest parts.

continental crust: the parts of Earth's crust that form the continents.

Earth's crust varies in thickness from 5 to 70 km (3 to 43 mi). The thinnest parts of the crust are under the oceans. These parts are called **oceanic crust**. The thickest parts of the crust are the continents. These parts are called **continental crust**. For example, the crust under the ocean is only about 5 km (3 mi) thick, and the continental crust in the Himalayan Mountains, where Mount Everest is located, is 75 km (47 mi) thick.

Although continental crust is thicker than oceanic crust, geologists know that the rocks making up the continental crust are less dense, with the particles of rock less packed together than those making up the oceanic crust. On average, the continental crust has a density of $2.7 g/cm^3$ and the density of the oceanic crust is $3.0 g/cm^3$. You will learn more about density later in this *Learning Set*.

EE 76

Discuss the characteristics of Earth's crust. It is composed of many different materials and chemical elements. Its thickness varies from 5 km (3 mi), under the ocean, to 75 km (47 mi), at the Himalayan Mountain Range. Ask students which locations they identified using the visualization software would have thinner crust. Which locations would have thicker crust? Generally, places with great depths are places where the crust is relatively thin. Places with great elevations are places where the crust is relatively thick.

Continental crust is thicker than oceanic crust. However, the rocks that make up the continental crust are less dense than the rocks of the oceanic crust.

NOTES

_____

_____

_____

_____

_____

_____

_____

_____

_____

_____

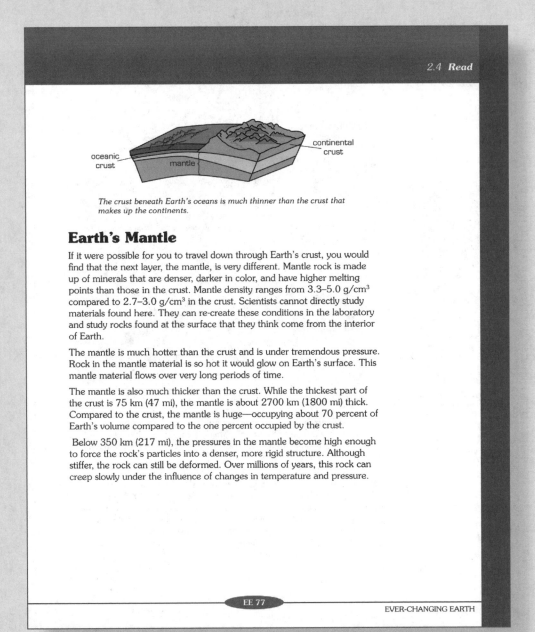

The crust beneath Earth's oceans is much thinner than the crust that makes up the continents.

Earth's Mantle

If it were possible for you to travel down through Earth's crust, you would find that the next layer, the mantle, is very different. Mantle rock is made up of minerals that are denser, darker in color, and have higher melting points than those in the crust. Mantle density ranges from 3.3–5.0 g/cm³ compared to 2.7–3.0 g/cm³ in the crust. Scientists cannot directly study materials found here. They can re-create these conditions in the laboratory and study rocks found at the surface that they think come from the interior of Earth.

The mantle is much hotter than the crust and is under tremendous pressure. Rock in the mantle material is so hot it would glow on Earth's surface. This mantle material flows over very long periods of time.

The mantle is also much thicker than the crust. While the thickest part of the crust is 75 km (47 mi), the mantle is about 2700 km (1800 mi) thick. Compared to the crust, the mantle is huge—occupying about 70 percent of Earth's volume compared to the one percent occupied by the crust.

Below 350 km (217 mi), the pressures in the mantle become high enough to force the rock's particles into a denser, more rigid structure. Although stiffer, the rock can still be deformed. Over millions of years, this rock can creep slowly under the influence of changes in temperature and pressure.

Earth's Mantle

5 min

Students read about the lower layer of Earth.

△ Guide

Discuss the composition of Earth's mantle. Here the rock has a higher melting point than rock in the crust and it is hotter. This rock is hot enough to glow. It is under great pressure, is denser than rock in the crust, and flows like ice in a glacier.

The mantle is very thick, making up 70 percent of Earth's volume. Point out that Earth's crust only makes up about 1 percent of Earth's volume.

Earth's Layers

< 5 min

Students read about what makes up the lithosphere and asthenosphere.

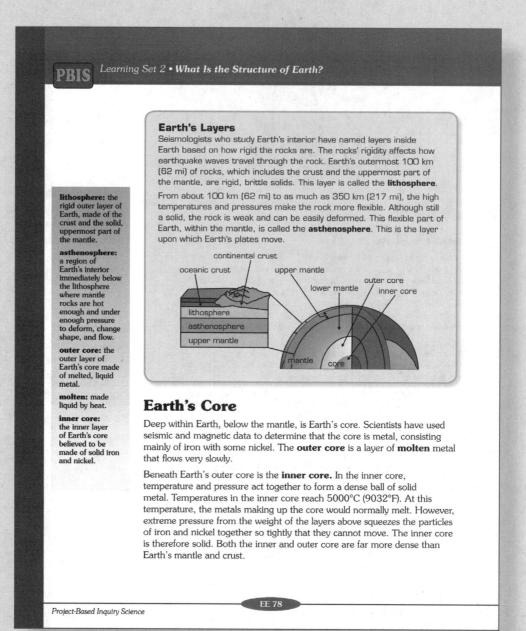

Earth's Layers

Seismologists who study Earth's interior have named layers inside Earth based on how rigid the rocks are. The rocks' rigidity affects how earthquake waves travel through the rock. Earth's outermost 100 km (62 mi) of rocks, which includes the crust and the uppermost part of the mantle, are rigid, brittle solids. This layer is called the **lithosphere**.

From about 100 km (62 mi) to as much as 350 km (217 mi), the high temperatures and pressures make the rock more flexible. Although still a solid, the rock is weak and can be easily deformed. This flexible part of Earth, within the mantle, is called the **asthenosphere**. This is the layer upon which Earth's plates move.

lithosphere: the rigid outer layer of Earth, made of the crust and the solid, uppermost part of the mantle.

asthenosphere: a region of Earth's interior immediately below the lithosphere where mantle rocks are hot enough and under enough pressure to deform, change shape, and flow.

outer core: the outer layer of Earth's core made of melted, liquid metal.

molten: made liquid by heat.

inner core: the inner layer of Earth's core believed to be made of solid iron and nickel.

continental crust
oceanic crust
upper mantle
lower mantle
outer core
inner core
lithosphere
asthenosphere
upper mantle
mantle
core

Earth's Core

Deep within Earth, below the mantle, is Earth's core. Scientists have used seismic and magnetic data to determine that the core is metal, consisting mainly of iron with some nickel. The **outer core** is a layer of **molten** metal that flows very slowly.

Beneath Earth's outer core is the **inner core.** In the inner core, temperature and pressure act together to form a dense ball of solid metal. Temperatures in the inner core reach 5000°C (9032°F). At this temperature, the metals making up the core would normally melt. However, extreme pressure from the weight of the layers above squeezes the particles of iron and nickel together so tightly that they cannot move. The inner core is therefore solid. Both the inner and outer core are far more dense than Earth's mantle and crust.

△ Guide

Discuss the layers within the mantle and crust that seismologists have identified. These layers are distinguished by the rigidity of the rock. The outermost layer, which contains Earth's crust and the outer portion of the mantle, called the lithosphere. Below the lithosphere is the asthenosphere, a layer of flexible rock. The pressure below that layer makes the rock very dense and rigid.

△ Guide

Discribe to the class that below the mantle is Earth's core. The outer core is composed of molten metal, similar to the mantle.

Beneath the outer core is the inner core, which is believed to consist of dense, solid metal with temperatures as high as 4982°C (9000°F). Ordinarily, the metal in the core would melt at these temperatures, but the pressure in the core makes the metal act as a solid.

Earth's Core

5 min

Students read about the composition of Earth's core.

NOTES

Stop and Think

10 min

Students have a class discussion of the questions.

Stop and Think

1. Compare Earth's layers. Which one of the layers is the least dense? Which is the most dense? Which layer has the highest temperature? Which layer has the lowest temperature?

2. The mantle is often described as molten. Why is this word used? Compare the molten mantle to the core. The temperature of the core is higher, but it acts more like a solid? Why?

What's the Point?

Using observations and inferences, Earth scientists have determined that Earth is made of three layers—the crust, the mantle, and the core. The crust is the outer layer, broken into large pieces called plates. The edges of the plates are called plate boundaries. These plates move and shift, resulting in earthquakes, volcanic eruptions, and changes in the topographic features of Earth. The crust is less dense than the layers under it.

Beneath the crust is the mantle. The mantle is hotter than the crust. The thickness of the mantle is also greater than that of the crust. The mantle has two layers. The outer layer is part of the lithosphere, along with the crust. The inner layer is molten. It is a solid, but it flows very slowly. The core is the center of Earth and is also divided into two layers: the outer core, which is molten metal, and the inner core, which is solid. The temperature and pressure in the core makes the inner core solid.

The continental crust in the Himalayas is 75 km (47 mi) thick. Mount Everest, the highest mountain in the world, is part of the Himalayas.

EE 79

EVER-CHANGING EARTH

⬡ Get Going

Have students answer the *Stop and Think* questions on their own, but let them know that they will discuss the questions with the class. Give them a few minutes to answer the questions.

△ Guide and Assess

When students have had time to answer the questions, lead a class discussion of their answers. Listen for the following in students' answers:

1. Students should note that the crust is the least dense and the core is the most dense. More specifically, they should explain that the inner core is more dense than the outer core. The inner core is also the hottest, while the crust has the lowest temperature.

2. Students should explain that the mantle is described as molten because the heat is great enough to melt the rock in the mantle and the pressure is not high enough to make the rock rigid. They should note that while the pressure is high enough to make mantle rock solid, the rock is still able to flow like the ice of glaciers. The core is hotter than the mantle, so the temperature in the core is also hot enough to melt the rock. However, the pressure is also higher, high enough to make the rock rigid.

NOTES

More to Learn: Density

5 min

Students are introduced to the investigation.

META NOTES

Students may conclude prematurely that the materials in Earth's layers rise or fall because of their density. There are many factors involved in the increased density towards the center of Earth, including increased pressure. The point of this discussion is to consider densities in the lithosphere, where the relatively low density of Earth's plates allows them to float on the denser molten rock of the mantle.

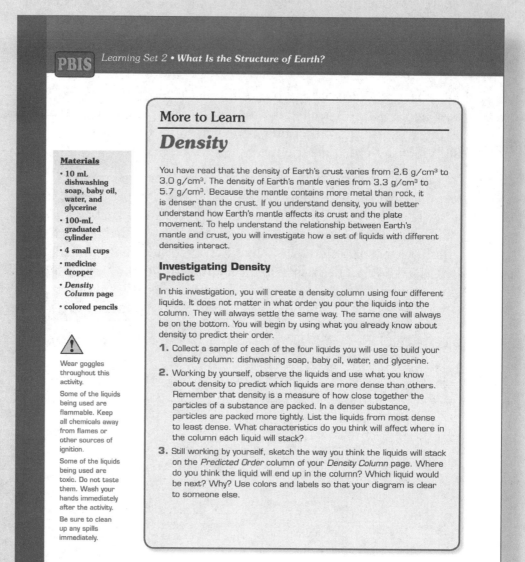

More to Learn

Density

You have read that the density of Earth's crust varies from 2.6 g/cm³ to 3.0 g/cm³. The density of Earth's mantle varies from 3.3 g/cm³ to 5.7 g/cm³. Because the mantle contains more metal than rock, it is denser than the crust. If you understand density, you will better understand how Earth's mantle affects its crust and the plate movement. To help understand the relationship between Earth's mantle and crust, you will investigate how a set of liquids with different densities interact.

Investigating Density
Predict

In this investigation, you will create a density column using four different liquids. It does not matter in what order you pour the liquids into the column. They will always settle the same way. The same one will always be on the bottom. You will begin by using what you already know about density to predict their order.

1. Collect a sample of each of the four liquids you will use to build your density column: dishwashing soap, baby oil, water, and glycerine.

2. Working by yourself, observe the liquids and use what you know about density to predict which liquids are more dense than others. Remember that density is a measure of how close together the particles of a substance are packed. In a denser substance, particles are packed more tightly. List the liquids from most dense to least dense. What characteristics do you think will affect where in the column each liquid will stack?

3. Still working by yourself, sketch the way you think the liquids will stack on the *Predicted Order* column of your *Density Column* page. Where do you think the liquid will end up in the column? Which liquid would be next? Why? Use colors and labels so that your diagram is clear to someone else.

Materials
- 10 mL dishwashing soap, baby oil, water, and glycerine
- 100-mL graduated cylinder
- 4 small cups
- medicine dropper
- *Density Column* page
- colored pencils

Wear goggles throughout this activity.

Some of the liquids being used are flammable. Keep all chemicals away from flames or other sources of ignition.

Some of the liquids being used are toxic. Do not taste them. Wash your hands immediately after the activity.

Be sure to clean up any spills immediately.

○ Engage

Point out that the rock beneath Earth's crust is molten. This rock flows slowly, but the plates in Earth's crust do not sink through this flowing rock. Ask students why they think the plates do not sink.

Remind students that the density of rock in Earth's crust is between 2.6 g/cm³ and 3.0 g/cm³, while the density of rock in Earth's mantle is between 3.3 g/cm³ and 5.7 g/cm³. Ask students if they have ideas about why it is important that Earth's crust is less dense than its mantle. How can this help to explain why the plates in Earth's crust do not sink?

△ Guide

Tell students they are now going to investigate how liquids of different densities interact. They are going to observe several liquids and predict which of them is most dense and which is least dense. Based on this, they will predict the order in which the liquids settle when they are combined. They will combine the liquids in a graduated cylinder and observe the order they settle in.

⬡ Get Going

Distribute samples of liquids, graduated cylinders, beral pipettes, colored pencils or markers, and the *Density Column* pages, or have students get them from a materials station. Emphasize that students should not put liquids into the graduated cylinders yet. Have them make predictions about what the density column will look like and draw their predictions in the *My predicted order* column of the *Density Column* page.

Investigating Density: Predict

10 min

Students predict the order of liquids in their density columns.

Spills should be cleaned up promptly to prevent injury.

NOTES

Conference

5 min

META NOTES

It is important for students to understand that density is mass per volume. One mL of a high-density liquid is heavier than one mL of a low-density liquid because it has more mass. Therefore, 1 mL of a high-density material will displace 1 mL of a low-density material in a density column, and a high-density liquid will be lower in a density column than a low-density liquid, even when the volume of the low-density liquid is much greater.

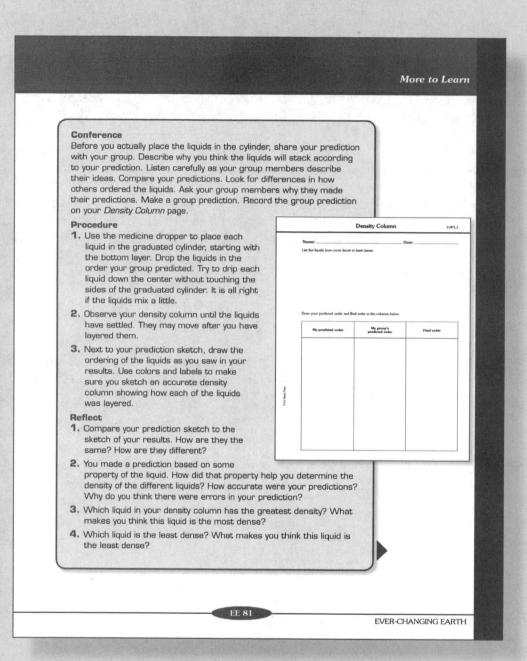

More to Learn

Conference

Before you actually place the liquids in the cylinder, share your prediction with your group. Describe why you think the liquids will stack according to your prediction. Listen carefully as your group members describe their ideas. Compare your predictions. Look for differences in how others ordered the liquids. Ask your group members why they made their predictions. Make a group prediction. Record the group prediction on your *Density Column* page.

Procedure

1. Use the medicine dropper to place each liquid in the graduated cylinder, starting with the bottom layer. Drop the liquids in the order your group predicted. Try to drip each liquid down the center without touching the sides of the graduated cylinder. It is all right if the liquids mix a little.

2. Observe your density column until the liquids have settled. They may move after you have layered them.

3. Next to your prediction sketch, draw the ordering of the liquids as you saw in your results. Use colors and labels to make sure you sketch an accurate density column showing how each of the liquids was layered.

Reflect

1. Compare your prediction sketch to the sketch of your results. How are they the same? How are they different?

2. You made a prediction based on some property of the liquid. How did that property help you determine the density of the different liquids? How accurate were your predictions? Why do you think there were errors in your prediction?

3. Which liquid in your density column has the greatest density? What makes you think this liquid is the most dense?

4. Which liquid is the least dense? What makes you think this liquid is the least dense?

EE 81

EVER-CHANGING EARTH

△ Guide and Assess

Have students share their predictions with their groups. As groups discuss their predictions, ask them what ideas they have discussed and why they think certain liquids may be lower or higher in the density column. If a student says that a liquid will sink because it is heavy, ask them if the liquid is heavy in all quantities. Would a small amount of the liquid be just as heavy? If a student says a liquid is light, ask them if a large amount of the liquid would be just as light. After discussing their own density column predictions they should all agree on a predicted order of the liquids. Have students record this in the *My group's predicted order* column on their *Density Column* pages. Note any misconceptions about density to discuss later in the investigation.

⬡ Get Going

Have students put the liquids into the graduated cylinders with the beral pipettes. They should start by putting 10 mL of each liquid into the cylinders by dripping each liquid down the center of the cylinder. Point out that they can use the beral pipettes to measure the amount of liquid, and then check their measurements with the graduated cylinder.

△ Guide and Assess

As students complete their density columns, monitor their progress and make sure they record the results in the *Final order* column on their *Density Column* pages. Ask them if the actual order of the density column surprises them and how.

When students have created their density columns, ask them what would happen if they doubled the amount of liquid in the top layer. Would the layer sink? Why or why not? Have students add an extra 10 mL of baby oil to their density columns and observe what happens. They should observe that the baby oil stays at the same place in their density column.

△ Guide

After students have completed their *Density Column* pages, have them answer the *Reflect* questions with their groups. Emphasize that they should be prepared to discuss their answers with the class.

Once groups have had a few minutes to answer the *Reflect* questions, ask the class what the density column for the continental crust, the oceanic crust, and the mantle should look like. Draw the density column on the board following students' suggestions. You should end up with a density column with the continental crust on top, the oceanic crust in the middle, and the mantle at the bottom.

Procedure

5 min

Students create their density columns.

These liquids are not for consumption. Ensure that students do not drink them.

Reflect

10 min

Students answer the Reflect *questions with their groups.*

NOTES

....

....

....

....

Density and Earth's Crust and Mantle

5 min

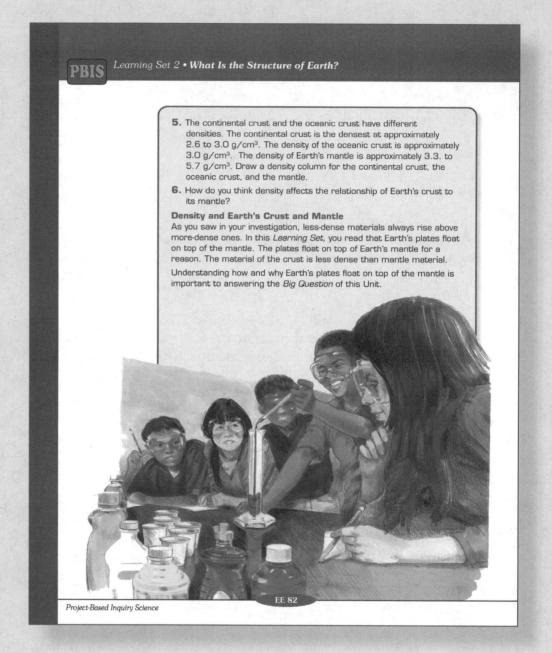

5. The continental crust and the oceanic crust have different densities. The continental crust is the densest at approximately 2.6 to 3.0 g/cm³. The density of the oceanic crust is approximately 3.0 g/cm³. The density of Earth's mantle is approximately 3.3. to 5.7 g/cm³. Draw a density column for the continental crust, the oceanic crust, and the mantle.

6. How do you think density affects the relationship of Earth's crust to its mantle?

Density and Earth's Crust and Mantle

As you saw in your investigation, less-dense materials always rise above more-dense ones. In this *Learning Set,* you read that Earth's plates float on top of the mantle. The plates float on top of Earth's mantle for a reason. The material of the crust is less dense than mantle material.

Understanding how and why Earth's plates float on top of the mantle is important to answering the *Big Question* of this Unit.

Project-Based Inquiry Science

EE 82

△ Guide and Evaluate

Ask students why plates float on the mantle. What did they see in this investigation that could help them understand how the crust floats? Students should recognize that the crust floats because it is less dense than the mantle. This is similar to the way some of the liquids they put in their density column rose above other liquids.

"Now that you have investigated how materials with different densities interact, what can you say about why plates float on Earth's mantle? How is the interaction of the plates and the mantle similar to the interaction of liquids in your density column?"

Assessment Options

Targeted Concepts, Skills, and Nature of Science	How do I know if students got it?
Interactions between Earth's crustal plates can result in mountain building, rift valleys, and geologic activity such as earthquakes and volcanoes. Underwater volcanic activity may form underwater mountains, which can thrust above the ocean's surface to become islands.	**ASK:** What kinds of geologic activity can happen at plate boundaries? What causes those types of geologic activity? **LISTEN:** Students should explain that earthquakes, volcanoes, and mountain formation can occur at plate boundaries. The motion of the plates—away from each other, against each other, or in collision—causes these geologic events.
Earth is a system made up of different layers, each with a distinctive composition and set of characteristics. These layers interact, driving the processes that shape Earth.	**ASK:** What layers make up Earth? **LISTEN:** Students should identify the core, mantle, and crust. They may also more specifically identify the inner core, outer core, inner mantle, outer mantle, lithosphere, asthenosphere, and mesosphere.

NOTES

....

....

Teacher Reflection Questions

- What evidence do you have that students understand how plate motion leads to geologic activity? How can you help students with any remaining difficulties?

- How were you able to use class discussion and other tools to help students with the concepts in this section? What might you try next time?

- What were some effective ways of guiding students through the content in this section? What could you try next time?

NOTES

_____

_____

_____

_____

_____

_____

_____

_____

_____

_____

2.5 Explore

Modeling Earth's Structure

◀ *1 class period*

A class period is considered to be one 40 to 50 minute class.

Overview

Students write letters to Benny describing the strengths and weaknesses of his model. They draw their own models of Earth's structure, synthesizing what they have learned about Earth's structure and the characteristics of its parts. Students present their models to the class and the class discusses the strengths and weaknesses of each model. This reinforces students' understanding of how the characteristics of Earth's parts relate to its structure and helps them evaluate methods of representing Earth's structure.

Targeted Concepts, Skills, and Nature of Science	Performance Expectations
Scientists often work together and then share their findings. Sharing findings makes new information available and helps scientists refine their ideas and build on others' ideas. When another person's or group's idea is used, credit needs to be given.	Students should share models with the class and discuss the strengths and weaknesses of each model.
Scientists must keep clear, accurate, and descriptive records of what they do so they can share their work with others and consider what they did, why they did it, and what they want to do next.	Students should use their notes while they participate in the group and class discussions.
Scientists use models and tools, such as Geographic Information Systems, and a variety of maps to develop claims and explanations from evidence in the data.	Students should develop a model of Earth's structure using what they have learned through their readings, their observations, and their inferences.

Materials	
1 per student	Crayon or colored pencil

Homework Options

Reflection

- **Science Content:** What information would you need to make your model more complete? How could you obtain that information? *(This question is meant to engage students in thinking about what remains to be learned about Earth's structure.)*

NOTES

....

....

....

....

....

....

....

....

....

....

...

SECTION 2.5 IMPLEMENTATION

2.5 Explore

Modeling Earth's Structure

In Benny's letter, he described some ideas he and his teacher had about Earth's structure. You now know enough to better identify the strengths and weaknesses of Benny's model and to suggest a better model. You will write a letter back to Benny telling him what you think about his model. In your letter, you will include a sketch that presents your understanding of Earth's structure.

Write a Letter to Benny

Read Benny's letter again. Think about the hard-boiled egg as a model for Earth. Based on what you now know about Earth's structure, identify the strengths and weaknesses of Benny's egg model. Think about the details missing from Benny's model.

Working with your partner, write a letter to Benny. Your letter should include what you think are the strengths and weaknesses of Benny's egg model and what you think is missing from his model.

EE 83

EVER-CHANGING EARTH

2.5 Explore

Modeling Earth's Structure

5 min

Students are introduced to the activity.

Write a Letter to Benny

10 min

Students review Benny's model, together with the class, and create their own models.

△ Guide

Let students know they will write a letter to Benny giving him feedback on his model of Earth.

Read Benny's letter with the class again. Emphasize that students now know a lot more about Earth's structure than when they first read the letter. Point out Benny's drawings and tell them they will now draw their own models of Earth's structure.

*A class period is considered to be one 40 to 50 minute class.

META NOTES

You may need to remind students what a model is by using some examples. Benny's hard-boiled egg is a model, but models do not have to use familiar objects to represent their subject. For instance, a map is a model, but a map resembles only the area it represents. Similarly, globes are models that are made specifically to represent Earth. Students' models may make analogies with familiar objects, but it is not necessary. It is, important that students' drawings accurately represent the parts of Earth and their significant characteristics.

Have students work with their groups to identify the strengths and weakness of Benny's model and what information the model lacks. Have them record this in a letter to Benny.

Have students draw their own models of Earth's structure to send to Benny. These models should address any weaknesses in Benny's model and include the information that Benny's model left out. Emphasize that they will need to represent Earth's layers, and the plates in Earth's crust with their boundaries. They should also include descriptions of the characteristics of each layer, including its density, consistency, composition, and temperature.

△ Guide and Evaluate

As students work on their letters and models, monitor their progress and evaluate their models. If their models are unclear about any characteristics of the parts of Earth, ask them questions about the characteristics. If a group appears to be excluding information, point out that their model is incomplete. If you think several groups are excluding information or are making unclear models, stop the class and discuss what information you expect to be in the models and the importance of making the models clear.

As you evaluate groups' models, look for the information that was missing from Benny's model. Benny's model included Earth's core, mantle, and crust. However, it did not include information about the lithosphere, asthenosphere, outer core, and inner core. In their models, students should show that the lithosphere is divided into plates. As Benny suggested, the movement of molten rock in the mantle causes the plates to move. Students' models should show that the rock in the asthenosphere is molten and moves the plates. Students' models should also indicate the composition and thickness of the different layers, along with the pressures, temperatures, and whether or not the rock in the layer is solid.

NOTES

....

....

....

....

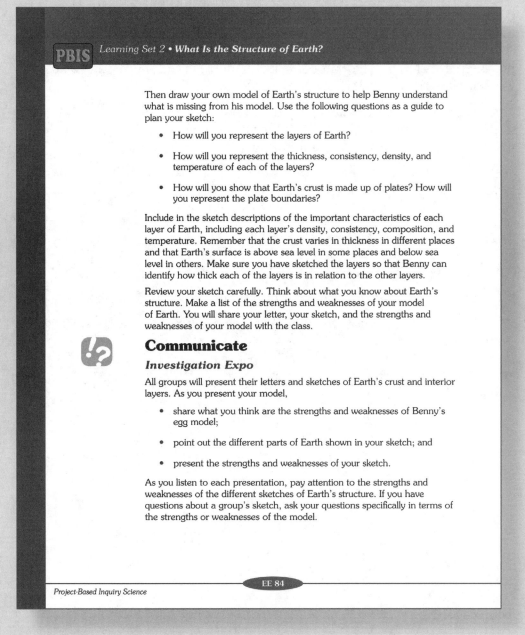

Then draw your own model of Earth's structure to help Benny understand what is missing from his model. Use the following questions as a guide to plan your sketch:

- How will you represent the layers of Earth?

- How will you represent the thickness, consistency, density, and temperature of each of the layers?

- How will you show that Earth's crust is made up of plates? How will you represent the plate boundaries?

Include in the sketch descriptions of the important characteristics of each layer of Earth, including each layer's density, consistency, composition, and temperature. Remember that the crust varies in thickness in different places and that Earth's surface is above sea level in some places and below sea level in others. Make sure you have sketched the layers so that Benny can identify how thick each of the layers is in relation to the other layers.

Review your sketch carefully. Think about what you know about Earth's structure. Make a list of the strengths and weaknesses of your model of Earth. You will share your letter, your sketch, and the strengths and weaknesses of your model with the class.

Communicate

Investigation Expo

All groups will present their letters and sketches of Earth's crust and interior layers. As you present your model,

- share what you think are the strengths and weaknesses of Benny's egg model;

- point out the different parts of Earth shown in your sketch; and

- present the strengths and weaknesses of your sketch.

As you listen to each presentation, pay attention to the strengths and weaknesses of the different sketches of Earth's structure. If you have questions about a group's sketch, ask your questions specifically in terms of the strengths or weaknesses of the model.

Communicate: *Investigation Expo*

20 min

Students present their letters and models in an Investigation Expo.

△ Guide

Remind students what an *Investigation Expo* is. An *Investigation Expo* contains two parts: a presentation including posters or other visual materials, and a discussion. In this case, students will present sketches of their models and the letters they wrote to Benny. The class will discuss each group's letter and model, give feedback to each group, share ideas, and improve their models.

Give groups a few minutes to prepare presentations of their letters and models. Emphasize that in their *Investigation Expo,* each group should share the strengths and weaknesses they identified in Benny's model, point out the parts of Earth shown in the sketch, and present the strengths and weaknesses of their sketches.

Once students have had a few minutes to prepare, have each group present to the class. Emphasize that as each group presents, students should note the strengths and weakness of their model and then ask questions.

Start a short discussion after each presentation. Remember to model the kinds of comments and questions you expect from students.

TEACHER TALK

"I agree with … because …

I don't understand how Benny's representation of … was weak.

I don't understand how the model's representation of … is stronger than Benny's."

NOTES

_____

_____

_____

_____

_____

_____

_____

Reflect

1. You were able to see different models of Earth's structure. Pick the model that you think best represents Earth. Describe why you selected that model.

2. Which characteristic of Earth's layers was the most difficult to represent? Why?

What's the Point?

Examining and making models of Earth can help you apply what you are learning about Earth's structure. By evaluating the strengths and weaknesses of Benny's model, your model, and those of your classmates, you can better understand the layers of Earth and their composition.

EE 85

EVER-CHANGING EARTH

Reflect

10 min

The class has a discussion of the Reflect *questions.*

△ Guide

Once the class has discussed all of the models presented, lead a discussion of the *Reflect* questions. As students discuss which model they think best represents Earth's structure, encourage them to support their judgments with reasons. If students disagree about the best model, encourage them to discuss the strengths and weaknesses of the different models. Encourage students to identify specific difficulties they had representing characteristics of Earth.

More to Learn:
Earth Systems

10 min

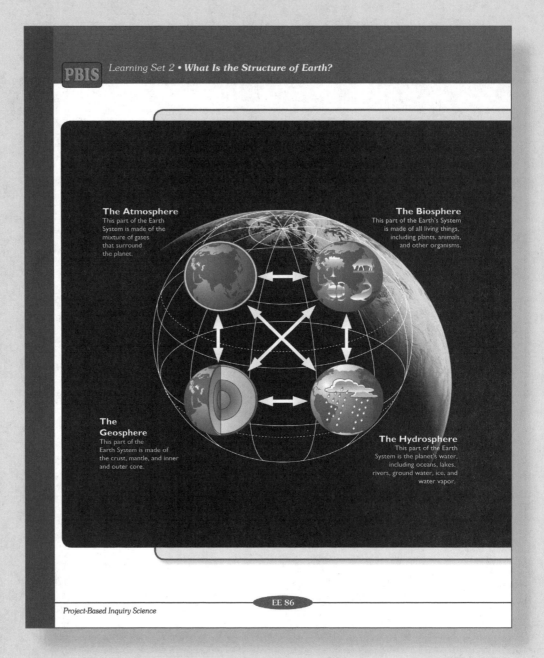

The Atmosphere
This part of the Earth System is made of the mixture of gases that surround the planet.

The Biosphere
This part of the Earth's System is made of all living things, including plants, animals, and other organisms.

The Geosphere
This part of the Earth System is made of the crust, mantle, and inner and outer core.

The Hydrosphere
This part of the Earth System is the planet's water, including oceans, lakes, rivers, ground water, ice, and water vapor.

Project-Based Inquiry Science

EE 86

△ Guide

Introduce the idea of Earth systems to the class. Explain that Earth has four main systems that work together. Descriptions of each of these—the atmosphere, the biosphere, the hydrosphere, and the geosphere—are given in the student text. Ask students if they are familiar with any of these systems. They have probably heard of the atmosphere. The atmosphere is made up of the gases (the air) that surround Earth. The atmosphere is

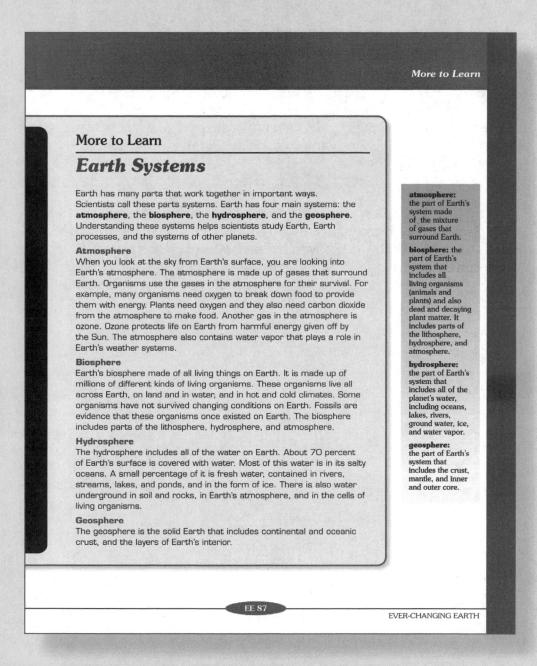

More to Learn

Earth Systems

Earth has many parts that work together in important ways. Scientists call these parts systems. Earth has four main systems: the **atmosphere**, the **biosphere**, the **hydrosphere**, and the **geosphere**. Understanding these systems helps scientists study Earth, Earth processes, and the systems of other planets.

Atmosphere
When you look at the sky from Earth's surface, you are looking into Earth's atmosphere. The atmosphere is made up of gases that surround Earth. Organisms use the gases in the atmosphere for their survival. For example, many organisms need oxygen to break down food to provide them with energy. Plants need oxygen and they also need carbon dioxide from the atmosphere to make food. Another gas in the atmosphere is ozone. Ozone protects life on Earth from harmful energy given off by the Sun. The atmosphere also contains water vapor that plays a role in Earth's weather systems.

Biosphere
Earth's biosphere made of all living things on Earth. It is made up of millions of different kinds of living organisms. These organisms live all across Earth, on land and in water, and in hot and cold climates. Some organisms have not survived changing conditions on Earth. Fossils are evidence that these organisms once existed on Earth. The biosphere includes parts of the lithosphere, hydrosphere, and atmosphere.

Hydrosphere
The hydrosphere includes all of the water on Earth. About 70 percent of Earth's surface is covered with water. Most of this water is in its salty oceans. A small percentage of it is fresh water, contained in rivers, streams, lakes, and ponds, and in the form of ice. There is also water underground in soil and rocks, in Earth's atmosphere, and in the cells of living organisms.

Geosphere
The geosphere is the solid Earth that includes continental and oceanic crust, and the layers of Earth's interior.

atmosphere: the part of Earth's system made of the mixture of gases that surround Earth.

biosphere: the part of Earth's system that includes all living organisms (animals and plants) and also dead and decaying plant matter. It includes parts of the lithosphere, hydrosphere, and atmosphere.

hydrosphere: the part of Earth's system that includes all of the planet's water, including oceans, lakes, rivers, ground water, ice, and water vapor.

geosphere: the part of Earth's system that includes the crust, mantle, and inner and outer core.

important because organisms use its gases to survive. Discuss some of the ways that organisms use gases to survive. When people breathe, they are taking in oxygen, which helps them break down food for energy. Plants take in carbon dioxide, which allows them to produce food. Most organisms benefit from the ozone in the atmosphere, which helps to protect them from some of the Sun's harmful rays.

Students are less likely to know the term biosphere. Tell them that the biosphere is made up of the living organisms on Earth, including the organisms that live under water. The hydrosphere is made up of the bodies of water covering much of Earth's surface. The oceans make up most of the hydrosphere, but it also contains rivers, lakes, and the water that is under the ground, in living things, and in the atmosphere. The geosphere is made up of solid Earth. It contains Earth's crust and all the layers under it.

TEACHER TALK

"Earth has four main systems that work together—the atmosphere, biosphere, hydrosphere, and geosphere. What can you tell me about the atmosphere? Does anyone know what the atmosphere is made of? The atmosphere is important because organisms depend on it for survival. When you breathe, you are taking in oxygen from the atmosphere. You need that oxygen to survive."

NOTES

Assessment Options

Targeted Concepts, Skills, and Nature of Science	How do I know if students got it?
Scientists often work together and then share their findings. Sharing findings makes new information available and helps scientists refine their ideas and build on others' ideas. When another person's or group's idea is used, credit needs to be given.	**ASK:** What ideas did you get from other groups' models? How was it helpful to think about the strengths and weaknesses of different groups' models? **LISTEN:** Students should discuss ways that some models were stronger than others and how sharing their ideas allows groups to develop the best model.
Scientists must keep clear, accurate, and descriptive records of what they do so they can share their work with others and consider what they did, why they did it, and what they want to do next.	**ASK:** How were you able to use your notes during discussions of the models? **LISTEN:** Students should have been able to use their notes to identify information that was missing and to think about how well the model represented parts of Earth.
Scientists use models and tools, such as Geographic Information Systems, and a variety of maps to develop claims and explanations from evidence in the data.	**ASK:** How can creating models of Earth's structure help you understand what causes geologic activity? **LISTEN:** Students should recognize that creating models helps them to visualize structures that are too large to investigate directly. This can give them insights into how Earth's structure causes geologic activity.

NOTES

....

Teacher Reflection Questions

- What strengths and weaknesses did students identify in their models? Did you identify additional strengths and weaknesses? How can you help students model real-world phenomena effectively?

- How were you able to guide students to create good models without telling them what to draw? What might you try next time?

- What disagreements did students have during class discussions? How were you able to help students discuss them constructively?

NOTES

_____

_____

_____

_____

_____

_____

_____

_____

_____

_____

Back to the Big Question

What Processes Within Earth Cause Geologic Activity?

◀ *1 class period*

A class period is considered to be one 40 to 50 minute class.

Overview

Students list the geologic terms they have learned in this *Learning Set* and make sketches to show the defining features of each term. They record connections between them, synthesizing the geologic ideas they have learned. Using this information, they create explanations of how the movement within Earth's layers leads to geologic activity and causes changes in Earth's surface. They consider what information would help them better explain what causes geologic activity and changes in Earth's surface and they update the *Project Board*.

Targeted Concepts, Skills, and Nature of Science	Performance Expectations
Scientists often work together and then share their findings. Sharing findings makes new information available and helps scientists refine their ideas and build on others' ideas. When another person's or group's idea is used, credit needs to be given.	Students should work together in small groups to create explanations. Then they should share their explanations with the class and discuss how different groups supported their claims.
Scientists must keep clear, accurate, and descriptive records of what they do so they can share their work with others and consider what they did, why they did it, and what they want to do next.	Students should keep clear, accurate, and descriptive records of the geologic concepts they have learned and of their claims and supporting evidence.
Graphs and tables are an effective way to analyze and communicate results of scientific investigation.	Students should use the *Project Board* and other tables to organize information. These should assist students to analyze information and share with others.

Targeted Concepts, Skills, and Nature of Science	Performance Expectations
Explanations are claims supported by evidence. Evidence can be experimental results, observational data, and other accepted scientific knowledge.	Students should create explanations, supporting their claims with evidence and scientific knowledge.
Scientists make claims (conclusions) based on evidence obtained (trends in data) from reliable investigations.	Students should construct claims based on observations and use these in their explanations.
Earthquake activity, volcanic activity, and topography are all evidence that Earth's crust is moving and changing.	Students should use evidence from their observations of earthquake activity, volcanic activity, and topography to support their claims about changes to Earth's crust.

Materials	
1 per student	*Create Your Explanation* page
100 per group	Index cards
1 per class	Class *Project Board*

Homework Options

Reflection

- **Science Content:** What evidence from your observations did you use in your explanations? *(Students should identify evidence from observations they made with visualization softwares and from photographs.)*

◄ *1 class period* *

Learning Set 2

Back to the Big Question

What Processes Within Earth Cause Geologic Activity?

People around the world and through many generations have observed and experienced changes in Earth's surface topography. People have explained these changes and events using what they know. Before people knew about Earth's layers, they described Earth's changes using myths and magic. They might have thought that giants' footsteps caused big valleys or that a fire goddess built Earth. Now that scientists know about Earth's layers, their explanations of Earth's changes take into account the composition of each layer and how the layers affect one another.

You have read a lot about the structure of Earth, and it is time to record what you have learned and apply that understanding to answer the *Big Question*. You will use what you have been learning to explain the processes that cause mountains to grow, islands to expand, volcanoes to erupt, and the ground to shake. You have read about some of these changes, described and compared the topography of parts of the crust where these changes have been observed, and heard about characteristics of Earth's crust and other layers. You will first update your *Picture Map*, and then use what you know to explain the processes changing and shaping Earth's crust.

Add to Your *Picture Map*

The goal of this *Learning Set* was to understand Earth's structure. While you were working on this goal, you learned these geologic terms: *crust, mantle, core, plate, inner core, outer core, oceanic crust, continental crust, plate boundary, seismology,* and *molten*. You have also learned about *earthquakes* and *volcanoes*.

As you did in *Learning Set 1*, write each term on a separate index card. Then, next to the term, draw a picture to show what the geologic term means. Make your picture as accurate as possible. Be sure to include features that would help someone else understand the geologic term.

EE 88

Project-Based Inquiry Science

△ Guide

Remind students that the *Big Question* for the Unit is *What processes within Earth cause geologic activity?* Emphasize that in *Learning Set 2* students learned a lot of information about the structure of Earth they can use to answer the *Big Question*. Tell them they will now use that information to explain the processes that cause the geologic activity and topographic features they have observed. They will update their *Picture Maps* and then construct explanations of the processes that change and shape of Earth's crust.

*A class period is considered to be one 40 to 50 minute class.

197

EVER-CHANGING EARTH

"In this *Learning Set,* you have learned a lot about the structure of Earth. You learned that molten rock moves in the mantle of Earth and you learned that Earth's crust has plates that move. This knowledge will help you answer the *Big Question: What processes within Earth cause geologic activity?* You are now going to use this knowledge to explain the geologic activity and topographic features you observed. To begin, you'll add to your *Picture Map.***"**

Add to Your Picture Map

10 min

Students map the concepts they have learned using index cards.

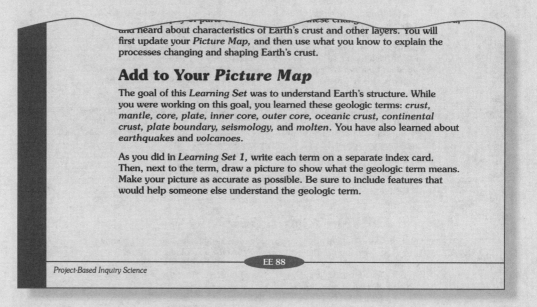

...and heard about characteristics of Earth's crust and other layers. You will first update your *Picture Map,* and then use what you know to explain the processes changing and shaping Earth's crust.

Add to Your *Picture Map*

The goal of this *Learning Set* was to understand Earth's structure. While you were working on this goal, you learned these geologic terms: *crust, mantle, core, plate, inner core, outer core, oceanic crust, continental crust, plate boundary, seismology,* and *molten.* You have also learned about *earthquakes* and *volcanoes.*

As you did in *Learning Set 1,* write each term on a separate index card. Then, next to the term, draw a picture to show what the geologic term means. Make your picture as accurate as possible. Be sure to include features that would help someone else understand the geologic term.

Project-Based Inquiry Science

EE 88

△ Guide

Tell students that they will add to their *Picture Maps* by writing important terms on index cards, as they did in *Learning Set 1.* They will draw a picture of each term to communicate what the term means. Emphasize that their drawing should help people who are not familiar with the terms to understand what they mean.

When students have completed their cards, they should share them with their group. Each student should listen to other members' descriptions of the terms and think about information they can add to their own cards or changes they can make to their drawings.

Return to the cards you created after *Learning Set 1*. You now know more about some of those concepts than you knew when you made those cards. Revise your pictures to make them more accurate.

When you have completed your cards, share them with a group of classmates. Listen carefully as someone in your group describes each geologic term. For each card, notice if there is additional information or if there are changes you need to make to your drawing or definition.

Now, work with your group to create a map that shows how the geologic terms go together. For example, *plate* might be connected to *plate boundary* and *earthquake*. Lay the cards on the table to show how each idea connects with another.

Discuss the connections with your group. If you cannot come to an agreement now, record your disagreement. As you learn more about the geologic terms, you will be better able to connect the ideas together. You can then revise your cards and connections.

On the back of each card, record the connections you made by writing the terms that are on the connecting cards. In the example, you would write *plate boundary* and *earthquake* on the back of the *plate* card. Record each connection on all cards that are connected to one another. Be as specific as possible. Record any disagreements your group had about connections and any connections you do not understand.

Explain

It is time to make your first explanation of how processes in Earth's layers are causing changes at Earth's surface. Use a *Create Your Explanation* page to help you. Remember that a good explanation has several parts to it:

- **your claim:** a statement of what you understand or a conclusion you have reached

- **your evidence:** data collected from investigations that support your claim

- **your science knowledge:** knowledge about how things work that supports your claim

- **your explanation:** a logical statement connecting your evidence and science knowledge to your claim in a way that can convince someone that your claim is valid. Good explanations tell what is happening that makes the claim valid.

EE 89

EVER-CHANGING EARTH

Students should work with their groups to find how the terms go together. They should arrange their cards on the table to show how the ideas connect. When they have agreed on how the ideas connect, they should record the connections on the back of the cards. If members of the group disagree about how the ideas connect, they should record their disagreement.

⬡ Get Going

Distribute index cards and go over the list of terms that students should include in their *Picture Maps.* Emphasize that each student should create a set of cards illustrating the terms.

△ Guide and Assess

As students work on their cards, monitor their progress and assist them with any difficulties they encounter. If they need guidance as they create sketches to illustrate their geologic terms, have them imagine they are trying to explain these ideas to another person. Ask them questions about the ideas to guide them toward statements they can illustrate.

When students share their cards with their groups, listen to how they discuss differences in the information on their cards and how they discuss the best arrangement of their cards. Emphasize that students should ask questions and make comments constructively. If students have difficulty arranging their cards, ask them what the most important connections between the ideas they have illustrated are. Ask which of the ideas they would use to explain one of the new terms. Those ideas should be connected to the new term in their *Picture Map.*

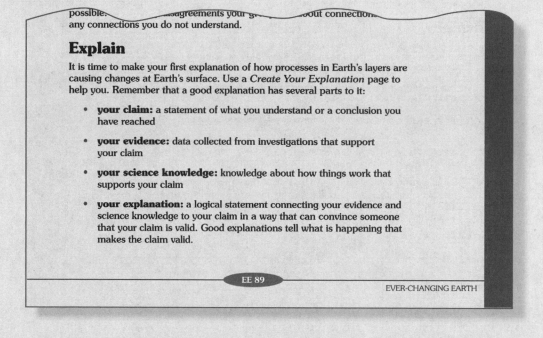

possible. ...agreements your g... ...out connection any connections you do not understand.

Explain

It is time to make your first explanation of how processes in Earth's layers are causing changes at Earth's surface. Use a *Create Your Explanation* page to help you. Remember that a good explanation has several parts to it:

- **your claim:** a statement of what you understand or a conclusion you have reached

- **your evidence:** data collected from investigations that support your claim

- **your science knowledge:** knowledge about how things work that supports your claim

- **your explanation:** a logical statement connecting your evidence and science knowledge to your claim in a way that can convince someone that your claim is valid. Good explanations tell what is happening that makes the claim valid.

EE 89

EVER-CHANGING EARTH

Explain

5 min

Students create explanations of the ways that movements in Earth's layers cause changes in Earth's surface.

△ Guide

Let students know they will now create explanations of the ways that movements of Earth's layers cause changes in Earth's surface. They will use evidence from their drawings and models, and they will use science knowledge from their reading.

Review the parts of a good explanation with the class (the claim, the evidence, the science knowledge) and that the explanation should connect the evidence and the science knowledge to the claim. A good explanation could have the form: "The movements of Earth's layers cause Earth's surface to change by… We know this because we observed…and we learned that …" Students should use the bulleted list in the student text as a reference for creating explanations.

Emphasize that students' claims should be statements about the ways that movement of Earth's layers cause changes in Earth's surface. These claims should be as clear and accurate as possible.

☐ Assess

As groups work on their explanations, monitor their progress and help them with any difficulties they are having. Ask them what evidence and science knowledge they are using to support their claims.

Note the similarities and differences among groups' claims. During presentations, you might consider having two groups with very similar claims present one after the other so that students can compare how they supported their claims.

NOTES

Communicate: Share Your Explanation

15 min

Groups present their explanations.

Your claim will be your clearest, most accurate statement about the ways that movements of Earth's layers cause changes in Earth's surface. Your evidence comes from the drawings you have made and the modeling you have done. Your drawings and sketches can be useful in helping you imagine how Earth's processes work. Your science knowledge comes from your reading. Work with your partner to create the best explanation you can. You will have a chance later in the Unit to revise your explanation. Use what you have learned so far to make the best explanation you can right now. It may be easier to express your explanation by attaching phrases to sketches than to simply use words. Feel free to combine sketches and words in your explanation.

Communicate

Share Your Explanation

Present your explanation to the class. As you listen to the explanations of others, notice how well each explanation connects what is happening in Earth's layers to changes on Earth's surface. As a class, develop your best explanation of the ways that processes happening in Earth's layers are affecting Earth's surface.

Reflect

1. What else do you need to learn to improve your explanation?

2. You have read that changes at Earth's surface happen because plates are moving. Do you know where the plates are? How would knowing the locations of the plates help you explain your Earth structure? What information would help you find the plate boundaries?

Update the *Project Board*

As you update the class *Project Board,* include what you have learned about the structure of Earth. Remember that any information added to the *What are we learning?* column should be supported with evidence in the *What is our evidence?* column. As you add ideas to the *What are we learning?* column, remember to think about how these ideas are going to help you answer the *Big Question.* There are some things you still need to learn to fully explain how movement in Earth's layers causes geologic activity and changes to Earth's surface. Add these questions to the *What do we need to investigate?* column.

△ Guide

When groups have completed their explanations, have them present their explanation to the class. With the class, review each explanation and ask the class to identify its parts (claim, evidence, science knowledge). Encourage the class to suggest any different ideas they have for the explanations presented. Ask groups with similar interpretations if they used any different evidence and science knowledge to support their claims.

Once all groups have presented, lead a discussion of what the class claim should be. Record the claim on the board or a projector, and lead the class in developing an explanation. Students should identify the evidence and science knowledge presented that can support the new class claim.

☐ Assess

As the class discusses the presentations and the final class recommendation, listen to how students discuss their ideas. Do students ask each other about things that are not clear? Do they give constructive feedback?

△ Guide

Lead a class discussion of the *Reflect* questions. Ask students how they think they could improve their explanations. What information is missing that could help? Ask them how knowing where the boundaries of the plates in Earth's crust could help them. How could that help them explain their Earth structures?

△ Guide

Update the *Project Board* with the class. Ask students what they have learned since they last updated the *Project Board*. Record their answers in the *What are we learning?* column. This should include the claims from the class explanation. For everything that students put in the *What are we learning?* column, ask student what evidence they have. Record the evidence in the *What is our evidence?* column. Finally, ask students what they still need to investigate, and record their answers in the *What do we need to investigate?* column. Students should suggest that they need to investigate where the boundaries of the plates in Earth's crust are.

Reflect

10 min

The class dicusses the Reflect *questions.*

Update the Project Board

10 min

The class has a discussion to update the Project Board.

NOTES

Assessment Options

Targeted Concepts, Skills, and Nature of Science	How do I know if students got it?
Scientists often work together and then share their findings. Sharing findings makes new information available and helps scientists refine their ideas and build on others' ideas. When another person's or group's idea is used, credit needs to be given.	**ASK:** How did listening to other groups' explanations help you refine your own explanations? **LISTEN:** Students should have identified evidence and science knowledge in other groups' explanations they could use. They should also have considered the strengths and weaknesses of other groups' explanations.
Scientists must keep clear, accurate, and descriptive records of what they do so they can share their work with others and consider what they did, why they did it, and what they want to do next.	**ASK:** Why was it important to record what you have learned along with your evidence on the *Project Board*? **LISTEN:** Students should recognize that recording what they did in the *Learning Set* allowed them to track their progress toward answering the *Big Question*.
Graphs and tables are an effective way to analyze and communicate results of scientific investigation.	**ASK:** How did organizing geologic terms by their connections with other terms help you? How did recording the things you have learned in a list with your drawing help? **LISTEN:** Students should recognize that organizing terms by their connections helped them to understand how all of these geologic terms are related and can be applied to understanding Earth structures. Making a list of the things they learned with the drawings should have helped students see how individual observations were related to their final interpretations.

Targeted Concepts, Skills, and Nature of Science	How do I know if students got it?
Explanations are claims supported by evidence. Evidence can be experimental results, observational data, and other accepted scientific knowledge.	**ASK:** How did you use scientific knowledge in your explanations? **LISTEN:** Students should have used scientific knowledge as evidence to support the claims in their explanations.
Scientists make claims (conclusions) based on evidence obtained (trends in data) from reliable investigations.	**ASK:** How is an interpretation different from an explanation? **LISTEN:** Students should be able to recognize that in an explanation, claims are supported by the observations (evidence) and science knowledge.
Earthquake activity, volcanic activity, and topography are all evidence that Earth's crust is moving and changing.	**ASK:** What evidence did you use to support your explanations? **LISTEN:** Students should have used evidence from their observations of earthquakes, volcanic activity, and topographic features.

Teacher Reflection Questions

- What concepts in this *Learning Set* were difficult for students? How can you help them master these concepts?

- What evidence do you have that students have been responding to your feedback? What might you try to engage students in your feedback?

- What kind of discussions did the class have as you updated the *Project Board?* How were you able to keep discussions constructive?

NOTES

LEARNING SET 3 INTRODUCTION

Learning Set 3

What Happens at Plate Boundaries?

◄ $11\frac{1}{2}$ *class periods*

A class period is considered to be one 40 to 50 minute class.

Overview

Students investigate plate boundaries and geologic activity in their regions. They begin by modeling plate interactions with blocks of clay. They make observations and interpret their observations. Their interpretations are refined and built as they read about the science of earthquakes. They are introduced to the seismic waves, seismographs, and the ways scientists measures earthquake magnitude and intensity. Using what they have learned about seismic waves and seismographs, students locate the epicenter of an earthquake using data from three seismograph stations, learning how scientists use triangulation. Students analyze current earthquake data from the United States Geological Survey (USGS) to develop a greater familiarity with geologic activity worldwide. They look for patterns in earthquake data from the past week, and begin to infer the locations of plate boundaries. They examine a map showing earthquake data from a one-year period and realize there are sometimes gaps in data. They record the plate boundaries they can identify in their regions and realize where the map has too much or too little data. To complete their plate boundary inferences, they use *My World* to select the best data. Once students have identified plate boundaries in their regions, they meet with students who were assigned neighboring regions and determine how their plate boundaries interconnect. Finally, the class creates a map of plate boundaries around the world.

LOOKING AHEAD

Students should have access to computers for *Sections 3.5* and *3.6*. In *Section 3.5* they will need access the USGS Web site. You will need to ensure beforehand that computers have working Internet access, that the USGS Web site is accessible, and that you know how to navigate the USGS Web site.

Targeted Concepts, Skills, and Nature of Science	Section
Scientists often work together and then share their findings. Sharing findings makes new information available and helps scientists refine their ideas and build on others' ideas. When another person or group's idea is used, credit needs to be given.	3.1, 3.4, 3.5, 3.6, 3.7, 3.BBQ

Targeted Concepts, Skills, and Nature of Science	Section
Scientists must keep clear, accurate, and descriptive records of what they do so they can share their work with others and consider what they did, why they did it, and what they want to do next.	3.1, 3.2, 3.4, 3.5, 3.6, 3.7, 3.BBQ
Graphs and tables are an effective way to analyze and communicate results of scientific investigation.	3.5, 3.6, 3.7, 3.BBQ
Scientific investigations and measurements are considered reliable if the results are repeatable by other scientists using the same procedures.	3.6, 3.7
Scientists make claims (conclusions) based on evidence obtained (trends in data) from reliable investigations.	3.5, 3.6, 3.7, 3.BBQ
Explanations are claims supported by evidence, accepted ideas, and facts.	3.BBQ
Scientists use models and tools, such as Geographic Information Systems, and a variety of maps to develop claims and explanations from evidence in the data.	3.5, 3.6, 3.7
Scientists measure and record earthquake activity using the Richter Scale and the Modified Mercalli Intensity Scale. The Richter Scale is used for measuring the magnitude of an earthquake. The Modified Mercalli Intensity Scale is used to measure the intensity.	3.3
Earthquake activity, volcanic activity, and topography are all evidence that Earth's crust is moving and changing.	3.1, 3.2, 3.3, 3.4, 3.5, 3.BBQ
Interactions between Earth's crustal plates can result in mountain building, rift valleys, and geologic activity such as earthquakes and volcanoes. Underwater volcanic activity may form underwater mountains, which can thrust above the ocean's surface to become islands.	3.2, 3.3, 3.5

Students' Initial Conceptions and Capabilities	• Students may have difficulty constructing explanations about the causes of earthquakes. (Duschl, Smith, Kesidou, Gitomer, & Schauble, 1992)
	• Students may think that earthquakes are only likely to occur in certain places, like California. Others may think they happen everywhere.
	• Students may believe that earthquakes are rare and always destructive.

LEARNING SET 3 IMPLEMENTATION

Learning Set 3

What Happens at Plate Boundaries?

The rocky plates making up the surface of Earth fit together like pieces of broken shell on a boiled egg. The breaks between the plates are areas where parts of the crust can move. Geologic activity resulting from these movements is often visible at the surface but occurs throughout the depths of the crust as well. In this *Learning Set*, you will investigate one type of geologic activity that happens where plates meet—earthquakes.

By investigating earthquakes in your region—what causes them, what happens during an earthquake, and how scientists determine where earthquakes have occurred—you will be able to identify where plates are interacting with each other in your area.

Many earthquakes and volcanic eruptions occur where plates are interacting with each other, making geologic activity a good indicator of the location of plate boundaries.

Investigating earthquakes and identifying where plates are interacting will help you understand the following:

- the geologic activity in your region;

- patterns of geologic activity across regions;

- what is happening within Earth that causes geologic activity.

After investigating earthquakes, you will use what you have learned to make your first predictions about where Earth's plates meet and interact. You will then use this information as you move forward, answering the *Big Question* for this Unit, *What processes within Earth cause geologic activity?*

EE 91

Learning Set 3

What Happens at Plate Boundaries?

5 min

Students are introduced to the Learning Set.

△ Guide

Begin by asking students what they know about the places in Earth's crust where the plates meet. Students should already know that volcanic activity and earthquakes occur at these places. They should also have some ideas about how earthquakes occur at these places due to plate interactions. How do these interactions cause the changes students have observed where earthquakes have occurred? What would students need to learn to be able to map the edges of plates?

*A class period is considered to be one 40 to 50 minute class.

Tell students that in this *Learning Set* they will investigate earthquakes, identifying where plates interact and developing their understanding of the geologic activity in their regions, the patterns of geologic activity across regions, and what processes within Earth cause geologic activity.

NOTES

3.1 Understand the Question

Think About What Happens at Plate Boundaries

◀ $1\frac{1}{2}$ *class periods*

A class period is considered to be one 40 to 50 minute class.

Overview

Students use blocks of clay to model Earth's plates and simulate several types of plate interaction. After recording observations from their simulations, they develop interpretations of their observations. They share these interpretations with the class and discuss what they think they now know about plate interaction. The class records what they think they know and what they need to investigate in the *Project Board*.

Targeted Concepts, Skills, and Nature of Science	Performance Expectations
Scientists often work together and then share their findings. Sharing findings makes new information available and helps scientists refine their ideas and build on others' ideas. When another person's or group's idea is used, credit needs to be given.	Students should work with their partners to simulate plate interactions and make observations. They should present their results to the class and discuss their interpretations with their classmates.
Scientists must keep clear, accurate, and descriptive records of what they do so they can share their work with others and consider what they did, why they did it, and what they want to do next.	Students should keep clear, accurate, and descriptive records of their simulations, their interpretations of the results, and what they learned from class discussions.
Earthquake activity, volcanic activity, and topography are all evidence that Earth's crust is moving and changing.	Students should recognize that interaction between plates may cause earthquake activity and changes to the topography of a region. Conversely, the presence of earthquakes and topographic features may be evidence of interaction between plates.

Materials	
2-3 per group	Flat blocks of modeling clay
1 sheet per group	Wax paper
1 per student	*Simulating Plate Interactions* page
1 per class	Class *Project Board*

Activity Setup and Preparation

In this section, students will simulate plate interactions by moving blocks of clay across a table or desk. They may need to put sheets of wax paper down to keep the clay from sticking to the table or desktop. Try the simulation with blocks of clay before class to see what the most effective way of doing it is

Homework Options

Reflection

- **Science Process:** In what ways do you think your simulation accurately predicts the events that occur when plates interact? What are some things you could do to test these predictions? *(This question is meant to engage students in evaluating the strengths of their model and thinking about what they should investigate.)*

Preparation for 3.2

- **Science Content:** Do you think the different types of plate interaction cause different types of earthquake activity? Why? *(This question is meant to engage students in imagining how the different types of plate interaction generate earthquakes.)*

SECTION 3.1 IMPLEMENTATION

3.1 Understand the Question

Think About What Happens at Plate Boundaries

The places where the edges of plates meet are called plate boundaries. When plates meet at plate boundaries, they apply forces on one another. These forces can include different types of pushes and pulls. The plates can slide past each other, pull apart, or meet and push against one another. Plate interactions and geologic activity cause changes in topography.

To help you think about how plates interact, you will simulate plate movements using blocks of clay. The blocks of clay are models of the plates making up Earth's crust.

Get Started

Simulate Plate Interactions

Working with your partner, you will move clay blocks in the ways that the plates move. Each time you push the clay blocks together, pull them apart, or slide them past each other, you will observe what happens to the clay as a result of each kind of interaction. Pay attention to what happens at the edges of each block, how the blocks change, and what causes those changes.

As you make observations, record your data in the *Observations* column of a *Simulating Plate Interactions* page.

EE 92

Project-Based Inquiry Science

3.1 Understand the Question

Think About What Happens at Plate Boundaries

5 min

Students are introduced to the activity.

△ Guide

Tell students that they will first investigate how plates interact. Discuss with the class how at plate boundaries, plates apply forces on each other. Since students cannot directly observe this interaction, they will use a simulation. They will use blocks of clay as models of the plates in Earth's crust.

*A class period is considered to be one 40 to 50 minute class.

TEACHER TALK

"Now we are going to investigate how plates interact. Because we cannot directly observe Earth's plates interacting, we are going to use blocks of clay as a model of Earth's plates. Use these blocks of clay to simulate how Earth's plates interact."

Get Started: Simulate Plate Interactions

5 min

Students simulate plate interactions with blocks of clay.

...making up Earth's cr...

Get Started

Simulate Plate Interactions

Working with your partner, you will move clay blocks in the ways that the plates move. Each time you push the clay blocks together, pull them apart, or slide them past each other, you will observe what happens to the clay as a result of each kind of interaction. Pay attention to what happens at the edges of each block, how the blocks change, and what causes those changes.

As you make observations, record your data in the *Observations* column of a *Simulating Plate Interactions* page.

△ Guide

Show students the clay blocks they will use and briefly discuss the procedure. They will lay two blocks of clay on a table and push them together and record their observations (Step 1). Continuing to apply steady pressure, they should observe what happens (Step 2). Then they should slide the clay blocks sideways against each other and observe what happens. They should record their observations using arrows to indicate direction (Step 3). Then they should pull on one clay block from opposite ends and observe what happens (Step 4). Finally, they should lay two clay blocks next to each other and pull them apart, recording their observations (Step 5).

NOTES

....

....

....

....

Procedure

1. Lay two blocks of clay flat on a table or desk, about 7.5 cm (3 in.) apart. Push them together using steady, firm pressure. The sides of the clay blocks should just touch. Notice what happens to the edges of each clay block. Record your observations on your *Simulating Plate Interactions* page. Draw pictures of the clay to show what happens to the blocks. Be sure to sketch all parts of the clay block.

2. Continue pushing firmly while paying attention to the edges of the blocks. Make careful observations and record them on your *Simulating Plate Interactions* page.

3. Now start again. Push two clay blocks together and slide them sideways past each other in opposite directions. Sketch the blocks and draw arrows to show how they are sliding past each other. Record what happens to the clay and describe how it feels as the blocks are sliding past each other. Record your observations on your *Simulating Plate Interactions* page.

4. Use one clay block and pull on it from opposite ends. Observe the middle of the clay as you are pulling. How is the middle of the clay block changing? What happens as you continue pulling? What if you pull with more force? Record your observations on your *Simulating Plate Interactions* page. Draw a picture of what your block of clay looks like once you stop pulling.

5. Place two clay blocks next to each other so they are touching. Pull them away from each other. Record your observations on your *Simulating Plate Interactions* page.

Simulating Plate Interactions

Name: _____ Date: _____

Record your observations from the plate interaction simulation.

Interactions Between Clay Plates	Observations— What happens at the edges of each block when they interact?	Data Analysis— What geologic activity might this interaction represent?	Communicate— What have you learned from others?
Plates move toward each other			
Plates continue moving toward each other			
Plates in contact slide past each other			
One plate is pulled from two sides			
Two plates are pulled away from each other			

Materials
- 2 or 3 flat blocks of clay
- *Simulating Plate Interactions page*

Procedure

15 min

Students start their simulations.

⬡ Get Going

Distribute *Simulating Plate Interactions* pages and blocks of clay and have the class begin their simulations.

☐ Assess

As students run their simulations, ask them what observations they have made. Look at the observations they have recorded. Their observations and drawings should include deformations of the clay. They should draw pictures of the clay in each interaction to show how the blocks of clay are affected. The drawings of blocks sliding past each other should include arrows to show the direction of motion.

Analyze
Your Data

10 min

Students interpret their observations.

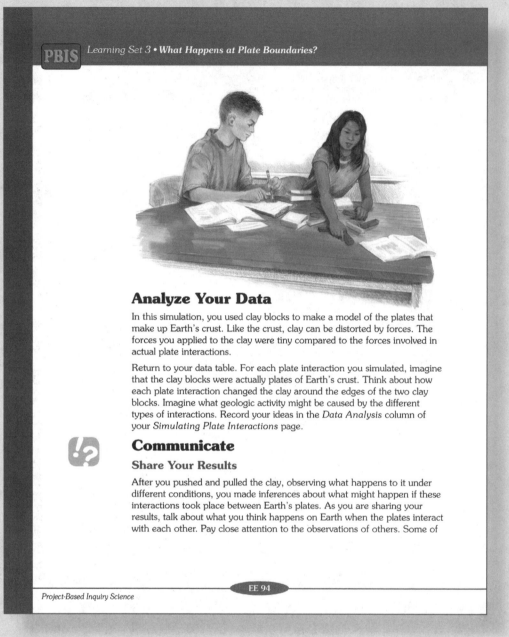

Analyze Your Data

In this simulation, you used clay blocks to make a model of the plates that make up Earth's crust. Like the crust, clay can be distorted by forces. The forces you applied to the clay were tiny compared to the forces involved in actual plate interactions.

Return to your data table. For each plate interaction you simulated, imagine that the clay blocks were actually plates of Earth's crust. Think about how each plate interaction changed the clay around the edges of the two clay blocks. Imagine what geologic activity might be caused by the different types of interactions. Record your ideas in the *Data Analysis* column of your *Simulating Plate Interactions* page.

Communicate

Share Your Results

After you pushed and pulled the clay, observing what happens to it under different conditions, you made inferences about what might happen if these interactions took place between Earth's plates. As you are sharing your results, talk about what you think happens on Earth when the plates interact with each other. Pay close attention to the observations of others. Some of

EE 94

Project-Based Inquiry Science

△ Guide

When students have finished running their simulations, have them discuss what their observations suggest about real interactions between plates in Earth's crust with their groups. Together, they should develop interpretations of their observations for each interaction they simulated, and record their interpretations in the *Data Analysis* column of their *Simulating Plate Interactions* pages. Emphasize that they should imagine their blocks of clay are plates in Earth's crust. They can then imagine how plates in Earth's crust might be deformed in ways similar to the blocks of clay.

◇ Evaluate

As students are discussing interpretations of their observations, ask what ideas they have discussed. Listen for ideas about deformations of plates leading to the formation of mountain ranges and plate interactions that cause earthquakes. It is not necessary that all students have developed these ideas, but most of these ideas should be thought of. Some students will also think about volcanoes occurring between plates or at places where plates are stretched thin, but this is not necessary.

△ Guide

When Students have had time to interpret their results, have them share the results along with their interpretations. They should describe what they observed when they simulated the plate interactions with the clay, and they should describe what they think their observations suggest about interactions of plates in Earth's crust.

Emphasize that students should listen carefully to other students' observations and examine their drawings. They should record anything they learned from other students in the *Communicate* column of their *Simulating Plate Interactions* pages.

☐ Assess and Guide

As students share their results and interpretations with the class, listen for ideas about earthquakes, land deformations—including mountain ranges— and volcanoes. It is not necessary for students to develop accurate ideas at this point. It is more important for students to connect observations of their simulations to real-world processes. In particular, they should connect their observations to earthquakes.

It is also important for students to pay attention to each other's ideas. Listen to the kinds of questions students ask presenting groups. They should ask questions constructively and make constructive comments. Emphasize that if they are confused about a group's results, they should ask the group to demonstrate how they got the result. Emphasize that students should record new ideas in the *Communicate* column of their *Simulating Plate Interactions* pages.

Note any observations that any groups missed. If any pairs missed observations, they should have a second chance to make them. Have a group that made the observations simulate the plate interaction where the observations were missed for the class. As they simulate the plate interaction again, the groups that missed the observations should use colored pencils to record their observations and interpretations on their *Simulating Plate Interactions* page. Do not let this take a long time. The group should not simulate all of the plate interactions again unless necessary.

Communicate: Share Your Results

15 min

Groups share their results and interpretations.

Ideally, some students will have observed that plates can move over or under each other. If no one has observed this, note this as something to bring up in the *Reflect* discussion. You will want to elicit students' ideas about what could happen when plates move under or over each other and record their ideas on the *Project Board*.

NOTES

_____

_____

_____

_____

_____

_____

_____

_____

_____

_____

_____

_____

_____

your classmates may have made different observations or may use different words to describe what they saw. Look carefully at the pictures they drew. If you are confused about a group's results, ask them to demonstrate what they did in their investigation. Record what you have learned from others in the *Communicate* column of your *Simulating Plate Interactions* page.

Reflect

1. Make a sketch showing two different ways Earth's plates interact. For each interaction, imagine the type of geologic activity that you think might happen due to that interaction. Label your sketches and include any information you learned from other groups.

2. Given the topography and geologic events that might occur where plates interact, what do you think you need to know to identify where Earth's plate boundaries are located?

3. Why do you think you need to identify where Earth's plates are interacting?

Update the *Project Board*

As a class, update the class *Project Board*. In the *What do we think we know?* column, record what you think you know about the ways Earth's plates interact at or near their edges and what you think happens when they interact that way. Also, record what you think you know about the geologic events caused by those interactions.

Record your ideas for investigations in the *What do we need to investigate?* column. Think about different kinds of geologic events and what you need to investigate to identify the location of Earth's plate boundaries. Remember to think about earthquakes, volcanoes, and mountain building.

What's the Point?

Earth's plates can interact with one another in a number of ways. By simulating ways in which Earth's plates interact, you found that Earth's plates may collide, slide past one another, or move away from one another. Each type of interaction can distort the land and change the features of the crust. This can result in geologic activity and changes to Earth's surface. Because of this, geologic activity can provide clues about the locations of plate boundaries.

Reflect
10 min

The class has a discussion of the Reflect *questions.*

△ Guide

Have students answer the *Reflect* questions. Let them know they will share their answers with the class.

When students have had a few minutes to answer the *Reflect* questions, lead a class discussion of their answers. Ask students what kind of information would help them to identify where Earth's plate boundaries are located. As students give their answers, record their ideas on the *Project Board*. Some of these ideas, such as those about the geologic events that occur at plate boundaries, can go into the *What do we think we know?* column.

Other ideas, like ideas about finding plate boundaries, can go in the *What do we need to investigate?* column. Listen for questions about where specific geologic events occur. Students should have questions about where volcanoes and mountain ranges arise in relation to plates. They should also have questions about what kinds of activity happen at plate boundaries. Students should be thinking about investigating whether earthquakes happen only at plate boundaries and, if not, how far from plate boundaries they happen; where earthquake zones are geographically; and what happens when plates move over or under each other.

Ask students why they need to identify where Earth's plates are interacting. Listen for ideas about how knowing where plate boundaries are and how plates are moving and interacting can help students recognize global patterns and explain the geologic activity and topographic features of their Earth structure. Record any new ideas in the *What do we think we know?* and *What do we need to investigate?* columns of the *Project Board*.

Update the Project Board

10 min

The class has a discussion to update the Project Board.

3. Why do you think you need to identify where Earth's plates are interacting?

Update the *Project Board*

As a class, update the class *Project Board*. In the *What do we think we know?* column, record what you think you know about the ways Earth's plates interact at or near their edges and what you think happens when they interact that way. Also, record what you think you know about the geologic events caused by those interactions.

Record your ideas for investigations in the *What do we need to investigate?* column. Think about different kinds of geologic events and what you need to investigate to identify the location of Earth's plate boundaries. Remember to think about earthquakes, volcanoes, and mountain building.

What's the Point?

Earth's plates can interact with one another in a number of ways. By ~~ting way~~ ~~plates~~

△ Guide

Ask students what they think they know about how plates interact. They should have discussed some ideas during the *Reflect* discussion, but they may have some additional ideas. Record their ideas in the *What do we think we know?* column of the *Project Board*. Ask them what they still need to investigate and record their answers in the *What do we need to investigate?* column of the *Project Board*. Make sure that students have questions about what causes earthquakes.

Assessment Options

Targeted Concepts, Skills, and Nature of Science	How do I know if students got it?
Scientists often work together and then share their findings. Sharing findings makes new information available and helps scientists refine their ideas and build on others' ideas. When another person's or group's idea is used, credit needs to be given.	**ASK:** How did class discussion help you develop your interpretations? **LISTEN:** Students should identify specific ideas they got from their classmates.
Scientists must keep clear, accurate, and descriptive records of what they do so they can share their work with others and consider what they did, why they did it, and what they want to do next.	**ASK:** How was it useful to record your observations, interpretations, and the ideas from your discussions? **LISTEN:** Students should recognize that recording what their observations, interpretations, and ideas helped them consider what they had done and how it led to their ideas about plate interactions and earthquakes.
Earthquake activity, volcanic activity, and topography are all evidence that Earth's crust is moving and changing.	**ASK:** Based on the ideas you have developed about plate interactions so far, what conclusion might you draw if you saw that a lot of earthquakes occurred in one location? **LISTEN:** Students should recognize that this might indicate the presence of a plate boundary.

Teacher Reflection Questions

- What misconceptions do students hold about earthquakes or plate interactions? How can you challenge those misconceptions?

- How were you able to engage students in developing their understanding of plate interaction? How can you engage students going forward?

- How were you able to keep discussions focused and constructive?

NOTES

3.2 Read

What Causes Earthquakes and What Happens When They Occur?

◀ $1\frac{1}{4}$ *class periods*

A class period is considered to be one 40 to 50 minute class.

Overview

Students learn more about the science of earthquakes, developing a more accurate understanding of how plate interactions cause earthquakes. They are introduced to the seismic waves that carry energy from the epicenter of an earthquake. They watch a demonstration of how longitudinal waves (similar to P waves) and transverse waves (similar to S waves) travel through a spring, developing an understanding of the characteristics of these different seismic waves and how they affect Earth's surface. Finally, they record what they have learned on the *Project Board,* connecting this science knowledge to the ideas they developed through simulations and observations.

Targeted Concepts, Skills, and Nature of Science	Performance Expectations
Scientists must keep clear, accurate, and descriptive records of what they do so they can share their work with others and consider what they did, why they did it, and what they want to do next.	Students should record new science knowledge on the *Project Board.*
Earthquake activity, volcanic activity, and topography are all evidence that Earth's crust is moving and changing.	Students should demonstrate understanding that the geologic processes in Earth can cause powerful earthquakes that result in great destruction.
Interactions between Earth's crustal plates can result in mountain building, rift valleys, and geologic activity such as earthquakes and volcanoes. Underwater volcanic activity may form underwater mountains, which can thrust above the ocean's surface to become islands.	Students should demonstrate understanding that the motion of plates in Earth's crust causes faults and that earthquakes occur when the rock at these faults moves.

Materials	
1 per class	Coiled spring toy
	Ribbon
	Class *Project Board*
	World map

Activity Setup and Preparation

In this section, you will demonstrate how longitudinal waves and transverse waves travel through materials using a spring. Before class, tie a ribbon to the spring. Put the ribbon on a coil far enough from either end of the spring so that students can clearly view it. Try sending longitudinal and transverse waves through the spring before class so that you know how the spring will behave. To do this, tie one end of the spring to a secure object, or have a colleague hold one end of it. Stretch the spring out and use your free hand to gently bat the back of the hand holding the spring. This will send a longitudinal wave through the spring. To demonstrate a transverse wave, use your free hand to gently bat the side of the hand holding the spring.

Homework Options

Reflection

- **Science Content:** P waves usually reach the epicenter of an earthquake before S waves. Do you think the distance between the first P waves and the first S waves increases, decreases, or stays the same as they travel away from the focus? *(This question is meant to engage students in analyzing the behaviors of P and S waves. The distance between the first P waves and the first S waves increases. If P waves travel X miles per hour faster than S waves, then after 1 hour the distance between the first P waves and the first S waves will be x miles, while after 2 hours it will be 2x.)*

Preparation for 3.3

- **Science Content:** You know that some earthquakes are stronger than others. How do you think earthquakes are measured? *(The purpose of this question is to get students thinking about how scientists measure earthquakes.)*

SECTION 3.2 IMPLEMENTATION

3.2 Read

What Causes Earthquakes and What Happens When They Occur?

The time is 4:11 PM on May 22, 1960. The most powerful earthquake ever recorded is shaking the coast of Chile. With a sudden lurch, the ocean floor heaves and plunges along a nearly 1000 km-long (620 mi) rupture. The violent shuddering that spreads outward through the crust levels buildings, triggers huge landslides, and changes the course of rivers. Cities along the coast sink and are flooded by ocean waters. The sudden shifting of the ocean floor creates a series of fast-moving ocean waves, called a **tsunami**.

tsunami: a series of huge ocean waves often triggered by an underwater earthquake.

Traveling at speeds up to 320 km (200 mi) per hour, these waves devastate the coast of Chile as well as coastlines across the Pacific Ocean—some as far as 15,000 km (9000 mi) away. Tsunamis caused 61 deaths and severe damage in Hawaii, where waves reached heights of 10.6 m (35 ft). Think about what could have occurred within Earth to set off such a destructive event.

The 1960 Chilean earthquake was the most powerful earthquake ever recorded. It was followed by a devastating tsunami.

Stop and Think

Before you investigate what causes earthquakes, answer these questions:

1. Where is Chile? Find Chile on the *Big World* map. Is Chile within the region of any group in the class?

3.2 Read

What Causes Earthquakes and What Happens When They Occur?

5 min

The class discusses the 1960 Chilean earthquake.

○ Engage

Point out the photograph in the student text. Ask students to describe what they think happened where the photograph was taken. Have they ever seen anything that looks like this photograph?

---

*A class period is considered to be one 40 to 50 minute class.

△ Guide

Discuss the events that caused the destruction. An earthquake near the coast of Chile ruptured the ocean floor, and vibrations spread outwards through Earth's crust. The shifting of the ocean floor caused a tsunami, which sent waves crashing at 320 km (200 mi) per hour onto coasts around the Pacific Ocean. Emphasize that students will soon be able to explain how events within Earth caused this destruction.

Stop and Think

5 min

Students answer the Stop and Think *questions.*

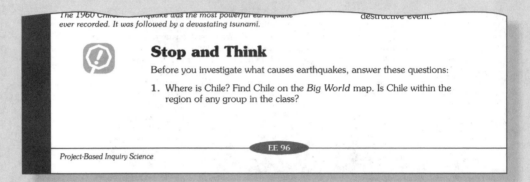

The 1960 Chilean earthquake was the most powerful earthquake ever recorded. It was followed by a devastating tsunami.

Stop and Think

Before you investigate what causes earthquakes, answer these questions:

1. Where is Chile? Find Chile on the *Big World* map. Is Chile within the region of any group in the class?

Project-Based Inquiry Science   EE 96

⬡ Get Going

Have students answer the *Stop and Think* questions individually. Let students know they should be prepared to share their answers with the class.

Ask students where Chile is. With the class, locate Chile on a world map. Make sure that students identify Mount Aconcagua as an Earth structure in Chile. Ask students for a few ideas about what it would be like to experience the earthquake. Try to engage students in thinking about the magnitude of such an event.

TEACHER TALK

❝What do you think it would be like to experience this earthquake? Do you have any experiences you can compare it to? How do you think people deal with something like this?❞

NOTES

....

....

2. Imagine that you were in Chile at the time of the earthquake. Write a paragraph about what it might have been like.

What Causes an Earthquake?

The account of the earthquake in Chile tells a lot about what happens during an earthquake. Earthquakes cause loss of life and destruction of property, so it is very important to know why they occur. As you read about the causes of earthquakes, keep in mind the simulation you did earlier in this *Learning Set,* using clay blocks to model Earth's plates.

As the plates bump into and slide past one another, they exert forces. The forces can be very strong, causing the crust to bend and break. Think about bending a wooden ruler. At first, when you grab the ends and push them toward each other, the ruler only bends. When enough force is applied, the ruler breaks.

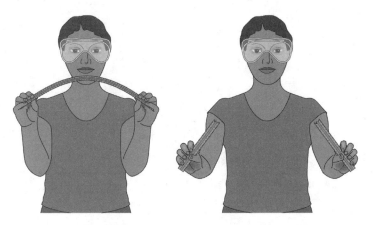

Like the ruler, the rocks of Earth's crust can bend and then break when enough force is applied. When the rocky crust breaks, the result is a fault in the crust. Faults may be as small as a few hundred meters or several hundred kilometers long.

EE 97

EVER-CHANGING EARTH

What Causes an Earthquake?

10 min

The class discusses how faults form and generate earthquakes.

△ Guide

When students have had a few minutes to answer the *Stop and Think* questions, discuss the causes of earthquakes. Tell students they should think about their simulations of plate interactions as they learn about the causes of earthquakes. Emphasize that their simulations and the story of the earthquake in Chile provide information that will help them understand the causes of earthquakes.

Discuss how the plates that students modeled with clay can bump into and slide past each other. The force of these interactions is great, and can cause the crust to bend and break. In this case, the crust bends until it breaks, then the pieces of the crust snap back. The student text uses the example of a wooden ruler. Point out the picture at the bottom of the page. The student in the picture is bending a wooden ruler. When the ruler breaks, the two pieces become straight again.

Tell students that when this happens in Earth's crust, the fracture is known as a fault. Discuss the importance of faults in earthquakes. As the student text points out, most earthquakes occur when the rock on either side of a fault moves. Earthquakes may occur along part of the fault. The magnitude of the earthquake is determined by how much of a fault or how much of a fault zone is involved in the earthquake.

NOTES

The force needed to move one of Earth's plates is less than the force needed to break the plate. Most earthquakes occur when a large area of rock making up a plate on either side of a fault moves.

Sometimes, when two plates are pushed together, the jagged edges become stuck. If the plates are sliding past each other, the edges remain stuck together while the rest of each plate keeps moving. This creates a lot of **stress** in the rock of the crust along the fault. Energy builds up due to the stress on the rock at the fault. Some types of rocks are more resistant to this stress than others. However, sooner or later, all rocks reach the point when the tremendous amount of stress causes rocks next to the fault to break loose and move suddenly along the fault. The stored energy that was building up in the rock is released as an earthquake.

stress: a force that squeezes rocks together, stretches or pulls them apart, or pushes them in different directions.

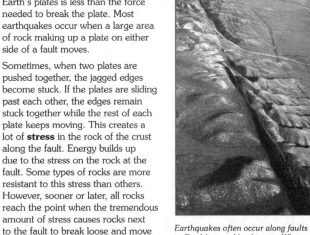

Earthquakes often occur along faults in Earth's crust like this one. When enough force is applied, the rocks on either side of the fault break loose and scrape past one another.

Normal Fault

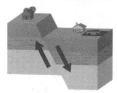

One side of a normal fault slips below the other side. The result is stress that moves the two sides apart.

Reverse Fault

One side of a reverse fault is thrust above the other side. The result is stress that moves the two sides together.

Strike-Slip Fault

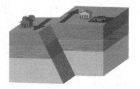

The two sides of a strike-slip fault slide past each other. The result is stress that moves the two sides past each other.

Tell students that different types of plate interactions can form faults. One important way plates interact and form faults is when two plates sliding past each other become stuck. The rest of the plates keep moving, and the stuck part creates a tremendous stress. Eventually, the stress causes rock along the fault to break loose and snap back to their original position in the plates. The release of energy causes an earthquake. Three types of faults are illustrated in the student text. It is not important for students to know how different plate interactions cause each kind, but they should understand that each of these types represent a different way Earth's crust can move past each other.

Stop and Think

5 min

The class has a discussion of the Stop and Think *questions.*

Stop and Think

1. What determines the strength of an earthquake?

2. How are faults related to earthquakes?

How Does Energy From an Earthquake Travel?

Earthquakes occur when parts of the crust break loose and move suddenly along a fault. The point where the parts of the crust first break and move is called the **focus** of the earthquake. Usually, an earthquake has one focus. It can be right at the surface of Earth's crust, or it can be very deep within the crust.

Think about the wooden ruler. The two halves of the ruler snap back after the ruler breaks. The rocks of the crust also snap back after they break loose in an earthquake. When this happens, the rock at the focus pushes against the surrounding rock with enough force to start a series of back-and-forth motions. These back-and-forth motions, called **vibrations**, carry energy through the surrounding rock. These vibrations spread outward in all directions as seismic waves.

The shaking is strongest and felt first on Earth's surface directly above the focus. This point is known as the **epicenter** of the earthquake. Scientists use the location of the epicenter as data to find exactly where an earthquake occurred.

focus: the point where part of the crust breaks loose and moves suddenly, causing an earthquake.

vibrations: back-and-forth motions that carry energy from one place to another.

epicenter: the point on the surface of Earth directly above the focus of an earthquake; often where the most damage from an earthquake occurs.

The relationship between the fault, focus, and epicenter is seen here. The fault is the fracture along which rocks move in relation to one another. The focus is the point underground where rocks break and the earthquake begins. The epicenter is the point on Earth's surface directly above the focus.

EVER-CHANGING EARTH

◇ Evaluate

Check students' understanding by briefly discussing the *Stop and Think* questions. Ask them what determines the strength of an earthquake. They should understand that it is the overall area of fault zone that determines the strength of an earthquake. Emphasize that an earthquake may take place at only a portion of a fault. If 10 km of a fault is involved in one earthquake and 5 km of the fault is involved in a second earthquake, the first will be stronger.

Ask how faults are related to earthquakes. Students should be able to describe how the motion of rock on either side of a fault can release energy, causing earthquakes.

TEACHER TALK

66**What determines how strong an earthquake is? This isn't surprising, is it? If more of a fault is vibrating, it makes sense that more energy would be released.**99

△ **Guide**

Discuss what happens at the focus of an earthquake. The focus is the spot where the rock breaks. As stress builds at this point, the rocks push against the surrounding rock until it is deformed. Just as the two parts of the bent ruler snap back to their original shape when the ruler breaks, the parts of the crust on either side of a fault snap back to their original shape when they break free in an earthquake. The energy of this back-and-forth motion (vibration) travels outward from the focus through surrounding rock in waves, called seismic waves. These waves shake Earth's surface.

The seismic waves shake Earth with the greatest force directly above the focus, at a point known as the epicenter.

How Does Energy from an Earthquake Travel?

5 min

The class discusses how seismic waves spread from an earthquake's focus.

NOTES

_____

_____

_____

_____

_____

_____

_____

Stop and Think

10 min

Lead a class discussion of the Stop and Think *questions.*

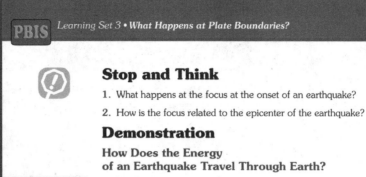

Stop and Think

1. What happens at the focus at the onset of an earthquake?

2. How is the focus related to the epicenter of the earthquake?

Demonstration

How Does the Energy of an Earthquake Travel Through Earth?

body waves: seismic waves that travel through Earth.

surface waves: seismic waves that travel along the surface of Earth.

P (primary) waves: longitudinal seismic waves that can travel through solids, liquids, or gases and are the fastest type of seismic waves.

S (secondary) waves: transverse seismic waves that can travel only through solids and are slower than P waves.

longitudinal wave: a type of wave that travels through Earth in a push-pull pattern.

The energy of an earthquake starts at the focus and travels outward in all directions. There are two different types of seismic waves created by an earthquake. **Body waves** are the seismic waves that travel through Earth. When body waves reach Earth's surface, they set in motion **surface waves** that transmit energy along the surface.

Body Waves

There are two types of body waves, **P waves** and **S waves**. Each has its own characteristic speed and substances through which it can travel.

P waves start as a pulse of energy released at the focus of an earthquake. These waves travel by pressing rock particles together and spreading them apart. Rock particles are squeezed, or compressed, and then spread apart, or expand, as each wave passes through. This compressing and expanding continues as the P wave travels through the surrounding rock. After the waves are finished passing through, the rock in the crust returns to its original position. P waves can travel through solids, liquids, and gases because these forms of matter can all be compressed and will return to their original position after the pulse of energy has passed.

Longitudinal Waves

Waves that travel in this push-pull pattern are called **longitudinal waves**. Watch as your teacher demonstrates this type of wave using a spring.

Begin by watching as the spring is pulled and pushed in line with the coils. You will notice that some coils squeeze closer together (compress) while others spread farther apart (extend). The compressions and expansions then move down the spring in an accordion-like motion.

EE 100

Project-Based Inquiry Science

◇ Evaluate

Check students' understanding by briefly discussing the *Stop and Think* questions. Ask students what happens at the focus of an earthquake. They should understand that the focus is where the rock creating tension and deforming surrounding rock breaks and releases waves of energy. Ask students how the focus is related to the epicenter. They should understand that the epicenter is directly above the focus.

△ Guide

Discuss the waves that carry an earthquake's energy through Earth. Tell students that body waves travel through Earth. When they reach Earth's surface, they cause surface waves, which travel along the surface.

Discuss the two types of body waves, P waves and S waves. P waves travel faster than S waves. As they travel, they push particles of rock into the particles ahead of them, expanding and contracting the rock they travel through. These waves are also able to travel through liquids and gases. These waves compress and expand in the same way the rock does that it is passing through. Waves that move in this way are called longitudinal waves. Tell students that you will demonstrate how longitudinal waves travel.

Demonstration: How Does the Energy of an Earthquake Travel Through Earth?

10 min

Students watch a demonstration of how P waves and S waves travel through Earth using a spring.

NOTES

Longitudinal Wave

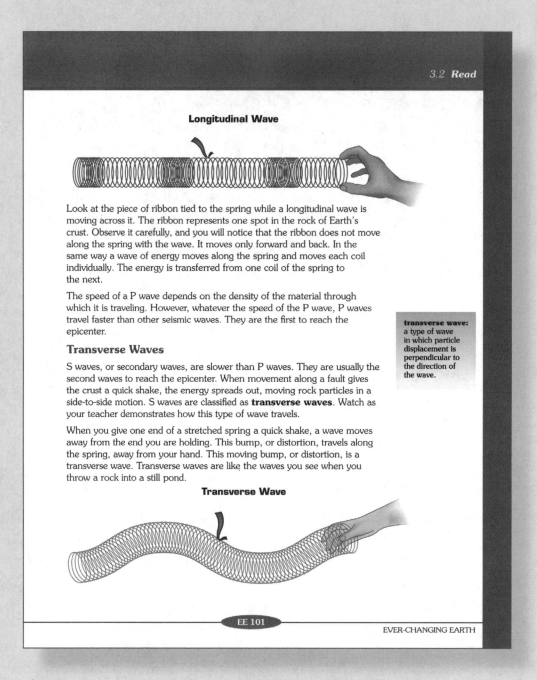

Look at the piece of ribbon tied to the spring while a longitudinal wave is moving across it. The ribbon represents one spot in the rock of Earth's crust. Observe it carefully, and you will notice that the ribbon does not move along the spring with the wave. It moves only forward and back. In the same way a wave of energy moves along the spring and moves each coil individually. The energy is transferred from one coil of the spring to the next.

The speed of a P wave depends on the density of the material through which it is traveling. However, whatever the speed of the P wave, P waves travel faster than other seismic waves. They are the first to reach the epicenter.

Transverse Waves

S waves, or secondary waves, are slower than P waves. They are usually the second waves to reach the epicenter. When movement along a fault gives the crust a quick shake, the energy spreads out, moving rock particles in a side-to-side motion. S waves are classified as **transverse waves**. Watch as your teacher demonstrates how this type of wave travels.

When you give one end of a stretched spring a quick shake, a wave moves away from the end you are holding. This bump, or distortion, travels along the spring, away from your hand. This moving bump, or distortion, is a transverse wave. Transverse waves are like the waves you see when you throw a rock into a still pond.

transverse wave: a type of wave in which particle displacement is perpendicular to the direction of the wave.

Transverse Wave

EE 101

△ Guide

Demonstrate how longitudinal waves travel through materials using a spring with a ribbon tied to it. Lay the spring on a table where students can see it. Then stretch it. Tie one end of the spring to a stationary object, or have a student hold one end. Point out the ribbon and emphasize that they should observe how the ribbon moves as longitudinal waves pass through it.

With the spring stretched out, send a compression wave through the spring by lightly flicking your hand towards the opposite end of the spring. If you have a free hand, you can hit the back of the hand holding the spring. Point out the waves of compression and expansion moving through the spring. Ask them what happens to the ribbon. They should observe that the ribbon does not move along the spring. It only moves forward and back with each wave. Repeat the demonstration a few times so that students will be able to observe the waves of compression and expansion.

Tell students about the other type of body waves. S waves, or secondary waves, are slower than P waves and move particles in a side-to-side motion. They happen when movement along a fault jerks the crust. Unlike P waves, S waves can only travel through solids. S waves displace particles, so they do not return to their original positions. These waves are classified as transverse waves.

Demonstrate how transverse waves travel through matter by giving one end of the spring a quick shake. If you have a free hand, you can use it to hit the hand holding the spring. This time, hit the side of your hand. Emphasize that students should watch the ribbon on the spring as transverse waves pass through it. Now the ribbon moves side to side.

NOTES

....

....

....

....

....

....

Observe the spring as it moves side to side in a transverse wave. Watch the piece of ribbon as the transverse wave moves past it. The ribbon in a transverse wave also does not move along the spring. The ribbon stays on the coil, but the coil transfers the energy to the next coil. In a transverse wave, the ribbon moves side to side compared to the direction the energy moves. The energy is transferred along the spring through this side to side motion.

Like P waves, S waves change speed depending on the density of material through which they are traveling. However, S waves can travel only through solids. They cannot pass through liquids or gases. In a liquid or gas, particles are free to move. Once pushed out of place by the energy of the S wave, the particles will not return to their original position, and so the energy is not transmitted.

Surface Waves

Surface waves are the slowest of all seismic waves. They are set in motion when the energy transmitted by body waves reaches the surface. Earth's surface rises and falls with each passing body wave, much like waves travel in an ocean. Surface waves may also move side-to-side, moving like a slithering snake. The action of body waves bends and tears Earth's surface, causing most of the damage in an earthquake. The motion of the surface can cause buildings to collapse and shake loose rock and soil on slopes, causing landslides.

EE 102

△ Guide

Introduce surface waves. Surface waves travel more slowly than body waves. Surface waves appear when body waves reach Earth's surface. Surface waves may cause Earth's surface to rise and fall, like the waves in a body of water. Or they may move from side to side, like a slithering snake. Point out the illustration of P waves, S waves, and surface waves in the student text.

3.2 Read

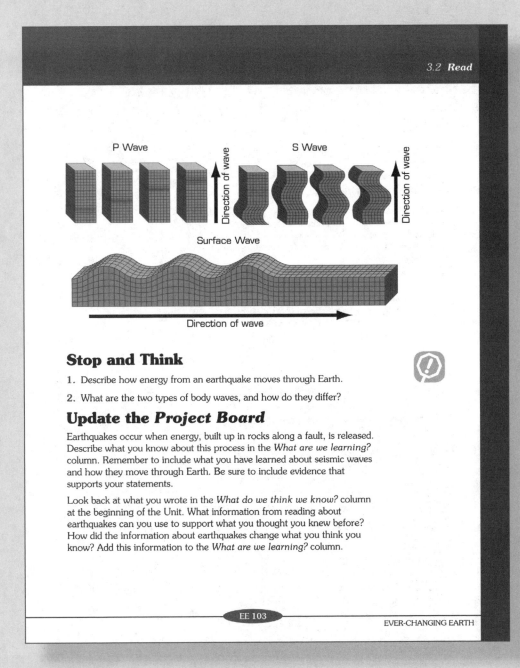

P Wave

S Wave

Direction of wave

Direction of wave

Surface Wave

Direction of wave

Stop and Think

1. Describe how energy from an earthquake moves through Earth.

2. What are the two types of body waves, and how do they differ?

Update the *Project Board*

Earthquakes occur when energy, built up in rocks along a fault, is released. Describe what you know about this process in the *What are we learning?* column. Remember to include what you have learned about seismic waves and how they move through Earth. Be sure to include evidence that supports your statements.

Look back at what you wrote in the *What do we think we know?* column at the beginning of the Unit. What information from reading about earthquakes can you use to support what you thought you knew before? How did the information about earthquakes change what you think you know? Add this information to the *What are we learning?* column.

EE 103

EVER-CHANGING EARTH

Stop and Think

5 min

Lead a class discussion of the Stop and Think *questions.*

△ Guide

Before updating the *Project Board,* lead a class discussion of the *Stop and Think* questions. Listen for the following answers to these questions:

1. Students should understand that in P waves, particles move closer together and farther apart along the direction the waves are traveling. In S waves, particles move back and forth, perpendicular to the direction the waves are traveling.

2. P waves and S waves are body waves. P waves are longitudinal waves; S waves are transverse waves. Transverse waves are slower than longitudinal waves and they are not able to pass through gases and liquids. Therefore, transverse waves usually reach the epicenter and other locations after longitudinal waves, and they are interrupted by places in Earth where there is liquid or gas.

Update the Project Board

10 min

Lead the class in a discussion to update the Project Board.

2. What are the two types of body waves, and how do they differ?

Update the *Project Board*

Earthquakes occur when energy, built up in rocks along a fault, is released. Describe what you know about this process in the *What are we learning?* column. Remember to include what you have learned about seismic waves and how they move through Earth. Be sure to include evidence that supports your statements.

Look back at what you wrote in the *What do we think we know?* column at the beginning of the Unit. What information from reading about earthquakes can you use to support what you thought you knew before? How did the information about earthquakes change what you think you know? Add this information to the *What are we learning?* column.

EE 103

EVER-CHANGING EARTH

△ Guide and Evaluate

Once the class has discussed the *Stop and Think* questions, ask students what they now know about how earthquakes occur. What can they put in the *What are we learning?* column of the *Project Board?* Students should suggest information about seismic waves, including the characteristics and behaviors of P waves and S waves. Record students' answers in the *Project Board*.

Draw students' attention to the *What do we think we know?* column. Ask them if they can use information from the reading to support any of the things in this column. Is there anything they need to modify? Record this in the *What are we learning?* column.

NOTES

....

....

What's the Point?

Earth's plates interact in different ways depending on the direction in which they move. They can move together, move away from each other, or slide past each other. These plate interactions begin a process that can result in an earthquake. When two plates slide past each other at a fault, their jagged edges can get stuck, creating strain on the rocks. Like a rubber band stretched as far as it can go, the two sides of the fault eventually break loose and snap back. Energy that is released results in an earthquake.

The point along a fault at which an earthquake begins is called the focus. The focus may be near the surface or deep within Earth. The point on Earth's surface directly above the focus is called the epicenter. During an earthquake, two types of body waves—P waves and S waves—move through Earth's interior. P waves can move through liquids, solids, or gases. S waves can move only through solids. Surface waves occur when P waves and S waves reach the surface. They are responsible for most of the damage caused by an earthquake.

The Great San Francisco Earthquake of 1906 ruptured only for a short time but devastated the city.

EE 104

NOTES

....

....

Teacher Reflection Questions

- Students will soon use seismic waves to locate the epicenter of an earthquake. What do you think they need to learn before they can do this successfully?

- How were you able to identify misconceptions about seismic waves? What might you try next time?

- How were you able to assess students' engagement in the demonstrations? What might you try next time?

NOTES

3.3 Read

How Do Scientists Collect and Evaluate Data from Earthquakes?

◄ *1 class period*

A class period is considered to be one 40 to 50 minute class.

Overview

Students are introduced to magnitude and intensity as measures of an earthquake's severity. They learn that the magnitude of an earthquake depends on the energy released in the earthquake and can be measured with a seismograph, which records the heights of seismic waves. They learn that the intensity of an earthquake depends on the effects of the earthquake and is estimated using observations of the earthquake's effects. They differentiate between these two measures and learn that magnitude is usually expressed by a number on the Richter Scale, while intensity is usually expressed by a number on the Modified Mercalli Intensity Scale.

Targeted Concepts, Skills, and Nature of Science	Performance Expectations
Scientists measure and record earthquake activity using the Richter Scale and the Modified Mercalli Intensity Scale. The Richter Scale is used for measuring the magnitude of an earthquake. The Modified Mercalli Intensity Scale is used to measure the intensity.	Students should discuss how scientists measure earthquakes.
Earthquake activity, volcanic activity, and topography are all evidence that Earth's crust is moving and changing.	Students should demonstrate understanding that scientists used observations of the Great San Francisco Earthquake and of the San Andreas fault to develop theories about how movements within Earth cause earthquakes.
Interactions between Earth's crustal plates can result in mountain building, rift valleys, and geologic activity such as earthquakes and volcanoes. Underwater volcanic activity may form underwater mountains, which can thrust above the ocean's surface to become islands.	Students should recognize that the Great San Francisco Earthquake of 1906 resulted from motion of the rock along the San Andreas fault.

Homework Options

Reflection

- **Science Content:** An earthquake in City A measures 5.5 on the Richter Scale. An earthquake in City B measures 7.5 on the Richter Scale. How much greater was the energy released in the earthquake in City B? (*Students should explain that each increase of 1 on the Richter Scale represents 32 times the energy released. Therefore, an increase of 2 on the Richter Scale represents 32^2, or 1024 times the energy released. It is not important that students calculate the value of 32^2; they only need to understand that an increase of 2 on the Richter Scale means that the energy is 32x32 times greater.*)

Preparation for 3.4

- **Science Process:** What clues do you think could help you find the epicenter of an earthquake? What tools could help you? (*Students will learn how scientists find the epicenter of an earthquake in the next section. This question is meant to engage them in thinking about the problem and how they could use what they know now to solve it.*)

NOTES

3.3 Read

How Do Scientists Collect and Evaluate Data From Earthquakes?

At the time it occurred, the Great San Francisco Earthquake of 1906 was the largest recorded earthquake in history. This earthquake ruptured 477 km (296 mi) of Earth's surface along the San Andreas Fault and was felt from Oregon to just south of Los Angeles, California. The violent shocks broke gas lines and caused electric lines to fall, sparking a catastrophic fire that burned for days. People were awakened by a loud rumbling noise and then a huge blast. Buildings shook, and pieces of buildings crashed to the ground. There was wave after wave of vibrations. The first was the strongest, occurring at 5:13 in the morning and lasting 47 seconds. This was followed by a series of shorter and weaker vibrations at 5:18 AM, 5:20 AM, and 5:25 AM. The vibrations stopped but began again at 8:13 AM.

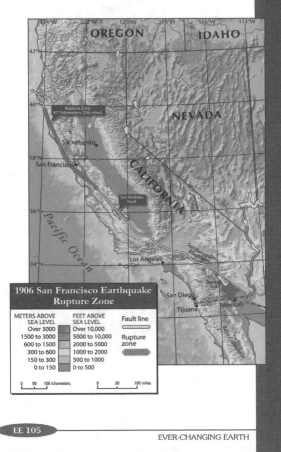

1906 San Francisco Earthquake Rupture Zone

METERS ABOVE SEA LEVEL	FEET ABOVE SEA LEVEL	Fault line
Over 3000	Over 10,000	
1500 to 3000	5000 to 10,000	Rupture zone
600 to 1500	2000 to 5000	
300 to 600	1000 to 2000	
150 to 300	500 to 1000	
0 to 150	0 to 500	

0   50   100 kilometers   0   50   100 miles

EE 105

EVER-CHANGING EARTH

3.3 Read

How Do Scientists Collect and Evaluate Data from Earthquakes?

10 min

The class discusses how seismographs work.

△ Guide

Begin by discussing the effects of the Great San Francisco Earthquake. The earthquake was a catastrophe, breaking gas lines and starting a fire that burned for days. At the time it occurred, it was the largest recorded earthquake.

Ask students how they think scientists record the strength of an earthquake. How do scientists know if one earthquake is stronger than another? Students may suggest that scientists observe the effects of the earthquake, such as damage to buildings. Tell them this is correct and they will soon learn more about this method of measuring an earthquake. Tell students that scientists are also able to directly measure the strength of the seismic waves generated by an earthquake.

*A class period is considered to be one 40 to 50 minute class.

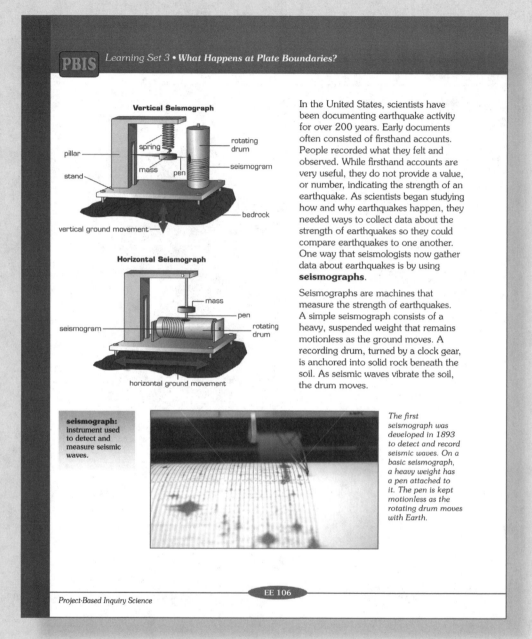

Vertical Seismograph

pillar
spring
rotating drum
mass
pen
seismogram
stand
bedrock
vertical ground movement

Horizontal Seismograph

mass
pen
seismogram
rotating drum
horizontal ground movement

In the United States, scientists have been documenting earthquake activity for over 200 years. Early documents often consisted of firsthand accounts. People recorded what they felt and observed. While firsthand accounts are very useful, they do not provide a value, or number, indicating the strength of an earthquake. As scientists began studying how and why earthquakes happen, they needed ways to collect data about the strength of earthquakes so they could compare earthquakes to one another. One way that seismologists now gather data about earthquakes is by using **seismographs**.

Seismographs are machines that measure the strength of earthquakes. A simple seismograph consists of a heavy, suspended weight that remains motionless as the ground moves. A recording drum, turned by a clock gear, is anchored into solid rock beneath the soil. As seismic waves vibrate the soil, the drum moves.

seismograph: instrument used to detect and measure seismic waves.

The first seismograph was developed in 1893 to detect and record seismic waves. On a basic seismograph, a heavy weight has a pen attached to it. The pen is kept motionless as the rotating drum moves with Earth.

EE 106

Project-Based Inquiry Science

Briefly discuss the history of scientific measurement of earthquakes. Early documentation of earthquakes often consisted of eyewitness accounts. Scientists have only recently developed the ability to measure the strength of earthquakes on a numerical scale. Describe the instrument that scientists developed to record seismic waves, the seismograph. A basic seismograph runs a sheet of paper against the tip of a pen that is attached to a suspended weight. Because they are suspended, the weight and pen stay stationary as seismic waves pass through the ground. The paper, however, shakes with the ground. As a result, the pen traces a graph of the waves on the paper. This graph is called a seismogram. Point out the diagram of a seismograph in the student text.

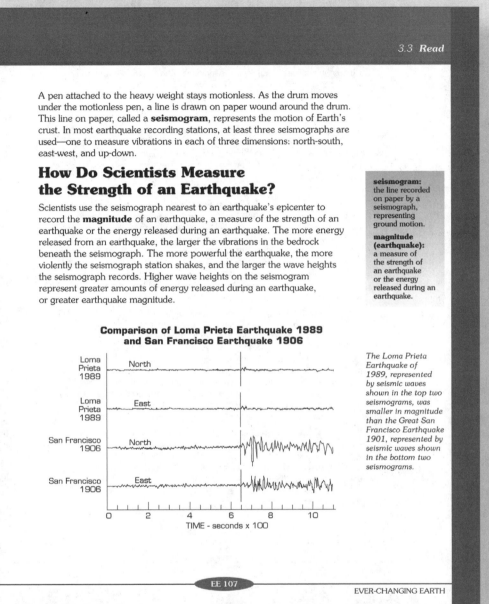

A pen attached to the heavy weight stays motionless. As the drum moves under the motionless pen, a line is drawn on paper wound around the drum. This line on paper, called a **seismogram**, represents the motion of Earth's crust. In most earthquake recording stations, at least three seismographs are used—one to measure vibrations in each of three dimensions: north-south, east-west, and up-down.

How Do Scientists Measure the Strength of an Earthquake?

Scientists use the seismograph nearest to an earthquake's epicenter to record the **magnitude** of an earthquake, a measure of the strength of an earthquake or the energy released during an earthquake. The more energy released from an earthquake, the larger the vibrations in the bedrock beneath the seismograph. The more powerful the earthquake, the more violently the seismograph station shakes, and the larger the wave heights the seismograph records. Higher wave heights on the seismogram represent greater amounts of energy released during an earthquake, or greater earthquake magnitude.

seismogram: the line recorded on paper by a seismograph, representing ground motion.

magnitude (earthquake): a measure of the strength of an earthquake or the energy released during an earthquake.

Comparison of Loma Prieta Earthquake 1989 and San Francisco Earthquake 1906

Loma Prieta 1989	North	
Loma Prieta 1989	East	
San Francisco 1906	North	
San Francisco 1906	East	

TIME - seconds x 100

The Loma Prieta Earthquake of 1989, represented by seismic waves shown in the top two seismograms, was smaller in magnitude than the Great San Francisco Earthquake 1901, represented by seismic waves shown in the bottom two seismograms.

EE 107

EVER-CHANGING EARTH

How Do Scientists Measure the Strength of an Earthquake?

10 min

Students are introduced to the Richter Scale.

△ Guide

Discuss how scientists use seismographs to measure the magnitude of an earthquake. Point out that scientists have seismographs at earthquake recording stations around the world. When an earthquake occurs, they use the seismograph nearest the earthquake to measure its magnitude. The greater the magnitude of the earthquake—that is, the more energy the earthquake releases—the larger the vibrations under the seismograph, and the more violently the seismograph shakes. The more violently the seismograph shakes, the higher the peaks of the waves on the seismogram.

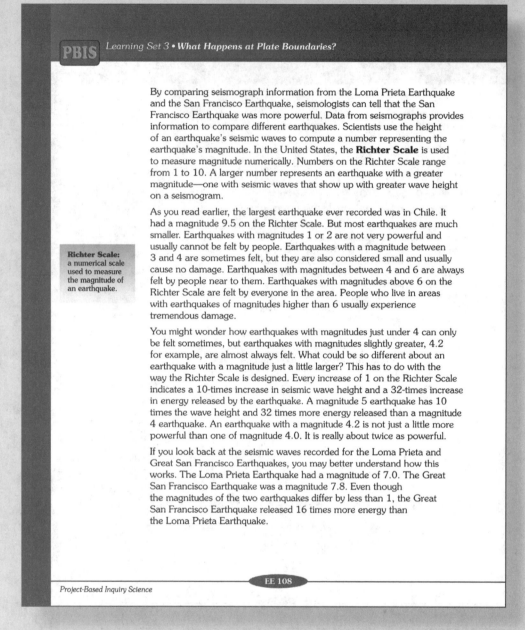

By comparing seismograph information from the Loma Prieta Earthquake and the San Francisco Earthquake, seismologists can tell that the San Francisco Earthquake was more powerful. Data from seismographs provides information to compare different earthquakes. Scientists use the height of an earthquake's seismic waves to compute a number representing the earthquake's magnitude. In the United States, the **Richter Scale** is used to measure magnitude numerically. Numbers on the Richter Scale range from 1 to 10. A larger number represents an earthquake with a greater magnitude—one with seismic waves that show up with greater wave height on a seismogram.

Richter Scale: a numerical scale used to measure the magnitude of an earthquake.

As you read earlier, the largest earthquake ever recorded was in Chile. It had a magnitude 9.5 on the Richter Scale. But most earthquakes are much smaller. Earthquakes with magnitudes 1 or 2 are not very powerful and usually cannot be felt by people. Earthquakes with a magnitude between 3 and 4 are sometimes felt, but they are also considered small and usually cause no damage. Earthquakes with magnitudes between 4 and 6 are always felt by people near to them. Earthquakes with magnitudes above 6 on the Richter Scale are felt by everyone in the area. People who live in areas with earthquakes of magnitudes higher than 6 usually experience tremendous damage.

You might wonder how earthquakes with magnitudes just under 4 can only be felt sometimes, but earthquakes with magnitudes slightly greater, 4.2 for example, are almost always felt. What could be so different about an earthquake with a magnitude just a little larger? This has to do with the way the Richter Scale is designed. Every increase of 1 on the Richter Scale indicates a 10-times increase in seismic wave height and a 32-times increase in energy released by the earthquake. A magnitude 5 earthquake has 10 times the wave height and 32 times more energy released than a magnitude 4 earthquake. An earthquake with a magnitude 4.2 is not just a little more powerful than one of magnitude 4.0. It is really about twice as powerful.

If you look back at the seismic waves recorded for the Loma Prieta and Great San Francisco Earthquakes, you may better understand how this works. The Loma Prieta Earthquake had a magnitude of 7.0. The Great San Francisco Earthquake was a magnitude 7.8. Even though the magnitudes of the two earthquakes differ by less than 1, the Great San Francisco Earthquake released 16 times more energy than the Loma Prieta Earthquake.

Point out the seismograms in the student text from the Loma Prieta Earthquake in 1989 and the Great San Francisco Earthquake of 1906. Ask students which earthquake was stronger. They should be able to tell from the higher peaks in the graph of the San Francisco earthquake that it was stronger.

Tell students that scientists in the United States express the magnitude of an earthquake using the Richter Scale. The Richter Scale ranges from 1 to 10, with higher numbers representing greater magnitudes. Describe how the numbers on the scale correspond to what people experience during the earthquake. The earthquake in Chile that students read about earlier had a magnitude of 9.5 on the Richter Scale, the highest ever recorded. By contrast, people usually cannot feel earthquakes with

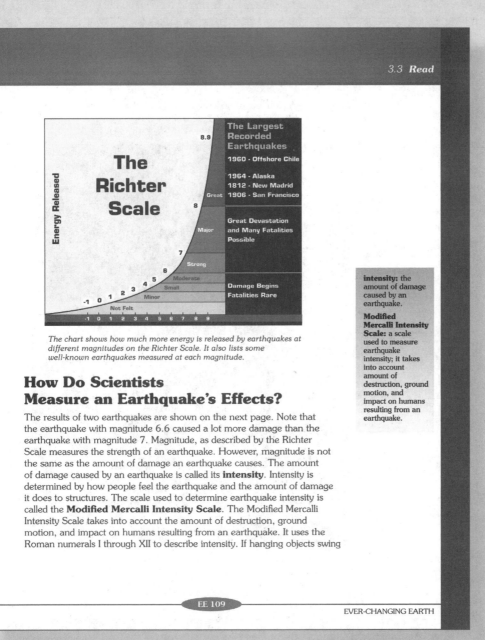

The chart shows how much more energy is released by earthquakes at different magnitudes on the Richter Scale. It also lists some well-known earthquakes measured at each magnitude.

How Do Scientists Measure an Earthquake's Effects?

The results of two earthquakes are shown on the next page. Note that the earthquake with magnitude 6.6 caused a lot more damage than the earthquake with magnitude 7. Magnitude, as described by the Richter Scale measures the strength of an earthquake. However, magnitude is not the same as the amount of damage an earthquake causes. The amount of damage caused by an earthquake is called its **intensity**. Intensity is determined by how people feel the earthquake and the amount of damage it does to structures. The scale used to determine earthquake intensity is called the **Modified Mercalli Intensity Scale**. The Modified Mercalli Intensity Scale takes into account the amount of destruction, ground motion, and impact on humans resulting from an earthquake. It uses the Roman numerals I through XII to describe intensity. If hanging objects swing

intensity: the amount of damage caused by an earthquake.

Modified Mercalli Intensity Scale: a scale used to measure earthquake intensity; it takes into account amount of destruction, ground motion, and impact on humans resulting from an earthquake.

magnitudes around 1 or 2. Earthquakes with magnitudes around 3 or 4 usually do not cause damage, though they may be felt. Earthquakes with magnitudes between 4 and 6 are felt by people nearby, and earthquakes with magnitudes above 6 cause a lot of damage.

Discuss the nonlinear increase in strength along the Richter Scale. Every increase of 1 on the Richter Scale indicates a tenfold increase in seismic wave height. This means that an earthquake with magnitude 5 has 10 times the wave height of an earthquake with magnitude 4. The increase in energy is even greater. An increase of 1 on the Richter scale indicates 32 times the energy. The Richter Scale in the student text illustrates how the strength of earthquakes increases.

How Do Scientists Measure an Earthquake's Effects?

10 min

The class discusses how scientists quantify an earthquake's intensity.

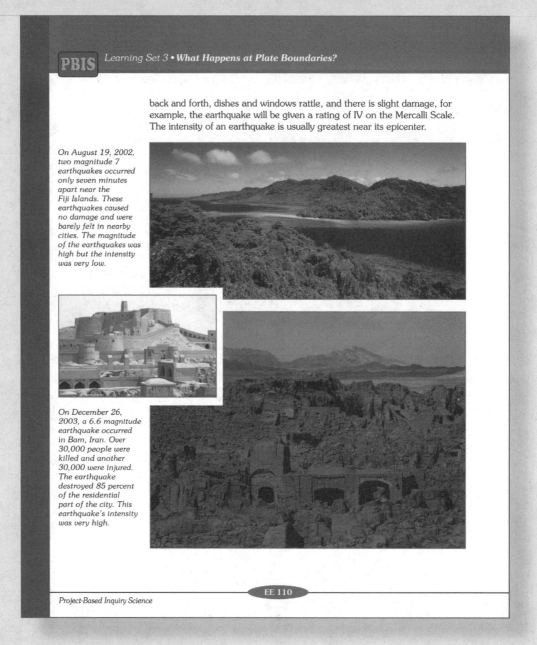

back and forth, dishes and windows rattle, and there is slight damage, for example, the earthquake will be given a rating of IV on the Mercalli Scale. The intensity of an earthquake is usually greatest near its epicenter.

On August 19, 2002, two magnitude 7 earthquakes occurred only seven minutes apart near the Fiji Islands. These earthquakes caused no damage and were barely felt in nearby cities. The magnitude of the earthquakes was high but the intensity was very low.

On December 26, 2003, a 6.6 magnitude earthquake occurred in Bam, Iran. Over 30,000 people were killed and another 30,000 were injured. The earthquake destroyed 85 percent of the residential part of the city. This earthquake's intensity was very high.

Project-Based Inquiry Science

EE 110

△ Guide

Draw students' attention to the photographs in the student text. The first picture shows the Fiji islands, where two magnitude 7 earthquakes occurred in quick succession. The second shows Bam, a city in Iran where a 6.6 magnitude earthquake occurred. The magnitude 7 earthquakes near the Fiji islands caused no damage and were barely felt by people nearby. Emphasize that even though the magnitude 7 earthquakes where much stronger than the magnitude 6.6 earthquake, the effects an earthquake will vary from place to place.

Scientists call the severity of an earthquake's effects the intensity of the earthquake. They use a different scale to measure intensity. In the United States, scientists usually use the Modified Mercalli Intensity Scale. The Modified Mercalli Intensity Scale uses Roman numerals I–XII to describe

Below is the Modified Mercalli Intensity Scale. On the next page is a map showing the intensity of the San Francisco Earthquake of 1906 in different areas near and far from the fault.

Modified Mercalli Scale	
I	Detected only by sensitive instruments
II	Felt by few persons at rest, especially on upper floors; delicately suspended objects may swing
III	Felt noticeably indoors, but not always recognized as an earthquake; standing autos rock slightly, vibration like passing truck
IV	Felt indoors by many, outdoors by few, at night some may awaken; dishes, windows, doors disturbed; motor cars rock noticeably
V	Felt by most people; some breakage of dishes, windows, and plaster; disturbance of tall objects
VI	Felt by all, many frightened and run outdoors; falling plaster and chimneys, damage small
VII	Everybody runs outdoors; damage to buildings varies depending on quality of construction; noticed by drivers of cars.
VIII	Panel walls thrown out of frames; walls, monuments, chimneys fall; sand and mud ejected; drivers of cars disturbed
IX	Buildings shifted off foundations, cracked, thrown out of plumb; ground cracked; underground pipes broken
X	Most masonry and frame structures destroyed; ground cracked; underground pipes broken
XI	Few structures remain standing; bridges destroyed; large cracks in ground; pipes broken; landslides; railroad tracks bent
XII	Damage total: ground moves in waves or ripples, large numbers of rocks move, objects thrown into air

The Modified Mercalli Intensity Scale assigns an intensity value based on firsthand observations of the effects of an earthquake.

earthquake intensity. Point out the Modified Mercalli Scale in the student text.

After you discuss the descriptions in the Modified Mercalli Scale, ask students what factors might make the events described more likely to occur. For instance, an earthquake with intensity X destroys most masonry and frame structures. What factors make this likely to happen? Students should recognize that the magnitude of the earthquake is one factor, but it is also important to understand that the presence of masonry and frame structures in a community is a factor. Another factor is the distance of communities from the epicenter of an earthquake. If a community with poorly constructed masonry buildings is directly over the epicenter of an earthquake, even a relatively moderate magnitude earthquake may reach intensity X.

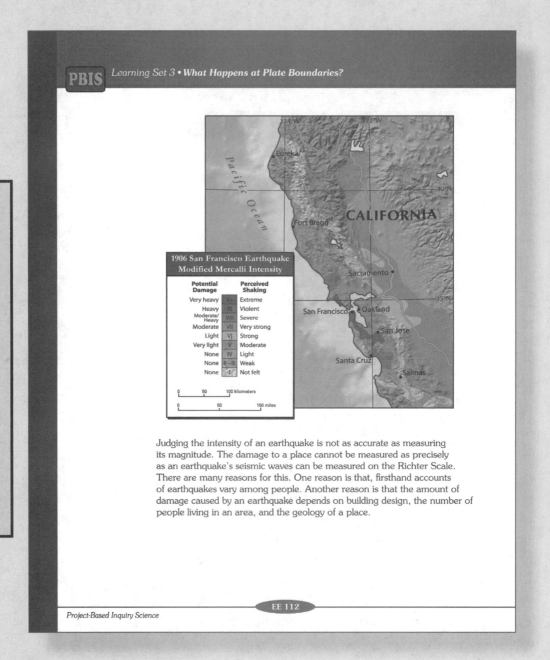

PBIS *Learning Set 3 • What Happens at Plate Boundaries?*

Judging the intensity of an earthquake is not as accurate as measuring its magnitude. The damage to a place cannot be measured as precisely as an earthquake's seismic waves can be measured on the Richter Scale. There are many reasons for this. One reason is that, firsthand accounts of earthquakes vary among people. Another reason is that the amount of damage caused by an earthquake depends on building design, the number of people living in an area, and the geology of a place.

EE 112

Project-Based Inquiry Science

Draw students' attention to the map of California in the student text. Ask students if the intensity of the earthquake is the same in all areas of the map. What is the range of the intensities? They should recognize that the intensity of the earthquake varied. Within California, the intensity varied from about II or III to IX. Emphasize that the earthquake had only one magnitude, the magnitude measured by the seismograph nearest the epicenter, but the effects of the earthquake were different in different areas.

Earthquake Safety

Good preparation is important in an area where earthquakes happen often. There are many things you can do before, during, and after an earthquake to remain safe. Here are a few ways to ensure your safety:

- Before an earthquake, have an emergency plan, including where household members will reunite if they are separated during a disaster.

- Be prepared for any disaster with an emergency preparedness kit that includes bottled water and enough nonperishable food for at least three days, a first-aid kit, flashlights, battery-operated radios, batteries, medications, and a wrench that can be used for shutting off gas and waterlines if necessary.

- If you are indoors during an earthquake, stay there. Get underneath and hold onto a sturdy desk or table. Stay away from outside walls and windows and other things that can fall on you.

- If you are outside, stay in the open. Keep away from buildings, power lines, and anything that can fall on you.

- If you are in a crowded public building with nothing you can use for cover, stay low and cover your head and neck with your hands and arms.

- After the earthquake, listen to the radio for important information and instructions.

Stop and Think

1. Compare the Richter and Modified Mercalli Intensity Scales.

2. What factors affect the intensity of an earthquake?

Earthquake Safety

5 min

The class has a discussion about guidelines for earthquake safety.

△ Guide

Briefly discuss earthquake safety. Ask students if they know of any safety guidelines for earthquakes. The bulleted list in the student text describes safety guidelines to follow during an earthquake. Discuss each of these with the class.

Stop and Think

10 min

Lead a class discussion of the Stop and Think *questions.*

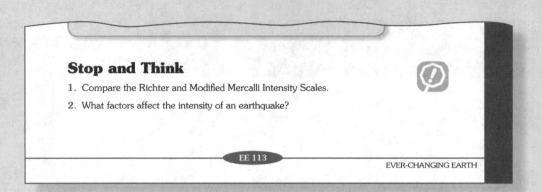

Stop and Think

1. Compare the Richter and Modified Mercalli Intensity Scales.

2. What factors affect the intensity of an earthquake?

EE 113

EVER-CHANGING EARTH

△ Guide and Evaluate

Before discussing the history of earthquake science, lead a class discussion of the *Stop and Think* questions. Ask students what the similarities and differences between the Richter and the Modified Mercalli Intensity Scales are. Students should understand that the Richter Scale measures the magnitude of earthquakes (the height of the seismic waves) and the Modified Mercalli Intensity Scale measures the intensity of earthquakes (the effects of the earthquake). They should also be able to tell you that the Richter Scale runs from 0 to 10, while the Mercalli Intensity Scale runs from I to XII, and that the Modified Mercalli Intensity Scale is less accurate than the Richter Scale.

Ask students what factors affect the intensity of earthquakes. Students may have many ideas about this. They should mention that the kind of structures present in the areas affected by an earthquake and the distance of the structures from the epicenter of the earthquake affect the intensity.

NOTES

PBIS *Learning Set 3 • What Happens at Plate Boundaries?*

Be a Scientist

How Do Scientists Know so Much About Earthquakes and Seismic Activity?

The Great San Francisco Earthquake of 1906 is one of the major disasters in United States history. Yet, out of the rubble and ashes came another historical landmark, the beginning of the age of modern earthquake science. Three days after the earthquake, the governor of California established a group of scientists to record what happened. These scientists established the existence of a fault line and named it the San Andreas Fault. These scientists developed a **theory**. A theory is an explanation of why and how a specific natural phenomenon occurs that is based on the support of considerable evidence and testing. The new theory from this study was called the *elastic rebound theory*. This theory suggested that energy is built up in Earth's crust as rocks along the fault move past each other, 2.5 to 5 cm (1 to 2 in.) per year. The energy is suddenly released when the plates slip back rapidly, lurching 3 to 6 m (10 to 20 ft).

In most earthquakes, people die from building or bridge collapses, not from the earthquake itself. Detailed surveys in the report issued by the scientists revealed that damage from the earthquake was dependent on the design and construction of structures and local geology. Evidence of the strongest shaking was found in areas with soft sedimentary soil. Areas built on solid bedrock experienced less violent shaking. Today, scientists and engineers work to build structures that can withstand earthquakes and save lives.

Scientists working on the team traveled the entire length of the San Andreas Fault, either on foot or horseback. Their detailed maps showing where and how much the fault slipped provided other scientists with the basis for predicting future earthquake activity.

Andrew Lawson from the University of California, Berkeley, headed a group of 25 scientists appointed by the governor to study the San Francisco Earthquake of 1906. The report they published, known as the Lawson Report, remains a highly respected document among geologists today.

theory: an explanation of why and how a specific natural phenomenon occurs. A theory is based on the support of considerable evidence and testing. Hypotheses that have been subjected to considerable testing and scrutiny, and have not been disproved, can evolve into theories. In turn, theories may be redefined as new hypotheses are tested.

Be a Scientist: How Do Scientists Know so Much About Earthquakes and Seismic Activity?

10 min

The class discusses the development of earthquake science.

△ Guide

Discuss the development of modern earthquake science. Much of what scientists know about earthquakes was learned in the days after the Great San Francisco Earthquake of 1906. A group of scientists determined that a fault line, the San Andreas Fault, ran through California. They developed a new theory, the elastic rebound theory, which suggests that energy builds up in Earth's crust as rock along a fault moves. Many of these scientists' findings were of great practical significance. They found that most fatalities in an earthquake are due to structural failures.

What's the Point?

One way seismologists gather data about earthquakes is by using a seismograph. Seismographs are machines that create seismograms, which show the strength of earthquakes. The higher the wave height on the seismogram, the greater the magnitude of the earthquake. Seismologists use the Richter scale to represent how much energy an earthquake has released, or its magnitude. They calculate the magnitude using the height of the seismic waves recorded by the seismograph closest to the earthquake's epicenter. For every increase of 1 on the Richter scale, an earthquake's energy is 32 times greater.

The Modified Mercalli Intensity Scale is used to represent the intensity of an earthquake—the amount of damage it causes. The intensity measurement is determined from firsthand accounts and by how much damage is done to buildings. The Modified Mercalli Intensity Scale depends on observations and not measurements.

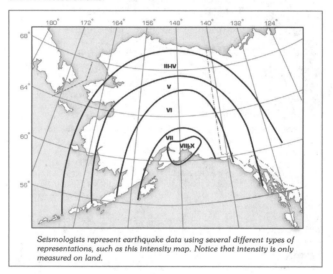

Seismologists represent earthquake data using several different types of representations, such as this intensity map. Notice that intensity is only measured on land.

They also found that structures resting on bedrock experienced less violent shaking than structures on sedimentary soil. This has helped scientists and engineers build structures that can withstand earthquakes and prevent a great number of fatalities.

Emphasize that the team explored the entire length of the San Andreas Fault and mapped it. Their maps helped other scientists predict earthquake activity in the region.

Assessment Options

Targeted Concepts, Skills, and Nature of Science	How do I know if students got it?
Scientists measure and record Earthquake activity using the Richter Scale and the Modified Mercalli Intensity Scale. The Richter Scale is used for measuring the magnitude of an earthquake. The Modified Mercalli Intensity Scale is used to measure the intensity.	**ASK:** Do earthquakes with greater magnitudes have greater intensity? If an earthquake with magnitude 7 on the Richter Scale occurred in a densely populated city with poorly built structures, would you expect the intensity of the earthquake to be high? If an earthquake with magnitude 7 occurred in the middle of an uninhabited desert, would you expect the intensity to be high? **LISTEN:** Students should understand that the magnitude of an earthquake contributes to its intensity. It is likely that an earthquake with a high magnitude will also have a high intensity. Because intensity measures the effects of an earthquake, the intensity of an earthquake in a densely populated city is likely to be high. Since intensity is a subjective measure, the intensity of an earthquake in an uninhabited area with no structures cannot be estimated.
Earthquake activity, volcanic activity, and topography are all evidence that Earth's crust is moving and changing.	**ASK:** You read about the Great San Francisco Earthquake of 1906 and scientists' studies of the San Andreas fault. What evidence was there in your reading that Earth's crust is moving and changing? **LISTEN:** Students should recognize that the earthquake itself and the existence of the San Andreas fault are evidence that Earth's crust is moving and changing. Scientists studying the earthquake and the San Andreas fault concluded that the movement of rock around the fault caused the earthquake.

Targeted Concepts, Skills, and Nature of Science	How do I know if students got it?
Interactions between Earth's crustal plates can result in mountain building, rift valleys, and geologic activity such as earthquakes and volcanoes. Underwater volcanic activity may form underwater mountains, which can thrust above the ocean's surface to become islands.	**ASK:** What causes faults? Why does the rock in faults move? **LISTEN:** Students should recognize that the interaction of plates in the crust causes faults and the motion of the plates causes the rock in the faults to move.

Teacher Reflection Questions

- What difficulties did students have differentiating between the Richter Scale and the Modified Mercalli Intensity Scale? What difficulties did students have differentiating between magnitude and intensity? How can you help them with this?

- How were you able to engage students in learning about seismology? What might you try next time?

- How were you able to assess students' involvement and understanding in this section?

NOTES

_____

_____

_____

_____

3.4 Explore

How Do Scientists Find the Epicenter of an Earthquake?

◀ $1\frac{1}{2}$ *class periods*

A class period is considered to be one 40 to 50 minute class.

Overview

Students use data from three seismograph stations to locate the epicenter of an earthquake. First, they examine a map of the Chilean earthquake of 1960 that shows a seismograph station and a circle representing the possible locations of the epicenter based on its distance from the station. They try to determine the location of the epicenter, engaging in the problem of finding epicenters. Then, they are given P wave and S wave arrival times from a seismograph station in Salt Lake City recorded during a different earthquake. They use a graph relating the differences of arrival times for P waves and S waves, and the distance from an epicenter to find how far the epicenter is from Salt Lake City. They draw a circle on their maps to show possible locations of the epicenter. They recognize that they do not have enough information to determine the location of the epicenter, and they calculate the distance of the epicenter from two other seismograph stations. By examining how the three circles overlap on their map, they can locate the epicenter. They learn that this process, called triangulation, is important to scientists in several fields.

Targeted Concepts, Skills, and Nature of Science	Performance Expectations
Earthquake activity, volcanic activity, and topography are all evidence that Earth's crust is moving and changing.	Students should recognize that the data collected at seismograph stations is evidence that Earth's crust is moving.
Scientists often work together and then share their findings. Sharing findings makes new information available and helps scientists refine their ideas and build on others' ideas. When another person or group's idea is used, credit needs to be given.	Students should work with their groups to find the epicenter and then discuss their ideas with the class.

Targeted Concepts, Skills, and Nature of Science	Performance Expectations
Scientists must keep clear, accurate, and descriptive records of what they do so they can share their work with others and consider what they did, why they did it, and what they want to do next.	Students should record their calculations and the location of the epicenter on their maps.

Materials	
1 per group	Compass (with a sharp pencil) Straight edge *Finding the Epicenter* page (United States map)

Homework Options

Reflection

- **Science Process:** Describe triangulation. What is required to triangulate the location of something? *(Students should know that when they found the location of an epicenter, they used triangulation. To triangulate a location, it is necessary to know the distance of the point from three locations.)*

Preparation for 3.5

- **Science Content:** Why do you think it is important to locate the epicenters of earthquakes? How can this help you understand how the interaction of plates causes geologic activity? *(Students should recognize that identifying the epicenters of earthquakes can help them find plate boundaries. Identifying plate boundaries can help find what kinds of geologic activity happen at plate boundaries.)*

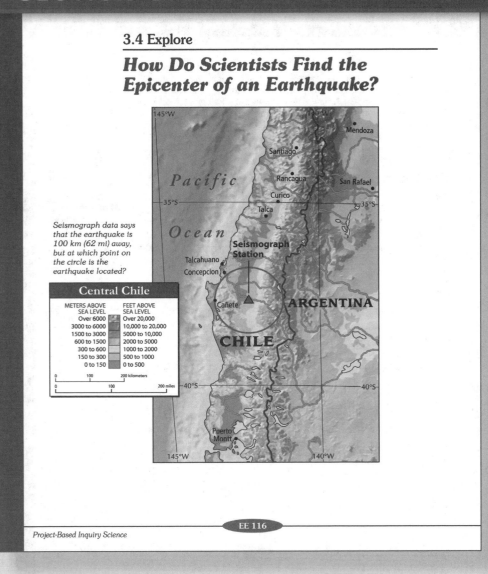

3.4 Explore

How Do Scientists Find the Epicenter of an Earthquake?

Seismograph data says that the earthquake is 100 km (62 mi) away, but at which point on the circle is the earthquake located?

Central Chile

METERS ABOVE SEA LEVEL		FEET ABOVE SEA LEVEL
Over 6000		Over 20,000
3000 to 6000		10,000 to 20,000
1500 to 3000		5000 to 10,000
600 to 1500		2000 to 5000
300 to 600		1000 to 2000
150 to 300		500 to 1000
0 to 150		0 to 500

EE 116

Project-Based Inquiry Science

3.4 Explore

How Do Scientists Find the Epicenter of an Earthquake?

5 min

Students are introduced to the problem: How do scientists find the epicenter of an earthquake?

⃝ Engage

Remind students that during an earthquake, energy spreads out from the focus in seismic waves. Point out that the average observer will not be able to tell where an earthquake's focus and epicenter are. The epicenter is the point on the surface directly over the focus of the earthquake and there is nothing to distinguish it from other areas in an earthquake. Ask students how they think scientists identify an earthquake's epicenter.

Tell students that when an earthquake occurs, scientists use data from several seismograph locations to find the epicenter and they will now determine how scientists do this.

*A class period is considered to be one 40 to 50 minute class.

Conference

5 min

Groups discuss the location of the epicenter of the Chilean earthquake using a map.

When an earthquake occurs, the seismic waves move out from its focus in all directions. Finding the exact location of the epicenter is very important, both to study the earthquake and to know what might happen next. To find the epicenter, scientists must have data from several seismograph locations. Seismologists have made it easy to identify the epicenters of earthquakes by placing seismographs all over the world and recording their data in files that scientists around the world can examine. After an earthquake occurs, seismologists look at the data files to determine which seismic data they need for their calculations.

Conference

The map shows the Chilean coast where the largest earthquake ever recorded hit in 1960. A seismic station near the coast has received the P and S waves, and the data has been recorded on the seismogram. Using the map, determine where the epicenter of the earthquake might be.

Discuss in your group where you each think the epicenter of the earthquake is. Make sure that each member of your group describes in detail why they have located the epicenter in that place.

Reflect

1. What disagreements did you have in your group about where the epicenter is?

2. Did you have enough data to make a good judgment about the epicenter?

3. How might you get more data to make a more accurate judgment?

There may have been disagreements in your group about where the epicenter of the earthquake was. It is impossible to know where an earthquake's epicenter is by looking at the P waves and S waves at only one station. One set of data tells you only how far away an earthquake is from the station, but it cannot tell you the direction from which the waves came. The epicenter could be located at any point in any direction that is the right distance from the seismograph. You need more information to pinpoint the location of the epicenter.

Materials
- compass with a sharp pencil
- United States map
- straight edge

EE 117

EVER-CHANGING EARTH

△ Guide

Draw students' attention to the map of Chile in the student text. Tell students that the map shows the area on the Chilean coast where the 1960 earthquake hit. Explain that the map shows a seismic station, and that scientists at the station determined that the epicenter of the earthquake was 100 km away. A circle around the seismic station shows locations that are 100 km away from the station.

Have students discuss where they think the epicenter was with their group. Emphasize that students should give reasons why they chose the location they did.

As groups discuss where they think the epicenter was, monitor their progress. Note what they are discussing. Students should find that it is difficult to resolve disagreements about the location of the epicenter. Note any groups that have reached agreement about the location of the epicenter. They should discuss their conclusions with the class as part of the *Reflect* discussion.

△ Guide

When students have had several minutes to discuss where they think the epicenter of the 1960 earthquake was, have them work with their groups to answer the *Reflect* questions. Tell them they should be prepared to share their answers with the class.

When students have had a few minutes to discuss the *Reflect* questions, ask the class if any groups were able to determine where the epicenter was. Ask the class if they agree with these groups' conclusions. Do these groups have enough data to support their conclusions?

Ask the class if they have enough data to judge where the epicenter is. Students should begin to see that they cannot make any conclusions about the location of the epicenter with the data they have.

Finally, ask students how they think they might get more data to make a more accurate judgment. Emphasize that there is no way to tell what direction seismic waves are coming from.

Let students know that they will now use data from several seismograph stations to determine the epicenter of an earthquake.

Reflect

10 min

Groups discuss the Reflect *questions and lead a class discussion.*

META NOTES

In this *Reflect* discussion, students should discover that they have enough information to know that the epicenter was on the circle drawn on the map, but that they do not have enough information to determine where on the circle the epicenter was. Once students begin to see this, you can reinforce their discovery by telling them that one station cannot give them enough data to locate the epicenter.

NOTES

....

....

....

....

Procedure

5 min

Students are introduced to the activity.

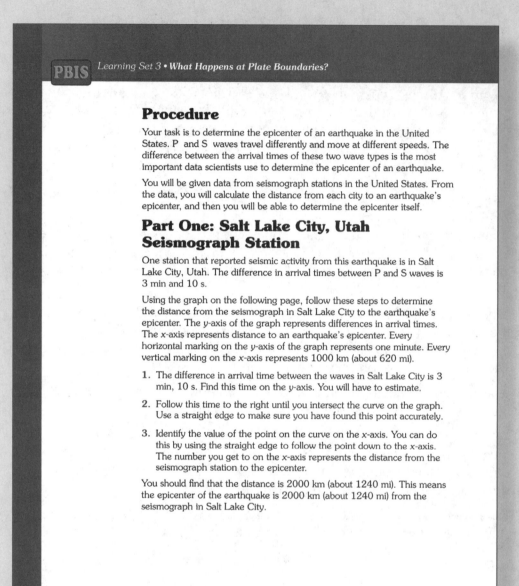

Procedure

Your task is to determine the epicenter of an earthquake in the United States. P and S waves travel differently and move at different speeds. The difference between the arrival times of these two wave types is the most important data scientists use to determine the epicenter of an earthquake.

You will be given data from seismograph stations in the United States. From the data, you will calculate the distance from each city to an earthquake's epicenter, and then you will be able to determine the epicenter itself.

Part One: Salt Lake City, Utah Seismograph Station

One station that reported seismic activity from this earthquake is in Salt Lake City, Utah. The difference in arrival times between P and S waves is 3 min and 10 s.

Using the graph on the following page, follow these steps to determine the distance from the seismograph in Salt Lake City to the earthquake's epicenter. The y-axis of the graph represents differences in arrival times. The x-axis represents distance to an earthquake's epicenter. Every horizontal marking on the y-axis of the graph represents one minute. Every vertical marking on the x-axis represents 1000 km (about 620 mi).

1. The difference in arrival time between the waves in Salt Lake City is 3 min, 10 s. Find this time on the y-axis. You will have to estimate.

2. Follow this time to the right until you intersect the curve on the graph. Use a straight edge to make sure you have found this point accurately.

3. Identify the value of the point on the curve on the x-axis. You can do this by using the straight edge to follow the point down to the x-axis. The number you get to on the x-axis represents the distance from the seismograph station to the epicenter.

You should find that the distance is 2000 km (about 1240 mi). This means the epicenter of the earthquake is 2000 km (about 1240 mi) from the seismograph in Salt Lake City.

△ Guide

Tell students that they will be given data from several seismograph stations. Using the difference in arrival times between P and S waves, they will calculate the distance of the epicenter from each seismograph station. Then they will be able to use this information to determine the location of the epicenter.

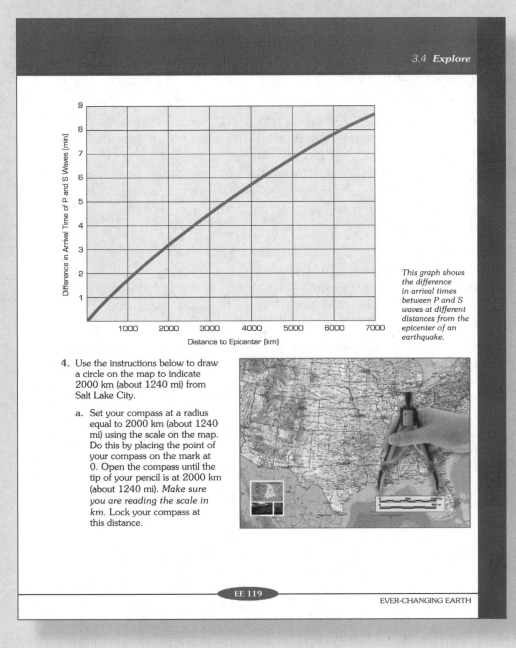

3.4 Explore

Difference in Arrival Time of P and S Waves (min) vs Distance to Epicenter (km)

This graph shows the difference in arrival times between P and S waves at different distances from the epicenter of an earthquake.

4. Use the instructions below to draw a circle on the map to indicate 2000 km (about 1240 mi) from Salt Lake City.

   a. Set your compass at a radius equal to 2000 km (about 1240 mi) using the scale on the map. Do this by placing the point of your compass on the mark at 0. Open the compass until the tip of your pencil is at 2000 km (about 1240 mi). *Make sure you are reading the scale in km.* Lock your compass at this distance.

EE 119

EVER-CHANGING EARTH

Part One: Salt Lake City, Utah Seismograph Station

10 min

Students calculate the distance of the epicenter from the Salt Lake City seismograph station and draw circles on their maps to show possible locations of the epicenter.

△ Guide

Distribute the *Finding the Epicenter* pages to groups and discuss how students will find the distance of the epicenter from the Salt Lake City seismograph station. Begin this discussion by pointing out the graph in the student text. Remind students that P waves travel faster than S waves so that the farther away you are from the epicenter, the greater the difference between the time the first P waves hit and the time the first S waves hit. A seismograph station by the epicenter will record almost the same arrival times for P waves and S waves. A seismograph station far from the epicenter will record later arrival times for S waves than for P waves.

Tell students that the graph in the student text shows how the difference between the arrival time of P and S waves increases as the distance from the epicenter increases. As they move out to the right on the graph, the distance from the epicenter increases and the difference between the arrival times of P and S waves increases. Ask students what the difference between the arrival times of P waves and S waves is at 1000 km (*about 1.75 min*). Ask students what the difference between the arrival times of P and S waves is at 5000 km (*about 6.8 min*).

Tell students they will find the difference of arrival times at the Salt Lake City seismograph station (*3 min and 10 s*) on the graph. They will then use a ruler and the graph to find the distance of the epicenter from the seismograph station. The student text gives detailed instructions for finding this distance. Go over these as necessary.

After students have determined the distance, they will use a compass to draw a circle to scale around Salt Lake City on their *Finding the Epicenter* pages with a radius that represents the distance that they found. They can get the correct radius for their compass by putting the point of the compass on the 0 end of the map's scale and opening the compass until the pencil tip is at the distance the found (which should be 2000 km).

Have students work with their groups to determine the distance of the epicenter from the Salt Lake City station.

NOTES

....

....

....

....

....

....

b. Draw a circle on your map by placing the point of your compass on Salt Lake City and rotating the compass to draw a complete circle. Draw your circle on the map very carefully.

Finding the Epicenter

Stop and Think

1. Where is the epicenter of the earthquake? The distance to the epicenter from Salt Lake City is 2000 km (about 1240 mi). How many different places are within 2000 km (about 1240 mi) of Salt Lake City?

2. What do you think should be the next step to determine the epicenter of this earthquake?

Part Two: Houston, Texas Seismograph Station

1. Another seismograph station is in Houston, Texas. The difference in arrival time between the P and S waves in Houston was 2 min, 0 s.

△ Guide and Evaluate

As groups work on finding the distance from the epicenter, monitor their progress and help them with any difficulties they may be having. Students may need help using the graph. They may also need help finding the correct radius for their compass using the scale of the map.

Check to make sure that groups got the correct answer (*2000 km*) and that they drew a circle with the correct radius on their map.

Stop and Think

5 min

Students discuss the Stop and Think questions.

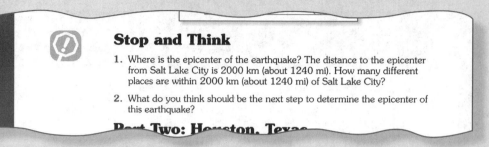

Stop and Think

1. Where is the epicenter of the earthquake? The distance to the epicenter from Salt Lake City is 2000 km (about 1240 mi). How many different places are within 2000 km (about 1240 mi) of Salt Lake City?

2. What do you think should be the next step to determine the epicenter of this earthquake?

Part Two: Houston, Texas

△ Guide and Assess

Lead a class discussion of the *Stop and Think* questions. Ask students if they can say where the epicenter of the earthquake is. They know the distance of the epicenter from Salt Lake City. How many points can they locate with that distance from Salt Lake City? They should recognize that any point on the circle they drew could be the epicenter. Ask them what the next step to determining the epicenter is. At this point, students will begin to see that having information from more than one station could help them locate the epicenter, although it is not necessary. The important thing is that students are engaged in the problem.

Part Two: Houston, Texas Seismograph Station

5 min

Students calculate the distance of the epicenter from the Houston seismograph station and draw circles on their maps showing possible locations of the epicenter.

what do you think sho... ...ne next step to dete... ...picenter of this earthquake?

Part Two: Houston, Texas Seismograph Station

1. Another seismograph station is in Houston, Texas. The difference in arrival time between the P and S waves in Houston was 2 min, 0 s.

⬡ Get Going

Have students repeat the procedure for the seismograph station in Houston. Emphasize that for Salt Lake City, the difference in arrival times was 3 min and 10 s; but for Houston it is only 2 min and 0 s.

△ Guide and Evaluate

As groups find the distance of the epicenter from the Houston station, monitor their progress and help them with any difficulties. Make sure that the circles they draw on their *Finding the Epicenter* page overlap with the first circles they drew, and that they have the correct radius. There should be two possible locations for the epicenter after they draw the second circle.

Repeat the steps from Part One, but use the differences in arrival times for the seismograph station in Houston.

Stop and Think

1. Now that you have drawn the circle to show the distance between the epicenter and Houston, what do you now know about where the epicenter was?

2. Do you think you are closer to knowing the location of the epicenter? Why?

3. What do you still need to do?

Part Three: Savannah, Georgia Seismograph Station

1. Savannah, Georgia, also reported seismic activity. They reported a difference in arrival times of 1 min, 50 s. Using the same procedure, determine how far the epicenter is from Savannah. Remember to draw the circle carefully so the data are represented accurately on the map.

Reflect

1. Where did you determine the epicenter of the earthquake to be?

2. Why were three seismic stations required for you to accurately locate the earthquake's epicenter?

3. Describe why the epicenter might not always appear as a single point.

4. If someone suggested that you needed to plot the information for one more station, what would be your response?

5. When would seismographs in two different cities record the same difference in arrival times of P waves and S waves?

6. When would a seismograph show no difference in the arrival times of P waves and S waves?

7. How can seismograph information help you determine where plate boundaries are?

Stop and Think

5 min

The students are led in a class discussion of the Stop and Think *questions.*

△ Guide and Assess

Lead a class discussion of the *Stop and Think* questions. Ask students if they know where the epicenter was. They should not have enough information to be certain where the epicenter was. Ask them if they have gotten closer to being able to find the epicenter. They should recognize that before they drew the second circle, any point on their first circle was a possible answer. Now they have ruled out all but two points on the circle.

Finally, ask students what they still need to do. At this point, students should have some sense that knowing the distance of the epicenter from a third seismograph station would further limit the possibilities—solving the problem.

Part Three: Savannah, Georgia Seismograph Station

5 min

Students calculate the distance of the epicenter from the Savannah seismograph station and draw circles on their maps showing possible locations of the epicenter.

3. What do you still need to do?

Part Three: Savannah, Georgia Seismograph Station

1. Savannah, Georgia, also reported seismic activity. They reported a difference in arrival times of 1 min, 50 s. Using the same procedure, determine how far the epicenter is from Savannah. Remember to draw the circle carefully so the data are represented accurately on the map.

Reflect

⬡ Get Going

Have students repeat the procedure for the station in Savannah. Emphasize that for this station the difference in arrival times is 1 min and 50 s.

△ Guide and Evaluate

As groups find the distance of the epicenter from the Savannah station, monitor their progress and help them with any difficulties. Make sure that their third circles overlap with their earlier circles. All three circles should meet in or near Lake Superior.

Reflect

15 min

Groups answer the Reflect questions, and have a class discussion.

determin...   ...he epicenter is from ...   ...member to d... the circle carefully so the data are represented accurately on the map.

Reflect

1. Where did you determine the epicenter of the earthquake to be?

2. Why were three seismic stations required for you to accurately locate the earthquake's epicenter?

3. Describe why the epicenter might not always appear as a single point.

4. If someone suggested that you needed to plot the information for one more station, what would be your response?

5. When would seismographs in two different cities record the same difference in arrival times of P waves and S waves?

6. When would a seismograph show no difference in the arrival times of P waves and S waves?

7. How can seismograph information help you determine where plate boundaries are?

△ Guide

Have students answer the *Reflect* questions with their groups. Emphasize that they should be prepared to share their answers with the class.

Project-Based Inquiry Science

☐ Assess

As groups discuss the *Reflect* questions, ask them what ideas they discussed. Encourage group discussion by asking other members of a group if they agree with the ideas suggested. What are some other ideas? Make sure that students support their ideas with reasons.

△ Guide and Evaluate

Lead a class discussion of groups' answers to the *Reflect* questions. Listen for the following in students' responses:

1. Students should have found that the epicenter of the earthquake was under Lake Superior.

2. However students answer this question, it is important for them to understand that with one station, scientists can only determine that the epicenter lies in the area of a circle. With two stations, scientists can only determine that the epicenter lies on one of two intersections of two circles. With three stations, scientists can determine a more precise location for the epicenter.

3. Students should recognize that there is always some amount of error in measurements. The radius of the circles used in triangulation will never be exactly the distance to the epicenter, but will be close. If the circles are a little too large or a little too small, there will be an area where the circles overlap or where they do not quite meet.

   Students may also recognize that the focus of an earthquake may be some depth below the epicenter, in which case the source of the waves—the focus—may be a little farther from the seismograph stations than the epicenter. If the focus is farther from the seismograph stations than the epicenter, then the radius of each circle used to triangulate the epicenter will extend past the epicenter, so that the circles overlap.

4. Since students have already discussed that they are able to identify a more precise location with three stations, they should realize that a fourth station might confirm the location, but will not provide any new information.

5. Students should understand that two seismographs in two different cities could record the same difference in arrival times of P and S waves when both cities were the same distance from the epicenter.

6. Students should explain that a seismograph would show no difference in arrival times of P and S waves when the seismograph was located on the epicenter. Because the epicenter is close to the focus of the earthquake, the P and S waves often reach it at about the same time. But because the P waves move faster, they will reach any location farther from the focus earlier than the S waves.

7. This question is meant to help students connect what they have just learned to their investigation of what happens at plate boundaries. Students should think about how seismograph information can help them triangulate the location of an earthquake's epicenter. This can help them identify places where Earth's plates are interacting. Knowing where Earth's plates interact can help students determine where plate boundaries are.

NOTES

....

....

....

....

....

....

....

....

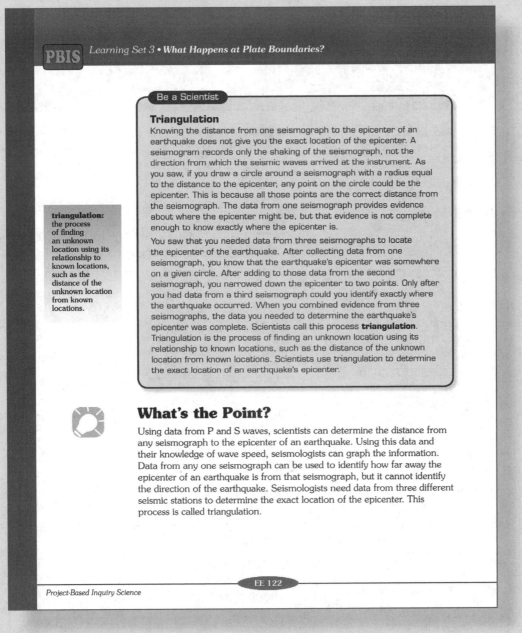

Be a Scientist

Triangulation

Knowing the distance from one seismograph to the epicenter of an earthquake does not give you the exact location of the epicenter. A seismogram records only the shaking of the seismograph, not the direction from which the seismic waves arrived at the instrument. As you saw, if you draw a circle around a seismograph with a radius equal to the distance to the epicenter, any point on the circle could be the epicenter. This is because all those points are the correct distance from the seismograph. The data from one seismograph provides evidence about where the epicenter might be, but that evidence is not complete enough to know exactly where the epicenter is.

You saw that you needed data from three seismographs to locate the epicenter of the earthquake. After collecting data from one seismograph, you know that the earthquake's epicenter was somewhere on a given circle. After adding to those data from the second seismograph, you narrowed down the epicenter to two points. Only after you had data from a third seismograph could you identify exactly where the earthquake occurred. When you combined evidence from three seismographs, the data you needed to determine the earthquake's epicenter was complete. Scientists call this process **triangulation**. Triangulation is the process of finding an unknown location using its relationship to known locations, such as the distance of the unknown location from known locations. Scientists use triangulation to determine the exact location of an earthquake's epicenter.

triangulation: the process of finding an unknown location using its relationship to known locations, such as the distance of the unknown location from known locations.

What's the Point?

Using data from P and S waves, scientists can determine the distance from any seismograph to the epicenter of an earthquake. Using this data and their knowledge of wave speed, seismologists can graph the information. Data from any one seismograph can be used to identify how far away the epicenter of an earthquake is from that seismograph, but it cannot identify the direction of the earthquake. Seismologists need data from three different seismic stations to determine the exact location of the epicenter. This process is called triangulation.

Be a Scientist: Triangulation

5 min *

The class learns about and discusses triangulation.

* Optional, if times allows

⚠ Guide

Briefly reinforce what students learned from the procedure by discussing how each seismograph station narrowed down the possible locations of the epicenter, but three were required to determine exactly where the epicenter was. Tell students that scientists call this triangulation. Discuss with the class that to triangulate means to make a measurement using three data points.

Assessment Options

Targeted Concepts, Skills, and Nature of Science	How do I know if students got it?
Earthquake activity, volcanic activity, and topography are all evidence that Earth's crust is moving and changing.	**ASK:** How does data collected at the seismograph stations support the conclusion that Earth's plates are moving? **LISTEN:** Students should recognize that seimograph stations provide earthquake data, showing evidence of interaction between Earth's plates.
Scientists often work together and then share their findings. Sharing findings makes new information available and helps scientists refine their ideas and build on others' ideas. When another person or group's idea is used, credit needs to be given.	**ASK:** What ideas did you get from class discussions? How did the discussions help you? **LISTEN:** Students should have discovered that groups could not locate the epicenter without data from three seismograph stations. They may also have got ideas about triangulation from their classmates.
Scientists must keep clear, accurate, and descriptive records of what they do so they can share their work with others and consider what they did, why they did it, and what they want to do next.	**ASK:** Why was it necessary to keep records of the distances of the epicenter from the seismograph stations? **LISTEN:** Students should recognize that they needed to use their calculations for all three of the seismograph stations to find the location of the epicenter.

NOTES

....

....

Teacher Reflection Questions

- What part of learning to triangulate the epicenter of an earthquake presented the greatest challenge for students? How can you help students master the concepts involved in calculating the distance of the epicenter and triangulating the location of the epicenter?

- How were you able to guide students to discover the concepts they needed while ensuring that they were active in making those discoveries? What might you try next time?

- How did students use discussion with their group members to solve problems in this section? What can you do to encourage this collaboration?

NOTES

_____

_____

_____

_____

_____

_____

_____

_____

_____

_____

NOTES

3.5 Explore

What Can Earthquake Data Tell You About the Location of Plate Boundaries?

◄ *2 class periods*

A class period is considered to be one 40 to 50 minute class.

Overview

Students use current data from the United States Geological Survey Web site to investigate recent earthquakes. They analyze the data to find the most recent earthquake, the number of earthquakes globally and locally in the past week, and the earthquakes with the greatest and smallest magnitudes. Then they collect and analyze data from the Web site on recent earthquakes in their regions. They begin to identify patterns in the locations of earthquakes. Working with the class, they find earthquakes globally from the past week and look for patterns. Based on this, they begin to infer the locations of plate boundaries. Once the class has discussed their confidence in their predictions about plate boundaries and what more they want to learn, they update their *Region Project Board* and the class *Project Board*. They record their ideas about plate boundaries in their regions and around the world and what they think they should learn to make their predictions more accurate.

Targeted Concepts, Skills, and Nature of Science	Performance Expectations
Earthquake activity, volcanic activity, and topography are all evidence that Earth's crust is moving and changing.	Students should gather data on earthquake activity and begin to infer where plates meet in Earth's crust.
Scientists often work together and then share their findings. Sharing findings makes new information available and helps scientists refine their ideas and build on others' ideas. When another person's or group's idea is used, credit needs to be given.	Students should work with their partners to gather and analyze data on earthquakes in their regions and globally. Then they should share their ideas and data with the class.

Targeted Concepts, Skills, and Nature of Science	Performance Expectations
Scientists must keep clear, accurate, and descriptive records of what they do so they can share their work with others and consider what they did, why they did it, and what they want to do next.	Students record earthquake data on their *Three-page Map* and on the *Big World Map*.
Scientists use models and tools, such as Geographic Information Systems, and a variety of maps to develop claims and explanations from evidence in the data.	Students should use tables and maps on the United States Geological Survey Web site to infer where plates in Earth's crust meet.
Interactions between Earth's crustal plates can result in mountain building, rift valleys, and geologic activity such as earthquakes and volcanoes. Underwater volcanic activity may form underwater mountains, which can thrust above the ocean's surface to become islands.	Students should recognize that the recent earthquakes recorded on the United States Geological Survey Web site are evidence of interaction between plates in Earth's crust.
Graphs and tables are an effective way to analyze and communicate results of scientific investigation.	Students should analyze data on recent earthquakes, using tables of earthquake data.
Scientists make claims (conclusions) based on evidence obtained (trends in data) from reliable investigations.	Students should identify where they think plate boundaries are based on earthquake data.

Materials

1 per student	*Three-page Map*
1 per class	*Big World Map*
1 per group	Computer with Internet access
1 per class (optional)	Computer with Internet access Projector Projection screen

Materials	
1 set per group	Crayons or colored pencils
1 per student	Blue marker

Activity Setup and Preparation

In this section, students will be investigating recent earthquakes using the United States Geological Survey Web site. They will need computers with Internet access. Verify that the site is accessible before class. Since the structure and addresses of Web sites sometimes change, you should take the time to explore the USGS site and to locate the information that students will need before class. You can find the current URL by entering *USGS earthquakes* in an Internet search engine.

Consider setting up a computer with a projector, projection screen, and Internet access so that you can show the class how to navigate the USGS Web site. It is not necessary, but it may save class time.

Homework Options

Reflection

- **Science Content:** Which regions of the world experienced earthquakes with the greatest magnitude recently? Which regions of the world experienced the greatest number of earthquakes recently? *(Students should look at a map of the world with earthquake data on the USGS Web site. Typically, high-magnitude earthquakes are clustered around the coastal regions of Asia, from the South Pacific and Indonesia to the Sea of Japan, and in Central America and western South America. There are also typically a great number of earthquakes clustered around the Bering Straight and California.)*

- **Science Content and Process:** How did your plate boundary predictions change since the start of this *Learning Set?* What did you base those changes on? *(Students should describe how their predictions changed with new data.)*

Preparation for 3.6

- **Science Content and Process:** How much more earthquake data do you think you would need to be sure of your plate boundary predictions? *(The purpose of this question is to get students thinking about the data they have and what further data they need. Students will access data in* My World *to revise their plate boundary predictions in the next section.)*

NOTES

....

....

....

....

....

....

....

....

....

....

....

....

SECTION 3.5 IMPLEMENTATION

3.5 Explore

What Can Earthquake Data Tell You About the Location of Plate Boundaries?

Seismologists are constantly recording earthquake data from around the world. They use seismograph information to determine the epicenter and magnitude of each earthquake.

Analyzing earthquake data can help seismologists determine how often and where earthquakes occur. The information can also tell scientists a lot about what is happening in Earth's crust. In this section, you will analyze some data to identify where earthquakes occurred in the past week. Along with your class, you will then plot that information and see what you can find out about plate boundaries.

Although the 1994 California earthquake is known as the Northridge earthquake, seismologists later determined that the epicenter was actually located in Reseda, California, and not in the community of Northridge.

EE 123

EVER-CHANGING EARTH

3.5 Explore

What Can Earthquake Data Tell You About the Location of Plate Boundaries?

5 min

Students are introduced to the activity.

○ Engage

Remind students that they were able to locate the epicenters of earthquakes using data from seismograph stations. This is important because identifying the epicenters of earthquakes can help scientists recognize global patterns of earthquake activity. Ask students how they can learn more about global earthquake patterns. What would they need to know in order to identify plate boundaries around the world?

*A class period is considered to be one 40 to 50 minute class.

Tell students they will now analyze data to identify where earthquakes have occurred in the past week. They will plot the data to see if the data tells them anything about plate boundaries.

TEACHER TALK

"You were able to locate the epicenter of an earthquake using data from seismograph stations the way scientists do. This is important, because identifying the epicenters of earthquakes allows scientists to learn about global earthquake patterns. To help you identify patterns in earthquake activity, what more do you think you need to learn?

In this section, you are going to identify where earthquakes occurred in the past week using data that scientists have gathered from seismograph stations. Then you will plot the data and see if it tells you anything about plate boundaries."

NOTES

What Data Is Recorded About Earthquakes?

The United States Geological Survey (USGS) collects earthquake data from around the world. This data is included on their Web site, organized on maps and in lists. In this first exploration of earthquake data, you will work with your partner to identify the locations of recent earthquakes. You will also look at the data geologists use to describe them. To find this information, navigate the Web site and answer the questions below.

1. Where in the world do most earthquakes occur?

2. Where in the world was the most recently recorded earthquake? Record the magnitude, intensity, and depth of the earthquake.

3. When and where in the United States was the last recorded earthquake? Record the magnitude, intensity, and depth of that earthquake.

4. How many earthquakes were recorded worldwide in the past week? What is the range of the magnitudes and depths of these earthquakes?

Materials
- *Three-page Map*
- *Big World Map*
- **purple marker**

5. Find and record the magnitude, intensity, and depth of the most recent earthquake closest to where you live.

6. How many earthquakes were recorded in your home state this week? What was the largest magnitude earthquake? What was the smallest magnitude earthquake? What was the depth of these earthquakes?

(Students in California can skip question 7.)

7. How many earthquakes have been recorded in California this week? What was the largest magnitude earthquake? What was the smallest magnitude earthquake? Record the depth of the deepest earthquake.

Communicate

Share Your Ideas

Share your answers to the questions with the class. Discuss the questions and make sure everyone understands how to find information on the Web site. You will need to be able to navigate the Web site easily to find data about your region.

What Data Is Recorded About Earthquakes?

10 min

Students gather data from the United States Geological Survey Web site.

META NOTES

The research in this activity can be largely self-directed. If you have time for students to explore the Web site and to find the information they need independently, simply allow them to use any information they can find on the site to answer these questions.

△ Guide

Tell students they will work with computers to investigate recent earthquakes. Have students start a Web browser on their computers and navigate to the United States Geological Survey (USGS). If necessary, write the URL for USGS in a place where students can see it. If you have a computer with a projector, you can guide students by projecting your browser on a screen while you navigate the Web site.

Once students have found the USGS site, go over the questions in the student text. Emphasize that students may need to look at several different sets of data and maps on the site to answer these questions. The first question, for instance, requires them to look at data from around the world. The sixth question, by contrast, requires them to look at data for the United States, and their home state especially. Emphasize that pairs should keep track of how they got the information they used to answer the questions. Let them know they will share their answers and how they found them shortly.

△ Guide and Assess

As students research recent earthquake activity, monitor their progress and help them as needed. Note any differences in the ways students analyze the data. It will be important for students to discuss these.

Students may need help finding the data needed to answer the questions. You can help them individually or, if you have a computer with a projector, you can show the class how to navigate the site.

There are a number of maps and lists of data that students can use to tell where most of the earthquakes in the world occur. A map of earthquakes with magnitude 4.5 and higher around the world can give students a good idea of where most earthquakes occur. The earthquakes in this map should be clustered around East Asia, the South Pacific, and the west coasts of North and South America.

One way to determine where the most recent earthquake occurred is to look at lists of earthquakes in specific areas from the past week. The USGS Web site has regional lists that include small, medium, and large earthquakes.

The USGS Web site also lists earthquakes in the United States with magnitudes of 1 or greater. Students can use this list to find the most recent earthquake in the United States.

Communicate:
Share
Your Ideas

15 min

Students discuss their answers after exploring USGS data.

Communicate
Share Your Ideas

Share your answers to the questions with the class. Discuss the questions and make sure everyone understands how to find information on the Web site. You will need to be able to navigate the Web site easily to find data about your region.

◯ Get Going

When students have finished answering the questions in the student text, have them share their answers with the class. Emphasize that they should tell the class how they got their answers. The rest of the class should be able to find the information they used on the Web site. If any students have analyzed the data in different ways, make sure this is discussed with the class.

3.5

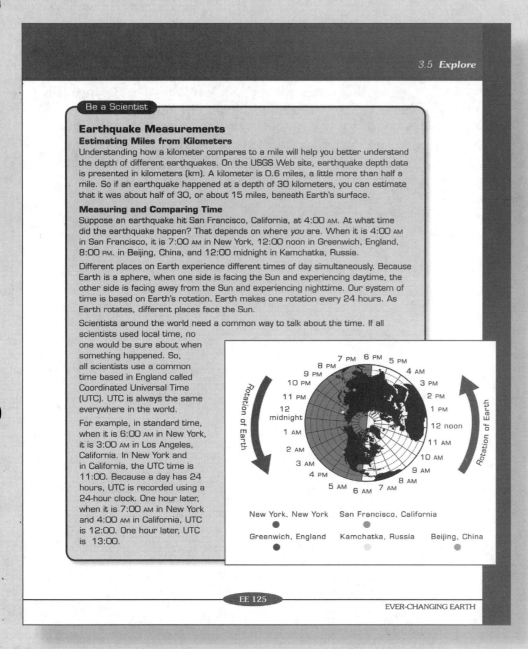

3.5 Explore

Be a Scientist

Earthquake Measurements
Estimating Miles from Kilometers

Understanding how a kilometer compares to a mile will help you better understand the depth of different earthquakes. On the USGS Web site, earthquake depth data is presented in kilometers (km). A kilometer is 0.6 miles, a little more than half a mile. So if an earthquake happened at a depth of 30 kilometers, you can estimate that it was about half of 30, or about 15 miles, beneath Earth's surface.

Measuring and Comparing Time

Suppose an earthquake hit San Francisco, California, at 4:00 AM. At what time did the earthquake happen? That depends on where *you* are. When it is 4:00 AM in San Francisco, it is 7:00 AM in New York, 12:00 noon in Greenwich, England, 8:00 PM. in Beijing, China, and 12:00 midnight in Kamchatka, Russia.

Different places on Earth experience different times of day simultaneously. Because Earth is a sphere, when one side is facing the Sun and experiencing daytime, the other side is facing away from the Sun and experiencing nighttime. Our system of time is based on Earth's rotation. Earth makes one rotation every 24 hours. As Earth rotates, different places face the Sun.

Scientists around the world need a common way to talk about the time. If all scientists used local time, no one would be sure about when something happened. So, all scientists use a common time based in England called Coordinated Universal Time (UTC). UTC is always the same everywhere in the world.

For example, in standard time, when it is 6:00 AM in New York, it is 3:00 AM in Los Angeles, California. In New York and in California, the UTC time is 11:00. Because a day has 24 hours, UTC is recorded using a 24-hour clock. One hour later, when it is 7:00 AM in New York and 4:00 AM in California, UTC is 12:00. One hour later, UTC is 13:00.

New York, New York   San Francisco, California

Greenwich, England   Kamchatka, Russia   Beijing, China

EE 125

EVER-CHANGING EARTH

Be a Scientist: Earthquake Measurements

5 min

Students read how to interpret units of measure for distance and time.

△ Guide

Briefly discuss how to estimate miles from kilometers. A kilometer is a little more than half a mile. If the depth of an earthquake is given in kilometers, you can divide the number of kilometers by two to estimate the number of miles.

META NOTES

Note that these examples refer to standard time. At present, San Francisco—along with most of the United States—follows daylight savings time in the summer, shifting its local time an hour ahead. San Francisco standard time is UTC - 8 hours, as in these examples; but San Francisco daylight savings time is UTC - 7 hours. Students do not need to know this, but if they ask about daylight savings time, you can explain that UTC does not change seasonally, while local time may.

△ Guide

Point out that times are usually expressed according to local time zone, but scientists use Coordinated Universal Time (UTC). Tell students that when it is 4 AM in San Francisco, it is noon in Greenwich, and 8 PM in Beijing. This is because the spherical shape of Earth results in different experiences of time in different countries. When the Sun is rising in San Francisco, it is directly overhead in Greenwich, and it is setting in Beijing. Scientists use Coordinated Universal Time to avoid ambiguity. UTC is always the same wherever you are in the world. When it is 3 AM in San Francisco, the UTC time is 11 AM.

NOTES

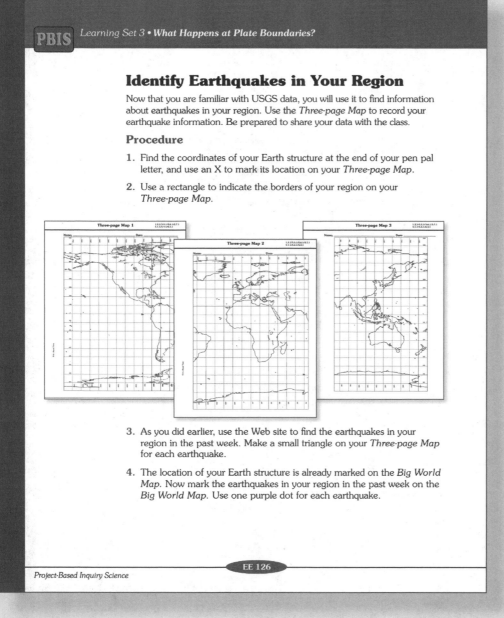

PBIS *Learning Set 3 • What Happens at Plate Boundaries?*

Identify Earthquakes in Your Region

Now that you are familiar with USGS data, you will use it to find information about earthquakes in your region. Use the *Three-page Map* to record your earthquake information. Be prepared to share your data with the class.

Procedure

1. Find the coordinates of your Earth structure at the end of your pen pal letter, and use an X to mark its location on your *Three-page Map*.

2. Use a rectangle to indicate the borders of your region on your *Three-page Map*.

3. As you did earlier, use the Web site to find the earthquakes in your region in the past week. Make a small triangle on your *Three-page Map* for each earthquake.

4. The location of your Earth structure is already marked on the *Big World Map*. Now mark the earthquakes in your region in the past week on the *Big World Map*. Use one purple dot for each earthquake.

EE 126

Project-Based Inquiry Science

Identify Earthquakes in Your Region: Procedure

10 min

Students use the USGS Web site to gather information on earthquakes in their regions.

⚠ Guide

Distribute *Three-page Maps* and blue markers. Go over the procedure with the class. Students should find their Earth structure on the map using the coordinates given in their pen pal letter. They should mark the location with an *X* and draw a rectangle to indicate the borders of their region. Then they should use the USGS data to find the earthquakes in their regions and mark the locations of the earthquakes on their *Three-page Maps* with triangles. They should use blue dots to mark the earthquakes in their region on the *Big World Map*.

Reflect

10 min

Students answer the Reflect *questions, and have a discussion of their responses.*

Reflect

1. Describe any patterns made by the locations of earthquakes in your region. What pattern do you think you would observe if you recorded earthquakes that have happened for the past month?

2. Look at the developing patterns of earthquakes on the *Big World Map*. What patterns are you starting to see in the earthquakes?

Identify Earthquakes Around the World

Now that you know where earthquakes have happened in your region in the past week, you will work as a class to identify where earthquakes have been happening worldwide during the past week.

The Web site you just used allows you to select particular time periods and view lists of earthquakes during that time. As a class, look at the list of earthquakes from the past week with magnitude 4.5 and greater. Notice how many earthquakes are in this list.

Your teacher will assign you and your partner a set of these earthquakes to find and mark on the *Big World Map*. Work with your partner and follow the next procedure.

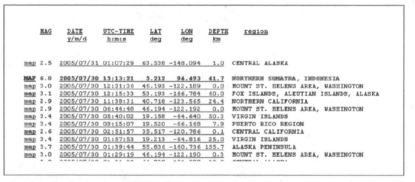

	MAG	DATE y/m/d	UTC-TIME h:m:s	LAT deg	LON deg	DEPTH km	region
map	2.5	2005/07/31	01:07:29	63.538	-148.094	1.0	CENTRAL ALASKA
MAP	6.0	2005/07/30	15:13:21	5.212	94.493	41.7	NORTHERN SUMATRA, INDONESIA
map	3.0	2005/07/30	12:31:36	46.193	-122.189	0.0	MOUNT ST. HELENS AREA, WASHINGTON
map	3.1	2005/07/30	12:15:33	53.193	-166.784	60.0	FOX ISLANDS, ALEUTIAN ISLANDS, ALASKA
map	2.9	2005/07/30	11:38:31	40.716	-123.565	24.4	NORTHERN CALIFORNIA
map	2.9	2005/07/30	06:44:46	46.194	-122.192	0.0	MOUNT ST. HELENS AREA, WASHINGTON
map	3.4	2005/07/30	05:40:02	19.158	-64.640	50.3	VIRGIN ISLANDS
map	3.4	2005/07/30	03:15:07	19.520	-66.168	7.9	PUERTO RICO REGION
map	2.6	2005/07/30	02:51:57	35.517	-120.786	0.1	CENTRAL CALIFORNIA
map	3.4	2005/07/30	01:57:53	19.213	-64.816	25.0	VIRGIN ISLANDS
map	3.7	2005/07/30	01:39:44	55.836	-160.736	155.7	ALASKA PENINSULA
map	3.0	2005/07/30	01:29:19	46.194	-122.190	0.3	MOUNT ST. HELENS AREA, WASHINGTON

Sample earthquake data from USGS Web site.

△ Guide

Have students work with their partners to answer the *Reflect* questions. Once pairs have answered the *Reflect* questions, lead a class discussion of their responses. Ask what patterns they observed in the locations of earthquakes. Students should have noticed that the earthquakes cluster in lines. If they included earthquakes from the past month, students should see the lines filled in and the pattern strengthened. Ask them what patterns they are beginning to see in earthquakes on the *Big World Map*. They should start to see emerging patterns indicating plate boundaries.

△ Guide

Have students navigate to the USGS site again, if necessary, to look at a list of earthquakes from the past week with magnitude 4.5 or greater. Ask students if the number of earthquakes surprises them. Were there more or fewer earthquakes than they expected?

Tell students that each group is going to find a set of these earthquakes on the map. Go over the procedure for locating earthquakes in the student text. They should understand that they should first use the coordinates to plot each earthquake on their *Three-page Map,* rounding the coordinates to the nearest tenth. They should check the location using the geographic name of the region given on the Web site. Then they should record the depth of each earthquake on their *Three-page Map.* Finally, they should put a blue dot on the *Big World Map* at the location of each of the earthquakes they found.

Identify Earthquakes Around the World

5 min

Students locate and gather information on earthquakes from the past week.

NOTES

Procedure

10 min

The class starts the activity.

Procedure

1. For each earthquake you are assigned, use its latitude and longitude coordinates to plot it on your *Three-page Map*. The latitude and longitude readings are precise to three decimal places. You will not be able to be that precise when you plot these locations. Instead, round your readings up to the next tenth.

2. The column on the far right of the earthquake data usually tells you where each earthquake was located. Use this information to verify the location you plotted on the map.

3. Mark the depth of each earthquake on your *Three-page Map*.

4. When you are confident that you have identified the correct locations of your earthquakes, mark them on the class's *Big World Map* by placing a purple dot over the coordinates that match the data. Save the depth information for later.

Materials
- *Three-page Map*
- **purple marker**
- **colored pencils**

When everyone is done, all of the earthquakes that happened over the last week will be plotted on the *Big World Map*.

Analyze Your Data

After the *Big World Map* has been marked, work with your partner to identify patterns in the seven days of earthquake data plotted. Begin by marking your *Three-page Map* with all the earthquakes marked on the *Big World Map*. Use the following questions to guide your analysis.

1. Look at the earthquakes in your region. Describe the patterns you see in the seven days of earthquake data. Identify bands (lines) of earthquakes and clusters of earthquakes. Identify any earthquakes that do not fit into patterns.

2. Describe the earthquake patterns around the world. Identify bands (lines) of earthquakes and clusters of earthquakes. Identify any earthquakes that do not fit into patterns.

3. What do these patterns suggest to you about the ways earthquakes occur?

⬡ Get Going

Divide the earthquakes from the past week into as many sets as there are groups in the class, and assign one set to each group. Have students locate the earthquakes on the maps and record their depths.

△ Guide and Evaluate

As students research earthquakes from the past week, assist them as necessary. Ask them if they verified the locations they found for earthquakes using the geographic names. If there were any discrepancies, ask them how they resolved them. Make sure that all groups have marked the locations of their earthquakes on the *Big World Map* before continuing.

△ Guide

Have students analyze the data they gathered using the questions in the student text as a guide. Distribute colored pencils or crayons for students to draw plate boundaries. Then have students mark the locations of all of the earthquakes that are on the *Big World Map* on their *Three-page Map*. Students should answer the first three *Analyze Your Data* questions using their *Three-page Map*. They should mark where they think plate boundaries are on their maps using the colored pencils or crayons and answer the last two questions.

△ Guide and Evaluate

Check students' work as they record and analyze their data. Ask them how they answered the first three questions. Students should recognize that the earthquake locations form lines, both in their regions and globally. They should see that this suggests that the plates in Earth's crust have edges, and that earthquakes occur where these edges meet. They should also identify some earthquakes that do not fit the pattern. Tell them that they will investigate what causes earthquakes far from plate boundaries later.

Analyze Your Data
5 min

The class analyzes their earthquake data.

NOTES

Communicate: Share Your Data and Ideas

20 min

Students share their answers to the Analyze Your Data *questions.*

---

4. On your *Three-page Map,* use a colored pencil to mark where you think there are plate boundaries.

5. For each plate boundary inference, how confident are you of the inference (a lot, a little)? What additional data would help support your plate boundary inference and make you more confident about it? Why?

6. In the places where you are still unsure of the plate boundaries, what data do you need to increase your confidence level?

Communicate

Share Your Data and Ideas

Share your plate boundary inferences with the class. At the same time, share the information you used. Observe each group's plate boundary inferences, and listen to their supporting ideas. Note what your classmates are unsure of and why. Pay careful attention to where others think plate boundaries are, especially those that are near your region. If you disagree with where others have identified plate boundaries, or if you think they have not used their supporting evidence well, offer your advice and the evidence that supports it. Be respectful, even when you disagree with one of your classmates.

You will probably agree with some groups' inferences about plate boundaries and disagree with others. There will be further opportunities to work with your classmates to better identify where plate boundaries are located. For now, notice what you disagree about and where people are unsure of boundary locations. Understand why they are unsure, and identify what further information is needed to resolve your disagreements. Also, think about how much or what type of data will increase your confidence about where plate boundaries are located.

As a class, answer these questions:

1. What patterns of earthquake activity do you see worldwide?

2. Based on the data you have looked at so far, where do you think there might be plate boundaries?

3. What else do you think you need to know to more accurately and completely identify Earth's plate boundaries?

EE 129

△ Guide

When students have finished recording their predictions and have answered the *Analyze Your Data* questions, have them share their data and predictions with the class. They should show their maps, pointing out their predictions for the locations of plate boundaries. When presenting, students should also point out the patterns in the earthquakes on their maps and any other information that led them to make their predictions.

Emphasize that students should listen to groups' supporting ideas and think about whether they agree with their predictions. If they disagree with any predictions or think any of the supporting ideas are weak, they should offer constructive comments. Emphasize that the class may not be able to come to an agreement right now, and that this is okay. The class will have opportunities later to work together to better identify where plate boundaries are. For now, they should note anything they cannot agree on so that they can come back to it later.

When all students have presented their predictions, lead a class discussion of the questions in the student text. Ask the class what patterns they see in earthquakes worldwide. Their answers should be based on clusters and bands of earthquakes on the *Big World Map*. Ask them where they think plate boundaries are. They should base their answers on the predictions different pairs made and the earthquakes marked on the *Big World Map*.

Ask students what else they need to know to more accurately and completely identify Earth's plate boundaries. This question is meant to engage students in thinking about how they can build on what they have learned to better identify plate boundaries. Students should recognize any gaps that remain in their inferred plate boundaries. The data from the past week probably does not provide a complete picture. Students should recognize that earthquake data over a longer period of time might help them better identify patterns. They should have questions about what they can learn from the depth of an earthquake. Is there anything they can learn from looking at the magnitudes of earthquakes? They should also recognize that there are many things they do not know about how earthquakes occur such as how plates move and why earthquakes sometimes occur far from plate boundaries.

NOTES

....

....

....

....

....

Update Your Region Project Board

5 min

Students record new information on their Region Project Boards.

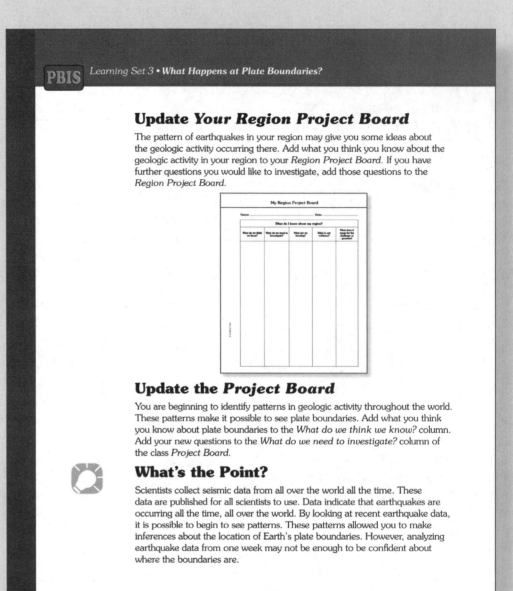

Update *Your Region Project Board*

The pattern of earthquakes in your region may give you some ideas about the geologic activity occurring there. Add what you think you know about the geologic activity in your region to your *Region Project Board*. If you have further questions you would like to investigate, add those questions to the *Region Project Board*.

Update the *Project Board*

You are beginning to identify patterns in geologic activity throughout the world. These patterns make it possible to see plate boundaries. Add what you think you know about plate boundaries to the *What do we think we know?* column. Add your new questions to the *What do we need to investigate?* column of the class *Project Board*.

What's the Point?

Scientists collect seismic data from all over the world all the time. These data are published for all scientists to use. Data indicate that earthquakes are occurring all the time, all over the world. By looking at recent earthquake data, it is possible to begin to see patterns. These patterns allowed you to make inferences about the location of Earth's plate boundaries. However, analyzing earthquake data from one week may not be enough to be confident about where the boundaries are.

EE 130

Project-Based Inquiry Science

△ Guide

Turn students' attention to their *Region Project Boards*. Now that they have discussed their predictions for plate boundaries and the patterns they found in earthquake data from their region, they should record what they think they know about their region in the *What do we think we know?* column of their *Region Project Board*. For everything they put in this column, they should record their evidence in this column. Finally, any questions they have should go in the *What do we need to investigate?* column.

△ Guide

When students have had a few minutes to update their *Region Project Boards,* lead a class discussion to update the class *Project Board.* Ask students what ideas about plate boundaries they can add to the *What do we think we know?* column. Ask them what questions they still have about plate boundaries that they can add to the *What do we need to investigate?* column. Record their responses on the class *Project Board.*

◇ Evaluate

Make sure that students have recorded any disagreements that arose over plate boundary predictions as investigative questions. Make sure they have recorded questions about how earthquakes occur, what they can learn from the magnitude and depth of earthquakes, and about what they might learn from longer term earthquake data.

Assessment Options

Targeted Concepts, Skills, and Nature of Science	How do I know if students got it?
Earthquake activity, volcanic activity, and topography are all evidence that Earth's crust is moving and changing.	**ASK:** How can you use the data you gathered from the USGS Web site as evidence that Earth's crust is moving and changing? **LISTEN:** Students should recognize that global patterns of earthquake activity suggest that Earth's crust has breaks, and that it is moving and changing.
Scientists often work together and then share their findings. Sharing findings makes new information available and helps scientists refine their ideas and build on others' ideas. When another person's or group's idea is used, credit needs to be given.	**ASK:** Why was it important to share your data and ideas with the class? **LISTEN:** Students should recognized that different pairs gathered data on different earthquakes, so the class needed everyone to share their findings. In addition, different pairs may have developed different ideas.

Update the Project Board

10 min

Lead a class discussion to update the Project Board.

Targeted Concepts, Skills, and Nature of Science	How do I know if students got it?
Scientists must keep clear, accurate, and descriptive records of what they do so they can share their work with others and consider what they did, why they did it, and what they want to do next.	**ASK:** Why was it important to record what you are learning on the *Project Boards?* **LISTEN:** Students should recognize that it is important for them to track their progress and the evidence they are gathering for their ideas.
Scientists use models and tools, such as Geographic Information Systems, and a variety of maps to develop claims and explanations from evidence in the data.	**ASK:** How does the United States Geological Survey data help you to develop ideas about plate boundaries? **LISTEN:** Students should recognize that without USGS's data, they would not be able to look for patterns in earthquakes around the world.
Interactions between Earth's crustal plates can result in mountain building, rift valleys, and geologic activity such as earthquakes and volcanoes. Underwater volcanic activity may form underwater mountains, which can thrust above the ocean's surface to become islands.	**ASK:** What do you think causes the patterns of earthquake activity that you are finding? **LISTEN:** Students should identify the interaction of plates as a cause of patterns of earthquake activity. Earthquakes cluster around places where two plates meet and interact.

Teacher Reflection Options

- What evidence do you have that students understand the importance of collaboration in science? How can you help students understand this?

- How were you able to guide students to effectively gather data from the USGS Web site? What might you try next time? How were you able to guide students to make inferences from the data? What might you try next time?

- How were you able to engage students in discussing their results and their ideas with the class? How were you able to keep them focused on the task? What else might you try?

3.6 Investigate

How Can One Year of Earthquake Data Help You Better Identify Plate Boundaries?

◄ $1\frac{3}{4}$ *class periods*

A class period is considered to be one 40 to 50 minute class.

Overview

Students gather data on earthquakes in their regions from the *Big Data Map*. Working with other students whose regions are geographically close, they infer where there are plate boundaries in their region and draw these plate boundaries on transparencies. They identify places on the *Big Data Map* where the clusters or bands of earthquakes are so thick that the exact location of the plate boundary cannot be found, or where there are too few earthquakes to find the plate boundary. Using *My World*, they examine maps that show earthquakes with a narrower range of magnitudes to find plate boundaries where the *Big Data Map* had too much data. They examine maps that show earthquakes over a greater period of time to find plate boundaries where the *Big Data Map* had too little data. They revise the plate boundaries they drew on their transparencies. Then they update their *Region Project Board* with new regional information and the class *Project Board* with new ideas about earthquakes and finding plate boundaries.

Targeted Concepts, Skills, and Nature of Science	Performance Expectations
Scientists often work together and then share their findings. Sharing findings makes new information available and helps scientists refine their ideas and build on others' ideas. When another person or group's idea is used, credit needs to be given.	Students should share ideas about earthquakes and plate boundaries with the class as they update the *Project Board*.
Scientists must keep clear, accurate, and descriptive records of what they do so they can share their work with others and consider what they did, why they did it, and what they want to do next.	Students should use old records and create new records of the earthquake data.

Targeted Concepts, Skills, and Nature of Science	Performance Expectations
Graphs and tables are an effective way to analyze and communicate results of scientific investigation.	Students should analyze one year of earthquake data plotted on a map and draw their inferences.
Scientific investigations and measurements are considered reliable if the results are repeatable by other scientists using the same procedures.	Students should evaluate the reliability of their plate boundary inferences based on the amount and clarity of the data they used. Students should also think critically about the amount of data needed, and consider why it is sometimes useful to analyze a smaller set of data.
Scientists make claims (conclusions) based on evidence obtained (trends in data) from reliable investigations.	Students should make claims about where their plate boundaries are based on their data.
Scientists use models and tools such, as Geographic Information Systems, and a variety of maps to develop claims and explanations from evidence in the data.	Students should use the *Big Data Map* and *My World* to predict where their plate boundaries are.

Materials

5-7 per classroom	*Big Data Map*
several per group	Blank transparencies
1 roll per group	Transparent tape
1 roll or box per group	Masking tape or paper clips
1 set per group	Black, red, and green transparency markers
1 per group	Computers with *My World* *Three-page Map*

Materials	
2 per group	Blue and yellow marker
1 per class	Class *Project Board*
1 per student	*Project Board* page

Activity Setup and Preparation

In this section, groups of students will be taping transparencies over large maps called *Big Data Maps*. If they use smaller sheets, they will need to tape them together with transparent tape. They can use masking tape to fix the transparencies to the *Big Data Maps*. Because the data maps are large, you may want to rearrange the room to accommodate them. You may need to put desks together, or lay the maps out on the floor.

Consider how to put pairs into larger groups to share *Big Data Maps*. Groups might look like this:

Big Data Map Group Assignments			
Eurasia	**North and South America**	**North and South America**	**South Pacific**
Mount Everest	Mount Aconcagua (Andes)	Mount Popo (Mexico)	Mount Fiji
Mount Kilimanjaro (Tanzania)	Mount Popo (Mexico)	Baja Peninsula	Java Trench
Iceland	Baja Peninsula	Hawaiian Islands	

Students will use *My World* in this section. They will need access to computers with *My World* and the *ESInquiry* project file installed. If possible, have students work at the computers they used earlier so they can access files from previous work. Have computers allocated for your students before class.

EVER-CHANGING EARTH

Homework Options

Reflection

- **Science Content and Process:** How did using the data in *My World* assist you in your plate boundary inferences? Were you able to find the right amount of data for your region? If not, did you have too much data or too little? *(Students should describe how they used the data in* My World, *what was useful about it, and if it was enough, too much, or too little.)*

- **Science Content and Process:** Describe what data you chose to use to support your plate boundary inferences and why? *(Students should describe the information they used (depth, magnitude, and so on) and why they used it to support their plate boundary prediction.)*

Preparation for 3.7

- **Science Content and Process:** How do you think your boundaries may change when you discuss them with other groups whose regions share the boundary? *(The purpose of this question is to get students to think about their plate boundary inferences and the other Earth structures that share the boundary.)*

NOTES

....

....

....

....

....

....

....

3.6 Investigate

How Can One Year of Earthquake Data Help You Better Identify Plate Boundaries?

You noticed that using one week of earthquake data left you with some gaps in your plate boundary inferences. If you had more data, you might be able to make better decisions about the locations of the plate boundaries.

You and your partner will use a tool called the *Big Data Map* to improve your plate boundary predictions. The *Big Data Map* is a large map of the world, very much like the *Big World Map,* but with earthquake data marked on it. You will be examining the *Big Data Map* to identify where earthquakes occurred in your region during a one-year period. You will use that data to make inferences about the location of the plate boundaries in or near your region. You and your partner will be sharing a *Big Data Map* with others whose regions are geographically close to yours.

When you have completed analyzing the map, you will use *My World* to fill in even more detail. With a year of data, you may have a better idea of where the plate boundaries are located in and near your region.

EE 131

EVER-CHANGING EARTH

3.6 Investigate

How Can One Year of Earthquake Data Help You Better Identify Plate Boundaries?

5 min

Students are introduced to the activity.

○ Engage

Point out that the plate boundary inferences students recorded on their *Three-page Maps* were incomplete. There were some places where students did not have enough data to make any inferences. Ask students how they think they could complete their inferences.

*A class period is considered to be one 40 to 50 minute class.

△ Guide

Tell students they are going to use a large map, similar to the *Big World Map,* that shows earthquake data. Students will examine this map, the *Big Data Map,* and identify places where earthquakes occurred in their region during a one-year period. Using this new data, they will make more inferences about the locations of plate boundaries. Once they have analyzed the data from the map, students will use *My World* to find more earthquake data. This will allow them to make more complete inferences about the location of plate boundaries in their region.

NOTES

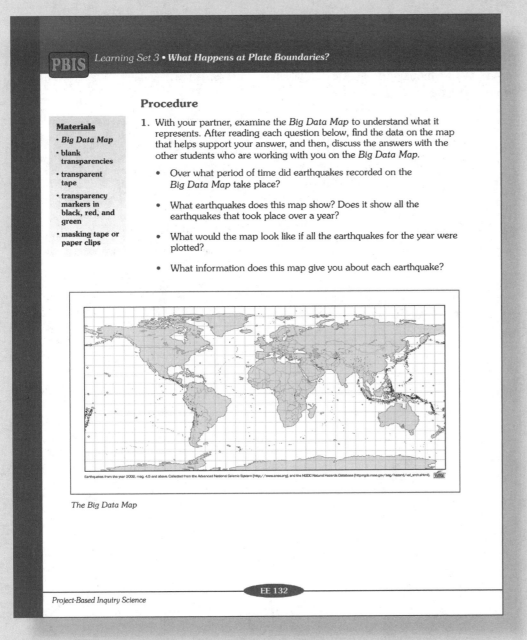

PBIS *Learning Set 3 • What Happens at Plate Boundaries?*

Procedure

Materials
• *Big Data Map*
• blank transparencies
• transparent tape
• transparency markers in black, red, and green
• masking tape or paper clips

1. With your partner, examine the *Big Data Map* to understand what it represents. After reading each question below, find the data on the map that helps support your answer, and then, discuss the answers with the other students who are working with you on the *Big Data Map*.

   • Over what period of time did earthquakes recorded on the *Big Data Map* take place?

   • What earthquakes does this map show? Does it show all the earthquakes that took place over a year?

   • What would the map look like if all the earthquakes for the year were plotted?

   • What information does this map give you about each earthquake?

Earthquakes from the year 2002, mag. 4.5 and above. Collected from the Advanced National Seismic System [http://www.anss.org], and the NGDC Natural Hazards Database [http://ngdc.noaa.gov/seg/hazard/vol_srch.shtml].

The Big Data Map

Project-Based Inquiry Science

EE 132

Procedure

20 min

Students examine the earthquake data in their regions on the Big Data Map *and draw plate boundary inferences on transparencies.*

Guide and Assess

Show students a *Big Data Map*. Get students into their regional groups and distribute *Big Data Maps*. Distribute blank transparencies, transparent tape, masking tape or paper clips, and black, green, and red markers.

Once regional groups have their *Big Data Maps* assembled, go over the questions in Step 1 with the class. These questions should help students understand what information the map contains. Ask the class each question, and lead a discussion of their responses. Look for the following in responses:

- Students should determine that the map recorded the data from earthquakes that took place over the period of a year.

- Students should recognize that the map does not show all earthquakes that took place over a year, only earthquakes of magnitude 4.5 and higher.

- Students should realize that with all the earthquakes of the year plotted, much of the additional data would be clustered in the same places as the data they have.

- Students should explain that the map gives them the location of each earthquake and each earthquake's magnitude.

NOTES

_____

_____

_____

_____

_____

_____

_____

_____

_____

2. Do not write or draw on the *Big Data Map*. You will use transparencies to record data and draw plate boundary predictions. Place transparencies over the part of the map where your region is located and tape them together. Secure your transparencies to the map using clips or masking tape. Trace enough latitude and longitude coordinates (intersections and numbers) from the *Big Data Map* onto your transparencies so you can place them back in the same spot on the *Big Data Map* each time you use it.

3. Observe the earthquake activity in your region. Look for bands and clusters of earthquakes. The bands and clusters you find will help you identify the plate boundaries in your region.

4. Discuss with your partner where you think there are plate boundaries in your region. To identify these boundaries accurately, you need to see a band of earthquake activity. There may be places on the map with so many dots that their pattern is hard to distinguish. There may also be places where there are not enough dots to be certain about a plate boundary. To help you identify where the plate boundaries are within your region, read *Identifying Plate Boundaries from Earthquake Data* on the next page.

5. Share the plate boundary you are identifying with the other students working with you at the *Big Data Map*. Take turns pointing to the bands and clusters you have identified, and together, sort them into three categories:

   • bands that seem to have the right amount of data for you to identify plate boundaries

   • bands or clusters where you think there is a boundary but have so much data that you are not sure where the boundary is

   • bands or clusters where you think there might be a boundary but where there is too little data for you to be sure

Mark each band or cluster with a different color marker.

Have students place transparencies over the *Big Data Map* and secure them with masking tape or paper clips. Each pair should place their transparencies over their region on the map. If they need several transparencies to cover their region, they should tape the transparencies together with transparent tape. Have students copy the coordinates of a few points from the map onto their transparencies so they can put the transparencies down in the same place later.

With the transparencies in place, students should look for bands and clusters of earthquakes in their region. They can mark these lightly on their transparencies. Using these bands and clusters of earthquakes, students will try to identify plate boundaries. This would be a good time to go over the following *Identifying Plate Boundary Zones from Earthquake Data* textbox with the class.

META NOTES

Having a large paper map provides opportunities for students to talk and justify their ideas using data.

When students are beginning to identify plate boundaries in their regions, they should share their ideas with the other pairs. Together, they should identify which bands have the right amount of data, which bands have too much data, and which bands have too little data for identifying plate boundaries. As groups begin to identify plate boundaries, ask them what ideas they have discussed. Ask if all of the bands of data in their region have the right amount of data. If some do not, ask if they have too much or too little data. Students should base their answers on whether the entire length of their boundaries can be clearly discerned from the data.

In the places where students decide they have the right amount of data, they should agree on the location of the plate boundary and draw it with a black marker. They should circle the bands and clusters where they have too much data with a green marker. They should circle the bands and clusters where they have too little data with a red marker.

NOTES

Identifying Plate Boundaries from Earthquake Data

Look at the Aleutian Islands, Alaska, on the data maps on the next page. Think about what each map tells you about the location of the plate boundary. The map with too much data shows you a wide band of earthquakes on the left and a huge cluster of earthquakes on the right. You can guess that the boundary zone on the left is between the red lines, but you cannot tell anything about the cluster toward the right. That cluster is not in a line. The boundary zone probably extends into that area, but you cannot tell which earthquakes are at the boundary and which are not. You need to narrow down the data in some way to identify the full plate boundary.

A satellite photograph of the Aleutian Islands.

Identifying the location of the plate boundary on the map with too little data is difficult because there are so few earthquakes shown. There is no clear line of earthquakes to guide your inference. Within the red lines, you can see a band of earthquakes, but you cannot tell exactly where the boundary might be. The cluster on the right of that map gives you even less information. There might be a band extending diagonally from the red lines, but with so few earthquakes, you cannot know how to draw the line. You need to see more earthquake activity to identify the plate boundaries on this map.

The map with just the right amount of data shows a clear line of earthquakes in the lower left side of the map that extends into the middle right side of the map. The plate boundary is much easier to see on this map than on the other two.

The amount of data you will see on any earthquake map depends on two things: the amount of time the map covers (how many years or months) and the magnitude of the earthquakes plotted. The *Big Data Map* you are using shows one year of earthquakes with magnitudes greater than 4.0. It does not include earthquakes with magnitudes less than 4.0. There are some places in the world with enough earthquakes with magnitudes of 4.0 occurring within a year to see easily where a plate boundary is. In other places, one year of data provides too little or too much data for you to be sure about where a plate boundary is.

EE 134

Project-Based Inquiry Science

Identifying Plate Boundaries from Earthquake Data

5 min

Students begin to understand how to evaluate the amount of information in a data map.

△ Guide

You can have students read this segment as they examine the *Big Data Maps* or you can go over it with the class. It is important for students to understand that there is no objective criterion for what the right amount of data is. The right amount of data is the amount of data that allows them to best determine where the plate boundary is. The student text uses data maps of the Aleutian Islands as an example.

How Much Data Is Enough?

Students analyze data maps of the Aleutian Islands.

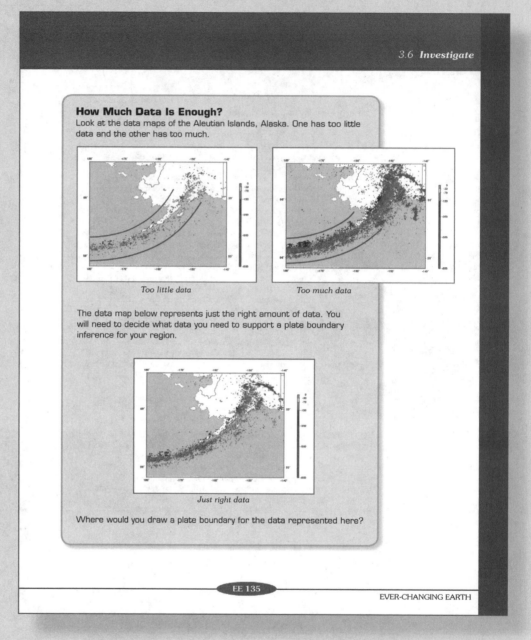

How Much Data Is Enough?

Look at the data maps of the Aleutian Islands, Alaska. One has too little data and the other has too much.

Too little data   *Too much data*

The data map below represents just the right amount of data. You will need to decide what data you need to support a plate boundary inference for your region.

Just right data

Where would you draw a plate boundary for the data represented here?

EE 135

EVER-CHANGING EARTH

To choose the right amount of data for the Aleutian Islands, a scientist or student would simply evaluate which of the data maps gave the clearest and most complete picture of where the plate boundary is. You can evaluate students' understanding as they sort bands and clusters of earthquakes in their data.

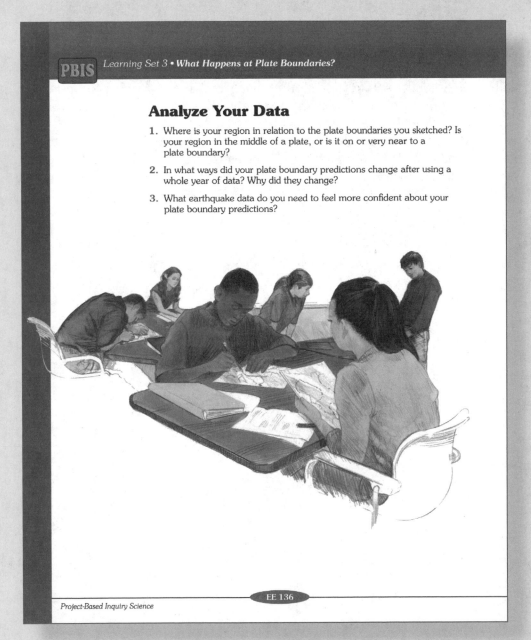

Analyze Your Data

1. Where is your region in relation to the plate boundaries you sketched? Is your region in the middle of a plate, or is it on or very near to a plate boundary?

2. In what ways did your plate boundary predictions change after using a whole year of data? Why did they change?

3. What earthquake data do you need to feel more confident about your plate boundary predictions?

Learning Set 3 • What Happens at Plate Boundaries?

PBIS

EE 136

Project-Based Inquiry Science

Analyze Your Data

5 min

Students answer the Analyze Your Data *questions.*

△ Guide

When students have finished sketching plate boundaries on their transparencies, have them analyze the data using the questions as a guide. Emphasize that as they answer these questions they should think about what they can learn about plates and geologic activity from the data, and how they can improve their inferences.

◇ **Evaluate**

As students analyze their data, check to see that they have evaluated how the additional data changed their inferences and what additional data they still need. Students should have found that they were able to make more complete inferences with the additional data. But they should have found places where the *Big Data Map* had too much or too little data. For places where there was too much data, they should recognize that they need to look at a data map with less data. For places where there was too little data, they should recognize that they need to look at a map with more data and identify what data they still need.

NOTES

3.6 Investigate

Refine Your Data to Improve Your Plate Boundary Inferences

To better identify where the plate boundaries are in your region, you will now use maps from *My World*. Using *My World*, you will be able to examine three years of data for earthquakes with magnitudes larger than 4.0. You will be able to select only the data you want. For example, if some part of your region has so many earthquakes that three years of data is too much, you can choose to look at only one or two years of data. If a year of data is too much in some part of your region, you can choose to look at less data. You can also change the way the world map appears. That is, you can change what you see to show the part of the globe you want to see and view the earthquake data more easily. For reminders about using *My World*, turn to the back of the book.

Materials

- transparencies with your plate boundary sketches
- blank *Three-page Map*
- markers: blue and yellow

Procedure

1. Working with your partner, review the earthquakes and plate boundaries sketched on your transparencies. Identify regions where you need more data to support your plate boundary predictions. Mark those areas on a *Three-page Map*. You will refer to the *Three-page Map* as you work on the computer.

2. Prepare a *My World* earthquake map by following these steps.

   a) **Open *My World*** by double-clicking on the *My World* icon on your computer screen.

   b) **From the *Data Library* drop-down menu, select *Earth Structures & Processes*.**

   c) **Open the *ESInquiry* file.** This map has information about your regions, including latitude and longitude, elevation and depth, earthquakes and volcanoes.

Refine Your Data to Improve Your Plate Boundary Inferences

5 min

Students use My World *to improve their inferences.*

△ Guide

Let students know that they will now use *My World* to better identify where the plate boundaries in their region are. Using *My World*, they will be able to select the amount of data that will best allow them to find plate boundaries. They may be able to find clear data for the bands and clusters they circled on their transparencies.

"You have found places where there was too much or too little data to identify plate boundaries confidently. Now you will use *My World* to select the right amount of data in these places so that you can identify the plate boundaries."

Procedure

30 min

Students use My World *to gather more earthquake data and revise their plate boundary inferences.*

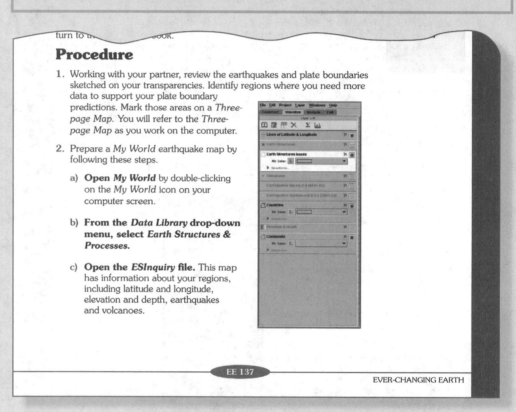

turn to the... ...book.

Procedure

1. Working with your partner, review the earthquakes and plate boundaries sketched on your transparencies. Identify regions where you need more data to support your plate boundary predictions. Mark those areas on a *Three-page Map*. You will refer to the *Three-page Map* as you work on the computer.

2. Prepare a *My World* earthquake map by following these steps.

   a) **Open *My World*** by double-clicking on the *My World* icon on your computer screen.

   b) **From the *Data Library* drop-down menu, select *Earth Structures & Processes*.**

   c) **Open the *ESInquiry* file.** This map has information about your regions, including latitude and longitude, elevation and depth, earthquakes and volcanoes.

EE 137

EVER-CHANGING EARTH

△ Guide

Distribute new *Three-page Maps* with blue and yellow markers. Go over the procedure with the class. Students should first examine their transparencies. They should find the places on their transparencies where there was too much or too little information to decide exactly where a plate boundary is and mark those areas on their new *Three-page Map*.

They should start *My World*, select *Earth Structures and Processes* in the *Library* dropdown, and open the *ESInquiry* file. In the *Layer List*, they should turn on *Earth Structures* boxes and *Earthquakes big*. They can select 3 years in the *Earthquakes big* layer. They should zoom in on their region and decide whether there is too much, too little, or the right amount of information. They can select a shorter time period if there is too much information. They can select *Earthquakes medium* if there is too little information. They should use *My World* to look closely at earthquakes in the areas they marked on their *Three-page Maps*. They should draw plate boundaries on their *Three-page Map* and record supporting information. When they have finished, they should revise the plate boundary inferences on their transparencies with different colored markers. They should use a blue marker for boundaries they are unsure of, and they should highlight places where they still do not have enough information with a yellow marker.

Once you have gone over the procedure, give students a timeframe and have them get started.

△ Guide and Assess

Help students with any difficulties they might have using *My World*. It may be difficult for them to see the earthquakes on the *My World* map. Tell them that they can change the color of the earthquakes by double clicking the *Earthquake big* layer, selecting the *Color* tab, and then clicking the *Edit* button.

Point out that students can display the earthquakes within a date range in one color and the earthquakes outside of the date range in another color, or they can simply hide earthquakes outside of the date range. To use two different colors, students can select *Color Selected (Yellow)* or *Color Selected (Magenta)* in the *Highlight Mode* dropdown. To hide any earthquakes outside the date range, they can select *Hide Unselected* in the dropdown.

As students work in *My World,* monitor their progress. Ask them what date range they have selected and whether they are looking at big earthquakes only, or big and medium earthquakes. How did they choose these parameters? Ask them if they are better able to make inferences about plate boundaries in the areas they marked on their *Three-page Map* with the new information. If they are not, ask them how they could change their parameters to improve the results. In some cases, students may not be able to identify plate boundaries accurately even with data from *My World.* Have students use the yellow marker to highlight areas where they cannot identify plate boundaries accurately.

NOTES

....

....

....

d) **Click on** *Earth Structure* **boxes.** Make sure the *Show/Hide* layer button is on (the *eye* icon is visible).

e) **Show the Earthquake data on your map.** In the *Layer List*, click *Earthquakes big*. This layer reveals all earthquakes with a magnitude of 6.0 or higher. If this layer is currently inactive, select the *Show/Hide* layer button on the right to reveal an eye. You now have the opportunity to choose how many years of data you wish to view. If there is not enough data when looking at only the big earthquakes, you can turn on the *Earthquakes medium* layer, which will reveal all earthquakes between the magnitudes of 4.0 and 5.9. If there is too much data, you can change the number of years of data shown.

f) **Zoom in and reposition the map to view the earthquakes in your region.**

3. Look at your *Three-page Map* to decide on which part of the plate boundary you need to focus.

4. Use *My World* to examine earthquake data in your region that will help you identify the locations of the plate boundaries.

5. As you identify plate boundaries, draw them on your *Three-page Map*. Annotate the map with earthquake data from *My World* that supports the inferences you make about your plate boundaries.

6. When you are finished gathering data, use the information you gathered from *My World* to revise the plate boundaries on your transparencies. Use a different colored marker than you used last time. Use a blue marker to mark plate boundary lines you are now sure of and yellow to highlight places where you still do not think you have enough data. You will be using the map to show the class your old and new plate boundary inferences.

NOTES

....

....

....

Update Your Region Project Board

You have looked at earthquake data in several ways to determine the plate boundaries for your region. Working with your partner, record what you have learned about earthquakes in your region in the *What are we learning column?* of the *Region Project Board*. In the *What do we think we know?* column, record what you can now infer about plate boundaries in your region. Include any questions you still have. Record these in the *What do we need to investigate?* column.

Reflect

You have made two iterations of plate boundary inferences. Think back to each one as you answer the following questions.

1. How have your inferences changed as you collected more data?

2. Why have your inferences changed?

3. How confident do you feel now about your plate boundary inferences? What has affected your level of confidence?

EE 139

EVER-CHANGING EARTH

Update Your *Region Project Board*

10 min

Students update their Region Project Boards.

△ Guide

Once students have finished revising the plate boundaries on their transparencies, have them work with their partners to update their *Region Project Board*. They should record new information about earthquakes in their region in the *What are we learning?* column. They should record inferences about plate boundaries in their region in the *What do we think we know?* column. Any questions they have or things they need more evidence for should be recorded in the *What do we need to investigate?* column.

Reflect

10 min

Groups evaluate and discuss their revised plate boundary inferences.

column, record what you can now infer about plate boundaries in your region. Include any questions you still have. Record these in the *What do we need to investigate?* column.

Reflect

You have made two iterations of plate boundary inferences. Think back to each one as you answer the following questions.

1. How have your inferences changed as you collected more data?

2. Why have your inferences changed?

3. How confident do you feel now about your plate boundary inferences? What has affected your level of confidence?

⬡ Get Going

Have students answer the three questions with their partners. Let them know their responses will be discussed during a class discussion.

△ Guide and Assess

Begin a class discussion by asking what students answered for the first two questions.

Have groups show their transparencies with plate boundary inferences and discuss the answers to the questions. They should point out specific changes they made to their plate boundary inferences on the transparencies and describe why they made those changes.

When answering these questions, students should consider these changes. They should recognize that having more information about earthquakes and what is happening on Earth's surface can help to shape their understanding of what is happening below. Students should feel more confident in their inferences because as they have more evidence to support their claims.

NOTES

Update the *Project Board*

You have been working with earthquake data to refine your plate boundary inferences. In the process, you have learned a lot about earthquakes and where they occur. You have also gathered evidence to justify the plate boundaries you have located. Now add what you have learned, along with the evidence to support it, to the *Project Board*.

As you worked on each iteration of your plate boundary map, you may have thought of more questions. For example, you know that the plates making up Earth's crust move, but you may not fully understand how they move. These questions should be added to the *What do we need to investigate?* column.

What's the Point?

Earthquake data can provide clues to the locations of the plate boundaries. These clues can be found in different amounts of earthquake data. Sometimes there is too much data, and it is difficult to see a pattern. With too little data, a pattern is also hard to find. It is important to identify the correct amount of data needed for answering different questions.

Project-Based Inquiry Science

EE 140

Update the *Project Board*

15 min

Lead a class discussion centered on updating the class Project Board.

△ Guide and Assess

Point out that students have been through two iterations of inferring the boundaries of plates from earthquake data. Ask them what they have learned during this process. Record students' ideas in the *What are we learning?* column of the *Project Board*. Listen for observations about patterns of earthquake activity around plate boundaries over time, and how data can best be selected for finding plate boundaries. Ask them what evidence they have for the things they have learned, and record their responses in the *What is our evidence?* column.

Ask the class if they have any questions they need to investigate to put in the *What do we need to investigate?* column of the *Project Board*.

Some students may say, "How are these plates moving? How does it move, why don't we feel it?"

Assessment Options

Targeted Concepts, Skills, and Nature of Science	How do I know if students got it?
Scientists often work together and then share their findings. Sharing findings makes new information available and helps scientists refine their ideas and build on others' ideas. When another person or group's idea is used, credit needs to be given.	**ASK:** Why was it important to share your data and ideas with the class? **LISTEN:** Students should recall that pairs studying different regions may have developed different ideas and that they were able to add to their understanding of their region.
Scientists must keep clear, accurate, and descriptive records of what they do so they can share their work with others and consider what they did, why they did it, and what they want to do next.	**ASK:** Why was it important to record what you are learning on the *Project Boards?* **LISTEN:** Students should recognize that it is important for them to track their progress and the evidence they are gathering for their ideas.
Scientific investigations and measurements are considered reliable if the results are repeatable by other scientists using the same procedures.	**ASK:** Were you more confident of your revised plate boundary inferences? Why? **LISTEN:** Students should base their confidence on the data they used for their revisions.
Scientists make claims (conclusions) based on evidence obtained (trends in data) from reliable investigations.	**ASK:** What claims did you make from the earthquake data and what did you base it on? **LISTEN:** Students should realize that their plate boundary inferences are their claims and are based on the trends in the earthquake data they used in the *My World* software.

Targeted Concepts, Skills, and Nature of Science	How do I know if students got it?
Scientists use models and tools, such as Geographic Information Systems, and a variety of maps to develop claims and explanations from evidence in the data.	**ASK:** What are the benefits of using the *Big Data Map* and the earthquake data in *My World*? **LISTEN:** Students should describe how maps are good models of Earth, and that plotting earthquake data on a map makes it easier to analyze and communicate that data. Some may mention how they can see or visualize the patterns which they use to determine their plate boundaries.

Teacher Reflection Questions

- What difficulties did students have deciding where they had too little data, too much data, or the right amount of data to be confident of their plate boundary inferences? What might you try to make this easier next time?

- How were you able to help students make inferences from the data in the *Big Data Map* and *My World?* What might you try next time?

- What difficulties did groups have working with *Big Data Maps* and *My World?* What can you try next time?

NOTES

NOTES

3.7 Explore

Where Are Plate Boundaries Located Across the Entire Earth?

◀ $1\frac{1}{4}$ *class periods*

A class period is considered to be one 40 to 50 minute class.

Overview

Students with neighboring regions meet to determine how the plate boundaries they have identified interconnect. Within a meeting, each pair presents their predictions for plate boundaries in their region along with supporting evidence. They settle disagreements about how the plate boundaries interconnect by examining their data. Once they have agreed on how the plate boundaries interconnect, they draw where they think the plate boundaries are throughout the larger area that contains all of their regions and share their predictions with the class. The class discusses whether they are confident in their plate boundary inferences, and they gather more data and revise their predictions if necessary. Once they are confident of their inferences, they create a class map on transparencies showing the plate boundaries around the world. Pairs independently create new maps of the plate boundaries in their regions using the class's map as a reference.

Targeted Concepts, Skills, and Nature of Science	Performance Expectations
Scientists often work together and then share their findings. Sharing findings makes new information available and helps scientists refine their ideas and build on others' ideas. When another person's or group's idea is used, credit needs to be given.	Pairs with neighboring regions should meet and make final revisions to their plate boundary inferences. They should share their inferences with the class and the class should agree and map out the plate boundaries for Earth.
Scientists must keep clear, accurate, and descriptive records of what they do so they can share their work with others and consider what they did, why they did it, and what they want to do next.	Students should use their records of plate boundary inferences to agree on the locations of the plate boundaries for Earth.

Targeted Concepts, Skills, and Nature of Science	Performance Expectations
Graphs and tables are an effective way to analyze and communicate results of scientific investigation.	Groups should use their *Big Data Maps* to communicate their results with the class.
Scientific investigations and measurements are considered reliable if the results are repeatable by other scientists using the same procedures.	Neighboring pairs should agree where they share a plate boundary based on their earthquake data.
Scientists make claims (conclusions) based on evidence obtained (trends in data) from reliable investigations.	Students should make claims about where plate boundaries are located around the world based on the earthquake data they have gathered.
Scientists use models and tools, such as Geographic Information Systems, and a variety of maps to develop claims and explanations from evidence in the data.	Students should make claims supported by the data they obtained from the *Big Data Map* and *My World*.

Materials	
several per group	Transparencies with plate boundary sketches (from *Section 3.6*)
1 per group	Transparent tape
1 per set of groups	Markers
1 per group	*Three-page Map* with plate boundaries and notes marked
a few per group	Blank transparencies
1 per class	Class *Project Board*
1 per student	*Region Project Board* page

Activity Setup and Preparation

In this section, pairs with neighboring regions will get together in *Neighbor Region Meetings*. You will need to decide how to divide the class into groups. Here is a possible division:

- Mt. Popo, Baja Peninsula, and Mt. Aconcagua

- Mt. Everest, Iceland, and Mt. Kilimanjaro

- Mt. Fiji, Java Trench, and Hawaii

In order to evaluate students' work, you should familiarize yourself with the plate boundaries of Earth. Before class, look at a couple of world maps showing plate boundaries. You can find some good maps showing plate boundaries on the Internet. Try searching Keywords like Earth plate maps, and look for Web sites by organizations such as USGS. Familiarizing yourself with Earth's plate boundaries will prepare you to help students make decisions about their own plate boundaries.

Set up the computer projection system with the *My World* project file for this section. If the class conversation leads students to revisit the data, you can use the projector.

Homework Options

Reflection

- **Science Content and Process:** Which of your plate boundaries did the class agree with you about? Which of your plate boundaries did some students disagree with you about? Why? *(Students should describe the reasons for others agreeing or disagreeing with their plate boundary inferences.)*

NOTES

....

....

....

....

....

NOTES

SECTION 3.7 IMPLEMENTATION

3.7 Explore

Where Are Plate Boundaries Located Across the Entire Earth?

The class will now work together to create a plate map covering Earth's entire crust. You will begin the process by working in pairs, focusing on regions that are near yours. This way, you can determine how the plate boundaries you have identified in your region connect to those others have identified. The class will then make a plate map of the entire Earth.

Conference

Neighboring Region Meeting

The class will divide into several groups, each focused on a different area of the world. Each pair of students will be working with two or three other pairs with the same, or neighboring regions. During a *Neighboring Region Meeting,* you will share your plate boundaries and the evidence used to develop them with others. Together, you will come to an agreement about the location of the plate boundaries in and between your regions.

You will be using all of the earthquake data and plate boundary sketches you have collected.

1. Begin by working with the other members of your group to arrange the transparencies so that corresponding areas are in line with each other. Tape the transparencies together so they can be moved later on. You might have several sets of transparencies for each region. If so, arrange them in several combinations.

2. Each pair of students should take a turn presenting their plate boundary inferences. They should share their current maps and point out the supporting evidence. They should also show their original plate boundary maps. Supporting evidence might include data on the map or data found in *My World.*

Materials

- transparencies with plate boundary sketches
- *Three-page Maps* with plate boundaries and notes on them
- *Region Project Board* pages
- markers

EE 141

EVER-CHANGING EARTH

3.7 Explore

Where Are Plate Boundaries Located Across the Entire Earth?

5 min

Students are introduced to the activity.

△ Guide

Let students know that they will now work together to create a map showing all of the plates in Earth's crust. They will start by sharing their plate boundary inferences with other students who examined earthquakes near their region. This will allow them to find how their plate boundaries connect with the plate boundaries other students identified. Once they have done this, they will work with the class to construct a world map showing plates and plate boundaries.

*A class period is considered to be one 40 to 50 minute class.

" Now you are going to meet with students who have made inferences about plate boundaries in regions close to your region. You will share your plate boundary inferences and determine how your plate boundaries connect with the plate boundaries in neighboring regions. Then we will be able to make a map of the plate boundaries around the world. **"**

Conference: Neighboring Region Meeting

20 min

Students meet to discuss how their plate boundaries connect with plate boundaries in neighboring regions.

regions tha̶t̶ ̶y̶o̶u̶r̶s̶. This way, you c̶
boundaries you have identified in your region connect to those others have
identified. The class will then make a plate map of the entire Earth.

Conference

Neighboring Region Meeting

The class will divide into several groups, each focused on a different area of the world. Each pair of students will be working with two or three other pairs with the same, or neighboring regions. During a *Neighboring Region Meeting,* you will share your plate boundaries and the evidence used to develop them with others. Together, you will come to an agreement about the location of the plate boundaries in and between your regions.

You will be using all of the earthquake data and plate boundary sketches you have collected.

1. Begin by working with the other members of your group to arrange the transparencies so that corresponding areas are in line with each other. Tape the transparencies together so they can be moved later on. You might have several sets of transparencies for each region. If so, arrange them in several combinations.

2. Each pair of students should take a turn presenting their plate boundary inferences. They should share their current maps and point out the supporting evidence. They should also show their original plate boundary maps. Supporting evidence might include data on the map or data found in *My World*.

Materials
- transparencies with plate boundary sketches
- *Three-page Maps* with plate boundaries and notes on them
- *Region Project Board* pages
- markers

△ Guide

Tell students they will now share their plate boundary inferences and evidence with other students working in the same area in *Neighboring Region Meetings*. In this meeting they will decide on the location of plate boundaries throughout the larger area containing all of the neighboring regions.

Divide the class into groups, distribute markers, and go over the instructions for the *Neighboring Region Meeting*. Groups will put their transparencies together, so they cover the neighboring regions on the map. Each pair should discuss the plate boundaries they drew on the transparencies, and share their *Three-page Maps* with supporting information.

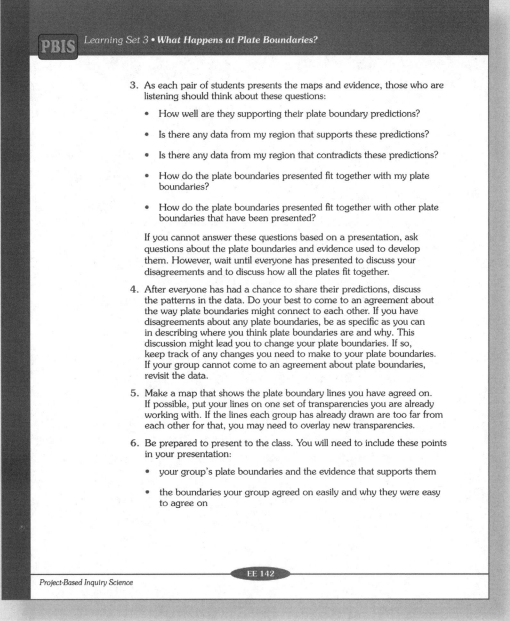

PBIS *Learning Set 3 • What Happens at Plate Boundaries?*

3. As each pair of students presents the maps and evidence, those who are listening should think about these questions:

- How well are they supporting their plate boundary predictions?

- Is there any data from my region that supports these predictions?

- Is there any data from my region that contradicts these predictions?

- How do the plate boundaries presented fit together with my plate boundaries?

- How do the plate boundaries presented fit together with other plate boundaries that have been presented?

If you cannot answer these questions based on a presentation, ask questions about the plate boundaries and evidence used to develop them. However, wait until everyone has presented to discuss your disagreements and to discuss how all the plates fit together.

4. After everyone has had a chance to share their predictions, discuss the patterns in the data. Do your best to come to an agreement about the way plate boundaries might connect to each other. If you have disagreements about any plate boundaries, be as specific as you can in describing where you think plate boundaries are and why. This discussion might lead you to change your plate boundaries. If so, keep track of any changes you need to make to your plate boundaries. If your group cannot come to an agreement about plate boundaries, revisit the data.

5. Make a map that shows the plate boundary lines you have agreed on. If possible, put your lines on one set of transparencies you are already working with. If the lines each group has already drawn are too far from each other for that, you may need to overlay new transparencies.

6. Be prepared to present to the class. You will need to include these points in your presentation:

- your group's plate boundaries and the evidence that supports them

- the boundaries your group agreed on easily and why they were easy to agree on

EE 142

Project-Based Inquiry Science

While groups share, students should evaluate their plate boundary inferences based others' evidence and their own data. They should use the bulleted questions in Step 3 as guidelines to evaluate predictions. The group should come to agreement about the plate boundaries in their neighboring regions. They should make a map showing the location of the plate boundaries they have agreed on and prepare a presentation. Some groups may not have room on their transparencies to trace their group's final plate boundary inference. Distribute new transparencies to groups as necessary. Their presentations should include information about how they decided on plate boundaries in their *Neighboring Region Meeting*. They should follow the guidelines in Step 6 as they prepare their presentations.

△ Guide and Assess

As students work with their groups, monitor their progress and assess how they are working together. Listen to the kinds of questions and feedback students have for each other. They may need tips about how to have a discussion in a constructive manner.

- Students should wait until a pair has finished sharing before they question or challenge their ideas.

- Students should support their ideas with data. When students disagree, they should examine the data to try to settle the disagreement.

- When anyone challenges another person's idea, he or she should describe the differences and similarities between their ideas.

Ask neighboring region groups what plate boundaries they have agreed on and what evidence they have for these plate boundaries. Is there any evidence that contradicts the locations for the plate boundaries they identified?

Ask groups what plate boundaries they disagree on. Do they think they need to change the plate boundaries they identified? What evidence do they have to support their ideas about where these plate boundaries are?

As groups work on their maps, check to make sure that the maps show the boundary lines they agreed on. Look for places where the plate boundaries that different groups identify are incompatible. Do not point these out now, but note them. Students should notice and discuss these places when groups share their plate boundaries with the class.

Emphasize that students should prepare to present their ideas to the class.

NOTES

3.7 Explore

- any areas where you had disagreements and the supporting evidence you used to work them out

- any plate boundary inferences that had been made earlier but were changed as a result of this meeting (and why they were changed)

- any plates your group has identified.

Communicate

Share Your Plate Boundary Inferences

All groups will now present their plate boundaries to the class. During each presentation, the group should show the transparent overlays of the agreed-upon plate boundaries and plates and present the material listed. Each pair of students should discuss changes they made to their plate boundary inferences during the *Neighboring Region Plate Meeting.*

As you are listening to presentations, notice plates and plate boundaries that overlap your map and plate boundaries that might connect to yours. Also, make sure you understand what supporting evidence each group used to determine plate boundaries and plates and how they think their plates fit in with other plates. If a presenting group has not made these points clear, ask them questions to clarify.

Reflect

After all the groups have presented, discuss and answer the following questions:

1. Where are the places along the plate boundaries that the class is most sure about?

2. Where are the places along the plate boundaries that the class is least sure about?

3. Where are there gaps in the data? What data do you need to fill in the gaps?

4. Where are there overlaps in the plates? What evidence do you have that these plates overlap?

EE 143

EVER-CHANGING EARTH

Communicate: Share Your Plate Boundary Inferences

10 min

Groups present their plate boundaries to the class.

△ Guide

Have groups present their plate boundaries to the class. Each group should begin by showing the transparent overlays with the plate boundaries they agreed on. They should discuss the evidence that supports the plate boundaries they identified. They should discuss which boundaries were easy to agree on, which were more difficult, and the reasons some were more difficult than others. They should also point out any plate boundaries they revised during the meeting. If they can identify any complete plates, they should do so.

Emphasize that as groups present, students in the audience should think about how the plate boundaries presented connect with the plate boundaries in their regions. Emphasize that students should ask questions to make sure they understand how the plate boundaries are supported by the group's data.

△ Guide and Assess

As groups present, listen to the questions students ask and the comments they offer. If there are any places where different groups' plate boundaries are incompatible, make sure that students notice this. If they do not notice it on their own, ask them guiding questions, such as: "How will these plate boundaries fit with the plate boundaries that the last group identified?"

Assess how students ask questions or make comments. Their questions and comments should be constructive. Model the kinds of questions you expect students to ask. You might ask a question like: "Can you explain what data you used to find the plate boundary in the upper left?"

Reflect

15 min

Lead a class discussion of the Reflect *questions.*

determ... ...s and plates ar...
with other plates. If a presenting group has not made these points clear, ask them questions to clarify.

Reflect

After all the groups have presented, discuss and answer the following questions:

1. Where are the places along the plate boundaries that the class is most sure about?

2. Where are the places along the plate boundaries that the class is least sure about?

3. Where are there gaps in the data? What data do you need to fill in the gaps?

4. Where are there overlaps in the plates? What evidence do you have that these plates overlap?

△ Guide

When all groups have presented, lead a class discussion of the *Reflect* questions. First, ask groups where along the plate boundaries the class is most sure about. They should identify places where they were able to make inferences based on clear evidence. Ask what places they are least sure about. These could be places where they were not able to get the right amount of data, or where they seemed to have contradictory evidence.

Ask students where there are gaps in the data. They should identify places where they cannot confidently complete the plate boundaries because they do not have enough data. Ask them where plates overlap. Ask them what evidence they have that the plates are overlapping. Students should be able to point out places where a fault zone covers a wide area.

If students decide that there are significant gaps in their data or that they have disagreements they need to resolve, consider having them use *My World* to examine the data again. They may also hold another *Neighboring Region Meeting*.

At the end of the class discussion, choose a student from each group to trace the agreed-on plate boundary zones on a new set of transparency sheets. Then post the new set of transparency sheets somewhere where the class can see it.

◇ Evaluate

The plate boundaries should look similar the widely accepted plate boundaries shown on many maps. When looking at students' transparencies, refer back to the maps you reviewed earlier of actual plate boundaries. Make sure the students have matched these maps.

NOTES

Conference

10 min

Pairs make new maps of the plate boundaries in their region.

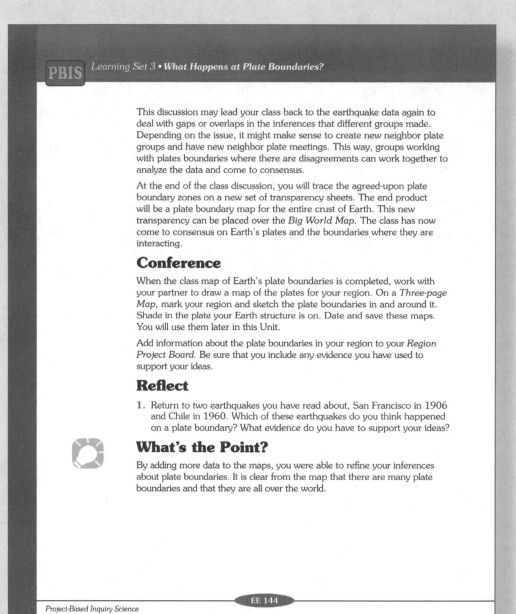

This discussion may lead your class back to the earthquake data again to deal with gaps or overlaps in the inferences that different groups made. Depending on the issue, it might make sense to create new neighbor plate groups and have new neighbor plate meetings. This way, groups working with plates boundaries where there are disagreements can work together to analyze the data and come to consensus.

At the end of the class discussion, you will trace the agreed-upon plate boundary zones on a new set of transparency sheets. The end product will be a plate boundary map for the entire crust of Earth. This new transparency can be placed over the *Big World Map.* The class has now come to consensus on Earth's plates and the boundaries where they are interacting.

Conference

When the class map of Earth's plate boundaries is completed, work with your partner to draw a map of the plates for your region. On a *Three-page Map,* mark your region and sketch the plate boundaries in and around it. Shade in the plate your Earth structure is on. Date and save these maps. You will use them later in this Unit.

Add information about the plate boundaries in your region to your *Region Project Board.* Be sure that you include any evidence you have used to support your ideas.

Reflect

1. Return to two earthquakes you have read about, San Francisco in 1906 and Chile in 1960. Which of these earthquakes do you think happened on a plate boundary? What evidence do you have to support your ideas?

What's the Point?

By adding more data to the maps, you were able to refine your inferences about plate boundaries. It is clear from the map that there are many plate boundaries and that they are all over the world.

EE 144

Project-Based Inquiry Science

⬡ Get Going

Distribute new *Three-page Maps* if necessary, and have pairs draw the plate boundaries in their regions using the class's plate map as a reference. They should shade in the plate their Earth structure is on. Have them save these maps; they will use them again later.

Before continuing, have students take a moment to record what they have learned about the plate boundaries in their region on their *Region Project Board.*

△ Guide

Lead a class discussion of the *Reflect* question. Ask students if the Chile earthquake of 1960 occurred on a plate boundary. Did the San Francisco earthquake of 1906 occur on a plate boundary?

Students should have found that plate boundaries run along the coast of Chile and through San Francisco. With this information, they can reasonably conclude that the earthquakes in Chile and San Francisco occurred on or near these plate boundaries.

Reflect

10 min

The class has a discussion of the Reflect question.

Assessment Options

Targeted Concepts, Skills, and Nature of Science	How do I know if students got it?
Scientists often work together and then share their findings. Sharing findings makes new information available and helps scientists refine their ideas and build on others' ideas. When another person's or group's idea is used, credit needs to be given.	**ASK:** What did you do during this section that you think best exhibits how you worked together, like scientists, to share your findings and refine your ideas? **LISTEN:** Students should describe how they discussed the plates in their regions with students in *Neighboring Region Meetings*.
Scientists must keep clear, accurate, and descriptive records of what they do so they can share their work with others and consider what they did, why they did it, and what they want to do next.	**ASK:** How did you use your *Three-page Map* and transparencies to develop ideas about the plate boundaries around the world? **LISTEN:** Students should have used their maps and transparencies as references as they discussed global plate boundaries.
Scientists make claims (conclusions) based on evidence obtained (trends in data) from reliable investigations.	**ASK:** Why was it important to have reliable data during your discussions of plate boundaries in and around your region? **LISTEN:** Students should recognize that they needed reliable data to support their ideas. In particular, they needed reliable data to settle disagreements about where plate boundaries are.

Teacher Reflection Questions

- What difficulties did students have agreeing on the plate boundaries of Earth?

- How did you evaluate students' contributions to the class discussion of global plate boundaries? What ideas do you have for encouraging students to actively participate in class discussions?

- How did you monitor the *Neighboring Region Meetings?* What ideas do you have for next time?

NOTES

Back to the Big Question

What Processes Within Earth Cause Geologic Activity?

◀ $1\frac{1}{4}$ *class periods*

A class period is considered to be one 40 to 50 minute class.

Overview

Students list the geologic terms they have learned in this *Learning Set* and make sketches to show the defining features of each term. They record connections between them, synthesizing the geologic ideas they have learned. Using the data they gathered, they create explanations of which plates in their regions interact to cause geologic activity. Finally, they consider what information would help them better explain what causes geologic activity and changes in their Earth structure, and they update the *Project Board*.

Targeted Concepts, Skills, and Nature of Science	Performance Expectations
Scientists often work together and then share their findings. Sharing findings makes new information available and helps scientists refine their ideas and build on others' ideas. When another person's or group's idea is used, credit needs to be given.	Students should work together in small groups to create explanations. They should share their explanations with the class, discussing how different groups supported their claims.
Scientists must keep clear, accurate, and descriptive records of what they do so they can share their work with others and consider what they did, why they did it, and what they want to do next.	Students should keep clear, accurate, and descriptive records of the geologic concepts they have learned and of their claims and supporting evidence.
Graphs and tables are an effective way to analyze and communicate results of scientific investigation.	Students should use the *Project Board* and possibly other tables to organize information. These should assist in analyzing the information and sharing it with others.

Targeted Concepts, Skills, and Nature of Science	Performance Expectations
Explanations are claims supported by evidence. Evidence can be experimental results, observational data, and other accepted scientific knowledge.	Students should create explanations, supporting their claims with evidence and scientific knowledge.
Scientists make claims (conclusions) based on evidence obtained (trends in data) from reliable investigations.	Students should construct claims based on observations and use these in their explanations.
Earthquake activity, volcanic activity, and topography are all evidence that Earth's crust is moving and changing.	Students should use evidence from their observations of earthquake activity, volcanic activity, and topography to support their claims about how plates in their regions cause geologic activity.

Materials

1 per student	*Create Your Explanation* page *Project Board* page
1 per class	Class *Project Board*
100 per group	Index cards

Homework Options

Preparation for Learning Set 4

- **Science Content:** What is occurring under Earth's crust to cause its plates to move? *(The purpose of this question is to elicit students' initial ideas about what is occurring in the mantle to cause the plates to move. Students will learn about convective currents in the next Learning Set.)*

Learning Set 3

Back to the Big Question

What Processes Within Earth Cause Geologic Activity?

Through investigation and analysis, you created a map of Earth's plates and a map of the plate for your Earth structure. You observed that earthquakes happen in different patterns, and you described and named those patterns. After *Learning Set 2,* you worked out your best explanation of the processes changing and shaping Earth's crust. You will have another chance to do that later in the Unit. However, before doing that, you will attempt to describe and explain the processes causing geologic activity in your region. This will help you later when you address the *Big Challenge* again.

Add to Your *Picture Map*

The goal of this *Learning Set* was to begin to understand how plate movements can cause earthquakes and to identify the location of Earth's plates and plate boundaries. While you worked on this goal, you came across many new geologic terms: *earthquake, tsunami, magnitude, depth, intensity, fault, seismic waves, seismograph, seismogram, body waves, surface waves, longitudinal wave, transverse wave, P waves, S waves, epicenter, focus, triangulation, Richter Scale, Modified Mercalli Intensity Scale,* and *plate boundary.* These scientific terms may have been new to you and may still be difficult to understand. When you learn new terms, it can be helpful to create pictures that show what the words mean, and build a map to show how the words relate to one another.

As you have done previously, write each term on a separate index card using large text so others will be able to read it from far away. Make cards with any other terms that were new to you and that you think are important. Next to the term or on the back of the card, draw a picture to show what the geologic term means. Make your picture as accurate as possible. Be sure to include features that would help someone else understand the geologic term.

EE 145

EVER-CHANGING EARTH

Learning Set 3

Back to the Big Question

5 min

Students are introduced to the activity.

○ **Engage**

Remind students of the *Big Question: What processes within Earth cause geologic activity?* Ask groups what claims they made for the processes that cause geologic activity in *Learning Set 2*. Tell them that they will now construct explanations of geologic activity in their regions. Have the class *Project Board* on display and point out where it is. Let students know they may want to refer to their *Project Board* as they are revising their explanations.

*A class period is considered to be one 40 to 50 minute class.

Add to Your Picture Map

10 min

Students map the concepts they have learned using index cards.

Add to Your *Picture Map*

The goal of this *Learning Set* was to begin to understand how plate movements can cause earthquakes and to identify the location of Earth's plates and plate boundaries. While you worked on this goal, you came across many new geologic terms: *earthquake, tsunami, magnitude, depth, intensity, fault, seismic waves, seismograph, seismogram, body waves, surface waves, longitudinal wave, transverse wave, P waves, S waves, epicenter, focus, triangulation, Richter Scale, Modified Mercalli Intensity Scale,* and *plate boundary.* These scientific terms may have been new to you and may still be difficult to understand. When you learn new terms, it can be helpful to create pictures that show what the words mean, and build a map to show how the words relate to one another.

As you have done previously, write each term on a separate index card using large text so others will be able to read it from far away. Make cards with any other terms that were new to you and that you think are important. Next to the term or on the back of the card, draw a picture to show what the geologic term means. Make your picture as accurate as possible. Be sure to include features that would help someone else understand the geologic term.

△ Guide

Tell students that they will add to their *Picture Maps* by writing important terms on index cards, as they did in *Learning Sets 1* and *2*. They will draw a picture of each term to communicate what it means. Emphasize that their drawings should help people who are not familiar with the terms understand what they mean. The student text mentions some of the words that may be new to students: earthquake, tsunami, magnitude, depth, intensity, fault, seismic waves, seismograph, seismogram, body waves, surface waves, longitudinal wave, transverse wave, P waves, S waves, epicenter, focus, triangulation, Richter Scale, Modified Mercalli Intensity Scale, and plate boundary.

NOTES

Return to the cards you created after *Learning Sets 1* and *2*. You know more now about some of those concepts than you knew when you made those cards. Revise your pictures to make them more accurate.

When you have completed your cards, share them with a group of classmates. Your teacher will tell you which group. Listen carefully as someone in your group describes each geologic term. For each card, notice if there is additional information or if there are changes you need to make to your drawing or definition.

As you did at the end of *Learning Sets 1* and *2,* work with your group to create a map showing how the geologic terms go together. Discuss the connections with your group. If you cannot come to an agreement now, record your disagreement. As you learn more about the geologic terms, you will be better able to connect the ideas together. You can then revise your cards and connections.

On each card, record the connections you made. Record each connection on the cards connected to one another. Be as specific as possible. Record any disagreements your group had about connections, and mark connections you do not understand.

Explain

Use your interpretations of the earthquake data to explain which plates are interacting to cause geologic activity in your region. Use a *Create Your Explanation* page to help you. Remember that a good explanation has several parts to it:

- **your claim:** a statement of what you understand or a conclusion you have reached

- **your evidence:** data collected from investigations that support your claim

- **your science knowledge:** knowledge about how things work that supports your claim

- **your explanation itself:** a logical statement connecting your evidence and science knowledge to your claim in a way that can convince someone that your claim is valid. Good explanations tell what is happening that makes the claim valid.

EE 146

Project-Based Inquiry Science

When students have completed their cards, they should share them with a group of students who were assigned to the same region. Each student should listen to other members' descriptions of the terms and think about information they can add to their own cards or changes they can make to their drawings.

They should work with their groups to find how the terms go together, including the terms from *Learning Sets 1* and *2*. They should arrange their cards on the table to show how the ideas connect. When they have agreed on how the ideas connect, they should record the connections on the back of the cards. If members of the group disagree about how the ideas connect, they should record their disagreement.

⬡ Get Going

Divide the class into regional groups, distribute index cards, and go over the list of terms that students should include in their *Picture Maps*. Emphasize that each student should create a set of cards illustrating the terms.

△ Guide and Assess

As students work on their cards, monitor their progress and assist them with any difficulties they encounter. If they need guidance as they create sketches to illustrate their geologic terms, have them imagine that they are trying to explain these ideas to someone using sketches. Ask them questions about the ideas to guide them towards statements they can illustrate.

When students share their cards with their groups, listen to how they discuss differences in the information on their cards and how they discuss the best arrangement of their cards. Emphasize that students should ask questions and make comments constructively. If students have difficulty arranging their cards, ask them what the most important connections between the ideas they have illustrated are. For each idea, what other ideas do they have to use in an explanation?

NOTES

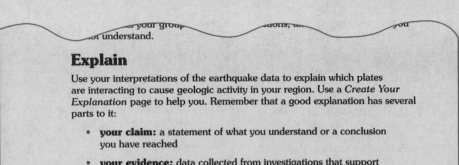

Explain

Use your interpretations of the earthquake data to explain which plates are interacting to cause geologic activity in your region. Use a *Create Your Explanation* page to help you. Remember that a good explanation has several parts to it:

- **your claim:** a statement of what you understand or a conclusion you have reached

- **your evidence:** data collected from investigations that support your claim

- **your science knowledge:** knowledge about how things work that supports your claim

- **your explanation itself:** a logical statement connecting your evidence and science knowledge to your claim in a way that can convince someone that your claim is valid. Good explanations tell what is happening that makes the claim valid.

Explain

10 min

Students create explanations of the ways that movements in Earth's layers cause changes in Earth's surface.

△ Guide

Let students know that they will now create explanations of which plates interact to cause geologic activity in their regions. They will use evidence from the earthquake data they gathered and science knowledge from their reading.

Review the parts of a good explanation with the class: the claim, the evidence, the science knowledge, and the explanation connecting the evidence and the science knowledge to the claim. A good explanation could have the form "The movements of Earth's layers cause Earth's surface to change by …. We know this because we observed … and we learned that …." Students should use the bulleted list in the text as a reference for creating explanations.

Emphasize that students' claims should be statements about the ways that movement of Earth's layers cause changes in Earth's surface. These claims should be as clear and accurate as possible.

NOTES

Your claim will be the best statement you can develop describing how movements of Earth's layers are causing changes in your region. Evidence to support your claim can come from the modeling you have done and the earthquake data patterns you have observed and described. Your drawings and sketches may be useful in helping you visualize the ways Earth's processes are working. Your science knowledge can come from your reading and the earthquake data you have observed. Work with your partner to create the best explanation you can. You will have a chance later in the Unit to revise your explanation. It may be easier to express your explanation by attaching phrases to sketches than using only words. Feel free to combine sketches and words in your explanation.

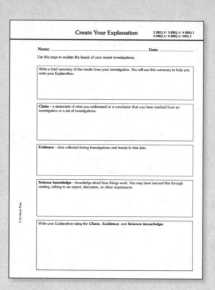

Conference

Share Your Explanation

Meet with other pairs assigned to your region to share the explanations you have developed for the changes that are happening in your region of the world. Listen and watch how others have explained the data patterns. Look for different ways Earth structure partners expressed their explanations. Think about ways you can improve your explanation. Revise your explanation based on what you learn from your peers.

As a group, select one explanation you think best explains geologic activity around your group's Earth structures. Your group will share this explanation with the rest of the class.

☐ Assess

As groups work on their explanations, monitor their progress and help them with any difficulties they are having. Ask them what evidence and science knowledge they are using to support their claims.

Note the similarities and differences among groups' claims. During presentations, you might consider having two groups with very similar claims present one after the other so that students can compare how they supported their claims.

△ Guide

When students have completed their explanations, have pairs meet with other pairs who studied the same region to share their explanations. As each pair presents their explanation, the other students in the group should listen and think about ways they can improve their explanations.

When all pairs in a group have presented, each pair should independently revise their explanation. If other pairs in the group used evidence that they did not use, they should include this evidence. If they realized that their interpretation of the data could be improved, they should revise their claims accordingly.

When pairs have revised their explanations, they should briefly share their revisions with the group. The group should discuss the explanations presented and choose the one that they think is best. The group will present this explanation to the class.

Conference: Share Your Explanation

15 min

Students share their explanations with other students assigned to the same region.

NOTES

_____

_____

_____

_____

_____

_____

Communicate

10 min

Groups present their explanations.

Communicate

Share your group's explanation with the rest of the class. As you are listening to others, look for ways they have explained patterns that are similar to yours.

Reflect

With your partner, answer the following questions:

1. What revisions did you make to your explanation after the group discussion?

2. How trustworthy and complete do you think your explanation is? To figure that out, think about how well it explains the earthquake patterns around other similar Earth structures.

3. What else do you need to investigate to make a better explanation of the processes causing changes in your Earth structure?

Update the *Project Board*

Now add to the *Project Board* what you know about the causes of earthquakes and how Earth's processes result in different kinds of earthquake patterns. Remember that any information added to the *What are we learning?* column should be supported with evidence in the *What is our evidence?* column.

Add any new questions you have identified to the *What do we need to investigate?* column. Also, add questions you need answered to help you better explain how processes deep within Earth are causing geologic activity and changes to Earth's crust, and questions you need answered to explain the geologic activity in and around your region.

△ Guide

When groups have discussed their explanations, have them present the explanation they chose. With the class, review the explanation and ask the class to identify the parts of the explanation. Encourage the class to suggest any different ideas they have for the explanations presented. Ask groups with similar interpretations if they used any different evidence and science knowledge to support their claims.

☐ Assess

As the class discusses the presentations and the final class recommendation, listen to how students discuss their ideas. Do students ask each other about things that are not clear? Do they give constructive feedback?

△ Guide

Once groups have presented their explanations to the class, have students answer the *Reflect* questions with their partners. Emphasize that they should be prepared to share their answers with the class.

△ Guide and Assess

When students have had time to answer the *Reflect* questions, lead a class discussion of their responses. Listen for the following in students' answers:

1. Students should specify the changes they made to their explanations. If their original explanations were supported by too little evidence, or if their claims did not match the evidence, they should have revised their explanations to use more data or to better interpret the evidence.

2. Students should honestly evaluate how well they have explained earthquake patterns in their regions, and how well their explanations can be applied to regions with similar Earth structures.

3. This question is meant to engage students in thinking about what they need to investigate. Students should have questions about what causes plates to move, what patterns they can find in volcanic activity, what causes volcanic activity, what they can learn from depth data, and why some earthquakes occur in the middle of plates.

△ Guide

Update the *Project Board* with the class. Ask students what they have learned since they last updated the *Project Board*. Record their answers in the *What are we learning?* column. This should include claims from groups' explanations. For everything that students put in the *What are we learning?* column, ask them what evidence they have. Record the evidence in the *What is our evidence?* column. Finally, ask students what they still need to investigate, and record their answers in the *What do we need to investigate?* column. Students should record the questions they identified in the *Reflect* discussion.

Reflect
10 min

Students answer the Reflect *questions and have a class discussion.*

Update the Project Board
10 min

Lead a class discussion to update the Project Board.

Assessment Options

Targeted Concepts, Skills, and Nature of Science	How do I know if students got it?
Scientists often work together and then share their findings. Sharing findings makes new information available and helps scientists refine their ideas and build on others' ideas. When another person's or group's idea is used, credit needs to be given.	**ASK:** How did listening to other pairs' explanations help you refine your own explanations? **LISTEN:** Students should have identified evidence and science knowledge in other pairs' explanations that they could use. They should also have considered the strengths and weaknesses of other pairs' explanations.
Scientists must keep clear, accurate, and descriptive records of what they do so they can share their work with others and consider what they did, why they did it, and what they want to do next.	**ASK:** Why was it important to record what you have learned along with your evidence on the *Project Board?* **LISTEN:** Students should recognize that this allows them to track their progress toward answering the *Big Question.*
Graphs and tables are an effective way to analyze and communicate results of scientific investigation.	**ASK:** How did organizing geologic terms by their connections with other terms help you? How did recording the things you have learned in a list with your drawing help? **LISTEN:** Students should recognize that organizing terms by their connections helped them to understand how all of these geologic terms are related and can be applied to understanding Earth structures. Making a list of the things they learned with the drawings should have helped students see how individual observations were related to their final interpretations (the drawings).

Targeted Concepts, Skills, and Nature of Science	How do I know if students got it?
Explanations are claims supported by evidence. Evidence can be experimental results, observational data, and other accepted scientific knowledge.	**ASK:** How did you use scientific knowledge in your explanations? **LISTEN:** Students should have used scientific knowledge as evidence to support the claims in their explanations.
Scientists make claims (conclusions) based on evidence obtained (trends in data) from reliable investigations.	**ASK:** How is an interpretation different from an explanation? **LISTEN:** Students should be able to recognize that in an explanation, claims are supported by the observations (evidence) and science knowledge.
Earthquake activity, volcanic activity, and topography are all evidence that Earth's crust is moving and changing.	**ASK:** What evidence did you use to support your explanations? **LISTEN:** Students should have used evidence from their observations of earthquakes, volcanic activity, and topographic features.

Teacher Reflection Questions

- What concepts in this *Learning Set* were difficult for students? How can you help them master these concepts?

- How have you been able to evaluate students' progress as they learn about geologic activity and Earth structures?

- What management issues arose when students worked with regional groups? What ideas do you have for addressing these issues next time?

NOTES

LEARNING SET 4 INTRODUCTION

Learning Set 4

◀ *5 class periods*

A class period is
considered to be one
40 to 50 minute class.

What Causes Earth's Plates to Move?

Overview

Students learn about density, convection, and convection currents. They apply these concepts to understanding how and why Earth's mantle moves and how this movement causes the plates that make up Earth's surface to move. It is important for students to understand that the plates move because the mantle is moving, and that some plates move apart and others move together. These ideas motivate and prepare students to investigate patterns in volcano data in the next *Learning Set*.

Targeted Concepts, Skills, and Nature of Science	Section
Scientists often work together and then share their findings. Sharing findings makes new information available and helps scientists refine their ideas and build on others' ideas. When another person or group's idea is used, credit needs to be given.	4.1, 4.2, 4.BBQ
Scientists must keep clear, accurate, and descriptive records of what they do so they can share their work with others and consider what they did, why they did it, and what they want to do next.	4.1, 4.2, 4.BBQ
Scientists use models to simulate processes that happen too fast, too slow, on a scale that cannot be observed directly (either too small or too large), or that are too dangerous.	4.2, 4.3
Earth is a system made up of different layers, each with a distinctive composition and set of characteristics. These layers interact, driving the processes that shape Earth.	4.3
The hot core of Earth drives the processes that bring about changes in the crust by creating convection currents in the mantle material. These convection currents drive plate motion.	4.3

Targeted Concepts, Skills, and Nature of Science	Section
Graphs and tables are an effective way to analyze and communicate results of scientific investigation.	4.BBQ
Explanations are claims supported by evidence. Evidence can be experimental results, observational data, and other accepted scientific knowledge.	4.BBQ
Scientists make claims (conclusions) based on evidence obtained (trends in data) from reliable investigations.	4.BBQ
Earthquake activity, volcanic activity, and topography are all evidence that Earth's crust is moving and changing.	4.BBQ

Students' Initial Conceptions and Capabilities

- Students may confuse mass, volume, and density. They tend to use phrases like lighter, heavier, smaller, or bigger interchangeably for these concepts (Lee et al., 1993; Stavy, 1990).

- If students do not understand what matter is, then they cannot accept mass as an intrinsic property of matter, or distinguish between mass and density (Carey, 1991; Smith et al., 1985; Smith, Snir, & Grosslight, 1987).

- Some students think that liquids and gases are weightless (do not contain matter) (Stavy, 1991; Mas, Perez, & Harris, 1987).

NOTES

Understanding for Teachers

Density

Density is mass per volume. Mass and volume are both measures of how much of something there is. Mass is a measure of how much matter or material there is and volume is a measure of how much space it occupies. Density is a measure of how much material there is per space or how tightly packed the material is in a given volume.

When fluids or gases of different densities are mixed together in a gravitational field, the least-dense substance rises to the top and the most-dense substance sinks to the bottom. This happens due to how gravity pulls on these substances. Students saw how this happens when they created density columns.

Convection

All fluids (liquids and gases) experience Brownian motion, or diffusion. If a drop of dye of approximately the same density as water is placed in a bowl of water, eventually the molecules of dye will mix evenly with the molecules of water due to the random motion of the molecules. This is known as Brownian motion. However, if you place a drop of dye in a heated (but not boiling) bowl of water you will observe convection currents. These currents occur because as you heat the water, the molecules of water gain thermal energy, or motion energy. As their motion increases, the molecules of water bounce farther apart from each other (and the bonds of the molecules of water move farther) so that the water's density decreases. As its density decreases, the hot water rises to the top of the bowl of water. At the top, it transfers some of its thermal energy to the air and the molecules again move closer together, increasing their density. These cooler, denser molecules then sink to the bottom of the bowl. (Note that during boiling, the bonds between the molecules are broken, forming gas bubbles that rise to the top.)

This is also observed with air, a type of fluid. You might notice on a warm day that the warmest air in a house is on the top floor and the coolest is on the lowest floor. This is because as the air gains thermal energy it becomes less dense and rises.

For more information, try an Internet search using Keywords such as density or convection currents.

LOOKING AHEAD

Students work in pairs in *Section 4.1*. When picking pairs, keep in mind that students will be working in these pairs in *Section 4.2* also.

Prepare and try out the simulation in *Section 4.2*. Also make sure to allocate a DVD player and monitor or television for the video demonstrations in *Section 4.2*.

NOTES

LEARNING SET 4 IMPLEMENTATION

Learning Set 4

What Causes Earth's Plates to Move?

People look for the reasons events happen to better understand their world. For example, if a football flew past your window, you might think that someone threw it or kicked it. You would know that the ball is moving, but you would not know what made it move. Some parts of an explanation are easier to fill in than others.

Similarly, you have evidence that Earth's plates move. Most geologic activity is caused by the movement of Earth's plates. Earthquakes occur when two plates collide or slide past each other. You may see or feel these movements if you are on Earth's surface, but evidence that Earth's plates are moving does not explain why they move. The question, *What causes Earth's plates to move?* has not yet been answered. In this *Learning Set,* you will explore the causes of plate movement.

EE 149

EVER-CHANGING EARTH

Learning Set 4

What Causes Earth's Plates to Move?

5 min

Students are introduced to the Learning Set.

○ Engage

Remind students that they have made progress toward explaining geologic activity around the world. They now know that the plates in Earth's crust move, causing earthquakes and other geologic activity, but they do not know what causes the plates to move. Compare this to the scenario in the student text. If you see a football fly by the window, you can explain that you see the ball outside the window because it is moving through the air, but you can only make conjectures about what sent it through the air. Maybe someone kicked it. Maybe someone threw it.

*A class period is considered to be one 40 to 50 minute class.

TEACHER TALK

"We have made a lot of progress. Now we can show that interactions between plates in Earth's crust cause earthquakes and other geologic activity. We can even show where the boundaries of plates are, but we cannot yet explain what causes the plates to move.

Think about if you saw a football fly past your window. You could explain that you saw the football through your window because it is flying through the air. But that is not really a complete explanation, right? You still want to know what sent it flying through the air. Did someone kick it? Did someone throw it? You probably want to know who kicked it or threw it.

That's about where we are with our explanation of geologic activity. We still need to find out what causes plates to move."

NOTES

4.1 Understand the Question

Think About Why Earth's Plates Move

◄ *1 class period*

A class period is considered to be one 40 to 50 minute class.

Overview

Students consider several ideas about what causes Earth's plates to move and describe why they agree or disagree with the ideas. They identify possible sources for the forces that move Earth's crust, examples of processes that illustrate how this could happen, and evidence to support their ideas about these forces. The class discusses these ideas and identifies investigation questions for the *Project Board*.

Targeted Concepts, Skills, and Nature of Science	Performance Expectations
Scientists often work together and then share their findings. Sharing findings makes new information available and helps scientists refine their ideas and build on others' ideas. When another person's or group's idea is used, credit needs to be given.	Groups should describe why they agree or disagree with any ideas about how and why Earth's crust moves, and how they may prove or disprove the idea. Then groups should share their ideas with the class.
Scientists must keep clear, accurate, and descriptive records of what they do so they can share their work with others and consider what they did, why they did it, and what they want to do next.	Students should update the class *Project Board*, making sure it contains all they know about Earth's crust and all the things they need to investigate to determine how and why Earth's plates move.

Materials	
1 per class	Class *Project Board*
1 per student	*Project Board* page

Homework Options

Reflection

- **Science Content and Process:** Write up an experiment you think could provide insights into how and why Earth's plates move. What variables would you measure and how would this information help you answer the questions of how and why Earth's plates move? *(The purpose of this question is to get students thinking about what variable they would measure to provide answers to how and why Earth's crust moves, and to think about the investigative process.)*

Preparation for 4.2

- **Science Content and Process:** Earth's crust is very large, and it is difficult to observe physical processes on the scale of Earth's crust. How might you investigate the physical processes that affect Earth's crust? *(Students may have a variety of ideas. It is important for students to recognize they could use models and simulations to investigate these processes, as with many other processes that happen on a large scale.)*

NOTES

....

....

....

....

....

....

....

....

SECTION 4.1 IMPLEMENTATION

4.1 Understand the Question

Think About Why Earth's Plates Move

You know that plates move and that this movement can result in geologic activity. You could stop there and think that you have answered the *Big Question*. However, if you think like a scientist, you will realize that knowing that the plates move raises new questions. One important question is: What tremendous forces are capable of moving the giant blocks of rock that make up Earth's plates?

It takes two large tractor trailers to move this house— imagine the force it must take to move a giant block of Earth's crust.

Get Started

On the next page, you will find some students' ideas about why Earth's plates move. Read each one carefully. Working with your partner, determine what evidence, if any, supports each idea. Make a list of this evidence.

Project-Based Inquiry Science

EE 150

4.1 Understand the Question

Think About Why Earth's Plates Move

5 min

Students are introduced to the activity.

○ Engage

Remind students of the *Big Question: What processes within Earth cause geologic activity?* Ask them what they think their best answer to the question is. At this point, students should be able to say that plates in Earth's crust move, causing earthquakes and other geologic activity. Ask them if they can say why the plates in Earth's crust move. Let them know they will investigate why the plates move in this *Learning Set*.

*A class period is considered to be one 40 to 50 minute class.

"Remember that the *Big Question* for the Unit is *What processes within Earth cause geologic activity?* At this point, what is the best answer you can give to that question? You can confidently say that the motion of plates in Earth's crust causes geologic activity, right? What can you say about what causes the plates to move? "

Get Started

15 min

Students read ideas about Earth's movement and record why they agree or disagree.

Get Started

On the next page, you will find some students' ideas about why Earth's plates move. Read each one carefully. Working with your partner, determine what evidence, if any, supports each idea. Make a list of this evidence.

Get Going

Go over the four ideas in the student text about why Earth's plates move. Emphasize that they should consider the great mass of the plates in Earth's crust and what forces could move such great mass. Have students discuss the ideas with their partners. They should think about the data they have examined and their science knowledge to determine if they have evidence to support any of the ideas. They should list the evidence they have that supports each idea. They should also think about what they would need to investigate to determine if each idea is correct. Let pairs know they will share their ideas with the class.

NOTES

....

....

....

....

4.1 *Understand the Question*

As you are thinking about each idea, consider the forces involved. Ask yourself if you think the forces suggested in each idea are big enough to move Earth's huge plates.

Leah: "I think lava, coming to the surface through breaks between the plates, pushes the plates apart. That would cause them to collide on the other side of the plate."

Joanne: "The plates float on Earth's mantle, like a raft or a chunk of ice floats in water. When the mantle moves, the plates move."

Consuela: "I think the plates just push and pull on each other, similar to bumper cars that sometimes run into each other and sometimes bounce off each other."

Jack: "Gravity is a very strong force. I learned that gravity causes the tides to change every day. It could be strong enough to make the plates move."

Conference

Discuss your ideas and compare lists with another pair of students. Use your lists to make a chart like the one below. In the *Source of force* column, list ideas about what causes Earth's plates to move. For each force, decide whether you think it can move Earth's plates and what role it might play. Enter the role you think each force can play in the middle column, and record supporting examples illustrating how the force might or might not be able to move an entire plate.

What causes Earth's plates to move?		
Source of force	What role might this force play in moving Earth's plates?	Supporting examples

Conference
10 min

Students discuss their responses to the ideas with other pairs and select an idea they think best explains what causes plates to move.

⬡ Get Going

When pairs have had time to respond to each idea, have each pair meet with another pair to form groups of four. (**NOTE:** Students will be working in these groups through the next section.) They should discuss the ideas and compare their lists of evidence. They should also discuss the sources of force they think might cause plates to move.

In their groups, students should create a table like the one in their text. In the left column, they should record the sources of force they discuss. For each force, they should identify a way the force could contribute to plate motion and record this in the middle column. In the third column, they should record examples to support their ideas.

△ Guide and Assess

As groups discuss their ideas, listen to how they discuss their ideas and how they support them. Look at the tables the students create. Students should give reasons for their responses to the ideas they read, and they should comment constructively on each other's reactions. For each source of force, they should articulate how the force causes plate motion, drawing on their knowledge of geologic activity and real-world phenomena for illustrative examples.

What causes Earth's plates to move?		
Source of force	What role might this force play in moving Earth's plates?	Supporting examples
Lava coming to the surface	The force of the rising lava could push the plates apart.	Volcanoes demonstrate that lava can force its way to the surface.
Motion in the mantle	When the mantle moves, it could carry the plates that float on it.	The density column provides evidence that less-dense materials can float on denser materials. Heavy ships with sails that can be moved by the wind.
Motion of neighboring plates	When neighboring plates move, they could push or pull on a plate, transferring force to it.	When a bumper car is hit by another bumper car, its motion is changed, and it may collide with more bumper cars as a result.
Gravity	Gravity could cause plates to move in the same way that it causes change in the tide.	The ocean has great mass, but the force of gravity is able to shift its mass around Earth's surface.

⬡ Get Going

Once groups have discussed each idea and created tables like the one above, have them choose the idea they think best explains what causes plates to move. They should develop their ideas about how the forces identified in the idea could cause plates to move. Make sure they identify evidence or models they can use to support their idea.

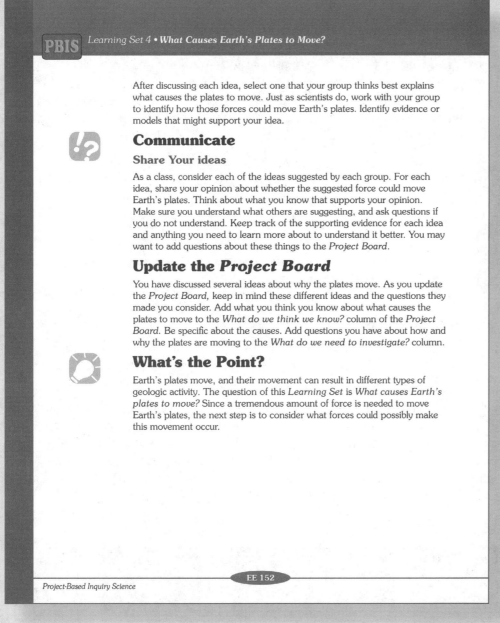

After discussing each idea, select one that your group thinks best explains what causes the plates to move. Just as scientists do, work with your group to identify how those forces could move Earth's plates. Identify evidence or models that might support your idea.

Communicate

Share Your ideas

As a class, consider each of the ideas suggested by each group. For each idea, share your opinion about whether the suggested force could move Earth's plates. Think about what you know that supports your opinion. Make sure you understand what others are suggesting, and ask questions if you do not understand. Keep track of the supporting evidence for each idea and anything you need to learn more about to understand it better. You may want to add questions about these things to the *Project Board*.

Update the *Project Board*

You have discussed several ideas about why the plates move. As you update the *Project Board,* keep in mind these different ideas and the questions they made you consider. Add what you think you know about what causes the plates to move to the *What do we think we know?* column of the *Project Board.* Be specific about the causes. Add questions you have about how and why the plates are moving to the *What do we need to investigate?* column.

What's the Point?

Earth's plates move, and their movement can result in different types of geologic activity. The question of this *Learning Set* is *What causes Earth's plates to move?* Since a tremendous amount of force is needed to move Earth's plates, the next step is to consider what forces could possibly make this movement occur.

EE 152

Communicate: Share Your Ideas

10 min

Groups share their ideas with the class.

△ Guide

Have each group share the idea they chose, along with their supporting evidence and models. Emphasize that students should ask questions of presenting groups if there is anything they do not understand. After each idea is presented, have students express whether they think the force could move Earth's plates. Encourage students to comment on each other's ideas. If there is anything the class feels they do not understand or if they think they need more evidence for any of the ideas, record these as investigative questions on the *Project Board.*

META NOTES

During the discussion, all ideas should be welcomed and discussed. The discussion should allow you to evaluate students' understanding. Consider noting some ideas to revisit later.

Update the Project Board

15 min

The class updates the Project Board.

△ Guide and Assess

During this discussion, students should begin to realize that the forces moving the plates must be coming from below. There is no force from above ground that would be capable of moving these massive plates. As students discuss possible sources for the forces that move the plates, challenge them to explain the mechanism by which the plates are moved. Students may not be able to provide much explanation at this point, but it is important for them to engage in trying to solve the problem.

want to add questions about these things to the *Project Board*?

Update the *Project Board*

You have discussed several ideas about why the plates move. As you update the *Project Board,* keep in mind these different ideas and the questions they made you consider. Add what you think you know about what causes the plates to move to the *What do we think we know?* column of the *Project Board.* Be specific about the causes. Add questions you have about how and why the plates are moving to the *What do we need to investigate?* column.

What's the Point?

△ Guide and Assess

Ask students what they think they know about what causes plates to move and record these ideas in the *What do we think we know?* column. Make sure to include ideas from the class discussion that everyone agreed on.

Ask students what ideas they had for things they should investigate. Record their ideas in the *What do we need to investigate?* column. Questions about how the mantle flows and how it moves plates should be put in this column. Students should also include specific questions about whether patterns can be found in the mantle's flow and whether these affect specific geologic events and topographic features.

Assessment Options

Targeted Concepts, Skills, and Nature of Science	How do I know if students got it?
Scientists often work together and then share their findings. Sharing findings makes new information available and helps scientists refine their ideas and build on others' ideas. When another person's or group's idea is used, credit needs to be given.	**ASK:** How was it useful to discuss your ideas with other pairs? **LISTEN:** Students should recognize that discussing their ideas with other pairs helped them to identify strengths and weaknesses in their own thinking.

Teacher Reflection Questions

- What difficulties did students have coming up with what they might investigate to determine which sources of force contribute to the motion of plates in Earth's crust?

- What difficulties did students have providing reasons of why they agree or disagree with an idea? How can you assist students with this?

- How were you able to encourage students to contribute to group and class discussions? What might you try next time?

NOTES

NOTES

4.2 Investigate

What Causes Earth's Mantle to Move?

◀ *2 class periods*

A class period is considered to be one 40 to 50 minute class.

Overview

Students build models of Earth's mantle using warm water with food coloring and cool, clear water. They simulate how heat affects material in Earth's mantle by releasing the warm water into the cool water. They share their observations and their ideas with the class in an *Investigation Expo*. Then they watch a simulation of cold water being released into warm water, and compare the results to the previous simulation. They determine that fluid that is warmer than the surrounding fluid rises, and fluid that is cooler than the surrounding fluid sinks. They watch a similar simulation with pieces of cardboard on the surface of the fluid, observing how the motion of the fluid due to temperature differences affects objects floating on the surface. This helps them to develop ideas about how the mantle causes Earth's plates to move.

Targeted Concepts, Skills, and Nature of Science	Performance Expectations
Scientists often work together and then share their findings. Sharing findings makes new information available and helps scientists refine their ideas and build on others' ideas. When another person's or group's idea is used, credit needs to be given.	Groups should predict what will happen when warm water that is dyed orange is released into cooler, clear water.
Scientists must keep clear, accurate, and descriptive records of what they do so they can share their work with others and consider what they did, why they did it, and what they want to do next.	Students should write clear descriptions of their observations of the simulation.
Scientists use models to simulate processes that happen too fast, too slow, on a scale that cannot be observed directly (either too small or too large), or that are too dangerous.	Students should learn about convection by observing dyed, warm water released into cooler, clear water.

Materials

Materials	
1 per group	2-L plastic bottle, cut off just above the label
	3-oz plastic cup
	3 in. x $\frac{1}{8}$ in. rubber band (size 18)
	4 in. x 4 in. square of aluminum foil
	Poster sheets
	Metric ruler
1 bottle of each per group	Red, yellow, and blue food coloring
2 per group	Long wooden pencil
1 per student	*Mantle Simulation* page
1 set per group	Markers
1 per class	DVD player with monitor or television
	Earth Science Content DVD
2 per class	1 cm x 1 cm squares of lightweight, non-corrugated cardboard.

Activity Setup and Preparation

Students will watch two videos in this section. Be sure to have a DVD player with a monitor set up before class. You may wish to give demonstrations instead of showing the videos. To give the demonstrations, you will need cups, a 2-L bottle, food coloring, hot and cold water, aluminum foil, rubber bands, pencils, and lightweight, non-corrugated cardboard. Instructions for giving the demonstrations can be found in the *Section 4.2 Implementation*.

Students will also run a simulation of convection. Perform this simulation before class so you can anticipate any difficulties. Mix a few drops of red and yellow food coloring in a cup. Fill the cup with warm water. Cover it with aluminum foil, poke two holes in the foil with a pencil about 2 cm apart and wrap a rubber band around the top of the cup to hold it in place. Then push a pencil under the rubber band to use as a handle.

If you are unable to do the simulation in class, you can show a demonstration of the simulation to the class from the video. The demonstration of a cup of hot water submerged in cold water is identical to the first simulation.

Homework Options

Reflection

- **Science Content:** If you performed the simulation from this section with a thicker fluid, such as motor oil, how do you think the results would be different? How would they be similar? *(This question is meant to engage students in thinking about how the thinness of water affects the results of the simulation. Students might expect a thicker fluid to move more slowly. They might also suggest that the heat could dissipate before the hotter fluid rose, meaning that the hotter fluid would cool down while still in its original position.)*

Preparation for 4.3

- **Science Content:** How can heat cause material to rise? What heats the mantle? Describe how you think the Earth's mantle is moving. *(This question is meant to engage students in thinking about what could cause the phenomena they observed.)* **NOTE:** Do not display this question until after students have run their simulations and watched the demonstrations.

NOTES

NOTES

4.2 Investigate

What Causes Earth's Mantle to Move?

A lot of force is needed to make the crustal plates move. The plates move because they are floating on the mantle, and the mantle is moving. So the next question that needs to be answered is, *What causes Earth's mantle to move?* To answer this question, you will model Earth's mantle and simulate the way it moves.

Remember that Earth's mantle is the layer just under the crust. It is above Earth's very hot core. Because the deepest parts of the mantle are so close to the core, those parts of the mantle are directly heated by the core. The core heats those parts of the mantle more than it heats the parts of the mantle farther from the core.

Earth's mantle is solid, but the way the core heats it makes the magma in the mantle behave like a liquid in an important way. Like a liquid, the mantle flows. However, because the mantle is solid, it does not flow like water and other liquids, such as milk and juice, that flow easily. Instead, the magma in the mantle flows very slowly. Magma is like a **viscous liquid**. A viscous liquid is very thick and resists flowing. It is also very difficult to make a viscous liquid start to flow. Keep these ideas in mind as you build your model of Earth's mantle and watch it flow. The model will allow you to observe the way one liquid moves when it is heated. This will help you imagine how other substances flow.

Like the raft floating on water, Earth's crust floats on top of the mantle because it is less dense than the mantle.

viscous liquid: a liquid that is very thick and resists flowing.

EE 153

EVER-CHANGING EARTH

4.2 Investigate

What Causes Earth's Mantle to Move?

10 min

Elicit students' ideas about how the mantle is moving and what causes it to move.

META NOTES

Having students articulate their initial ideas helps them organize their thoughts so they can evaluate their ideas and build new ideas as they learn.

○ Engage

Tell students the main reason the plates in Earth's crust move is that they float on the mantle, and the mantle is moving. Ask students to draw how they think the mantle is moving. What do they think causes the mantle to move? Record a list of their ideas.

*A class period is considered to be one 40 to 50 minute class.

△ Guide

Remind students that Earth's mantle is the layer that surrounds the core. The core is very hot. Discuss how the core heats the parts of the mantle that are close to it. The way the core heats the mantle has important affects on the mantle. Although the mantle is solid, the heat from the core causes it to flow like a viscous liquid. Explain that a viscous liquid is very thick and resists flow.

Let students know they will build a model of Earth's mantle to explore how it could move. As they build and observe their model, they should keep in mind that the material in the mantle is like a viscous liquid.

NOTES

Build Your Model

Procedure

1. Fill the cut-off 2-L bottle with cool tap water to about 5-6 cm from the top. Be careful not to spill water as you do this.

2. Put several drops of orange (red and yellow mixed) food coloring in the plastic cup. Then fill it to within about 1 cm from the brim with warm water.

3. Cover the cup with warm water using aluminum foil. Bend the foil down over the edges of the cup to make a tight seal. Hold the foil in place with a rubber band that has been doubled over. Make sure the rubber band is tight.

4. Push the point of the pencil through the aluminum foil in two places to make two holes about 2 cm apart. Each hole will be about as wide as the pencil. Be careful, the pencil can be very sharp.

5. Make a handle for the cup by sliding the point of the pencil under one loop of the rubber band and sliding the pencil down until the side of the pencil is secure against the side of the cup.

After you make your prediction, you will use the handle to lower the cup into the 2-L bottle. In this model, the warm water in the cup represents the part of Earth's mantle that is being heated by Earth's hot outer core. The cool water in the 2-L bottle represents material in Earth's mantle that is not being heated as much by the core.

Predict

In the procedure that follows, you will lower the cup of warm water into the 2-L bottle. The holes in the foil will allow the warm water to escape. Since it is colored orange, you will be able to see what happens to the warm water.

What do you think will happen when the warm water is released into the 2-L bottle of cool water? Why do you think this will happen? Record your prediction and ideas about why you think that will happen on your *Mantle Simulation* page.

Materials

- 2-L plastic bottle cut off just above the label (remove the label after cutting)
- 3 oz. plastic cup
- red and yellow food coloring (combined to make orange)
- 3 inch x 1/8 inch rubber band (size 18)
- 4-inch square of aluminum foil
- long wooden pencil (sharpened)

Build Your Model: Procedure

10 min

Students build their models.

Clean up spills promptly to prevent injury.

△ Guide

Display the materials and go over the procedure for building the model with the class. First, students will fill the 2-L bottles with water to about 5-6 cm from the top. Then they will put drops of red and yellow food coloring in their cups and fill them up to 1 cm from the brim with warm water. They will cover the cups with aluminum foil and wrap a rubber band around the top to hold the foil in place. Using a pencil, they will poke holes in the foil about 2 cm apart. Finally, they will put another pencil under the rubber band so that it can be used as a handle.

If the simulation cannot be run in class, you can show students the demonstration of a cup of hot water submerged in a bottle of cold water on video. Let them watch the whole video once to gain a general impression of what is happening. Then show it again, omitting the demonstration setup if time is short, and have students note which hole the water flows through and what direction it flows.

⬡ Get Going

Distribute materials, give students a timeframe, and have them build their model.

Predict

5 min

Students predict the results of the simulation.

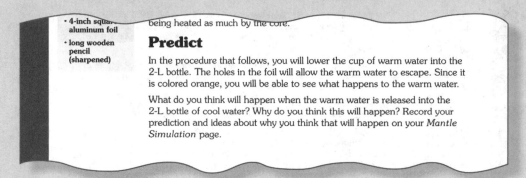

- 4-inch square aluminum foil
- long wooden pencil (sharpened)

being heated as much by the core.

Predict

In the procedure that follows, you will lower the cup of warm water into the 2-L bottle. The holes in the foil will allow the warm water to escape. Since it is colored orange, you will be able to see what happens to the warm water.

What do you think will happen when the warm water is released into the 2-L bottle of cool water? Why do you think this will happen? Record your prediction and ideas about why you think that will happen on your *Mantle Simulation* page.

△ Guide

When groups have completed their models, tell them they will lower the cup of warm water into the bottle of cool water, keeping the cup tilted so that one hole in the foil is higher than the other. Water will be able to flow through the holes in the foil. Before they do this, they should predict what will happen. Have them predict what will happen and record their predictions on the *Mantle Simulation* pages.

NOTES

4.2 Investigate

Run your Simulation

Procedure

1. Hold the pencil you put under the rubber band as a handle. Lower the cup into the 2-L bottle.

2. When the cup reaches the bottom, hold the handle so that the cup is slanted at the bottom of the 2-L bottle and one hole is higher than the other. Hold the cup steady.

3. Carefully observe the movement of the warm colored water as it comes out through the foil. Some air bubbles may come out of the cup before the water begins to flow. Those can be disregarded. Take note of which hole the warm water seems to exit from (upper or lower) or if it comes out of both holes.

4. Note the direction of flow of the warm, colored water. Pay close attention to the path the colored water takes. If you could follow one drop of water with your eyes, what path would it be taking? What do you think is happening inside the cup?

5. Draw a diagram on your *Mantle Simulation* page showing how the warm water moved after it flowed out from the cup and how the cool water in the 2-L bottle moved.

6. Label your diagram so that someone who did not see the simulation can understand how the warm, colored water moved.

⚠️

Do not use water that is so hot that it could scald you. The water only needs to feel warm to the touch, like you would use to wash your hands. It does not need to be hot.

Clean up any spills right away.

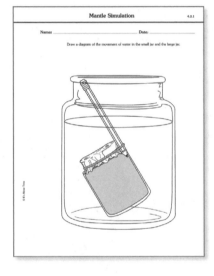

Mantle Simulation   4.2.1

Name: ....   Date: ....

Draw a diagram of the movement of water in the small jar and the large jar.

⚠️ Guide and Assess

Briefly go over the procedure with the class. Students will lower the cup into the jar at a slight tilt and observe the movement of the warm water. They should note which hole the warm water flows through, or if it flows through both holes. They should note the direction the warm water (which will be visible because of the orange food coloring) flows. Have the students draw a diagram on their *Mantle Simulation* pages showing how the warm water and how the cool water moved. Remind students that they should label their diagrams to clearly show how the warm water moved.

Have students run the simulation. As they run their simulations, help them with any difficulties that arise. Ask them what they observed, and how they think the warm and cool water move. Check to make sure they are labeling their diagrams clearly.

NOTES

Reflect

1. The water in a 2-L bottle represents most of Earth's mantle. The warm water in the small cup represents part of the mantle material that was heated by Earth's very hot core. Use what you observed in the simulation to sketch a diagram showing how you think Earth's mantle might move and why.

2. What do you think is causing the warm water to move as it did in the simulation? If you do not know, what questions would you need to answer to answer this question?

3. Water is a liquid that flows easily, but Earth's mantle is a solid that behaves like a viscous, or very thick, liquid. How do you think Earth's mantle might flow differently than the water?

4. What strengths does this model have for studying the movement of materials in Earth? What are its weaknesses?

5. Prepare a poster that shows the following:

   • your sketches and descriptions of how the water moved when the warm water was released into the cooler water

   • your ideas about what is causing the warm water to move

   • your diagram of the way you think Earth's mantle moves and why

   • what you think are the strengths and weaknesses of the model you built

Communicate

Investigation Expo

In this *Investigation Expo,* you will display your posters around the room. When all are displayed, walk around the room with your group looking at the diagrams and information in the posters. Observe everyone's sketches of how they saw the water move after it flowed out of the cup. Notice anything in the posters that is different from what your group found. Discuss these differences with your group. After everyone has examined each of the posters, take turns presenting your ideas. Each group should present their ideas about what caused the water to move as it is did in the simulation, the strengths and weaknesses of the models you built, and how and why

EE 156

Project-Based Inquiry Science

Reflect

10 min

Students answer the Reflect *questions.*

△ Guide

When groups have finished running the simulation, tell students that they will answer the *Reflect* questions with their groups and prepare posters for an *Investigation Expo.* Emphasize that each poster should address the four bulleted items in Question 5. It should show the group's observations, their interpretations of their observations, a diagram of how the water moved in their simulation, and an evaluation of the strengths and weaknesses of the model they built. Emphasize that an *Investigation Expo* should communicate what happened in a simulation, conclusions the group drew from their simulation, and their confidence in their conclusions.

⬡ Get Going

Distribute materials for creating posters and have students answer the *Reflect* questions.

◇ Evaluate

As groups work on the *Reflect* questions, check their diagrams of Earth's mantle. Ask how they used their observations from the simulation to draw the diagram. Check to see that they are evaluating the strengths and weaknesses of their models. They should recognize that water flows much more easily than magma, and that this is a weakness of the model they need to keep in mind.

When students create their posters, make sure they address all the bulleted points listed in the student text.

Communicate: *Investigation Expo*

15 min

Students review posters and present in an Investigation Expo.

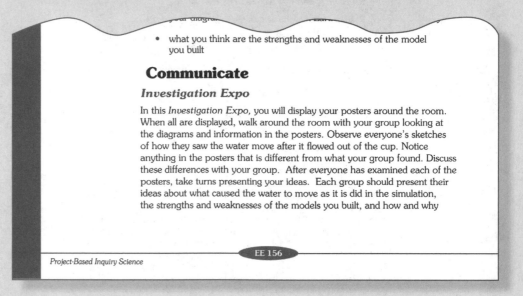

* what you think are the strengths and weaknesses of the model you built

Communicate

Investigation Expo

In this *Investigation Expo,* you will display your posters around the room. When all are displayed, walk around the room with your group looking at the diagrams and information in the posters. Observe everyone's sketches of how they saw the water move after it flowed out of the cup. Notice anything in the posters that is different from what your group found. Discuss these differences with your group. After everyone has examined each of the posters, take turns presenting your ideas. Each group should present their ideas about what caused the water to move as it is did in the simulation, the strengths and weaknesses of the models you built, and how and why

EE 156

Project-Based Inquiry Science

⬡ Get Going

Have groups display their posters around the room. Let groups walk around the room and examine the posters. They should note any observations or ideas in other groups' posters that are different from their findings.

△ Guide

When groups have had a chance to examine all of the posters, have each group present their ideas to the class.

Emphasize that presentations should include ideas about what caused the water to move the way it did, the strengths and weaknesses of the models they built, and how and why the mantle moves.

As each group presents, the rest of the class should take notes about things that can help explain how plates in Earth's crust move. Emphasize that they should ask questions to clarify things they do not understand.

☐ Assess

As groups present, note the differences in observations and ideas between groups. Note when presentations are unclear. Students should ask for clarification. Model the kinds of questions students should ask such as, "Can you explain which way the mantle is flowing in the top part of your diagram?"

△ Guide

If you think students are having trouble with the concept of density, remind them of the density columns they created earlier. Ask them what made the liquids in the density column sort into different layers. If they put a high-density liquid together with a low-density liquid, which will rise? Which will sink? Does it matter how much of each liquid there is? They should understand that a certain quantity of a high-density liquid will displace the same quantity of a low-density liquid, so that the high-density liquid will end up below the low-density liquid in a density column, regardless of the total volume of each.

Once groups have presented, lead a class discussion to develop a statement about how material in Earth's mantle moves and how it affects the movement of Earth's crustal plates. Let students know they will soon make more observations that will allow them to better explain this statement.

NOTES

....

....

....

....

....

Observe

10 min

Students watch a video of a cup of cold water submerged in hot water.

Earth's mantle moves. As you listen to each presentation, take notes about things you see and hear that can help you explain how the plates making up Earth's crust move. If you do not understand something that was presented, ask respectfully for clarification. After the presentations, work as a class to develop a statement about how material in Earth's mantle moves and how that affects the movement of Earth's crustal plates.

Observe

You will see a video that shows another simulation of Earth's mantle movements. The model is different than the model you built. You will be able to see more details in this simulation than the one you ran with your model. As you watch, notice the similarities and differences between what you see in the video and what you saw when you ran your simulation. In particular, pay attention to these details:

- Carefully observe the movement of the water. Note which hole the warm water seems to exit from and which hole the cool water seems to enter.

- Note the direction the water is flowing. Pay close attention to the path the colored water takes. What does it look like as it travels upward? What happens when it reaches the surface? Where does it go from there?

- What happens at the surface of the water? What movements do you see, if any?

Reflect

Work with your partner to answer these questions.

1. Draw a diagram showing how the warm water moved when it was released and how the cool water moved. Label your diagram so that someone who did not see the demonstration can understand the movements of the hot and cool water.

2. Why do you think the colored warm water moved the way it did in your simulation and in the video?

3. What do you think is causing Earth's mantle material to move?

4. Earth's mantle is constantly moving. Use what you observed in the simulation to describe why.

△ Guide

Let students know that they will watch a video of a different simulation of movement in Earth's mantle. Emphasize that students should pay careful attention to the similarities and differences between what they see in the video and their experience with the in-class simulation. Point out the list of details in the student text they should pay attention to: which hole the water in the cup exits, what direction the water flows, and what happens at the surface.

⬡ Get Going

Start the video showing the demonstration of a cup of cold water submerged in a bottle of hot water. Show the entire video once to give students a chance to become familiar with the setup. Then show it a second time. Have students note which hole the cold water flows through and what direction the cold water flows.

You can also give a hands-on demonstration of cold water submerged in warm water. The setup is similar to that of the first simulation. Put several drops of blue food coloring in a cup and fill the cup with cold water. Put aluminum foil over the cup, wrap a rubber band around the top, poke two holes in the foil, slip a pencil under the rubber band as a handle, and then submerge the cup at a tilt in a bottle of warmer water. The cold, blue water should flow out of the lower hole and sink.

△ Guide and Assess

Have students work with their groups to answer the *Reflect* questions. As they answer the questions, look at groups' diagrams and ask them what ideas they have discussed. Their diagrams should indicate that the cold water sank out of the lower hole when it was released. They may also indicate that the warmer water entered the cup through the upper hole.

Students should contrast the way the cold water sank with the way the warm water rose. For the second *Reflect* question, they may suggest that warm water rises, which forces cold water down. Ideally, they will suggest that some source of heat causes a similar process within Earth's mantle.

At this point, students probably cannot explain why the warm water rises and the cold water sinks. They should recognize that they need to understand why. They might suggest that they need to know whether the water rises only because it is warm or because it is warmer than the surrounding water. Does fluid rise whenever it is warmer than the surrounding fluid? Does it rise whenever it is warm? They might suggest that they need to know whether other fluids behave the same way. In particular, they should want to know whether the material in Earth's mantle behaves the same way.

The last question should elicit predictions, which students will test when they watch the next video.

Reflect

10 min

Students answer the Reflect *questions with their groups.*

Observe

5 min

The class watches the demonstration with pieces of cardboard.

---

5. What else do you need to know to better explain why the water moved the way it did? What else do you need to know to better explain how Earth's mantle could be moving?

6. Remember what you saw at the top surface of the water in the video. What do you think would happen if two pieces of cardboard were floated on the top of the water? Why?

Observe

Now you will see a video of another simulation. This time, the model includes two pieces of cardboard floating on top of water. The cardboard represents two of Earth's plates. You already predicted what you think would happen to cardboard floating on the water. Watch the simulation to see how the pieces of cardboard move.

Reflect

1. Describe the movements of the cardboard. Why do you think they moved the way they did?

2. What do you think is causing Earth's plates to move?

3. What else do you need to know to better explain what causes Earth's plates to move?

Update the *Project Board*

In the *What do we think we know?* column of the *Project Board,* record your ideas about what causes Earth's mantle material and plates to move. In the *What do we need to investigate?* column, record the questions you just developed.

What's the Point?

The warmer, colored water moved upward through the cooler water. As the warmer water rose, the cooler water moved down, or sank, replacing it. It works the same way in the mantle. As material in the mantle becomes warmer, it rises, and as it cools, it sinks. This sets up a repeating pattern of rising and sinking material in the mantle. The movements in the mantle cause the plates to move. The next section will help you understand why this continuous rising and sinking is happening.

EE 158

⬡ Get Going

Let students know they will now watch another simulation. In this simulation, two pieces of cardboard will be placed on the surface of the water, allowing them to test their predictions from the last *Reflect* question. Emphasize that these pieces of cardboard represent two of Earth's plates. The simulation will help students think about how movement in Earth's mantle affects plates in Earth's crust.

Show the video demonstrating convection currents with pieces of cardboard on the surface of water. Show the entire video once. Show it again and have students note how the pieces of cardboard move.

You can give a hands-on demonstration of this simulation. The setup is similar to the first simulation. Fill a cup with hot water and orange food coloring. With the foil pierced in two places fixed over the cup, submerge the cup in a bottle of hot water. Then put two pieces of lightweight, non-corrugated cardboard on the surface of the cold water. Each piece should be 1 cm x 1 cm.

△ Guide

After students have watched the video, lead a class discussion of the *Reflect* questions. Make sure that students make connections between what they saw in the simulation and what might happen in Earth's mantle. They should speculate that a process similar to the process they saw in the simulations causes Earth's plates to move. They should want to know what causes warm water to rise and cool water to sink, and they should want to know whether material in Earth's mantle behaves the same way.

△ Guide

As the class discusses what they need to know more about, draw their attention to the *Project Board*. Ask what they can now put in the *What do we think we know?* column. Students may be able to record a claim about warm fluids rising and cool fluids sinking. Ask what they can put in the *What do we need to investigate?* column. What they discussed in their responses to the third *Reflect* question should go in this column. These should include questions about what causes motion when a warm fluid is released into a cool fluid and when cold fluid is released into a warm fluid. Does the same thing happen in Earth's mantle?

Reflect
10 min

The students have a class discussion of the Reflect *questions.*

Update the Project Board
10 min

The class has a discussion to update the Project Board.

NOTES

....

....

....

....

....

Assessment Options

Targeted Concepts, Skills, and Nature of Science	How do I know if students got it?
Scientists often work together and then share their findings. Sharing findings makes new information available and helps scientists refine their ideas and build on others' ideas. When another person's or group's idea is used, credit needs to be given.	**ASK:** Why was it important to share your observations in an *Investigation Expo?* **LISTEN:** Some groups probably had different observations or ideas from other groups. *Investigation Expos* should give students a chance to see what they missed and identify things they need to learn more about.
Scientists use models to simulate processes that happen too fast, too slow, on a scale that cannot be observed directly (either too small or too large), or that are too dangerous.	**ASK:** Why is a simulation useful for investigating processes that take place in Earth's mantle? **LISTEN:** Students should recognize that because of the great size, high temperature, and inaccessibility of Earth's mantle, it is impossible to observe processes in the mantle directly.

Teacher Reflection Questions

- What difficulties do you think students will have with the concept of convection? What can you do to help students understand convection?

- How did you encourage students to provide reasoning to support their ideas?

- What management issues arose during the simulation? How will you address these in future implementations of this section?

4.3 Read

Why Does the Mantle Move the Way it Does?

◀ *1 class period*

A class period is considered to be one 40 to 50 minute class.

Overview

Students learn about convection currents, and how the heat of Earth's core causes convection currents in the mantle. Thinking about the simulations they observed earlier, and the real-world example of water boiling in a pot, students consider how differences in the heat energy of materials cause differences in their densities, which lead to convection currents. Students learn how lava rising through gaps in Earth's crust causes ocean-floor spreading, which contributes to plate motion. They learn that as new crust is formed at ocean ridges, old crust cools and becomes denser, sinking into the mantle.

Targeted Concepts, Skills, and Nature of Science	Performance Expectations
Scientists use models to simulate processes that happen too fast, too slow, on a scale that cannot be observed directly (either too small or too large), or that are too dangerous.	Students should draw models of the mantle and crust to show how the mantle moves and how its motion moves the crust.
Earth is a system made up of different layers, each with a distinctive composition and set of characteristics. These layers interact, driving the processes that shape Earth.	Students should focus on how the layers of Earth interact—the crust heats the mantle, which then moves due to convection currents, and the moving mantle moves the crust.
The hot core of Earth drives the processes that bring about changes in the crust by creating convection currents in the mantle material. These convection currents drive plate motion.	Students should be able to describe Earth's core as a heat source that creates convection currents in the mantle. These currents in the mantle cause the plates on Earth's surface to move.

Homework Options

Reflection

- **Science Content:** Describe how ridges are formed on an ocean floor. *(Students should describe ridges as being formed by two plates moving apart due to the convection currents in the mantle. As the plates move apart, a crack in the crust occurs and is filled with lava which solidifies.)*

Preparation for Learning Set 5

- **Science Process:** Write down everything you think you know about volcanoes. *(This is meant to get students thinking about what they think they know and provides you with their initial ideas about volcanoes to prepare for the upcoming Learning Set.)*

NOTES

....

....

....

....

....

....

....

....

....

4.3 Read

Why Does the Mantle Move the Way it Does?

In the demonstration, you observed warm water rising through cool water. You also observed cool water sinking to replace the warm water.

The movement of a fluid material caused by density differences is called **convection**. Convection carries heat energy from one location to another location within a fluid. Often, convection is driven by either heating from below or cooling from above the fluid. The warm water you observed carried heat energy as it moved from an area of higher temperature to an area of cooler temperature. You saw this happen in the demonstration as warm water from the cup moved upward through the cooler water until it reached the top.

cooling

rising

sinking

heating

convection: the movement of a fluid material caused by density differences. Often, convection is driven by either heating from below or cooling from above the fluid.

Convection occurs in many places. Think of what happens when a pot of water is heated on a stove. When the water reaches a full boil, the liquid will bubble and roll. However, long before the bubbles start forming, the heated water is already moving due to convection, even though it is hard to see. That is because the heat from the stove adds energy to the water molecules at the bottom of the pot.

Molecules are always moving and bumping into one another. In the pot, the heat energy from the stove will cause the water molecules to move faster and hit one another harder. This hitting causes them to spread apart.

EE 159

EVER-CHANGING EARTH

4.3 Read

Why Does the Mantle Move the Way it Does?

20 min

The class discusses how the heat of Earth's core causes convection in the mantle.

△ Guide

Begin by letting students know they will now learn about the kind of movement they observed in the simulations and that occurs in Earth's mantle. This will help them explain why Earth's crustal plates move.

Introduce the concept of convection. Convection is the movement of fluid material caused by density differences. When a fluid is less dense than the surrounding fluid, it will rise, causing motion in the fluid.

*A class period is considered to be one 40 to 50 minute class.

Convection is often caused by heating from below or cooling from above. When a fluid is heated, the molecules move faster, hitting each other harder, and spreading apart. This makes the fluid less dense where it is hotter. Because it is less dense, the hotter fluid will rise.

Ask students whether the orange water in the first simulation was more or less dense than the surrounding water. They should recognize that it was less dense than the surrounding water. This is because heat energy caused the molecules to spread out. Ask them whether the blue water in the second simulation was more or less dense than the surrounding water. They should recognize that it was more dense because the surrounding water was warmer than the blue water, and therefore the molecules of the surrounding water were more spread out. The orange water rose because it was less dense, while the blue water sank because it was more dense.

META NOTES

Varying how you implement reading material with the class helps keep students' attention and helps you adapt to students' reading ability. In addition to discussing what is in the reading material, consider having students take turns reading, summarizing after each paragraph or each segment, listing keywords in each paragraph, pairing readers based on ability, or reading to students.

TEACHER TALK

"In the first simulation, you released hot orange water into cooler water. Was the orange water more or less dense than the surrounding water? In the second simulation, you saw cold blue water released into warmer surrounding water. Was the blue water more or less dense than the surrounding water?"

The student text uses the example of a pot of water on a stove showing that as the water in the pot is heated, it begins to move due to convection. Point out the illustration in the student text. In the illustration, hot water rises directly over the flame. Near the surface, it is cooled as it is pushed to the outside of the pot by more rising water. As it cools, it becomes denser. This causes it to sink back to the bottom of the pot, where it is heated again.

NOTES

....

....

....

....

That spreading means that when water is hot, the same amount of space will have fewer molecules in it than when the water is cool. Where there are fewer water molecules in a space, the water is less dense. Like any liquid, water that is less dense than the surrounding liquid will rise. The warmer water on the bottom of the pot rises because it is less dense than the water around it.

The floating of the heated, less dense water is not all that happens in a pot of water on a hot stove. As the water molecules reach the top of the pot, they release some of their heat energy to material in the surroundings, such as air. As it releases its heat energy into other materials, the water cools. It becomes more dense, and it begins to sink. The heating and cooling of the water causes it to float and then sink in a process that can repeat many times. That process is what is known as convection.

convection current: the cycle of movement when warm, less-dense fluids rise and cool, and more-dense fluids sink due to differences in temperature.

When a substance rises and sinks due to differences in heat energy, the movement is called a **convection current.** A convection current is a flowing pattern in which warmer, less-dense quantities of a substance rise and are replaced by cooler quantities that sink because they are more dense.

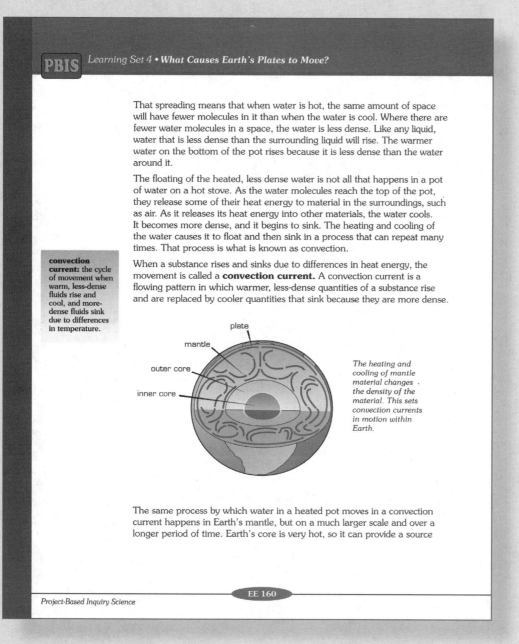

plate

mantle

outer core

inner core

The heating and cooling of mantle material changes the density of the material. This sets convection currents in motion within Earth.

The same process by which water in a heated pot moves in a convection current happens in Earth's mantle, but on a much larger scale and over a longer period of time. Earth's core is very hot, so it can provide a source

EE 160

This rising and sinking is an example of a convection current. In a convection current, warmer, less-dense fluid rises and is replaced by cooler fluid, which sinks because it is more dense. There are convection currents in Earth's mantle, as shown in the illustration in the student text. The convection currents in Earth's mantle take place over a much larger scale and a longer period of time.

of heat that causes convection in the mantle. Scientists have calculated that temperatures at Earth's core reach as much as 5000°C (over 9000°F). The mantle material that is farthest down is heated by the core. Remember that the mantle extends a long way from its upper to lower parts (its thickness is about 2700 km, or 1800 mi). Because of its thickness, temperatures in the upper mantle, nearest to the crust, are less hot (just under 900°C, about 1600°F), than the temperatures in the lower mantle, nearest the core (more like 2200°C, just under 4000°F). This temperature difference is thought by scientists to cause convection in Earth's mantle.

In Earth's mantle, convection occurs when the core heats material in the lower mantle. The molecules making up the mantle material begin to move more quickly and spread apart. As they spread farther apart, the mantle material nearest the core becomes less dense than the material above it, and it rises.

This heated, less dense mantle material eventually reaches the upper region of the mantle. As it rises up to just below the crust, the mantle material spreads outwards. As it spreads under the crust, the material loses heat energy. With less heat energy, the molecules move less quickly, and begin to get closer together. This loss of heat causes the material in the upper mantle to become more dense than the material below it, so it sinks slowly back down toward Earth's core. This rising and sinking due to differences in heat in the mantle material is a convection current.

plume: a hot, rising column of mantle material.

Some evidence indicates that convection currents in the Earth cause material that is hotter than the material around it to rise as a column of upward flowing magma in the mantle. This kind of hot, rising column of magma is called a **plume**. Scientists are studying the possibility that a plume may contribute to several kinds of geologic events.

EE 161

EVER-CHANGING EARTH

The convection currents in Earth's mantle are caused by the heat of Earth's core. Scientists think that the temperature at Earth's core can be as high as 5000°C (over 9000°F). Material that is farthest down in the mantle is heated by the core. Because the mantle is very thick (about 2700 km, or 1800 mi), material in the upper parts of the mantle remains much cooler. Scientists think that this difference in temperature causes convection in the mantle.

Discuss how this convection takes place. The core heats material close to it. This causes the molecules in the material to spread out, so that the material becomes less dense. Because it is less dense than the material above it, this material rises. The less-dense material eventually rises into the upper region of the mantle, where it is cooled. The molecules begin to move less quickly and closer together, increasing the material's density. As it cools, it becomes more dense than the material below it, which causes it to sink again.

Point out the illustration of a plume in the student text. Scientists think that hot material in Earth's mantle may rise in plumes like the one in the illustration.

NOTES

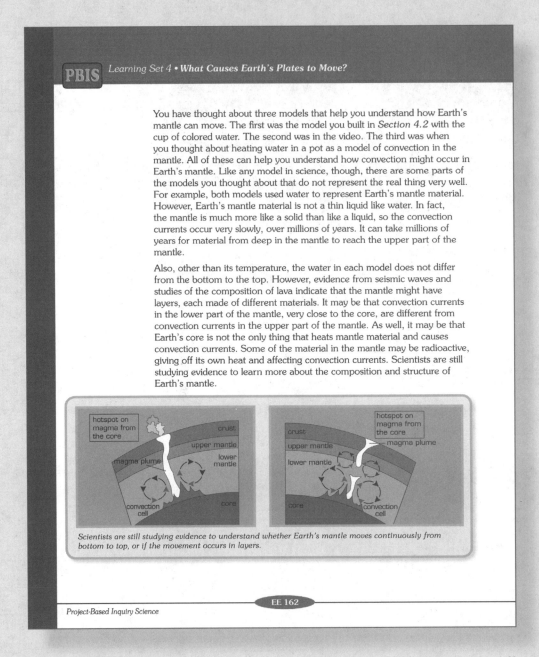

You have thought about three models that help you understand how Earth's mantle can move. The first was the model you built in *Section 4.2* with the cup of colored water. The second was in the video. The third was when you thought about heating water in a pot as a model of convection in the mantle. All of these can help you understand how convection might occur in Earth's mantle. Like any model in science, though, there are some parts of the models you thought about that do not represent the real thing very well. For example, both models used water to represent Earth's mantle material. However, Earth's mantle material is not a thin liquid like water. In fact, the mantle is much more like a solid than like a liquid, so the convection currents occur very slowly, over millions of years. It can take millions of years for material from deep in the mantle to reach the upper part of the mantle.

Also, other than its temperature, the water in each model does not differ from the bottom to the top. However, evidence from seismic waves and studies of the composition of lava indicate that the mantle might have layers, each made of different materials. It may be that convection currents in the lower part of the mantle, very close to the core, are different from convection currents in the upper part of the mantle. As well, it may be that Earth's core is not the only thing that heats mantle material and causes convection currents. Some of the material in the mantle may be radioactive, giving off its own heat and affecting convection currents. Scientists are still studying evidence to learn more about the composition and structure of Earth's mantle.

Scientists are still studying evidence to understand whether Earth's mantle moves continuously from bottom to top, or if the movement occurs in layers.

Point out how students can now see some ways in which their models differ from Earth's mantle. They used water in their models. However, the material in Earth's mantle is more like a solid than like water, and moves much more slowly. Warm water at the bottom of a 2-L bottle may approach the surface of the surrounding cooler water within minutes, it may take millions of years for material from the lower parts of the mantle to reach the upper part.

Another way that the models differ from Earth's mantle is that they contain only water. Earth's mantle may contain different materials in different layers. Evidence from seismic waves and the composition of lava indicate that there may be layers in Earth's mantle, each made of different materials. If there are layers within the mantle, there may be different convection currents within the different layers.

The core may not be the only source of heat within Earth. It is possible that there are radioactive materials in the mantle that give off heat. Such radioactive materials would also affect convection currents.

NOTES

Stop and Think

15 min

Students answer the Stop and Think *questions.*

Stop and Think

1. How do changes in heat energy affect the density of Earth's mantle material?

2. Write a short story detailing the journey of a cubic centimeter (cm^3) of mantle material through a convection current beginning at the core. Be sure to include information about what happens to its molecules. Support your story with sketches.

3. Draw a cross section of Earth, showing the core, mantle, and crust. Draw arrows to represent a convection current in Earth's mantle.

Sometimes called the Blue Planet, Earth's blue waters and land areas look very different from other planets in our solar system. However, beneath its cool and inviting crust is a very different scene where temperatures are high enough to melt rock.

EE 163

EVER-CHANGING EARTH

△ Guide

Have students answer the *Stop and Think* questions. These questions can also be assigned for homework. Look for the following in students' answers:

1. Students should recognize that heat energy causes molecules to spread out, making materials less dense. Materials in Earth's mantle become less dense when they are heated by Earth's core.

2. Students' stories should provide details about how heat energy causes molecules in the mantle material to spread out, making the material less dense. They should describe how this less-dense material rises until it loses heat energy (cools down) and returns to a higher density. When it gains density, it sinks again. Make sure that students' sketches accurately show the steps of their journey.

3. Students' drawings should show how material rises from the core, spreads under the crust, and then sinks. Make sure they accurately place the arrows in their convection current.

NOTES

What Else Drives Plate Motion?

15 min

The class discusses ocean-floor spreading, ridge push, and slab pull.

What Else Drives Plate Motion?

Scientists generally agree that circular motion created by convection in the mantle is the strongest force driving plate movement. But there are other forces, too, that cause Earth's plates to move. When Earth's plates move apart from each other, mantle material rises to Earth's surface. This causes two more forces that drive plate movement: ridge push and slab pull.

There are places where two plates are moving away from each other and mantle material reaches Earth's surface. One such place is within a large system of underwater mountains known as **mid-ocean ridges**. A deep crack runs through their center. Mantle material rises up from this crack, filling in the gap between the two plates. As this **lava** cools and hardens, it forms new crust on the ocean floor. This process is called **ocean-floor spreading**.

mid-ocean ridge: a continuous mountain range through the oceans, which is subject to earthquakes.

lava: fluid rock that comes from a volcano; also, the same material that becomes solid by cooling.

ocean-floor spreading: a process by which new ocean floor is created in the area where two plates are moving apart.

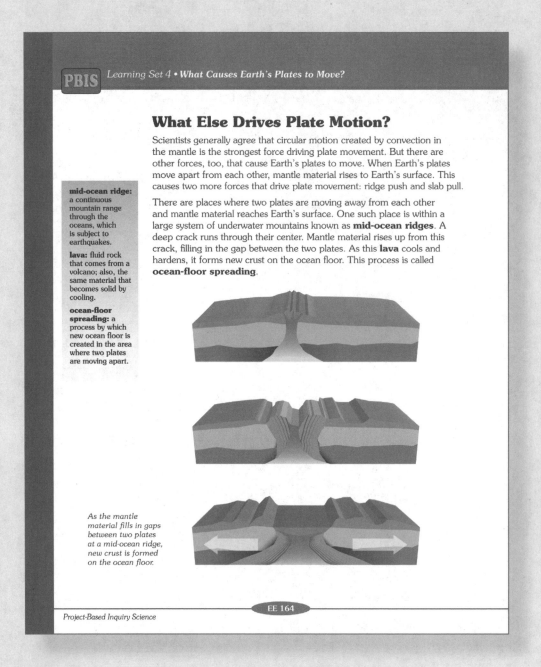

As the mantle material fills in gaps between two plates at a mid-ocean ridge, new crust is formed on the ocean floor.

EE 164

△ Guide

Discuss other contributing causes of plate motion. Emphasize that scientists agree that convection in the mantle is the primary cause of plate motion, but in addition, mantle material rising to the surface contributes to plate motion. This happens at mid-ocean ridges on the ocean floor. A crack in the crust runs through the ridges, and mantle material pushes up through the crack. This material cools and hardens, forming new crust. This is called ocean-floor spreading. The force of new crust pushing against the older crust is called ridge push.

In places where new ocean floor is being added, a depressed valley fills the gap between the plates. The valley is surrounded by the shoulders of the plates that are moving apart. The gap is filled in, but the plates continue to move. As the plates move farther apart, new gaps are created, and the same thing happens again. As new gaps form and fill again and again, a pattern forms on the seabed. At the mid-ocean ridge, where the plates meet, the crust is composed of young rocks. On either side, the rocks become older as you move away from the plate boundary. Successive bands of rock form, with the youngest rock near the current plate boundary and older rock on both sides of it. This evidence first led scientists to recognize that the sea floor was spreading apart at the mid-ocean ridges. The push of older crust away from the plate boundary, called **ridge push**, is a force that drives plate motion.

ridge push: the push of older crust away from a plate boundary.

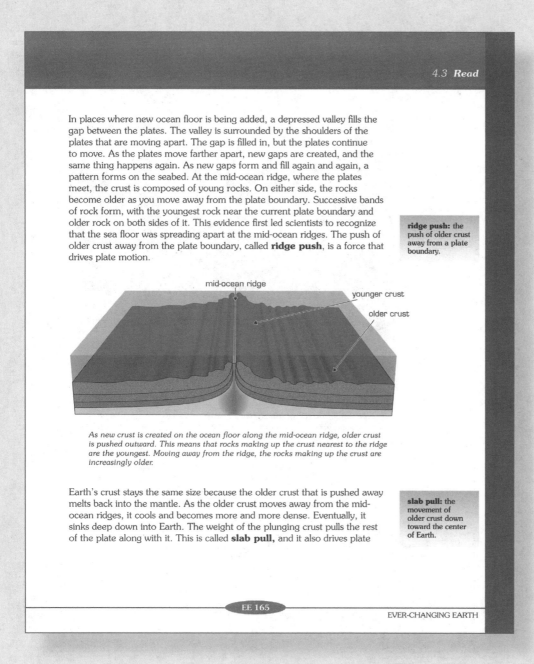

mid-ocean ridge

younger crust

older crust

As new crust is created on the ocean floor along the mid-ocean ridge, older crust is pushed outward. This means that rocks making up the crust nearest to the ridge are the youngest. Moving away from the ridge, the rocks making up the crust are increasingly older.

Earth's crust stays the same size because the older crust that is pushed away melts back into the mantle. As the older crust moves away from the mid-ocean ridges, it cools and becomes more and more dense. Eventually, it sinks deep down into Earth. The weight of the plunging crust pulls the rest of the plate along with it. This is called **slab pull,** and it also drives plate

slab pull: the movement of older crust down toward the center of Earth.

While new crust is formed by ocean-floor spreading, older crust which is usually far from the mid-ocean ridges melts back into Earth's mantle. It cools down and becomes more dense so that it can no longer float. The weight of the crust that is melting into the mantle pulls the plates in a motion called slab pull.

Reflect

15 min

Students answer the Reflect *questions.*

movement. When the rocks making up this crust move deep enough, they are melted by the heat of the Earth's core and, once more, their material becomes part of the mantle. Eventually, this material may rise once again to the surface in a mid-ocean ridge.

The Mid-Atlantic Ridge, the part of the mid-ocean ridges beneath the Atlantic Ocean, rises above the surface of the ocean in Iceland. This allows scientists to observe phenomena that more commonly occur deep under water.

Reflect

1. Look at your sketch of the convection current you drew earlier. Add arrows and notes to show how convection currents in the mantle cause the plates to move.

2. Think back to the example of the pot of water. If you take the water off the heat, the bubbling stops after a few seconds. Why does this happen? Why is this not happening on Earth?

3. Describe three factors that drive plate motion and discuss how they work together to move Earth's plates.

4. At the beginning of this *Learning Set,* you evaluated several ideas about the forces that cause Earth's plate to move. Reread and evaluate these ideas again. Which ideas do you now have evidence to support? Describe the evidence and how each force moves Earth's plates.

NOTES

....

....

....

△ Guide

Have students answer the *Reflect* questions. Like the *Stop and Think* questions, these can be assigned for homework. Look for the following in students' answers:

1. Students' drawings should indicate that the motion of the plates corresponds to the motion of the material in the mantle.

2. Students should recognize that when the heat is turned off, the water will stop boiling because it has lost its source of heat energy. Without this source of heat, convection cannot occur. Students should recognize that the convection currents in Earth's mantle are moved by the heat of Earth's core which can never be removed, making it impossible for convection to stop within Earth.

3. Students should discuss convection, ridge push, and slab pull. In their discussions of convection, they should describe how the core heats materials in the mantle, causing them to become less dense than the surrounding materials. This causes the hot materials to rise. Near Earth's crust, these rising materials spread and cool, moving the plates as they flow. In their discussions of ridge push, they should describe how gaps form when plates move apart. Lava rises in these gaps and forms new crust. The new crust presses against the old crust. In their discussions of slab pull, they should describe how old crust cools, becomes more dense, and sinks into the mantle. This sinking crust pulls on plates, contributing to their motion.

4. Students should evaluate the four ideas they discussed early in the *Learning Set*—lava rising through cracks in the surface pushes the plates apart, plates float on the mantle and move as the mantle moves, plates push and pull each other, and gravity causes the plates to move. Each idea describes a factor that contributes to plate motion. Students should use the science knowledge they have learned to describe how each factor contributes to plate motion and they should support their ideas with evidence.

NOTES

....

....

....

What's the Point?

Scientists have evidence that motion in Earth's mantle is caused by
convection currents. Convection currents are formed when material
is heated while other material around it is cooler. The heating causes
molecules in the material to move faster and spread apart, making the
material less dense. The less-dense material rises, while cooler material
sinks. This rising and sinking due to temperature differences is a convection
current. In Earth's mantle, material is heated by Earth's very hot core.
This heating causes mantle material to rise, possibly in the form of plumes
of heated magma. While convection currents in water move quickly,
convection currents within Earth's mantle move very slowly, taking many
millions of years to move material from the lower mantle up to Earth's crust.

Hot magma can escape through cracks in Earth's crust. As the magma
reaches the surface, it cools and forms new crust. This happens in the
ocean at mid-ocean ridges. As new crust forms at a mid-ocean ridge, older
crust is pushed aside exerting a force called ridge push. The formation
of new crust, along with the force of ridge push, means that usually the
crust material that is farther away from a mid-ocean ridge is older than the
material nearer to the center of the mid-ocean ridge. Eventually, that slab
of crust material is pushed to a place where it sinks deep into Earth. The
slab of crust material exerts a force as it sinks called slab pull, which helps
pull more crust material back down into Earth. As slabs of crust material
reach Earth's mantle, the heat there melts them. It may be that as the old
crust material melts, it is recycled, becoming magma that can eventually
contribute to the formation of new crust.

EE 167

EVER-CHANGING EARTH

NOTES

Assessment Options

Targeted Concepts, Skills, and Nature of Science	How do I know if students got it?
Scientists use models to simulate processes that happen too fast, too slow, on a scale that cannot be observed directly (either too small or too large), or that are too dangerous.	**ASK:** How can diagrams help you determine how convection currents flow? **LISTEN:** Students should recognize that by drawing diagrams, they can visualize convection currents and test whether their ideas make sense.
Earth is a system made up of different layers, each with a distinctive composition and set of characteristics. These layers interact, driving the processes that shape Earth.	**ASK:** What are the different layers within Earth? How do they interact? **LISTEN:** Students should identify the crust, mantle, and core. They may also identify the inner core, outer core, lithosphere, and asthenosphere. They should be able to describe how the core heats the mantle, and how movement in the mantle causes the plates in the crust to move. They should also be able to describe how magma rises to the surface in places, causing ocean-floor spreading, and older, denser parts of the crust to sink into the mantle.
The hot core of Earth drives the processes that bring about changes in the crust by creating convection currents in the mantle material. These convection currents drive plate motion.	**ASK:** How does Earth's core affect the mantle? How does the mantle affect the crust? **LISTEN:** Students should recognize that Earth's core heats the lower part of the mantle, causing convection currents. The convection currents in the mantle cause the material under the crust to flow, moving plates in the crust.

Teacher Reflection Questions

- What difficulties did students have understanding convection currents and how the mantle moves?

- How were you able to help students connect the concepts in this section with what they learned before?

- How did you manage the varying reading levels of your class? How did, or would, you treat this section with a non-English speaking student?

NOTES

_____

_____

_____

_____

_____

_____

_____

_____

_____

_____

Back to the Big Question

What Processes Within Earth Cause Geologic Activity?

◀ *1 class period*

A class period is considered to be one 40 to 50 minute class.

Overview

Students list the geologic terms they have learned in this *Learning Set* and make sketches to show the defining features of each term. They record connections between them, synthesizing their understanding of the geologic ideas. Using their observations from simulations and their science knowledge from reading, they revise their explanations of which plates in their regions interact to cause geologic activity. Finally, they consider what information would help them better explain what causes geologic activity and changes in their Earth structure, and update the *Project Board*.

Targeted Concepts, Skills, and Nature of Science	Performance Expectations
Scientists often work together and then share their findings. Sharing findings makes new information available and helps scientists refine their ideas and build on others' ideas. When another person's or group's idea is used, credit needs to be given.	Students should work together in small groups to revise their explanations. They should share their explanations with the class, and discuss how different groups supported their claims.
Scientists must keep clear, accurate, and descriptive records of what they do so they can share their work with others and consider what they did, why they did it, and what they want to do next.	Students should keep clear, accurate, and descriptive records of the geologic concepts they have learned and their claims and supporting evidence.
Graphs and tables are an effective way to analyze and communicate results of scientific investigation.	Students should use the *Project Board* and possibly other tables to organize information. This should assist in analyzing the information and sharing it with others.

Targeted Concepts, Skills, and Nature of Science	Performance Expectations
Explanations are claims supported by evidence. Evidence can be experimental results, observational data, and other accepted scientific knowledge.	Students should create explanations, supporting their claims with evidence and scientific knowledge.
Earthquake activity, volcanic activity, and topography are all evidence that Earth's crust is moving and changing.	Students should use evidence from their observations of earthquake activity, volcanic activity, and topography to support their claims about how plates in their regions cause geologic activity.

Materials	
1 per student	*Create Your Explanation* page *Project Board* page
1 per class	Class *Project Board*
100 per group	Index cards

Homework Options

Reflection

- **Science Content:** How did you revise the claim(s) in your explanation? *(Students should have revised their claims to show how the heat of Earth's core and the convection currents in the mantle cause plate motion.)*

Learning Set 4

Back to the Big Question

What processes within Earth cause geologic activity?

Throughout history, people have tried to explain natural phenomena such as earthquakes, volcanic eruptions, avalanches, and floods. Over time, as they have gathered more data and evidence, people's explanations have improved. Today, scientists and communities share information about the changes they observe or experience in a region. These changes are documented, and scientists study them to understand more about how and why these events occur.

At the start of this *Learning Set,* you explored several ideas about how and why Earth's plates are moving. You also came up with your own ideas. After updating your picture map, you will use what you have learned to update your explanation of how and why the plates of Earth's crust are moving.

Add to Your *Picture Map*

The goal of this *Learning Set* was to understand what processes cause Earth's plates to move. You came across many new geologic terms: *convection, convection currents, ocean-floor spreading, ridge push,* and *slab pull.* These scientific terms may have been new to you. As you have done in previous *Learning Sets,* before developing your explanation, sketch pictures representing each term to help you make sense of what the words mean, and identify how they relate to one another.

Return to the cards you made before. You now know more about some of those concepts than you knew when you first made those cards. Revise your pictures so they are more accurate. Pay particular attention to your density card. You probably know more now about density than you did when you made the card.

EE 168

Project-Based Inquiry Science

Learning Set 4

Back to the Big Question

5 min

Students are introduced to the activity.

○ **Engage**

Remind students of the *Big Question: What processes within Earth cause geologic activity?* Tell them that they will now update their *Picture Maps* and use the new information and concepts they have learned to revise the explanations they created in *Learning Set 3.* Have the class *Project Board* on display. Let students know they may want to refer to their *Project Board* as they are revising their explanations.

*A class period is considered to be one 40 to 50 minute class.

Add to Your *Picture Map*

10 min

Students map the concepts they have learned using index cards.

updating your picture map, you will use what you have learned...create your explanation of how and why the plates of Earth's crust are moving.

Add to Your *Picture Map*

The goal of this *Learning Set* was to understand what processes cause Earth's plates to move. You came across many new geologic terms: *convection, convection currents, ocean-floor spreading, ridge push,* and *slab pull.* These scientific terms may have been new to you. As you have done in previous *Learning Sets,* before developing your explanation, sketch pictures representing each term to help you make sense of what the words mean, and identify how they relate to one another.

Return to the cards you made before. You now know more about some of those concepts than you knew when you first made those cards. Revise your pictures so they are more accurate. Pay particular attention to your density card. You probably know more now about density than you did when you made the card.

△ Guide

Tell students that, as they did in previous *Learning Sets,* they will add to their *Picture Maps* by writing important terms on index cards. They will draw a picture of each term to communicate what it means. Emphasize that their drawings should help people who are not familiar with the terms understand what they mean. The student text mentions some of the words that may be new to students: convection, convection currents, ocean-floor spreading, ridge push, and slab pull.

Students should also revise the cards they made in previous *Learning Sets.* Emphasize that they have learned more about these concepts, especially density, and their cards should show what they have learned.

When students have completed their cards, they should share them with a group of students who were assigned to the same region. Each student should listen to other members' descriptions of the terms and think about information they can add to their own cards or changes they can make to their drawings.

Then they should work with their groups to find how the terms go together, including the terms from *Learning Sets 1, 2,* and *3.* They should arrange their cards on the table to show how the ideas connect. When they have agreed on how the ideas connect, they should record the connections on the back of the cards. If members of the group disagree about how the ideas connect, they should record their disagreement.

◯ Get Going

Divide the class into regional groups, distribute index cards, and go over the list of terms that students should include in their *Picture Maps.* Emphasize that each student should create a set of cards illustrating the terms.

△ Guide and Assess

As students work on their cards, monitor their progress and assist them with any difficulties they encounter. If they need guidance as they create sketches to illustrate their geologic terms, have them imagine they are trying to explain these ideas to someone using sketches. Ask them questions about the ideas to guide them towards statements they can illustrate.

When students share their cards with their groups, listen to how they discuss differences in the information on their cards and how they discuss the best arrangement of their cards. Emphasize that students should ask questions and make comments constructively. If students have difficulty arranging their cards, ask them what the most important connections between the ideas they have illustrated are. For each idea, what other ideas do they have to use in an explanation?

NOTES

Revise Your Explanation

15 min

Students revise their explanations of the ways movements in Earth's layers cause changes in Earth's surface.

When you have completed your cards, share them with a group of classmates. Listen carefully as someone in your group describes each geologic term. For each card, notice if there is additional information to add or changes you need to make to your drawing or to your definition.

As you did at the end of *Learning Sets 1, 2,* and *3,* work with your group to create a map that shows how the geologic terms go together. Discuss the connections with your group. If you cannot come to agreement now, record your disagreement. As you learn more about the geologic terms, you will be better able to connect the ideas together. Then you can revise your cards and connections.

On each card, record the connections you made. For example, *convection* is related to *convection current* and to *density.* Record each connection on both cards that are connected to each other. Be as specific as possible. Also record any disagreements your group had about connections, and mark any connections you do not understand.

Revise Your Explanation

Revisit and revise the explanation you created in *Learning Set 2.* At the end of that *Learning Set,* you developed your best explanation of how processes in Earth's layers are causing changes on the surface. You knew then that Earth had layers of different temperatures and that Earth's crust was made of plates that moved around. You did not know how the heat of the core causes convection currents in the mantle to make the plates move. Revise the parts of your explanation from *Learning Set 2* to include all the new things you now know about Earth's processes. Add to your old *Create Your Explanation* page or start a new one.

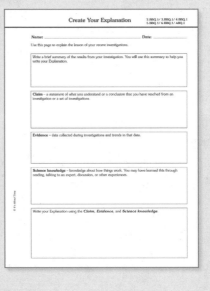

△ Guide

Let students know they will now revise their explanations of the ways that movements of Earth's layers cause changes in Earth's surface. They will use evidence from their drawings and models, and science knowledge from their reading.

Review the parts of a good explanation with the class—the claim, the evidence, the science knowledge, and that the explanation connects the evidence and the science knowledge to the claim. Students should revise their claims to connect the heat of Earth's core and convection currents in the mantle to changes on Earth's surface using what they have learned in this section about the heat of the core, convection, and convection currents.

☐ Assess

As groups work on their explanations, monitor their progress and help them with any difficulties they are having. Ask them what evidence and science knowledge they are using to support their claims.

Note the similarities and differences among groups' claims. During presentations, you might consider having two groups with very similar claims present one after the other so that students can compare how they supported their claims.

NOTES

Communicate: Share Your Explanation

15 min

Groups present their revised explanations to the class.

Your claim will be your best statement about how and why Earth's plates move. It might be a revision of the statement you wrote at the end of *Learning Set 2,* or you might want to write a new statement. Be sure to include information about convection and density in your statement. Your new evidence comes from the drawings you made during the convection activity. Your drawings and sketches can be useful in helping you imagine the ways processes are working. Your science knowledge comes from your reading. Work with your partner to create the best explanation you can. You will continue to revise your explanation as you move through the Unit.

Communicate

Share Your Explanation

Present your explanation to the class. As you listen to the explanations of others, notice how each explanation connects what is happening in the mantle to changes on Earth's surface. Notice the way other pairs' claims are supported by evidence and science knowledge. Be sure that you have seen the same evidence and science knowledge others report. If you have not, ask about the source of the evidence. If you think a claim is not supported well enough, or if you think someone's claim or explanation could be made more clear, raise your hand and say why. Be sure to be respectful. As a class, develop your best explanation of how and why Earth's plates are moving.

Update the *Project Board*

While exploring models of how and why the crust is moving, you learned some new things about the processes that are causing geologic activity in Earth's crust. Specifically, you learned that several factors work together to drive plate motion. Add these ideas to the *What are we learning?* column of the *Project Board*. Remember that any information added to the *What are we learning?* column must be supported in the *What is our evidence?* column.

Revising your explanation of Earth's process probably has led you to some new questions. Add these questions to the *What do we need to investigate?* column.

ES 170

△ Guide

When groups have finished revising their explanations, have them present to the class. Encourage the class to suggest any different ideas they have for the explanations presented, and to point out differences in their observations. Ask groups with similar interpretations if they used any different evidence and science knowledge to support their claims.

☐ Assess

As the class discusses the presentations, listen to how students discuss their ideas. Do students ask each other about things that are not clear? Do they give constructive feedback?

△ Guide

Ask students what they have learned since they last updated the *Project Board*. Record their answers in the *What are we learning?* column. This should include claims from groups' explanations. For everything that students put in the *What are we learning?* column, ask them what evidence they have. Record the evidence in the *What is our evidence?* column. Finally, ask students what they still need to investigate, and record their answers in the *What do we need to investigate?* column.

Assessment Options

Targeted Concepts, Skills, and Nature of Science	How do I know if students got it?
Scientists often work together and then share their findings. Sharing findings makes new information available and helps scientists refine their ideas and build on others' ideas. When another person's or group's idea is used, credit needs to be given.	**ASK:** How did listening to other pairs' explanations help you refine your own explanations? **LISTEN:** Students should have identified evidence and science knowledge in other pairs' explanations that they could use. They should have also considered the strengths and weaknesses of other pairs' explanations.
Scientists must keep clear, accurate, and descriptive records of what they do so they can share their work with others and consider what they did, why they did it, and what they want to do next.	**ASK:** Why was it important to record what you have learned along with your evidence on the *Project Board?* **LISTEN:** Students should recognize that the *Project Board* allows them to track their progress towards answering the *Big Question.*

Update the Project Board

15 min

The class has a discussion to update the Project Board.

Targeted Concepts, Skills, and Nature of Science	How do I know if students got it?
Graphs and tables are an effective way to analyze and communicate results of scientific investigation.	**ASK:** How did organizing geologic terms by their connections with other terms help you? How did recording what you learned in a list with your *Picture Map* help? **LISTEN:** Students should recognize that organizing terms by their connections helped them to understand how all of these geologic terms are related and can be applied to understanding Earth structures. Making a list of the things they learned with the drawings should have helped students see how individual observations were related to their final interpretations.
Explanations are claims supported by evidence. Evidence can be experimental results, observational data, and other accepted scientific knowledge.	**ASK:** What did you use to formulate your explanations? **LISTEN:** Students should have used scientific knowledge as evidence to support the claims in their explanations. In an explanation, claims are supported by the observations (evidence) and science knowledge.
Earthquake activity, volcanic activity, and topography are all evidence that Earth's crust is moving and changing.	**ASK:** What evidence did you use to support your explanations? **LISTEN:** Students should have used evidence from their observations of earthquakes, volcanic activity, and topographic features.

Teacher Reflection Questions

- What concepts in this *Learning Set* were difficult for students? How can you help them master these concepts?

- How have you been able to evaluate students' progress as they learn about geologic activity and Earth structures?

- What kind of discussions did the class have as you updated the *Project Board?* How were you able to keep discussions constructive?

Learning Set 5

What Can Volcanoes Tell You About Plate Interactions?

◀ $7\frac{1}{2}$ *class periods*

A class period is considered to be one 40 to 50 minute class.

Overview

Students examine volcano data in *My World,* finding patterns and comparing them to patterns in earthquakes. They observe the features of the three main volcano types and identify the characteristic features of each type. Based on this new knowledge, they develop descriptions of the type of volcano in their region. They read what scientists know about the types of volcanoes, and they revise their classification of the volcanoes in their regions. They learn about the shapes, eruptions, and lava characteristics of each type of volcano, and how the types of volcanoes are related to the movement of plates. Using this new science knowledge and the data they have gathered about volcanoes in their region, groups infer the direction the plates are moving in and around their region. The class discusses these inferences, and identifies inconsistencies in different groups' inferences. They record these inconsistencies as investigative questions on the *Project Board.*

Targeted Concepts, Skills, and Nature of Science	Section
Scientists often work together and then share their findings. Sharing findings makes new information available and helps scientists refine their ideas and build on others' ideas. When another person's or group's idea is used, credit needs to be given.	5.1, 5.2, 5.3, 5.4, 5.BBQ
Scientists must keep clear, accurate, and descriptive records of what they do so they can share their work with others and consider what they did, why they did it, and what they want to do next.	5.1, 5.2, 5.3, 5.4, 5.BBQ
Graphs and tables are an effective way to analyze and communicate results of scientific investigation.	5.1

Targeted Concepts, Skills, and Nature of Science	Section
Scientists use models and tools, such as Geographic Information Systems, and a variety of maps to develop claims and explanations from evidence in the data.	5.1
Scientists make claims (conclusions) based on evidence obtained (trends in data) from reliable investigations.	5.2, 5.4, 5.BBQ
Explanations are claims supported by evidence, accepted ideas, and facts.	5.BBQ
Earth's crust is constantly changing. These changes are usually a very slow process that is not immediately observable. Some changes are very rapid and are observable.	5.BBQ
Interactions between Earth's crustal plates can result in mountain building, rift valleys, and geologic activity such as earthquakes and volcanoes. Underwater volcanic activity may form underwater mountains, which can thrust above the ocean's surface to become islands.	5.2, 5.3, 5.BBQ
Earthquake activity, volcanic activity, and topography are all evidence that Earth's crust is moving and changing.	5.3 , 5.BBQ
New crust is formed at the mid-ocean ridge where the plates move apart. Oceanic crust is destroyed when it collides with continental crust and is subducted. In this way, Earth's crust is recycled.	5.4

NOTES

....

....

....

....

....

....

Understanding for Teachers

Volcanoes occur where magma is able to breach Earth's crust. When magma reaches Earth's surface it is called lava. This lava adds to Earth's crust.

Volcano Types

There are three main types of volcanoes: cinder cones, stratovolcanoes, and shield volcanoes.

Cinder cone volcanoes, also known as scoria cone volcanoes, form from pieces of congealed lava ejected from a single vent or opening. Eruptions are violent due to the high pressure of gas-filled lava. When the volcano initially erupts, pieces of the gas-filled lava solidify and fall as cinders around the vent, forming a circular or oval cone. During these initial eruptions, the deadliest of flows is possible—the pyroclastic flow. A pyroclastic flow is a mixture of solid to semi-solid fragments and hot, expanding gases that can move like an avalanche down the cone at speeds over 100 km/hr.

After gases have dissipated, rhyolitic lava usually flows down the surface of the volcano. The summit is usually a bowl-shaped crater. Cinder cone volcanoes are usually no more than 1000 ft above the surrounding ground level. These volcanoes have straight, steep sides and a large summit crater. The composition of this volcano is usually basaltic tephra, and occasionally andesitic. Cinder cone (or scoria cone) volcanoes have Strombolian eruptions.

Stratovolcanoes are sometimes called composite volcanoes. They are usually steep, symmetrical cones that contain alternating layers of lava flow, ash, cinders, blocks, and bombs. They reach heights of up to 8000 ft. They usually have a crater at the summit which contains a central vent, or a clustered group of vents. Lava flows from breaks in the crater wall, or from fissures on the flanks of the cone. Stratovolcanoes are composed of a conduit system through which magma from a deep reservoir rises to Earth's surface. These volcanoes have gentle slopes near the base, but steep, concave slopes near the summit. They also have a small summit crater. They are highly variable in their composition. They alternate from basaltic to rhyolitic lavas and have an overall andesitic composition. Stratovolcanoes have Plinian eruptions.

Shield volcanoes are built almost entirely of lava flows that pour in all directions from a central summit or vent. These cone-shaped volcanoes are broad and gently sloping. They are built up by thousands of lava flows over great distances. This type of volcano usually erupts from vents along fractures (rift zones) that develop on the sides of the cone. This type of volcano forms the largest volcanoes. For example, Mauna Loa is 97 km (60 mi) long, 48 km (30 mi) wide, and rises about 8742 m (28,680 ft) from its base on the sea floor. Shield volcanoes have basaltic lava flows and Hawaiian type eruptions.

Volcanic domes, also called lava domes, are formed when a small amount of very viscous lava flows a short distance. In this situation, lava piles over and around the vent of the volcano forming a dome. This occurs due to expansion from within the volcano. As the dome grows, it hardens and shatters causing fragments to fall down the sides of the volcano. Volcanic domes commonly occur within the craters or on the sides of composite volcanoes.

Eruption Types

Volcanoes may erupt in a variety of ways. The three main types of eruptions are Strombolian, Hawaiian, and Plinian.

Strombolian eruptions involve very large clots of lava bursting from the summit crater in luminous arcs through the sky. Lava clots fall on the side of the cone, as do lava streams. This type of eruption usually occurs from cinder cone (or scoria cone) volcanoes and sometimes from stratovolcanoes. The lava is basaltic tephra and occasionally andesitic.

Hawaiian eruptions are the calmest of the eruption types with the least amount of ejected material. They occur along fissures or fractures. Lava spurts from a fissure and feeds into lava streams. They may also occur at a central vent where a fountain of fiery lava can spurt several hundred feet. This lava often collects in old craters forming lava lakes or cones, or it feeds into radiating flows. The lava is basaltic, so it flows easily, and it has a low gas content.

Plinian eruptions are the most powerful. They consist of explosive ejections of viscous lava and can send ash and volcanic gas tens of miles into the air. The resulting ash fallout can affect large areas hundreds of miles downwind. These eruptions occur from stratovolcanoes and have variable lava types, from basaltic to rhyolitic. Pyroclastic flows, which are the deadliest, are associated with Plinian eruptions.

If more information is needed, try an Internet search using the Keywords volcano type, eruption type, and lava type.

NOTES

....

....

....

....

LEARNING SET 5 IMPLEMENTATION

◄ $7\frac{1}{2}$ *class periods**

Learning Set 5

What Can Volcanoes Tell You About Plate Interactions?

The *Big Question* for this Unit is *What processes within Earth cause geologic activity?* You have learned that earthquakes commonly occur along plate boundaries. You also know that plate movement associated with earthquakes is driven by convection currents in the mantle material. These same convection currents also play a role in volcanic eruptions. Volcanoes have different characteristics and styles of eruption depending on factors such as their location. Studying different volcanoes can offer insight into what is happening at different places on Earth's plates. In this *Learning Set,* you will find out where volcanoes are located in your region and what they show about plate interactions.

As with earthquakes, much volcanic activity is associated with convection currents in the mantle material.

EE 171

EVER-CHANGING EARTH

Learning Set 5

What Can Volcanoes Tell You About Plate Interactions?

5 min

Students are introduced to the question of this Learning Set.

○ **Engage**

Remind students that the *Big Question* of the Unit is *What processes within Earth cause geologic activity?* Briefly discuss how students examined earthquakes to learn about plate interactions. Tell them they can also learn about plate interactions from volcanoes. The question they will answer in this *Learning Set* is *What can volcanoes tell you about plate interactions?* Point out the picture of a volcano in student text. Ask them what they think causes the volcano to erupt.

*A class period is considered to be one 40 to 50 minute class.

NOTES

5.1 Understand the Question

Think About What Volcanoes Can Tell You About Plate Interactions

◀ $1\frac{3}{4}$ *class periods*

A class period is considered to be one 40 to 50 minute class.

Overview

Students use *My World* to gather and analyze data on volcanoes. They begin by working as a class to locate volcanoes in the Java Trench region and to find patterns of volcanic activity in the region. They work with their partners to locate volcanoes in their regions. They record the locations on their *Three-page Maps,* identify the types of the volcanoes, and look for patterns. Through this, they learn to analyze and interpret empirical data the way scientists do. They describe the patterns they found in volcanoes and compare them to the patterns they found in earthquakes, developing an understanding that volcanoes are related to the same geologic processes that cause earthquakes. Students share their results with the class, and consider the relationship of patterns of volcanic activity to patterns of earthquake activity worldwide. They then begin to make conjectures about how volcanic activity and earthquake activity are related.

Targeted Concepts, Skills, and Nature of Science	Performance Expectations
Scientists often work together and then share their findings. Sharing findings makes new information available and helps scientists refine their ideas and build on others' ideas. When another person's or group's idea is used, credit needs to be given.	Students should work in groups to analyze volcanic activity in their Earth structure region and compare it with earthquake activity in the region.
Scientists must keep clear, accurate, and descriptive records of what they do so they can share their work with others and consider what they did, why they did it, and what they want to do next.	Students should keep accurate and descriptive records of the data they gathered and the patterns they found in the data.

Targeted Concepts, Skills, and Nature of Science	Performance Expectations
Graphs and tables are an effective way to analyze and communicate results of scientific investigation.	Students should analyze volcano data plotted on maps, and plot this data on their *Three-page Maps*.
Scientists use models and tools, such as Geographic Information Systems, and a variety of maps to develop claims and explanations from evidence in the data.	Students should use *My World* to gather data on volcanoes in their regions.

Materials	
1 per student	*Three-page Map* (from *Learning Set 3*) *Region Project Board*
1 per pair	Computer with *My World* Red, blue, yellow, and black markers
1 per class	*Big World Map* with transparency layer Class *Project Board* *Ever-Changing Earth Teacher Notes* and *Suggested Data* table

NOTES

....

....

....

....

....

....

....

Activity Setup and Preparation

In this section, students will use *My World* to gather data on different types of volcanoes. To help them with this, you will give a demonstration on how to find data on volcanic activity for the Java Trench region. Before class, use the procedure in the student text to gather this data for the Java Trench as the students will do, so that you will be prepared to give the demonstration and be able to anticipate any difficulties the students will have. Ensure that you have computers with *My World* installed allocated for students to use. If possible, have a computer with a projector available for the demonstration.

Students will also need to refer to and update the *Big World Map* with transparencies from *Learning Set 3*. Put the *Big World Map* on display with the transparencies taped onto it.

Homework Options

Reflection

- **Science Content:** In what parts of the world are volcanoes most common? Are there places where there are many earthquakes, but not many volcanoes? *(Students should identify places in eastern Asia, from Indonesia to the eastern coast of China, and the western coasts of North and South America as places where volcanoes are common. They may also identify places along the mid-ocean ridge where there are many earthquakes and a number of volcanoes.)*

Preparation for 5.2

- **Science Content:** What information about volcanoes in the regions the class has been investigating would help you understand how volcanoes are related to other kinds of geologic activity? *(This question is meant to engage students in thinking about how volcanoes are related to other types of geologic activity and what they need to investigate.)*

NOTES

◄ $1\frac{3}{4}$ *class periods**

5.1 Understand the Question

Think About What Volcanoes Can Tell You About Plate Interactions

The question for this *Learning Set* is *What can volcanoes tell you about plate interactions?* You can approach this question by considering what you know. For example, you know that mantle material moves because of convection. As mantle material near the core gains heat energy, it becomes less dense and rises toward the crust.

When mantle material escapes to Earth's surface, it forms a volcano. Volcanoes are places in Earth's crust where material from the mantle reaches the surface. Volcanic eruptions have many different characteristics. They are not all the same. How the mantle material escapes to the surface can tell you a lot about how the plates in your region are moving and interacting with one another.

In this *Learning Set,* you will learn about different types of volcanoes and volcanic activity. You will also have opportunities to look at data showing the locations and types of volcanoes in your region. After you make connections between what you already know about plate movement and new things you will learn about volcanoes, you can develop a better understanding of the processes causing geologic activity.

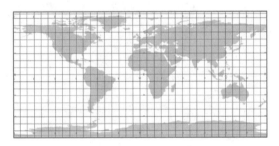

Project-Based Inquiry Science

5.1 Understand the Question

Think About What Volcanoes Can Tell You About Plate Interactions

5 min

Students are introduced to the activity.

△ **Guide**

Tell students that they have some science knowledge that will help them interpret volcanic activity and answer the *Learning Set* question. They know, for instance, that there are convection currents in Earth's mantle, which cause hot material in the mantle to rise toward the crust. Tell them that when mantle material escapes to Earth's surface, it forms a volcano. The characteristics of the resulting volcano can tell a lot about the plate interactions in the region. Students will learn about types of volcanoes and

*A class period is considered to be one 40 to 50 minute class.

volcanic activity in this *Learning Set*. They will look at data about volcanic activity in their regions and apply what they learn to answering the *Big Question*.

TEACHER TALK

"The question of this *Learning Set* is *What can volcanoes tell you about plate interactions?* You already have some science knowledge that will help you begin to think about volcanic activity. You know that plates in Earth's crust move, and that there are convection currents in Earth's mantle which cause hot material to rise towards the crust. Volcanoes occur when hot material in the mantle escapes through Earth's crust. By studying the characteristics of a volcano, you can learn a lot about plate interactions in the region. You will learn about different types of volcanoes, and you will look at data on volcanic activity in your region. Using this information, you will answer the question of the *Learning Set*. This will also help you to answer the *Big Question*."

NOTES

As you gather data about volcanoes in your region and around the world, you will observe patterns in their locations. These patterns will give you more clues about how the plates are moving and shaping Earth's crust.

Observe Volcanoes in the Java Trench Using *My World*

Demonstration

You will soon be using *My World* to collect data about the volcanoes in your region. Before you begin, you will practice with your class, identifying where volcanoes are located near the Java Trench. After the volcanoes are located, you will work together to describe the patterns they make.

Observe carefully as your teacher uses *My World* to locate volcanoes near the Java Trench. Notice that the first step involves showing the earthquake data for the area and locating the area you want to view. You will be able to use the plate map you drew on a *Three-page Map* to guide you in locating the area around your region.

Watch as your teacher goes to the *Layer List* and clicks on *Volcanoes*. This layer allows you to see the volcanoes near the Java Trench. With your class, practice finding the volcanoes in this region. When finished, mark the volcanoes on the *Big World Map*. Pay attention to where the volcanoes are located in relation to the plate boundaries. Note on which side of the plate boundary, or on which plate, each volcanoes is found.

MAP KEY

● Cinder cone volcano

▲ Shield volcano

■ Stratovolcano

cinder cone volcano: a cone-shaped hill made of ash and rock particles around the vent of a volcano.

shield volcano: a gently-sloping volcano formed when runny lava spreads out over a large area.

stratovolcano: a steep-sided, cone-shaped volcano made of alternating layers of ash and lava.

My World can also be used to identify different types of volcanoes. Watch as your teacher uses the buttons to show different types of volcanoes in the region. Using the map key, identify each type of volcano found near the Java Trench on the *Big World Map*. Circle **cinder cone volcanoes** using a red marker. Draw a blue triangle around **shield volcanoes** and a yellow box around any **stratovolcanoes**.

Later in this section, you will read more about each of these types of volcanoes. For now, notice and record their types to refer back to later.

Observe Volcanoes in the Java Trench Using *My World*

15 min

The class observes a demonstration of how to find volcanoes in My World.

△ Guide

Tell students that they will use *My World* to investigate volcanoes in their regions. They will practice investigating volcanoes in *My World* by investigating volcanoes in the Java Trench with the class. Use a projector or a large monitor to show the class what you are doing on your computer.

Start *My World*. Select *Earth Structures and Processes* from the *Library* dropdown. Then select the *ESInquiry* project file. When the project has loaded, select the *Java Trench* in the *Map View* dropdown.

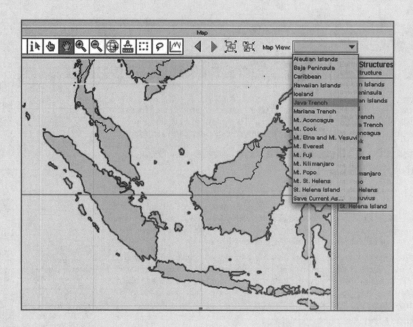

With the map centered on Java Trench, turn the *Volcanoes* layer on in the *Layer List*. Explain what you are doing so students will be able to navigate the *My World* interface on their own. Now the volcanoes in the region should be marked with red dots.

Ask the class to describe the pattern of volcanoes in the region. They should describe something like a curved string of volcanoes along Sumatra and Java. Draw students' attention to the *Big World Map* with the transparency showing plate boundaries. Ask them where the volcanoes are in relation to the plate boundary in the Java Trench region.

Have the class identify individual volcanoes in the region. Have them record these on the *Big World Map*. You might have one student record volcanoes while the others guide him or her. Emphasize that students should pay attention to where the volcanoes are in relation to the plate boundary. When the volcanoes are recorded on the *Big World Map,* it should be easy to see whether the volcanoes are on the plate boundary and, if not, which side of the boundary they are on.

Select the different types of volcano in the *Volcanoes* layer so that students can identify volcanoes of different types. Select *Cinder Cone* and help the class find cinder cone volcanoes in the region. Have them circle each cinder cone volcano with a red marker on the *Big World Map*. Then select *Shield Volcanoes* and help the class find shield volcanoes in the region. Have them draw a blue triangle around each shield volcano on the *Big World Map*. Select *Stratovolcanoes* and help the class find stratovolcanoes in the region. Have the class draw a yellow box around each stratovolcano on the *Big World Map*. There are many volcanoes shown in the *My World* map for which this information is unavailable. Students can simply mark these as unknown.

Practice analyzing the data with your class by answering the following questions about volcanoes near the Java Trench:

- How many volcanoes are located near the Java Trench?

- Describe the pattern formed by the volcanoes. Do they form a narrow line, a wide band, a tight cluster, or are they spread throughout the region?

- Compare the patterns made by earthquakes and volcanoes. How do you think earthquakes and volcanoes are related? Why?

You have now seen how to use *My World* to identify volcanoes in a region. Now you and your partner will use *My World* to explore the volcanoes found in your own region.

Observe Volcanoes in Your Region

Using the same steps demonstrated by your teacher, use *My World* to collect data about the volcanoes in your region. You will add this data to your *Three-page Map*, as well as to your *Region Project Board*. As you work, see what patterns you can find in the data.

Procedure

1. Prepare a *My World* plate map for examining volcano data by following these steps.

   a) **Open *My World*** by double-clicking on the *My World* icon on your computer screen.

   b) **Select *Earth Structures & Processes*** from the *Library* drop-down menu.

   c) **Open the *ESInquiry* file.** This file has information about elevation and depth, earthquakes, and volcanoes.

   d) **Show the medium earthquake data on your map.** In the *Layer List,* find the layer titled *Earthquakes medium.* If this layer is currently inactive, select the *Show/Hide* layer button on the right to reveal an eye icon.

Materials
- *Three-page Map*
- *My World* computer software
- colored markers or pencils—red, blue, yellow, black
- transparency layer of the *Big World Map* showing plate boundaries
- Region *Project Board*

EE 174

Once the class has identified and recorded the types of all the volcanoes for which the information is available, lead a class analysis of the data using the bulleted questions in the student text as guidelines.

Ask students how many volcanoes are located near the Java Trench. Have them refer to the *Big World Map*. They may have different interpretations of what they consider near. At the least, they should count volcanoes on the island of Java. They will probably want to exclude volcanoes in the Philippines, which may be related to another Earth structure. They may choose to count all of the volcanoes on Java, or all of the volcanoes in the band that runs through Sumatra and Java.

Ask students to describe the pattern formed by the volcanoes. Do they form a narrow line, a wide band, or a tight cluster? Or are they scattered? Students should recognize that the volcanoes form a narrow line that runs through the islands just north of the Java Trench and, compared to most of the earthquakes they have looked at, the volcanoes fall in a much narrower line.

Ask students to compare the patterns made by earthquakes and volcanoes. How do they think they are related? Students should notice that the volcanoes and the earthquakes follow the same curved line running through the islands. They may notice that the earthquakes in the region are much more spread out. They may also notice that the heaviest concentration of earthquakes tends to be a little south of the volcanoes.

Let students know that they will gather and analyze data on volcanoes in their region in the same way they gathered and analyzed volcano data in the Java Trench region.

TEACHER TALK

"You have used *My World* to gather data on volcanoes in the Java Trench region, and you have analyzed data on volcanoes in the region. Now you will use *My World* to gather data on volcanoes in your region. You will analyze the data, in the same way that you analyzed data on volcanoes in the Java Trench region.**"**

NOTES

....

....

....

....

....

....

....

- Three-p Map
- *My World* computer software
- colored markers or pencils—red, blue, yellow, black
- transparency layer of the *Big World Map* showing plate boundaries
- Region *Project Board*

...ound in your own region.

Observe Volcanoes in Your Region

Using the same steps demonstrated by your teacher, use *My World* to collect data about the volcanoes in your region. You will add this data to your *Three-page Map,* as well as to your *Region Project Board.* As you work, see what patterns you can find in the data.

Procedure

1. Prepare a *My World* plate map for examining volcano data by following these steps.

   a) **Open *My World*** by double-clicking on the *My World* icon on your computer screen.

   b) **Select *Earth Structures & Processes*** from the *Library* drop-down menu.

   c) **Open the *ESInquiry* file.** This file has information about elevation and depth, earthquakes, and volcanoes.

   d) **Show the medium earthquake data on your map.** In the *Layer List,* find the layer titled *Earthquakes medium.* If this layer is currently inactive, select the *Show/Hide* layer button on the right to reveal an eye icon.

Observe Volcanoes in Your Region

15 min

Students use My World *to examine volcanoes in their regions.*

△ Guide

Have pairs start *My World* at their computer stations. Have them load the *ESInquiry* project, following the instructions in the student text. Once they have the project loaded, they should turn the *Earthquakes medium* layer on. Then they should use the magnifier tool from the tool bar to zoom in on their region. When their map shows their region, they should turn the *Volcanoes* layer on and hide the *Earth Structure* and *Earth Structure boxes* layers.

NOTES

Finding volcanoes using *My World*

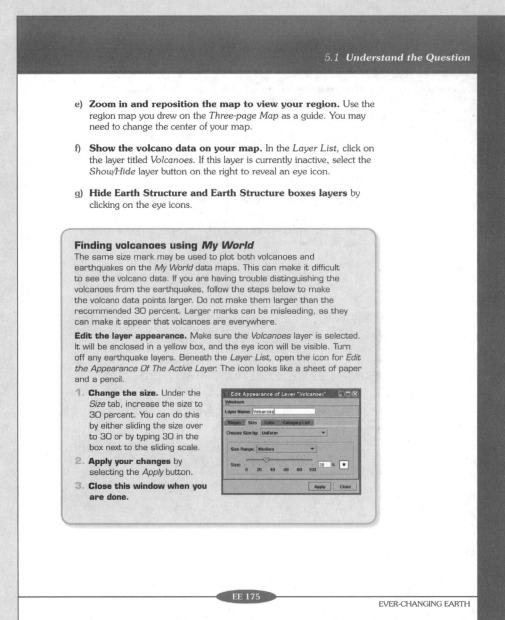

e) **Zoom in and reposition the map to view your region.** Use the region map you drew on the *Three-page Map* as a guide. You may need to change the center of your map.

f) **Show the volcano data on your map.** In the *Layer List,* click on the layer titled *Volcanoes.* If this layer is currently inactive, select the *Show/Hide* layer button on the right to reveal an eye icon.

g) **Hide Earth Structure and Earth Structure boxes layers** by clicking on the *eye* icons.

Finding volcanoes using *My World*
The same size mark may be used to plot both volcanoes and earthquakes on the *My World* data maps. This can make it difficult to see the volcano data. If you are having trouble distinguishing the volcanoes from the earthquakes, follow the steps below to make the volcano data points larger. Do not make them larger than the recommended 30 percent. Larger marks can be misleading, as they can make it appear that volcanoes are everywhere.

Edit the layer appearance. Make sure the *Volcanoes* layer is selected. It will be enclosed in a yellow box, and the eye icon will be visible. Turn off any earthquake layers. Beneath the *Layer List,* open the icon for *Edit the Appearance Of The Active Layer.* The icon looks like a sheet of paper and a pencil.

1. **Change the size.** Under the *Size* tab, increase the size to 30 percent. You can do this by either sliding the size over to 30 or by typing 30 in the box next to the sliding scale.

2. **Apply your changes** by selecting the *Apply* button.

3. **Close this window when you are done.**

EE 175

EVER-CHANGING EARTH

△ Guide

Tell students that they can use the *My World* controls to make it easier to view volcanoes and other data in their region. Instructions for doing this are given in the student text. Students should find the tool for editing the appearance of their active layer at the top of the *Layer List.* It looks like a pencil over a piece of paper. They should click this icon and select the *Size* tab in the pop-up window. Next to the slider there is a window showing the current size setting. Students should type *30* in this window and click the *Apply* button. This will enlarge the dots that mark the locations of volcanoes in their maps. Then students can close the window.

2. You should be able to see the earthquakes and volcanoes in your region. Examine the map to identify where volcanoes are located. Find volcanoes in your region and volcanoes on the plates your region sits on. Use a black marker to sketch the locations of the volcanoes on your *Three-page Map*. Volcanoes near your plate boundaries may be in your region, or they may be outside your region. Make sure you mark the map so you can tell which side of the plate boundaries, or on which plate, each volcano is located. Be very accurate when marking the locations on your *Three-page Map*.

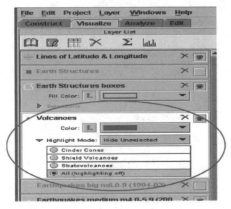

3. Prepare *My World* to show you the types of volcanoes around your region.

   a) **Make sure the Volcanoes layer is still selected.** You should see a yellow border around the *Volcanoes* box, and the eye icon will be visible.

   b) **Use the selection buttons inside the *Volcanoes* box to show the different types of volcanoes.** There are three different types of volcanoes to choose from: Cinder Cones, Shield Volcanoes, and Stratovolcanoes.

4. Identify the types of volcanoes using *My World*. On your *Three-page Map,* draw a red circle around any cinder cone volcanoes, a blue triangle around any shield volcanoes, and a yellow square around any stratovolcanoes.

5. Look for patterns in your volcano data. Look for groups of volcanoes that form a narrow line, a wide band, or a tight cluster. When you find a recognizable pattern of volcanoes, circle the pattern in pencil. Also, note how the volcanoes are spread throughout the region.

When students have the map in *My World* set up, have them identify volcanoes in their regions and on the plates that extend into their regions. Have them mark the locations of volcanoes with a black marker on their *Three-page Map*. (They should use the *Three-page Map* that they used in *Learning Set 3*.) Emphasize that they should mark the locations of volcanoes for the entire plates that their region sits on, and they should make it clear which side of a plate boundary each volcano is on.

Once students have recorded the locations of volcanoes in their region, have them use *My World* to identify the types of volcanoes. Step 3 tells students how to do this. In the *Volcanoes* box (found in the *Layer List*), they should select a type of volcano and record which of the volcanoes on their *Three-page Map* are of that type. They should repeat the process for the other two types of volcano. On their *Three-page Map,* they should draw red circles around cinder cone volcanoes, blue triangles around shield volcanoes, and yellow squares around stratovolcanoes. There may be some volcanoes in students' regions for which *My World* does not have type information.

As students record the types of the volcanoes in their regions, they should look for patterns in the data. They might find narrow lines, bands, or clusters. If they find any patterns, they should circle them with pencil.

NOTES

_____

_____

_____

_____

_____

_____

_____

_____

_____

Analyze Your Data

Use the data you just recorded on your *Three-page Map* to answer these questions.

1 Describe the shape of each pattern of volcanoes you found. For example, do the volcanoes make a narrow line, a wide band, or perhaps a triangle-shaped cluster? Maybe the volcanoes are scattered throughout the region and do not form any patterns.

2. For each pattern, describe the number of volcanoes. Are there fewer than five? Five to ten? More than ten?

3. For each pattern, describe where the volcanoes are in relation to the earthquakes. For example, the pattern of volcanoes might be parallel to or next to the pattern of earthquake activity. Or, the volcanoes might be scattered randomly within the pattern of earthquake activity.

4. Compare the patterns of earthquakes and volcanoes. What do the two patterns suggest about the relationship between earthquakes and volcanoes?

Conference

If other pairs of students in your class are working on the same region, work with them to prepare to present your data and analysis.

Prepare to share what you have found by marking the locations of volcanoes in and near your region on the transparency layer of the *Big World Map*. Be accurate when you mark them so the patterns are apparent. Be sure all volcanoes are marked on the correct sides of the plate boundaries. They should also be placed correctly with respect to the earthquakes. Do not mark the types of volcanoes on the *Big World Map* transparencies yet.

Be prepared to present the following to the class:

• descriptions of the volcano patterns, including their shapes and how many volcanoes are in each pattern

• the relationships between each of those patterns and the earthquakes that are nearby

• your ideas about the relationship between volcanoes and earthquakes

EE 177

EVER-CHANGING EARTH

Analyze Your Data

5 min

Students analyze the data they collect from My World.

⬡ Get Going

Have students work with their partners to answer the *Analyze Your Data* questions. Emphasize that they should be prepared to share their answers with the class.

△ Guide and Assess

As pairs answer the questions, monitor their progress, help them with any difficulties, and use the *Ever-Changing Earth Teacher Notes and Suggested Data* table in the Appendix to help you guide and assess students' analysis.

They should be able to describe the patterns they found in volcano data as either a narrow line, a wide band, or a cluster. They may also be able to describe other characteristics, such as a curve in a band or line, the shape of a cluster, or discontinuities. If the volcanoes are simply scattered, students should describe this. The *Ever-Changing Earth Teacher Notes and Suggested Data* table provides descriptions of patterns in volcano data that will help you assess students' work.

To answer the second question, students should simply count up the volcanoes in each circle they drew.

For Questions 3 and 4, students may use their *Three-page Maps* with their recorded data from *My World* to compare patterns in earthquakes to patterns in volcanoes. They should note whether the earthquakes are more or less spread out, whether they are in the same place as the volcanoes, and whether the pattern of volcanoes has about the same shape. The *Ever-Changing Earth Teacher Notes and Suggested Data* table provides comparisons of volcano and earthquake patterns that you can use to assess students' work.

Ask students what ideas they have discussed about the relationship between earthquakes and volcanoes. Students will not know enough about volcanoes to explain their relationship to earthquakes confidently at this point, but they should make an effort to develop ideas.

NOTES

two patterns suggest about the relationship between earthquakes and volcanoes?

Conference

If other pairs of students in your class are working on the same region, work with them to prepare to present your data and analysis.

Prepare to share what you have found by marking the locations of volcanoes in and near your region on the transparency layer of the *Big World Map*. Be accurate when you mark them so the patterns are apparent. Be sure all volcanoes are marked on the correct sides of the plate boundaries. They should also be placed correctly with respect to the earthquakes. Do not mark the types of volcanoes on the *Big World Map* transparencies yet.

Be prepared to present the following to the class:

* descriptions of the volcano patterns, including their shapes and how many volcanoes are in each pattern

* the relationships between each of those patterns and the earthquakes that are nearby

* your ideas about the relationship between volcanoes and earthquakes

Conference

10 min

Students discuss their data and data analysis in groups.

△ Guide

When students have finished analyzing their data, have them meet with other students with the same region. Together, they should prepare to present their data and data analysis to the class. Have them begin by marking the locations of volcanoes in and near their region on the transparency on the *Big World Map*. They should be careful to mark the locations accurately. They do not need to record the types of the volcanoes yet.

Have them briefly discuss their answers to the *Analyze Your Data* questions. They should come to agreement on descriptions of the volcano patterns and the relationships between those patterns and nearby earthquakes, and on ideas about the relationship between volcanoes and earthquakes. They will present these ideas to the class along with their data. Emphasize that they should use the bulleted list in the student text to guide them.

NOTES

....

....

....

....

Communicate: Share What You Know About Volcanoes in Your Region

15 min

Groups share their data and ideas.

Communicate

Share What You Know About Volcanoes in Your Region

After all of the volcanoes are marked on the *Big World Map*, take turns presenting what you found out about volcanoes in your region.

Begin your presentation by showing where volcanoes are located in and near your region. Point to each volcano you marked on the transparency layer of the *Big World Map*. Describe any patterns you identified in the locations of volcanoes. Discuss how the volcano patterns you identified compare with patterns in your earthquake data.

As part of your presentation, talk about any disagreements that came up as your group analyzed and compared data patterns. Discuss things you were confused about and anything your group wants to find out about the relationship between earthquakes and volcanoes.

As you listen to other groups present, look for similarities in the patterns of volcanoes or earthquake activity across different regions. Listen for differences of opinion about the relationships between earthquakes and volcanoes. If you disagree with a group's ideas, use evidence to support your ideas. Remember to be respectful.

After all the groups have presented, examine the whole *Big World Map* together as a class. Notice the earthquake patterns around the world. Notice the relationship between earthquakes and volcanoes around the world. Note the similarities and differences you see.

Reflect

Use the information from the presentations and the *Big World Map* to answer these questions. Think carefully about what you are seeing on the map and how these patterns might provide evidence to explain what is happening at plate boundaries.

1. What do you think is the relationship between earthquakes and volcanoes? Why might this relationship exist?

2. What do the patterns of volcanoes around the world tell you about the plate boundaries?

3. Are there any places in the world where the earthquake or volcanic activity does not seem to fit the patterns you identified? Describe them.

EE 178

△ Guide

When groups have marked their volcanoes on the *Big World Map* and discussed their ideas, have them present their data and ideas to the class. Each group should begin by pointing out the volcanoes they located on the *Big World Map*. Then they should discuss the patterns they identified and how these compare with patterns of earthquakes.

They should also discuss any disagreements that came up during their group's discussion, anything that they feel uncertain about, or would like to investigate.

☐ Assess

As groups present, assess how students are participating. Students should ask about anything that is unclear in a group's presentation.

△ Guide

After groups have presented, draw students' attention to the *Big World Map*. Ask students to describe the patterns they see in the volcano data. How do they compare to the patterns in earthquakes? They should observe that volcanoes, like earthquakes, tend to occur around plate boundaries. And the places where there are the heaviest concentrations of volcanoes are the same places where there are the heaviest concentrations of earthquakes. They should also notice that earthquakes appear to have a greater frequency, and the lines or bands of earthquakes reveal more of the plate boundaries than volcanoes do. Like earthquakes, volcanoes do not always occur at plate boundaries.

△ Guide and Assess

Lead a class discussion of the *Reflect* questions. Use the following guidelines to assess students' ideas:

1. Students probably cannot say very much with confidence about the relationship between earthquakes and volcanoes, but they should recognize that volcanoes tend to occur where earthquakes occur.

2. Knowing that volcanoes worldwide tend to cluster around the places where students identified plate boundaries should give students confidence in the plate boundaries they identified.

3. Students should identify outlying earthquakes or volcanoes that do not fit with any patterns.

Reflect

10 min

The class has a discussion of their answers.

NOTES

....

....

....

....

....

Conference

10 min

Groups update their Region Project Boards.

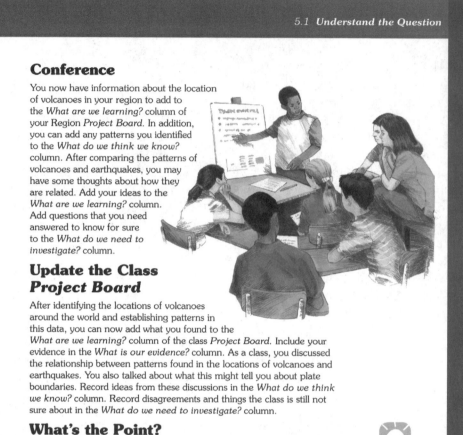

Conference

You now have information about the location of volcanoes in your region to add to the *What are we learning?* column of your Region *Project Board*. In addition, you can add any patterns you identified to the *What do we think we know?* column. After comparing the patterns of volcanoes and earthquakes, you may have some thoughts about how they are related. Add your ideas to the *What are we learning?* column. Add questions that you need answered to know for sure to the *What do we need to investigate?* column.

Update the Class Project Board

After identifying the locations of volcanoes around the world and establishing patterns in this data, you can now add what you found to the *What are we learning?* column of the class *Project Board*. Include your evidence in the *What is our evidence?* column. As a class, you discussed the relationship between patterns found in the locations of volcanoes and earthquakes. You also talked about what this might tell you about plate boundaries. Record ideas from these discussions in the *What do we think we know?* column. Record disagreements and things the class is still not sure about in the *What do we need to investigate?* column.

What's the Point?

Observing the number and spread of volcanoes in your region provides further evidence about where the plates of Earth's crust are located. Comparing the location of volcanoes with the location of earthquakes adds more evidence. Often, volcanoes and earthquakes occur near one another. This indicates that there may be a relationship between the two geologic events.

EE 179

EVER-CHANGING EARTH

⬡ Get Going

Have students meet with their groups to update their *Region Project Board.* They should record new information about the location of volcanoes in their regions to their *What are we learning?* column. They should record patterns they identified in the *What do we think we know?* column. They should record any ideas about how the volcanoes in their region are related to the earthquakes in their region in the *What are we learning?* column. Any questions about volcanoes (or earthquakes) in their region should go in the *What do we need to investigate?* column.

△ Guide

Lead a class discussion to update the class *Project Board*. Ask them what new information they can add to the *What are we learning?* column. For any claims they put in the *What are we learning?* column, they should put evidence in the *What is our evidence?* column.

Ask students what ideas from the class discussions they can record in the *What do we think we know?* column. They should record ideas about the relationship of volcanoes to earthquakes and plate boundaries. Ask them what they need to put in the *What do we need to investigate?* column. They should record questions about why earthquakes and volcanoes have similar patterns, why there are volcanoes that are not near plate boundaries, and why volcanoes happen. Ideally, students will also have questions about why there are not more volcanoes at the places where Earth's plates are pulling away from each other, why does the greatest number of volcanoes occur in the places where earthquakes occur, and where the plates are pushing together. They should also wonder what they can learn from the different types of volcanoes in their region.

Update the Class *Project Board*

10 min

The class updates the Project Board.

Assessment Options

Targeted Concepts, Skills, and Nature of Science	How do I know if students got it?
Scientists often work together and then share their findings. Sharing findings makes new information available and helps scientists refine their ideas and build on others' ideas. When another person's or group's idea is used, credit needs to be given.	**ASK:** Why is it important to share your data and ideas with the class? **LISTEN:** Students should recognize that different pairs gathered data on different volcanoes, so the class needs everyone to share their findings. In addition, different pairs may have developed different ideas.
Scientists must keep clear, accurate, and descriptive records of what they do so they can share their work with others and consider what they did, why they did it, and what they want to do next.	**ASK:** Why is it important to record what you are learning on the *Project Board?* **LISTEN:** Students should recognize that it is important for them to track their progress and the evidence they are gathering for their ideas.

Teacher Reflection Questions

- What difficulties did students have comparing earthquake activity to volcanic activity?

- How were you able to help students recognize and describe patterns in volcano data? What might you try next time?

- How were you able to encourage constructive group and class discussions?

NOTES

_____

_____

_____

_____

_____

_____

_____

_____

_____

5.2 Explore

How Do the Volcanoes in Your Region Compare to Those Around the World?

◄ $1\frac{1}{4}$ *class periods*

A class period is considered to be one 40 to 50 minute class.

Overview

Using pictures and data, students observe the features of four volcanoes, which include examples of the three major volcano types. They consider the differences and similarities of the volcanoes and compare them to volcanoes in their regions, analyzing their observations and data. From among the four volcanoes they observed, they identify one that is most similar to volcanoes in their region. They meet with other pairs that picked the same volcano from the four. Together, they identify the characteristics of volcanoes that they think are most important and develop a description of the type of volcano in their region. Finally, they present their ideas to the class, and the class records what they have learned on the *Project Board*.

Targeted Concepts, Skills, and Nature of Science	Performance Expectations
Scientists often work together and then share their findings. Sharing findings makes new information available and helps scientists refine their ideas and build on others' ideas. When another person or group's idea is used, credit needs to be given.	Students should work in groups to predict and describe the volcanoes they observed and to compare the volcanoes in their regions with these volcanoes.
Scientists must keep clear, accurate, and descriptive records of what they do so they can share their work with others and consider what they did, why they did it, and what they want to do next.	Students should refer to their class *Project Board* and *Region Project Board* as necessary, and may want to refer to their records from this section during future sections in this Unit.

Targeted Concepts, Skills, and Nature of Science	Performance Expectations
Scientists make claims (conclusions) based on evidence obtained (trends in data) from reliable investigations.	Students should make claims about which volcano is most similar to the volcanoes in their region. They support their claims with reasoning about which characteristics of volcanoes are most important, with their observations of photographs of volcanoes, and information from the pen pal letters.
Interactions between Earth's crustal plates can result in mountain building, rift valleys, and geologic activity such as earthquakes and volcanoes. Underwater volcanic activity may form underwater mountains, which can thrust above the ocean's surface to become islands.	Students should consider the relationships between volcanic activity and geographic features.

Materials	
1 per class	Class *Project Board* *Ever-Changing Earth Teacher Notes and Suggested Data* table

Homework Options

Reflection

- **Science Content:** Describe the differences you noticed between volcanoes in your region and volcanoes in other regions. What regions had the same type of volcano as your region? What regions had different volcano types from your region? *(The purpose of this question is to check and reinforce students' observations and categorizations of volcanoes.)*

SECTION 5.2 IMPLEMENTATION

5.2 Explore

How Do the Volcanoes in Your Region Compare to Those Around the World?

You know there are several volcanoes in your region, and you know their types. However, you do not yet know what the different types mean. Each type of volcano has a characteristic shape and structure, style of eruption, and type of material that is ejected. Some volcanoes are very explosive, shooting lava into the air. Others simply seep rivers of lava onto Earth's surface. Some are very tall, while others are broad and flat. These are some of the characteristics you will observe as you look at the following photographs. As you look at these different types of volcanoes, keep in mind the types of volcanoes found in your region.

Observe

Examine the photographs and descriptions of volcanic eruptions on the following pages. You will see examples of each volcano type. As you look at the shape of each volcano and its characteristics, identify similarities and differences among the types of volcanoes.

To gain firsthand knowledge about volcanoes, vulcanologists may face dangerous situations.

Project-Based Inquiry Science

EE 180

5.2 Explore

How Do the Volcanoes in Your Region Compare to Those Around the World?

5 min

Students are introduced to the activity.

META NOTES

To better guide students as they explore types of volcanoes, you may wish to review the *Understanding for Teachers* at the beginning of the *Learning Set*.

○ Engage

Ask students what they know about volcanoes. What do volcanoes look like? What happens at volcanoes? Students may be aware that different types of volcanoes have different shapes. They probably know that volcanoes can erupt and release lava and other materials. Tell them that in addition to having different shapes, different types of volcanoes have different kinds of activity. Let them know they will explore the different types of earthquakes in this section.

*A class period is considered to be one 40 to 50 minute class.

Observe

10 min

Students observe the characteristics of four different volcanoes.

photographs. As you look at these different types of volcanoes, keep in mind the types of volcanoes found in your region.

Observe

Examine the photographs and descriptions of volcanic eruptions on the following pages. You will see examples of each volcano type. As you look at the shape of each volcano and its characteristics, identify similarities and differences among the types of volcanoes.

△ **Guide**

Draw students' attention to the photographs of volcanoes in their text. Read the descriptions of each volcano with the class. Tell students to pay attention to the similarities and differences of the volcanoes. Emphasize that they should note the shapes of the volcanoes and the activities at the volcanoes. The first volcano, Koryaksky Sopka, is a cinder cone volcano and emits hot gas and rocks. The second volcano, South Sister (of the Three Sisters Volcanoes), is a stratovolcano and emits hot gas, rocks, and lava flows. The third, Kilauea, is a shield volcano, and emits lava flows. Unlike the preceding volcanoes, it is not explosive. The last volcano is also a shield volcano. It initially emitted steam and rock fragments, but now it emits lava flows.

META NOTES

This activity should familiarize students with volcanoes and help them begin to analyze the characteristics of volcanoes. It is not necessary for students to develop an accurate understanding of the different types of volcanoes at this point. They will learn more about volcanoes and the characteristics of the different types in the next section.

NOTES

....

....

....

....

....

....

....

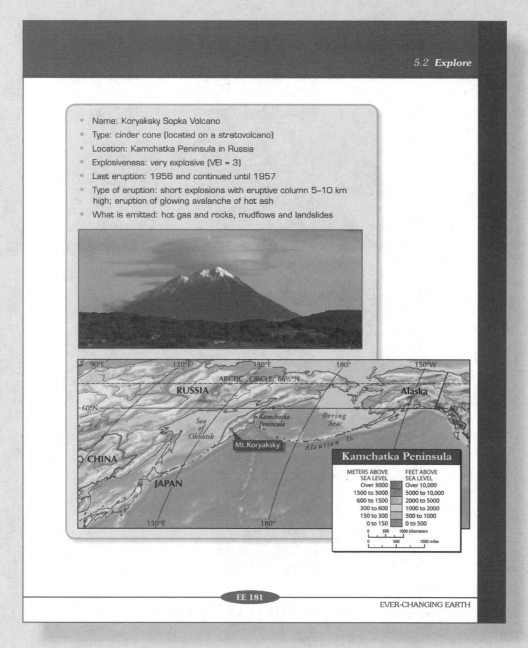

5.2 Explore

- Name: Koryaksky Sopka Volcano
- Type: cinder cone (located on a stratovolcano)
- Location: Kamchatka Peninsula in Russia
- Explosiveness: very explosive (VEI = 3)
- Last eruption: 1956 and continued until 1957
- Type of eruption: short explosions with eruptive column 5–10 km high; eruption of glowing avalanche of hot ash
- What is emitted: hot gas and rocks, mudflows and landslides

Kamchatka Peninsula

METERS ABOVE SEA LEVEL	FEET ABOVE SEA LEVEL
Over 3000	Over 10,000
1500 to 3000	5000 to 10,000
600 to 1500	2000 to 5000
300 to 600	1000 to 2000
150 to 300	500 to 1000
0 to 150	0 to 500

EE 181

EVER-CHANGING EARTH

Ask students what similarities and differences they noticed. How is the South Sister of the Three Sisters similar to Sopka? How is it different? Students should notice that they are both roughly conical, but that the South Sister is more irregular and rises to a sharp peak. The volcanoes are both very explosive, although the South Sister emits lava flows, while Sopka only emits hot gas, rocks, and mud slides. The South Sister also had long eruptions, producing a column of up to 50 km (30 mi). Sopka, by contrast, had short eruptions that produced columns of up to 10 km (6 mi).

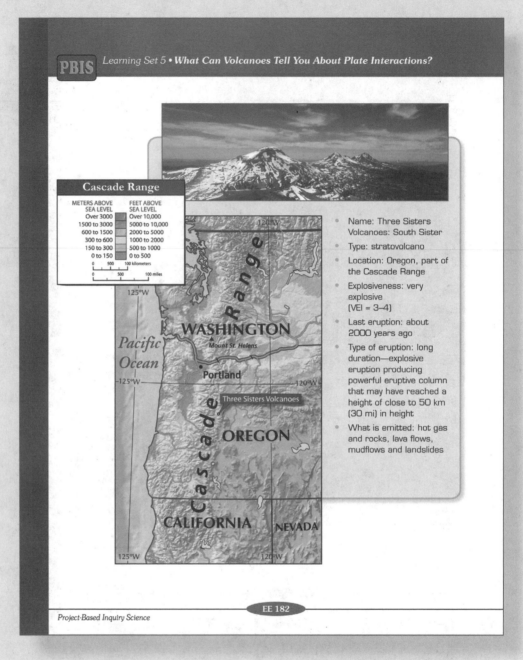

Cascade Range

METERS ABOVE SEA LEVEL	FEET ABOVE SEA LEVEL
Over 3000	Over 10,000
1500 to 3000	5000 to 10,000
600 to 1500	2000 to 5000
300 to 600	1000 to 2000
150 to 300	500 to 1000
0 to 150	0 to 500

- Name: Three Sisters Volcanoes: South Sister
- Type: stratovolcano
- Location: Oregon, part of the Cascade Range
- Explosiveness: very explosive (VEI = 3–4)
- Last eruption: about 2000 years ago
- Type of eruption: long duration—explosive eruption producing powerful eruptive column that may have reached a height of close to 50 km (30 mi) in height
- What is emitted: hot gas and rocks, lava flows, mudflows and landslides

WASHINGTON
Mount St. Helens
Portland
Three Sisters Volcanoes
OREGON
CALIFORNIA
NEVADA
Pacific Ocean

Ask them how Laki is similar to these two volcanoes. How is it different? Students should see that Laki has an elevation, just as the other two volcanoes do. They should also see that Laki is less steep towards the top than at the base, so that it has a mound, or shield shape, in contrast to the conical shape of the other two. Laki now only emits lava flows, unlike the other two volcanoes. It is described as violently explosive, having spewed steam, rocks, and gas and thrown lava into the air.

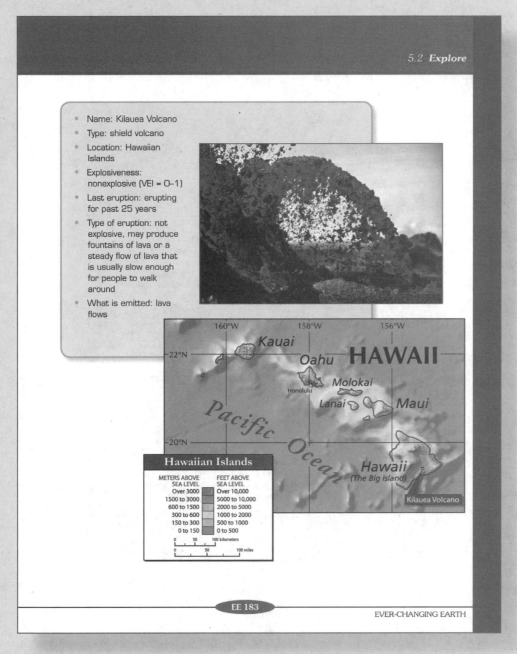

5.2 *Explore*

- Name: Kilauea Volcano
- Type: shield volcano
- Location: Hawaiian Islands
- Explosiveness: nonexplosive (VEI = 0–1)
- Last eruption: erupting for past 25 years
- Type of eruption: not explosive, may produce fountains of lava or a steady flow of lava that is usually slow enough for people to walk around
- What is emitted: lava flows

Hawaiian Islands

METERS ABOVE SEA LEVEL	FEET ABOVE SEA LEVEL
Over 3000	Over 10,000
1500 to 3000	5000 to 10,000
600 to 1500	2000 to 5000
300 to 600	1000 to 2000
150 to 300	500 to 1000
0 to 150	0 to 500

EE 183

It may be more difficult for students to characterize the shape of the other shield volcano, Kilauea, from the picture in their text. Point out the location of the volcano on the map of Hawaii. It is on the southeast side of the island, far from the summit of the island. Unlike Sopka and the South Sister, it is not a high peak. Unlike all of the other volcanoes, Kilauea is not explosive. Like the other shield volcano, Laki, it emits lava flows.

- Name: Laki
- Type: shield volcano
- Location: Iceland, peak of mid-ocean ridge
- Explosiveness: violently explosive (VEI = 6)
- Last eruption: 1783
- Type of eruption: Contact of magma with water resulted in an explosion of steam, water, and gas. This was followed by regular explosions with booming sounds that thrust small amounts of lava into the air. The explosion ended with a lava flow.
- What is emitted: The initial eruption produced steam and rock fragments, or volcanic bombs, followed by lava flows.

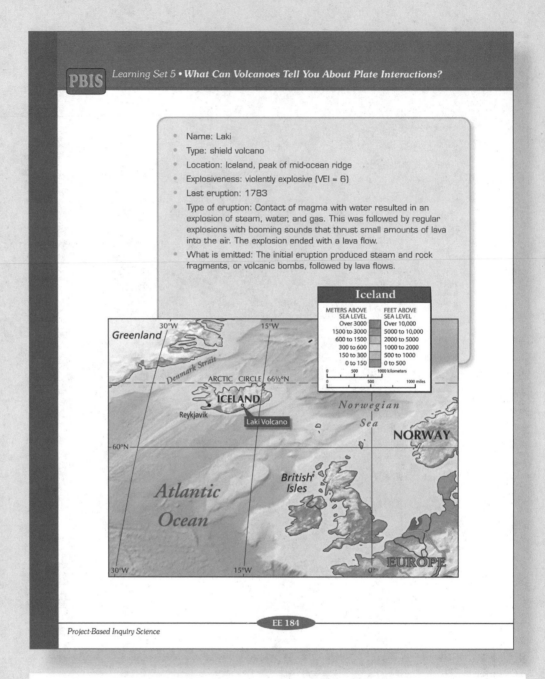

Iceland

METERS ABOVE SEA LEVEL	FEET ABOVE SEA LEVEL
Over 3000	Over 10,000
1500 to 3000	5000 to 10,000
600 to 1500	2000 to 5000
300 to 600	1000 to 2000
150 to 300	500 to 1000
0 to 150	0 to 500

NOTES

....

....

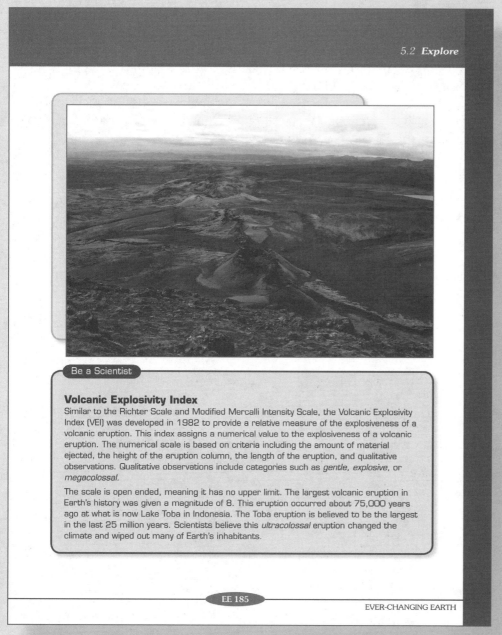

Be a Scientist

Volcanic Explosivity Index

Similar to the Richter Scale and Modified Mercalli Intensity Scale, the Volcanic Explosivity Index (VEI) was developed in 1982 to provide a relative measure of the explosiveness of a volcanic eruption. This index assigns a numerical value to the explosiveness of a volcanic eruption. The numerical scale is based on criteria including the amount of material ejected, the height of the eruption column, the length of the eruption, and qualitative observations. Qualitative observations include categories such as *gentle, explosive,* or *megacolossal.*

The scale is open ended, meaning it has no upper limit. The largest volcanic eruption in Earth's history was given a magnitude of 8. This eruption occurred about 75,000 years ago at what is now Lake Toba in Indonesia. The Toba eruption is believed to be the largest in the last 25 million years. Scientists believe this *ultracolossal* eruption changed the climate and wiped out many of Earth's inhabitants.

Be a Scientist: Volcanic Explosivity Index

5 min*

Students are introduced to the Volcanic Explosivity Index.

*Optional, if time allows.

△ Guide

Ask students how they think an explosive volcano is different from a nonexplosive volcano. What do they think explosive means? How do they think this quality of volcanoes is measured? Tell them explosive volcanoes emit large amounts of material and produce high columns of gases and other substances. Less explosive volcanoes may simply produce streams of lava.

Introduce the Volcanic Explosivity Index (VEI). Like the magnitude and intensity of earthquakes, the explosivity of volcanoes can be measured on a scale. The index assigns a number to the explosivity of a volcano based on the amount of material ejected, the height of the column, the length of the eruption, and other criteria. The largest volcanic eruption in Earth's history had an explosivity of 8. Scientists think this eruption, which took place around 75,000 years ago, changed the climate and wiped out many of Earth's inhabitants.

NOTES

447

Stop and Think

1. There are many types of volcanoes. Based on the pictures you have already seen, sketch each different shape. Label each type of volcano.

2. Locate the volcanoes you have read about on the *Big World Map*. How close are these volcanoes to other geologic activity marked on the map?

Compare the Volcanoes in Your Region

You observed several different types of volcanoes and have some of the same information scientists use to classify volcanoes. You can use this to start thinking about the volcanoes in your region in a more scientific way.

Working with your partner, reread your pen pal letter, focusing on volcanic activity in your region. Using the information provided with the photographs, complete as many details as you can about the volcanic activity in your region. For each volcano described in your pen pal letter, list its name, type, location, explosiveness, and last eruption, and what is emitted. Record your volcano information on a *Region Project Board* in the *What are we learning?* column.

Compare the volcanoes discussed in your pen pal letters to the volcanoes described in the photographs. Select one volcano from the photographs that you think is most like the volcano in your region. Discuss this selection with your partner. If you disagree about which volcano most closely matches, discuss how you made your selection. Share which characteristics you thought were most important—shape, location, eruption date, type of eruption. If you cannot agree on one similar volcano, you may keep two selections for now.

Conference

Form a group with others who selected the same volcano as you. Take turns describing the similar volcanoes in your regions and why you think they are similar to the volcano you all selected. Discuss the characteristics of volcanoes and decide which ones all of you consider to be the most important when looking for a match.

Finally, see if the volcano in your region is the same type as the volcano you selected from the photographs. Develop your best description of that type of volcano.

EE 186

Project-Based Inquiry Science

Stop and Think

10 min

Students have a class discussion of the Stop and Think *questions.*

△ Guide

Have students answer the *Stop and Think* questions independently. For the first question, have them sketch the different shapes of volcanoes they have identified. They should have identified volcanoes with conical shapes, volcanoes with sharp peaks, and mound-shaped volcanoes.

They should also locate the volcanoes they read about on the *Big World Map*. After students have had a moment to sketch the types of volcanoes and locate the volcanoes they read about, ask the class how close the volcanoes they read about are to other geologic activity marked on the *Big World Map*. Students should notice that Sopka and the South Sister lie in thick bands of volcanic and earthquake activity along plate boundaries. Laki lies in a cluster of volcanic and earthquake activity around Iceland. Iceland is on a plate boundary, but has far more geologic activity than nearby parts of the plate boundary. Kilauea is one of a cluster of volcanoes, but off the Hawaiian Islands there is not much surrounding geologic activity. Kilauea is not on a plate boundary.

Compare the Volcanoes in Your Region

10 min

Pairs compare the volcanoes in their region to the volcanoes in the photographs.

close are these volca... ...ther geologic activity marked on the map?

Compare the Volcanoes in Your Region

You observed several different types of volcanoes and have some of the same information scientists use to classify volcanoes. You can use this to start thinking about the volcanoes in your region in a more scientific way.

Working with your partner, reread your pen pal letter, focusing on volcanic activity in your region. Using the information provided with the photographs, complete as many details as you can about the volcanic activity in your region. For each volcano described in your pen pal letter, list its name, type, location, explosiveness, and last eruption, and what is emitted. Record your volcano information on a *Region Project Board* in the *What are we learning?* column.

Compare the volcanoes discussed in your pen pal letters to the volcanoes described in the photographs. Select one volcano from the photographs that you think is most like the volcano in your region. Discuss this selection with your partner. If you disagree about which volcano most closely matches, discuss how you made your selection. Share which characteristics you thought were most important—shape, location, eruption date, type of eruption. If you cannot agree on one similar volcano, you may keep two selections for now.

△ Guide

Have students meet with their partners to compare volcanoes in their regions. Have them begin by rereading their pen pal letter, thinking particularly of the volcanic activity in their region.

They should combine the information from the photographs of volcanoes of different types with the information from their pen pal letter. Have them list the name, type, location, explosiveness, and last eruption of each volcano in their region. They should record this information in the *What are we learning?* column of their *Region Project Board*.

Have students compare the volcanoes in their pen pal letters to the volcanoes in the photographs. They should discuss with their partners which volcano from the photographs is most like the volcanoes in their region. They should try to agree on one volcano. They should discuss which characteristics they think are most important, such as shape, location, eruption date, or type of eruption. If they cannot agree on one, they can choose two for the time being.

△ Guide and Assess

Using the *Ever-Changing Earth Teacher Notes and Suggested Data* table in the Appendix, check how students are progressing in identifying important information from their pen pal letters. Students may feel that they do not have enough information to make an accurate comparison. Emphasize that they will revise their ideas as they learn more about volcanoes. For now, they should use all of the information available to them.

selections for now.

Conference

Form a group with others who selected the same volcano as you. Take turns describing the similar volcanoes in your regions and why you think they are similar to the volcano you all selected. Discuss the characteristics of volcanoes and decide which ones all of you consider to be the most important when looking for a match.

Finally, see if the volcano in your region is the same type as the volcano you selected from the photographs. Develop your best description of that type of volcano.

△ Guide

Have students meet with other pairs who chose the same volcano. Each pair should describe the volcanoes in their region that they identified as similar to the group's volcano. They should describe the characteristics that are similar, and they should discuss which characteristic they think is most important when looking for similar volcanoes.

They should check the type of the volcanoes. Are they all the same type? Have them develop their best description of that type of volcano. Let them know that they will share their ideas with the class.

☐ Assess

As students work with their groups, ask them what ideas they discussed. How is their type of volcano different from other types of volcanoes? It is not necessary for students to have accurate descriptions of their volcano types at this point, but they should use the characteristics they identified as important and the specific features of the volcanoes they have examined to develop an initial description.

Conference
10 min

Students discuss and describe the types of volcanoes in their regions with other students who chose the same volcano.

NOTES

....

....

....

Communicate: Share Your Ideas

15 min

Groups share their ideas.

Communicate

Share Your Ideas

Take turns presenting the volcano you chose from the photographs, the volcanoes in your regions, and the characteristics your group decided were most important when comparing volcanoes. Share with the class your description of your volcano type.

As you are listening, make sure you understand what each group is presenting. If you do not understand something, or if you do not agree with something that is being presented, raise your hand, and share your question or disagreement. Remember to be respectful.

You are only beginning to learn about volcanic activity. Your class may have many disagreements. You may also find that there are many things you still need to learn to fully understand the volcanic activity in your region. Keep track of these things. You will use the ideas, agreements, and disagreements generated during this discussion as suggestions for the *Project Board*.

To complete this conference, mark on the *Big World Map* the location of the volcanoes mentioned in the letters. Use a dot to mark the spot as close to the location as you can. Label each volcano with its name.

Update the *Project Board*

As a class, update the *Project Board*. In the *What do we think we know?* column, list what you think you know about different types of volcanoes and how they erupt. The similarities and differences among different types of volcanoes, including the ones located in your region, should also be included.

Learning about different types of volcanoes probably raised more questions. In the *What do we need to investigate?* column, record what you need to investigate to better understand why there are different types of volcanoes and what volcanoes and their eruptions can tell you about plate movement.

EE 187

EVER-CHANGING EARTH

△ Guide

Once students have had time to develop descriptions of their type of volcano, have them share their ideas with the class. Have them present the volcano they chose from the photographs, the volcanoes in their region, the characteristics they decided were most important, and their description of their volcano type.

As students listen to other groups' presentations, they may disagree with something a group says, or they may not understand something a group says. If they disagree with something the group says, they should constructively state their disagreement. If something is not clear, they should politely ask questions. If students ask you questions about the volcanoes in a region, redirect the questions to the presenting group. You may need to model the kinds of questions students should be asking by asking presenting groups questions about why they chose the volcano they did or why they think a particular characteristic of volcanoes is important.

△ Guide

Ask students what they think they know about the different types of volcanoes. Record students' ideas in the *What do we think we know?* column of the *Project Board*. Ask them what the similarities and differences between the different types of volcanoes are. Record their answers in the *What do we think we know?* column.

Ask students what they need to investigate to better understand why there are different types of volcanoes. What do they need to investigate to understand what volcanoes can tell them about Earth's plates? Record their responses in the *What do we need to investigate?* column.

Update the Project Board

10 min

The class has a discussion to update the Project Board.

NOTES

 ## What's the Point?

There are several different types of volcanoes. The similarities and differences in volcanoes include shape and structure of the cone, style of eruption, and the type of material that is emitted. When scientists classify volcanoes, they use these properties. Different types of volcanoes occur in different places on Earth.

NOTES

....

....

....

Assessment Options

Targeted Concepts, Skills, and Nature of Science	How do I know if students got it?
Scientists often work together and then share their findings. Sharing findings makes new information available and helps scientists refine their ideas and build on others' ideas. When another person or group's idea is used, credit needs to be given.	**ASK:** What did you learn from the others who chose the same volcano? **LISTEN:** Some groups probably had different observations or ideas than other groups. *Investigation Expos* should give students a chance to see what they missed and identify things they need to learn more about.

Teacher Reflection Questions

- What difficulties did students have distinguishing the different types of volcanoes? Did the characteristics they identified as important help them distinguish the types? How can you help them with this?

- What concepts will you need to emphasize when students learn more about types of volcanoes? What gaps do you see in students' understanding?

- How were you able to engage students in discussing their ideas with their partners, with their groups, and with the class? How were you able to assess their participation? What might you try next time?

NOTES

NOTES

5.3 Read

What Is a Volcano?

◀ *2 class periods*

A class period is
considered to be one
40 to 50 minute class.

Overview

Students read about the basic features of volcanoes and volcanic eruptions.
They learn about the shapes, eruptions, and lava characteristic of the
different types of volcanoes. Using what they have learned, they revise
their classification of the volcanoes in their regions, connecting what they
have learned to their investigation of their regions and reflecting on their
developing understanding.

Targeted Concepts, Skills, and Nature of Science	Performance Expectations
Scientists often work together and then share their findings. Sharing findings makes new information available and helps scientists refine their ideas and build on others' ideas. When another person or group's idea is used, credit needs to be given.	Students should answer questions about the reading together and collaboratively update the *Project Board* based on what they learned about volcanoes, eruptions, and lava.
Scientists must keep clear, accurate, and descriptive records of what they do so they can share their work with others and consider what they did, why they did it, and what they want to do next.	Students should keep track of information on the class *Project Board* and refer to it throughout the Unit.
Earthquake activity, volcanic activity, and topography are all evidence that Earth's crust is moving and changing.	Students should be able to support their claim with evidence.
Interactions between Earth's crustal plates can result in mountain building, rift valleys, and geologic activities such as earthquakes and volcanoes. Underwater volcanic activity may form underwater mountains, which can thrust above the ocean's surface to become islands.	Students should be able to describe volcanic activity underwater, and how islands are formed in these areas.

Materials	
1 per student	*Volcano Table* page
	Region Project Board

Homework Options

Reflection

- **Science Content:** Beginning with your story of magma moving around in the mantle because of convection currents, write what would happen if the magma entered a volcano and reached the surface of Earth. Describe how it reaches Earth's surface and the topography of the crust. *(Students should describe the type of volcano, eruption, and lava.)*

NOTES

....

....

....

....

....

....

....

....

....

SECTION 5.3 IMPLEMENTATION

5.3 Read

What Is a Volcano?

Parícutin Volcano in Mexico

On February 20, 1943, a loud rumbling noise disturbed a small farming community in Mexico. The loud noise was Earth opening up. People first noticed the smell of rotten eggs, which was actually the smell of burning sulfur rising from below the surface. The smell was followed by smoke, ash-like particles, and heat. Overnight, a small cone-shaped structure formed in the middle of the cornfields. Lava that erupted from it flowed over the land, covering crops. People watched in amazement as over the weeks the volcano grew.

During the first year, the volcano rose to 336 m (1100 ft). Over the next eight years, layers of hot rock and lava piled up, adding another 88 m (290 ft) to the volcano. Today, many people come to visit this volcano, Parícutin, and the town near where it was born.

- Name: Parícutin
- Type: cinder cone
- Location: Mexico
- Explosiveness: very explosive (VEI = 4)
- Last eruption: 1952
- Type of eruption: regular explosions with an eruptive column several kilometers high; occasional large cannonlike explosions
- What is emitted: different-sized volcanic particles, including ash that rains down on the surrounding land; lava flows

EE 189

EVER-CHANGING EARTH

5.3 Read

What Is a Volcano?

Parícutin Volcano in Mexico

5 min

Students are introduced to the question addressed by this reading.

⃝ Engage

Begin by pointing out the picture of Parícutin in the student text. Discuss how Parícutin first erupted. The volcano opened up in the middle of a cornfield in Mexico in 1943. The people in the nearby farming community heard a loud rumbling, and smelled the burning sulfur from below Earth's surface. Soon the volcano produced smoke, volcanic ash, and heat. During its first year, it grew to 336 m (1100 ft) in height. It eventually grew to 88 m (290 ft). It last erupted in 1952.

*A class period is considered to be one 40 to 50 minute class.

Ask students what a volcano is. Could a volcano open up on the street in front of the school?

TEACHER TALK

"Imagine being one of the farmers who discovered the volcano. One day you smell rotten eggs in the cornfield, and then there's smoke and ash coming from the ground. Why would that happen? Could we have a volcano here? Out in the street? What is a volcano?"

NOTES

_____

_____

_____

_____

_____

_____

_____

_____

_____

_____

_____

_____

_____

5.3

The pictures you have seen show volcanoes of different shapes and sizes. They erupt in a variety of ways, and those eruptions emit different materials. In this section, you will learn more about volcanoes and the characteristics that make them different.

What Is a Volcano?

A volcano is any place in Earth's crust where mantle material and other substances reach the surface. The mantle material is a mixture of molten rock, rock particles, and dissolved gases called magma. As the magma travels to the surface, some rock in the lower crust is melted and mixes in with the rising magma. Once the magma reaches the surface, it is called lava. Lava is a mixture of mantle material and material from the lower crust. Substances that erupt from a volcano may be solid, liquid, or gas, depending on the makeup of the lava and the amount of pressure involved. An Earth structure formed by the accumulation of lava and other volcanic materials is also referred to as a volcano. Volcanoes of both types come in a variety of shapes and sizes.

Volcanoes are sometimes found in clusters called **volcanic fields.** Some volcanic fields are made up of multiple volcanoes, each formed by a single eruption. Parícutin is an example of such a volcano. It is part of an 1100 km (700 mi) line of similar volcanoes extending across southern Mexico.

volcanic field: a place on Earth's surface where there are clusters of volcanic activity, including anywhere from 10 to 100 volcanoes.

active volcano: a volcano that is currently erupting or is expected to erupt.

dormant volcano: a volcano that is currently not erupting, but has erupted in the past and is likely to erupt in the future.

extinct volcano: a volcano that is not currently active and is not likely to erupt again.

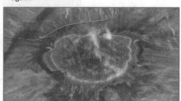

At 87° C (188° F), the water in the center of Grand Prismatic Hot Spring, in Yellowstone National Park, is just one indication that a very large dormant volcano may lie beneath the park. Although Yellowstone has not had an eruption in 70,000 years, it is considered to be an active volcano because there is earthquake activity around it and the ground has been rising to a higher elevation.

Another type of volcanic field is formed by multiple volcanic vents, all part of the same volcano. Volcanic fields such as this can cover hundreds of kilometers. Mauna Loa in Hawaii, the world's most active and largest volcano, is part of this type of volcanic field.

Some volcanoes are currently active, while others have been silent for thousands of years. If a volcano is currently erupting or shows signs of activity, such as the release of gases, scientists consider it an **active volcano**. Some scientists also consider a volcano active if it has erupted within recorded history. If a volcano is not currently active but could become so, it is considered to be a **dormant volcano**. If a volcano is not likely to erupt again, it is considered to be an **extinct volcano**.

EE 190

What Is a Volcano?

5 min

Students are introduced to the basic concepts of volcanoes.

META NOTES

There are many ways to implement a reading section. Consider alternating the way you implement these sections periodically to keep students engaged. You might have students read in pairs or take turns reading aloud before you discuss the content of the section. Or you might read the text to the class and have the students summarize what you read, recording the main ideas and key facts.

△ Guide

Discuss the two meanings of the word volcano. Volcano can mean a place in Earth's crust where mantle material reaches the surface. The mantle material is a mixture of rock, rock particles, and dissolved gases. Emphasize that when this material is in the mantle, it is called magma. When it reaches Earth's surface, it is called lava. Lava often includes materials from the lower crust, as well as magma from the mantle. The word volcano can also mean an Earth structure formed by the accumulation of lava and other volcanic materials.

Introduce the concept of volcanic fields. A volcanic field is a cluster of vents. A volcanic field may be composed of multiple volcanoes, or it may be a single volcano with multiple vents. The student text provides examples of both types of volcanic field. Parícutin is in a volcanic field that contains many different volcanoes. But Mauna Loa, in Hawaii, is part of a volcanic field comprised of a single volcano with multiple vents.

Discuss how not all volcanoes are active. Scientists consider a volcano active if it is currently erupting or showing signs of activity, such as a release of gases. Some scientists consider any volcano that has erupted within recorded history to be active. A volcano that is not active, but could become so, is considered dormant. A volcano that is unlikely to erupt again is considered extinct.

NOTES

Stop and Think

1. What are two definitions of volcano?

2. How would you classify a volcano as active, dormant, or extinct?

3. What is the difference between magma and lava?

How Does a Volcano Form?

As you know, mantle material is moving beneath Earth's surface in a convection current. Mantle material can collect in the crust in pockets called **magma chambers**. If the pressure in a magma chamber is great enough, the magma may find its way to Earth's surface by way of a **vent**. A vent is a pipe-like channel from a magma chamber to the surface. It is the opening through which volcanic material erupts.

A volcano can have more than one vent. Parícutin erupted from a single vent. Other volcanoes may have a vent at the top, as well as several vents down the sides. Central vents typically end at a bowl-shaped depression, called a **summit crater**, at the top of a volcano.

Parts of volcanoes may also collapse, resulting in new Earth structures. When large amounts of magma escape from beneath a volcano during an eruption, part of the structure can collapse, causing an enormous depression called a **caldera**.

magma chamber: a pocket, or reservoir, where magma collects beneath Earth's surface.

vent: a pipe-like channel through which magma travels from a magma chamber to Earth's surface.

summit crater: a bowl-like depression at the top of a volcanic structure where the central vent ends.

caldera: a large, bowl-shaped depression formed by the collapse of part of a volcano.

The Structure of a Volcano

Different types of volcanoes have different structures, but this one shows the parts shared by most volcanoes.

EE 191

Stop and Think

5 min

Students answer the questions and lead a class discussion of their responses.

△ Guide and Evaluate

Have students take a moment to answer the *Stop and Think* questions on their own. Then lead a class discussion of their responses. Use the following points as guidelines:

1. Students should understand that volcano sometimes means a place where materials from Earth's mantle reach the surface, and sometimes means an Earth structure that results from the accumulation of materials from Earth's mantle.

2. Students should describe that a volcano is usually considered active if it is currently erupting, or if it shows signs of activity, such as the emission of gases. Some scientists consider any volcano that has erupted within human history to be active. A volcano is considered dormant if it is not currently active, but could become active. A volcano is considered extinct if it is unlikely to erupt again.

3. Students should describe that magma is mantle material that has not risen to Earth's surface. Lava is mantle material that has risen to Earth's surface.

As the class discusses these questions, listen for misconceptions. If necessary, review the concepts in this section.

How Does a Volcano Form?

10 min

The class discusses the formation of volcanoes.

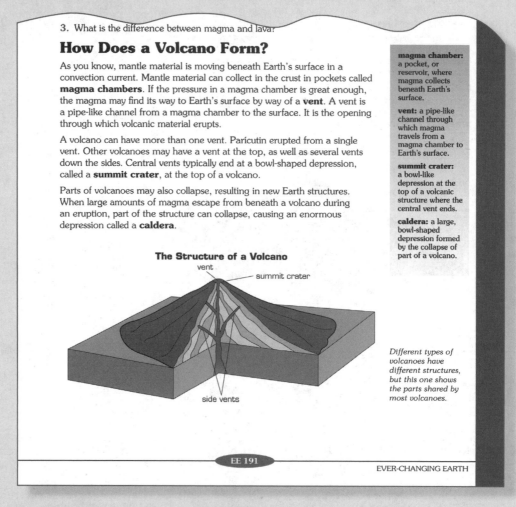

3. What is the difference between magma and lava?

How Does a Volcano Form?

As you know, mantle material is moving beneath Earth's surface in a convection current. Mantle material can collect in the crust in pockets called **magma chambers**. If the pressure in a magma chamber is great enough, the magma may find its way to Earth's surface by way of a **vent**. A vent is a pipe-like channel from a magma chamber to the surface. It is the opening through which volcanic material erupts.

A volcano can have more than one vent. Parícutin erupted from a single vent. Other volcanoes may have a vent at the top, as well as several vents down the sides. Central vents typically end at a bowl-shaped depression, called a **summit crater**, at the top of a volcano.

Parts of volcanoes may also collapse, resulting in new Earth structures. When large amounts of magma escape from beneath a volcano during an eruption, part of the structure can collapse, causing an enormous depression called a **caldera**.

magma chamber: a pocket, or reservoir, where magma collects beneath Earth's surface.

vent: a pipe-like channel through which magma travels from a magma chamber to Earth's surface.

summit crater: a bowl-like depression at the top of a volcanic structure where the central vent ends.

caldera: a large, bowl-shaped depression formed by the collapse of part of a volcano.

The Structure of a Volcano

vent — summit crater — side vents

Different types of volcanoes have different structures, but this one shows the parts shared by most volcanoes.

EE 191

EVER-CHANGING EARTH

○ **Engage**

Now that students know that volcanoes are places where magma rises to Earth's surface, ask them how they think volcanoes form. Why does magma rise to Earth's surface? Students may suggest that volcanoes form where plates pull apart or collide. Tell them this is often true, but it does not explain why magma rises to the surface. What pushes magma to the surface? Remind students that magma at the upper levels of the mantle is usually denser than the crust, so the crust floats on top of it.

△ Guide

Discuss how volcanoes form. Volcanoes can be caused by magma chambers. As material in the mantle moves in convection currents, some of it can collect in magma chambers, which are pockets in the crust. The pressure in these magma chambers can grow great enough to force magma to Earth's surface. The opening that the magma is forced through is called a vent. Vents are pipe-like channels.

Discuss possible configurations of vents in volcanoes. A volcano may consist of a single vent, or it may comprise several vents. A volcano may have a central vent at the top and several vents on the sides. Central vents typically have a bowl-shaped depression at the top, called a summit crater. Point out the diagram of a typical volcano in the student text. The illustration shows several vents and a summit crater at the opening of the central vent. Introduce calderas—depressions that result from parts of volcanoes collapsing as magma escapes from below them.

NOTES

Crater Lake in Oregon was formed when a volcano was drained of large amounts of lava during an eruption. The top collapsed, forming a huge caldera that later filled with water. One last eruption produced a small volcano in the middle of the lake. This Earth structure is now called Wizard Island.

You have learned how volcanoes form along the mid-ocean ridge. Recall that magma makes its way up through a gap in the ridge, created by two plates moving away from each other. As the magma cools and hardens, it becomes new ocean floor and pushes existing rock away on both sides of the ridge. Examples of volcanoes formed this way can be observed in Iceland, where the mid-ocean ridge rises above the surface of the ocean. Laki, seen in the photographs earlier in this *Learning Set,* is one such volcano.

Other types of volcanoes form as material, ejected during an eruption, accumulates around the vent. Each volcano is shaped by the eruption and the kind of material ejected. Some volcanoes form from thin, fast-moving lava that spreads over a broad area before cooling and hardening. Others form from lava that is thick and slow-moving and does not spread far from the central vent. Still others form from lava that is blasted into different-sized particles.

Stop and Think

1. Draw a diagram of a volcano, showing the basic structure and main parts. Label all parts of your diagram.

2. How does the movement of material in the mantle relate to the formation of volcanoes?

Discuss how volcanoes form where plates move apart. Just as convection currents can cause magma to collect in magma chambers, they can also cause it to rise up through the gaps where two plates are moving away from each other. This is what happens along the mid-ocean ridge. Point out that Laki, in Iceland, formed in this way.

Other volcanoes form as material ejected from an eruption accumulates. The type of eruption and the type of material ejected affect the shape of the volcano. Some volcanoes form from thin, fast-flowing lava that can spread over a wide area before cooling and hardening. Others form from thicker lava that does not spread much before cooling and hardening. Volcanoes can also form from lava that is blasted into small chunks.

△ Guide and Assess

Have students answer the *Stop and Think* questions independently. Let students know that they will share their responses with the class. As they work on answering the questions, monitor their progress and assess their work.

When students have had time to answer the questions, lead a class discussion of their responses to the second question. Students should recognize that convection currents force magma into magma chambers in the crust. If there is enough pressure in a magma chamber, it can cause a volcano to form.

Stop and Think

5 min

Students answer the Stop and Think *questions.*

NOTES

What Is a Volcanic Eruption?

10 min

The class discusses volcanic eruptions.

What Is a Volcanic Eruption?

A **volcanic eruption** is the release of material from under Earth's crust to its surface. Not all eruptions are alike. Extraordinary differences can occur in eruptions, depending on the location of the volcano and the material released. Lava, volcanic particles, and gases from Earth's mantle are all materials that may erupt from a volcano. Lava can be thin and runny, or it can be thick and move slowly. It can be fluid, or it can be in pieces.

Recall that hot mantle material is less dense than cool mantle material. This difference in density causes hot mantle material to rise upward toward the crust. If there are cracks, gaps, or weak spots in the crust, rising mantle material can fill them or break through.

Pressure from gases found within magma also exerts an upward push. Gases escape quite easily from thin lava, resulting in quiet eruptions that ooze out lava. If lava is very thick, gases cannot escape easily, and the pressure builds. Imagine shaking a can of soda and then opening it. The pressure that forces the liquid to spray out of a can is similar to the pressure that causes a volcano to erupt in an explosion. Large amounts of volcanic material are ejected from the crater.

Some volcanic eruptions last a long time, and some end swiftly. For example, Stromboli, in Italy, has been erupting continuously for over 2400 years, but when Mount St. Helens in the western United States erupted in 1980, the explosive phase lasted only nine hours. As you read this, there are volcanoes around the world oozing lava or blasting particles into the air. About 1300 volcanoes have been known to erupt during the last 10,000 years. It is estimated that over a million volcanoes, never observed or recorded, are adding crust deep on the ocean floor.

volcanic eruption: the release of material from under Earth's crust to its surface.

nuée ardente: a thick, rapidly moving, deadly, gaseous cloud produced by a volcano.

*A **nuée ardent** is a glowing avalanche made up of red-hot volcanic particles and hot gases. These glowing clouds can travel at speeds up to 250 km (155 mi) per hour and burn or suffocate anything in their path.*

EE 193

EVER-CHANGING EARTH

△ Guide

After students share their responses, discuss volcanic eruptions. Tell students that the location of a volcano and the material it releases affect its eruptions. Volcanoes may release lava, volcanic particles, and gases from the mantle. In addition, the viscosity of lava varies between volcanoes. Some volcanoes release thin, runny lava. Others release thick, slow-moving lava.

Tell students that the thickness of the lava in a volcano can have a dramatic effect on how the volcano erupts. In addition to the pressure from rising magma, gases within the magma also exert an upward push. When the lava is thin, the gases can escape easily, and the lava pours quietly out of the volcano. When the lava is thick, the gases are trapped, and pressure builds up. This can cause highly explosive eruptions. The student text uses the example of a can of soda that has been shaken to illustrate how the pressure of gases in the lava can lead to explosive pressure.

Eruptions also vary in their duration. Some can last thousands of years, and some last only a few hours. Emphasize that there are currently volcanoes around the world erupting, although many of the eruptions are not very explosive.

NOTES

Stop and Think

5 min

Students answer the Stop and Think *questions.*

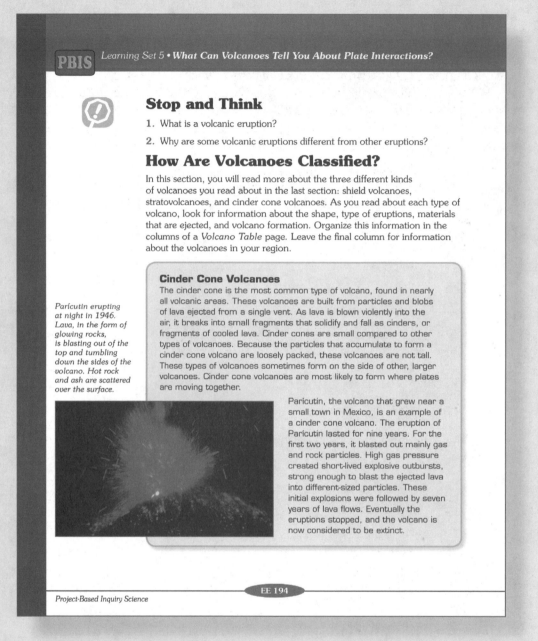

Stop and Think

1. What is a volcanic eruption?

2. Why are some volcanic eruptions different from other eruptions?

How Are Volcanoes Classified?

In this section, you will read more about the three different kinds of volcanoes you read about in the last section: shield volcanoes, stratovolcanoes, and cinder cone volcanoes. As you read about each type of volcano, look for information about the shape, type of eruptions, materials that are ejected, and volcano formation. Organize this information in the columns of a *Volcano Table* page. Leave the final column for information about the volcanoes in your region.

Parícutin erupting at night in 1946. Lava, in the form of glowing rocks, is blasting out of the top and tumbling down the sides of the volcano. Hot rock and ash are scattered over the surface.

Cinder Cone Volcanoes

The cinder cone is the most common type of volcano, found in nearly all volcanic areas. These volcanoes are built from particles and blobs of lava ejected from a single vent. As lava is blown violently into the air, it breaks into small fragments that solidify and fall as cinders, or fragments of cooled lava. Cinder cones are small compared to other types of volcanoes. Because the particles that accumulate to form a cinder cone volcano are loosely packed, these volcanoes are not tall. These types of volcanoes sometimes form on the side of other, larger volcanoes. Cinder cone volcanoes are most likely to form where plates are moving together.

Parícutin, the volcano that grew near a small town in Mexico, is an example of a cinder cone volcano. The eruption of Parícutin lasted for nine years. For the first two years, it blasted out mainly gas and rock particles. High gas pressure created short-lived explosive outbursts, strong enough to blast the ejected lava into different-sized particles. These initial explosions were followed by seven years of lava flows. Eventually the eruptions stopped, and the volcano is now considered to be extinct.

Project-Based Inquiry Science

EE 194

△ Guide and Evaluate

Have students answer the *Stop and Think* questions independently. Then lead a class discussion of their responses. Use the following as guidelines:

1. Students should be able to describe how lava, gases, and volcanic materials are emitted during a volcanic eruption. They should also be able to describe what causes eruptions (rising magma and pressure from gases).

2. Students should be able to explain how thick lava leads to explosive eruptions. Thick lava traps gases, so that the pressure from those gases builds. Thin lava, on the other hand, allows gases to escape easily, so that there is less pressure. Volcanoes with thin lava tend not to be very explosive.

△ Guide

Let students know that they will now learn more about the three major types of volcanoes. They have already seen examples of these types of volcanoes, identified some of their characteristics, and compared them to volcanoes in their regions. They should think about the volcanoes they have observed and the volcanoes in their regions as they learn more about the three types of volcanoes.

Distribute *Volcano Table* pages, and let students know they will use the table to organize information about volcanoes in their regions. Point out that the types of volcanoes will be recorded in the columns and the characteristics will be recorded in the rows. As students listen to or read information about the types of volcanoes, they should record facts about the characteristics of each type in the table. For instance, if they learn something about the shape of stratovolcanoes, they should record it in the first row of the second column.

△ Guide

Discuss cinder cone volcanoes. Tell students that cinder cones are the most common type of volcano. Describe the structure of a cinder cone volcano. Unlike some volcanoes, a cinder cone volcano is formed from a single vent. A cinder cone forms as small particles and blobs of lava from eruptions solidify and fall as cinders, forming a cone around the vent. Cinder cones are relatively small. Sometimes these volcanoes form on the sides of larger volcanoes.

Ask students what they remember about Parícutin, the volcano that grew near a small town in Mexico. If necessary, remind them that the volcano opened in a cornfield and erupted for several years. Tell them that this was a cinder cone volcano. For the first two years, it had explosive eruptions, which blasted the ejected lava into different-sized particles. The accumulation of these particles led to the rapid formation of a cone.

How Are Volcanoes Classified?
10 min

The class discusses the three major types of volcanoes.

Cinder Cone Volcanoes

Shield Volcanoes

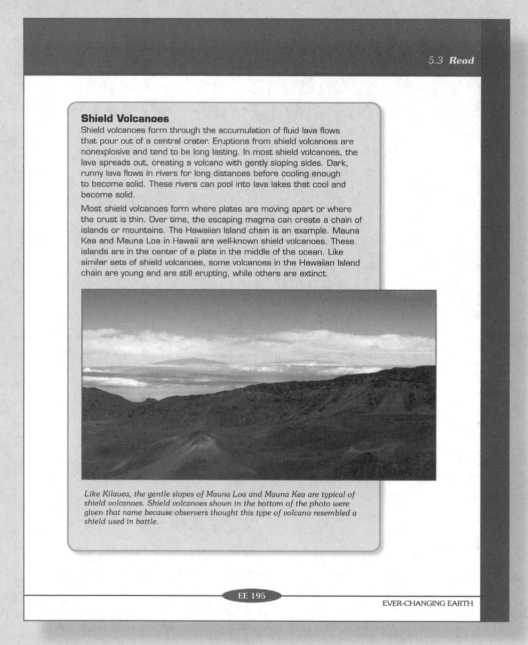

Shield Volcanoes

Shield volcanoes form through the accumulation of fluid lava flows that pour out of a central crater. Eruptions from shield volcanoes are nonexplosive and tend to be long lasting. In most shield volcanoes, the lava spreads out, creating a volcano with gently sloping sides. Dark, runny lava flows in rivers for long distances before cooling enough to become solid. These rivers can pool into lava lakes that cool and become solid.

Most shield volcanoes form where plates are moving apart or where the crust is thin. Over time, the escaping magma can create a chain of islands or mountains. The Hawaiian Island chain is an example. Mauna Kea and Mauna Loa in Hawaii are well-known shield volcanoes. These islands are in the center of a plate in the middle of the ocean. Like similar sets of shield volcanoes, some volcanoes in the Hawaiian Island chain are young and are still erupting, while others are extinct.

Like Kilauea, the gentle slopes of Mauna Loa and Mauna Kea are typical of shield volcanoes. Shield volcanoes shown in the bottom of the photo were given that name because observers thought this type of volcano resembled a shield used in battle.

EE 195

EVER-CHANGING EARTH

△ Guide

Discuss the structure of shield volcanoes. Tell students most shield volcanoes have gently sloping sides with a central crater. Point out the picture of Mauna Loa and Mauna Kea in the student text. These volcanoes have gently sloping sides typical of shield volcanoes. Shield volcanoes form from the accumulation of thin lava flows that spread far from the central crater before cooling and solidifying. Emphasize that because the lava from a shield volcano is thin and allows gases to escape easily, eruptions of shield volcanoes tend to be nonexplosive. They also tend to be long lasting.

Tell students that shield volcanoes typically form where plates are moving apart, or where the crust is thin. Shield volcanoes can sometimes form chains of mountains or islands, as they do in the Hawaiian Islands. Notably, the Hawaiian Islands are in the middle of a plate.

NOTES

Stratovolcanoes

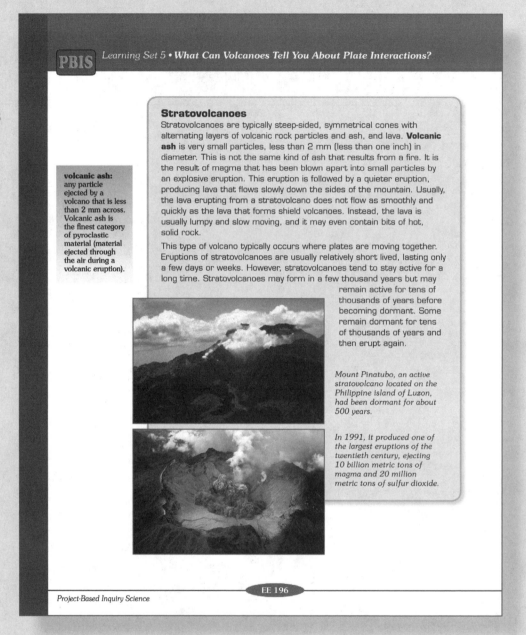

Stratovolcanoes

Stratovolcanoes are typically steep-sided, symmetrical cones with alternating layers of volcanic rock particles and ash, and lava. **Volcanic ash** is very small particles, less than 2 mm (less than one inch) in diameter. This is not the same kind of ash that results from a fire. It is the result of magma that has been blown apart into small particles by an explosive eruption. This eruption is followed by a quieter eruption, producing lava that flows slowly down the sides of the mountain. Usually, the lava erupting from a stratovolcano does not flow as smoothly and quickly as the lava that forms shield volcanoes. Instead, the lava is usually lumpy and slow moving, and it may even contain bits of hot, solid rock.

This type of volcano typically occurs where plates are moving together. Eruptions of stratovolcanoes are usually relatively short lived, lasting only a few days or weeks. However, stratovolcanoes tend to stay active for a long time. Stratovolcanoes may form in a few thousand years but may remain active for tens of thousands of years before becoming dormant. Some remain dormant for tens of thousands of years and then erupt again.

volcanic ash: any particle ejected by a volcano that is less than 2 mm across. Volcanic ash is the finest category of pyroclastic material (material ejected through the air during a volcanic eruption).

Mount Pinatubo, an active stratovolcano located on the Philippine island of Luzon, had been dormant for about 500 years.

In 1991, it produced one of the largest eruptions of the twentieth century, ejecting 10 billion metric tons of magma and 20 million metric tons of sulfur dioxide.

EE 196

△ Guide

Discuss the structure and composition of stratovolcanoes. Stratovolcanoes usually have cone shapes, somewhat like cinder cones, but are often steeper—especially toward the summit. They are composed of layers of lava, alternating with layers of volcanic rock and ash. Explain that volcanic ash is not ash in the usual sense. Volcanic ash is the result of magma that has been blown into small particles in an explosive eruption. The alternating layers are the result of the patterns of eruptions at stratovolcanoes. Typically, an explosive eruption—which releases volcanic ash and rock—is followed by a quieter eruption, which releases lava. The lava from a stratovolcano is usually lumpy and slow, unlike the lava from a shield volcano, so it is unlikely to flow very far. Tell students that stratovolcano eruptions are usually short, but that the volcanoes can stay active for a long time. Emphasize that they typically form where plates collide.

NOTES

Stop and Think

5 min

Students answer the Stop and Think questions and then lead a class discussion.

Stop and Think

1. Summarize the similarities and differences among cinder cone volcanoes, shield volcanoes, and stratovolcanoes.

2. How does the material that erupts from a volcano affect the structure that is formed?

3. Describe two types of volcano fields.

How Can Volcanoes Erupt in the Center of a Plate?

Most volcanoes around the world occur near plate boundaries. However, as you may have already observed, there are a few exceptions. For example, the Hawaiian Islands were formed in the middle of a plate where there are no gaps in the crust created by interacting plates. Geologists have determined that small, long-lasting, and very hot plumes of magma, called **hot spots**, form volcanoes in the middle of plates. As the plate moves over a hot spot, the magma melts through the crust and acts as a funnel, bringing hot magma to the surface. Some active volcanoes are found in regions where the plate is sitting over a hot spot.

> **hot spots:** places in the middle of plates where very hot plumes of magma rise for a short time, forming volcanoes.

Evidence of how hot spots work can be observed in places like the Hawaiian Islands. Currently, Kilauea on the Big Island, at the southeast end of the Hawaiian island chain, is erupting and has been erupting for the past 25 years. Rocks here date back 700 thousand years.

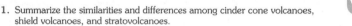

A satellite photo of the Hawaiian Islands

△ Guide and Assess

Have students answer the *Stop and Think* questions independently. Emphasize that they should use their *Volcano Tables* to answer the questions. Let them know they will share their answers with the class.

When students have had a few minutes to answer the questions, lead a class discussion of their answers, using the following guidelines:

1. Students should identify differences and similarities in the shapes of the volcanoes, the types of eruptions that occur at each type of volcano, and the places where each type of volcano forms. Cinder cones and stratovolcanoes have roughly conical shapes, but stratovolcanoes tend to have steeper slopes and tend to be larger. Shield volcanoes, on the other hand, are more rounded, and are generally mound-shaped. Cinder cone volcanoes tend to have violently explosive eruptions. Stratovolcanoes also have explosive eruptions, although these are usually followed by nonexplosive eruptions. Shield volcanoes usually have nonexplosive eruptions. Cinder cone volcanoes occur in most volcanic areas. By contrast, stratovolcanoes and shield volcanoes have a more restricted range. Stratovolcanoes tend to occur where plates collide, while shield volcanoes tend to occur where they pull apart.

2. Students should demonstrate understanding of how the materials emitted during eruptions lead to the different shapes of the three types of volcanoes. When the explosive eruptions of cinder cone volcanoes spew particles of lava into the air, they lead to cone-shaped accumulations. When the thin lava flows from shield volcanoes, it often spreads far before cooling and solidifying, leading to a structure with a wide base and gentle slopes. When the explosive eruptions of stratovolcanoes spew rocks and volcanic ash, a layer of these materials accumulates into a cone shape. When the explosive eruptions are followed by less-explosive eruptions that produce lava flows, a layer of hardened lava accumulates over the cone, so that these structures develop alternating layers.

3. Students should remember that volcano fields may either comprise one single volcano with multiple vents, or several separate volcanoes.

How Can Volcanoes Erupt in the Center of a Plate?

10 min

Students have a discussion on how volcanoes can erupt in the center of a plate.

that

3. Describe two types of volcano fields.

How Can Volcanoes Erupt in the Center of a Plate?

Most volcanoes around the world occur near plate boundaries. However, as you may have already observed, there are a few exceptions. For example, the Hawaiian Islands were formed in the middle of a plate where there are no gaps in the crust created by interacting plates. Geologists have determined that small, long-lasting, and very hot plumes of magma, called **hot spots**, form volcanoes in the middle of plates. As the plate moves over a hot spot, the magma melts through the crust and acts as a funnel, bringing hot magma to the surface. Some active volcanoes are found in regions where the plate is sitting over a hot spot.

Evidence of how hot spots work can be observed in places like the Hawaiian Islands. Currently, Kilauea on the Big Island, at the southeast end of the Hawaiian island chain, is erupting and has been erupting for the past 25 years. Rocks here date back 700 thousand years.

hot spots: places in the middle of plates where very hot plumes of magma rise for a short time, forming volcanoes.

○ Engage

Point out that all three of the volcano types students have learned about tend to occur at plate boundaries. Shield volcanoes tend to occur where plates are pulling apart, and stratovolcanoes tend to occur where plates are colliding. Cinder volcanoes can occur at either. Draw students' attention to the volcanoes of the Hawaiian Islands, which occur in the middle of a plate. Ask them if there is anything they have learned yet that would explain how this happens. Students may suggest that faults extend into the middle of the plate. Tell them that faults can extend into plates, but Hawaii is not in a fault zone. Tell them that they will now learn about how this happens.

△ Guide

Introduce the concept of hot spots. Hot spots are long-lasting plumes in the mantle, where hot magma from near the core rises to the crust. Tell students that some hot spots form volcanoes in the middle of plates. Explain that as a plate moves over a hot spot, the rising hot magma melts through the crust and rises to the surface.

Discuss how the Hawaiian Islands provide evidence of how this process can work. The island at the southeast end of the chain of islands, Big Island, is the site of an active volcano. Rocks on the island date back 700,000 years. Moving northwest, each island is older. The island at the northwest end of the chain, Kauai, is about 5.5 million years old. Scientists think this age difference happened because the plate is moving northwest. The hot spot formed a volcano at Kauai, and then the plate moved northwest, moving the volcano away from the hot spot. The volcano became extinct, and another formed over the hot spot, to the southeast of Kauai's new position.

Moving northwest, the islands get progressively older. The oldest rocks on Kauai date back about 5.5 million years, and the volcano is now extinct. Other similar island chains show the same pattern. As the plate moves over the hot spot, new volcanoes form and are active. Older ones, no longer sitting over the hot spot, become extinct.

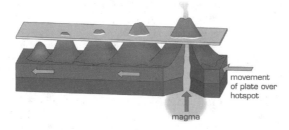

movement of plate over hotspot

magma

Conference

Using information organized on your *Volcano Table* page, compare what is in your pen pal letter to what you now know about volcanoes. Work with your partner to fill in the column on the *Volcano Table* for volcanoes in your region. Include all the information from your pen pal letter, as well as any other information you have.

Think about how you classified the volcanoes in your region earlier, based on photographs of different types of volcanoes. Think about the new information and evidence you have. Record this new evidence, as well as any other new information, in the volcano table and on your Region *Project Board*.

Then meet with others who are also assigned your region. Compare your volcano classifications, and try to come to an agreement. Prepare to share with the class new information about the volcanoes in your region. If you have changed your mind about what type of volcanoes are in your region, make sure you can describe how and why your ideas changed. If you have not changed your mind, describe the information that makes you even more certain of the characteristics and classification of the volcanoes in your region.

EE 198

Project-Based Inquiry Science

Point out the diagram in the text. The island at the left end of the chain would be equivalent to Kauai, while the island at the right end would be equivalent to Big Island. The arrows show the direction of the plate's movement.

Conference

10 min

The class reconsiders their classification of volcanoes in their region using new evidence.

Conference

Using information organized on your *Volcano Table* page, compare what is in your pen pal letter to what you now know about volcanoes. Work with your partner to fill in the column on the *Volcano Table* for volcanoes in your region. Include all the information from your pen pal letter, as well as any other information you have.

Think about how you classified the volcanoes in your region earlier, based on photographs of different types of volcanoes. Think about the new information and evidence you have. Record this new evidence, as well as any other new information, in the volcano table and on your Region *Project Board*.

Then meet with others who are also assigned your region. Compare your volcano classifications, and try to come to an agreement. Prepare to share with the class new information about the volcanoes in your region. If you have changed your mind about what type of volcanoes are in your region, make sure you can describe how and why your ideas changed. If you have not changed your mind, describe the information that makes you even more certain of the characteristics and classification of the volcanoes in your region.

△ Guide

Have students meet with their partners to discuss how they can combine what they have just learned about volcanoes with the information about volcanoes in their regions from their pen pal letters. Emphasize that they should consider the information they recorded in their *Volcano Table* page. Have them complete the *Volcanoes in my region* column of their *Volcano Table* page. Emphasize that they should use information from their pen pal letters and any other information that they think is relevant. They should think about new evidence they have to support (or contradict) their classifications. Have them record this new information in their *Region Project Board*.

When pairs have had a few minutes to complete their *Volcano Table* pages and to update their *Region Project Boards,* have them meet with other pairs that were assigned to the same region. Have them compare their classifications of volcanoes in their regions and try to come to an agreement. They should record any changes pairs make in their classification and the reasons for these changes, including new information they have learned about volcanoes. They should prepare to present their classification, their reasoning, and the discussions they had to the class.

☐ Assess

As groups revise their classifications of the volcanoes in their regions, monitor their progress. Use the *Ever-Changing Earth Teacher Notes and Suggested Data* table to assess their ideas. Students may have difficulty deciding what type of volcano is in their region. In addition, some regions have more than one type of volcano. Even if students have trouble deciding what type of volcano is in their region, they should be able to support their ideas with evidence from the pen pal letters and the reading.

Communicate

Now that you have gathered new information about the volcanoes in your region, take time to share it with your class. When it is your turn to present, discuss how each pair had initially classified the volcanoes in the region by comparing them to the photographs in *Section 5.2*. If you changed the way you classified the volcanoes, explain why and what you based your decision on. If you are even more confident of your first classification, tell the class what you learned that supports your ideas.

As others present their ideas, listen carefully, as you may hear something that makes you think about the volcanoes in your own region. Perhaps you will hear something that raises a new question that you would like to investigate further. Keep these things in mind, as they can be added later to the *Project Board*.

When everyone has finished presenting, answer the following questions together, as a class.

Reflect

1. The shape of a volcano is determined by the way it erupts. Choose one type of volcano and describe how its shape is determined by the materials that erupt from it.

2. Some volcanoes erupt quickly and are short lived while others erupt for very long periods. How does pressure and material type affect the length of the eruption?

3. You know a lot now about different volcanoes. What does this knowledge tell you about the ways plates might interact with each other?

4. Suppose you know what types of volcanoes are in your region. What can that information tell you about the interactions between the plates in your region?

Volcano Table

Fill in the columns with information about volcano types. Use the last column to fill in information about your region.

	Shield Volcanoes	Stratovolcanoes	Cinder Cone Volcanoes	Volcanoes in my region
Common shape				
Type of eruption				
Materials that are ejected				
How the volcanoes form				
Where the volcanoes form				
Other information				
Location in our region				
Questions				

△ Guide

Have groups present their ideas to the class, including their current classification of the volcanoes in their region, each pair's original classification, and the reasons for any changes they made. If the new information supports their original classifications, they should say how. If they revised their classifications, they should explain why.

Tell students to ask questions of presenting groups if anything is unclear. Emphasize that they should think about how the ideas discussed by groups can be applied to the investigation. If they think of any investigative questions, they can put these on the *Project Board* later.

Communicate

10 min

Students share their ideas with the class.

Reflect

10 min

The class discusses the Reflect questions.

When everyone has finished presenting, answer the following questions together, as a class.

Reflect

1. The shape of a volcano is determined by the way it erupts. Choose one type of volcano and describe how its shape is determined by the materials that erupt from it.

2. Some volcanoes erupt quickly and are short lived while others erupt for very long periods. How does pressure and material type affect the length of the eruption?

3. You know a lot now about different volcanoes. What does this knowledge tell you about the ways plates might interact with each other?

4. Suppose you know what types of volcanoes are in your region. What can that information tell you about the interactions between the plates in your region?

△ Guide and Assess

Once all groups have presented, tell them they will now answer the questions in the student text as a class. To begin, read the first question and have the class choose a type of volcano. Have them describe how the materials ejected from the volcano determine its shape. Students should demonstrate understanding of the qualities of the materials ejected from the different types of volcanoes and how these qualities lead to the shapes of the different types of volcanoes. The table below includes information that should be in students' descriptions.

	Cinder cone volcano	**Shield volcano**	**Stratovolcano**
Shape of volcano	*small cone*	*rounded shape with gently sloping sides*	*large cone with steep sides*
Materials and how these determine shape	*particles and blobs of thick lava* *The particles and blobs accumulate around the vent, forming a cone.*	*runny, flowing lava* *The lava runs from the vent and may flow some distance before it cools and solidifies. Because the lava spreads far before solidifying, the volcano typically has a wide base and gently sloping sides*	*rock and volcanic ash alternating with slow-moving lava* *The rock and volcanic ash accumulate around the vent, forming a cone. Then the lava flows over the accumulated rock and ash. Because it is thick and slow-moving, it does not travel far. This leads to a steep-sided cone, as the lava builds up around the vent.*

Discuss the second question with the class. This question is meant to help students synthesize the information they have learned about materials emitted from volcanoes and eruptions. It may help to ask students to summarize what they know about what materials the different types of volcanoes emit and what kind of eruptions they have. You can write this information on the board as students suggest it. In general, volcanoes with thicker lava tend to have shorter, more explosive eruptions. The thick lava provides resistance to the upward pressure of the gases and magma, so that eruptions do not occur until great pressure builds up. When eruptions do occur at these volcanoes, they are violently explosive, as the built-up pressure is released. Volcanoes with thinner lava provide little resistance to the pressure from gases and magma, so that eruptions occur readily. At many volcanoes with thin lava, eruptions occur continuously. Because pressure does not build up, the eruptions at these volcanoes are nonexplosive.

When students have explained how pressure and material type affect the length of eruptions, discuss the third question. This question is meant to help students connect what they are learning to the larger question of how plates interact with each other. Students may have difficulty answering this question. This is okay, the next question will help them to identify specific knowledge about plate interactions that they can gain from learning about volcano types.

Students should recognize that stratovolcanoes and shield volcanoes give them information about the kind of plate interaction in their region. Stratovolcanoes typically occur where plates collide, so if there are stratovolcanoes in their regions, this is evidence that plates are colliding there. Similarly, cinder cone volcanoes are most likely to form where plates collide, so they provide some evidence of plate collision. Shield volcanoes typically occur where plates pull apart, so if there are shield volcanoes in their regions, this is evidence that plates are pulling apart there. Shield volcanoes can also occur away from plate boundaries, over hot spots, but when they occur on plate boundaries they provide information about the plate interaction.

Be a Scientist: Predicting if a Volcano Will Erupt

10 min*

Students discuss how scientists predict if a volcano will erupt.

Be a Scientist

Predicting if a Volcano Will Erupt

Volcanoes can occur in some of the most beautiful locations in the world. People will always want to live in these places, despite the danger of living in the shadow of a fiery volcano. People need places to live as the world's population is growing. This sometimes forces them to accept the risks and live near one of Earth's volcanoes. But this can put hundreds, or even hundreds of thousands, of humans at risk. Fortunately, volcanoes usually provide some early-warning signs that, when interpreted correctly, can save lives.

Three warning signs used by scientists to predict volcanic eruption are small earthquakes and vibrations caused by the movement of magma, changes in the quantity and composition of gases released by a volcano, and swelling or bulges on the slope of the volcano caused by a buildup of magma.

Similar to the way weather forecasters predict weather, scientists can predict volcanic eruptions. However, just like a weather forecaster, they can only predict the chance of an eruption. They cannot predict the severity or duration of an eruption. To successfully predict a volcanic eruption, scientists need three things—a detailed eruptive history, proper instrumentation installed at the volcano, and a way to continuously monitor and interpret data from the instruments. This limits the number of volcanoes that can be watched, as it is not possible to monitor every volcano site in the world.

Recorded histories are not available for most volcanoes, but volcanoes leave some records of their own. Scientists dig through the remains of previous eruptions looking for clues that can tell them about the type of eruption, duration, direction of lava flows, or the explosiveness. They may map old lava flows or sift through volcanic particles. Today, scientists can use data collected for worldwide distribution on the Internet, just like you did, to collect information.

If scientists had been able to detect the early warning signs of a volcanic eruption in 79 A.D. near Pompeii, Italy, more than 10,000 people who died in the two-day eruption of Mt. Vesuvius might have been saved.

*Optional, if time allows.

○ Engage

Point out the photograph of human remains at Pompeii in the student text. Tell students that the people living at Pompeii in 79 A.D. were unable to escape the ash and poisonous gas that spewed from Mt. Vesuvius because they did not have enough time. If they had known in advance, they might have been able to evacuate.

Emphasize that even though volcanoes remain a grave threat, people still live near them. For this reason, it is important to be able to predict volcanoes. Ask students if they can think of any volcanoes that may erupt again. They may suggest Mount St. Helens or Yellowstone Volcano. Ask them what they think some warning signs before an eruption at one of these volcanoes might be.

TEACHER TALK

"Just like the people at Pompeii, there are people today who live near active volcanoes. Without advance warning of eruptions, these active volcanoes can be just as deadly as Mt. Vesuvius was. So scientists need ways to predict eruptions ahead of time.**"**

△ Guide

Discuss the warning signs that scientists use to predict volcanic activity. Small earthquakes and vibrations caused by magma moving in the crust, changes in the quantity and composition of gases released by a volcano, and swelling on the side of a volcano caused by building magma are three warning signs. Knowing what warning signs to look for is not enough to predict where volcanic eruptions will occur. For each volcano that is considered a risk, scientists need a detailed eruptive history, instrumentation installed at the volcano, and a way to continuously monitor and interpret the data from the instruments. For this reason, it is not possible to make predictions for every volcano in the world. It is also not possible to predict the severity or duration of volcanic eruptions. Scientists can only predict the chance of an eruption occurring.

Tell students that the detailed eruptive history that scientists use does not always come from recorded history. Often, scientists must dig through the remains of previous eruptions to determine the type of eruption, duration, and explosiveness.

NOTES

....

....

One of the most important tools used by scientists to predict eruptions is a seismograph. This instrument detects and records the small earthquakes produced by the movement of magma. Other instruments measure amounts of sulfur dioxide. Remember the smell of rotten eggs that preceded the eruption of Paricutin. That was the tell-tale smell of sulfur dioxide that increases in concentration right before an eruption. Other instruments are used to detect any swellings or bulges in the slopes of a volcano, indicating that magma is building up.

Today, satellites are also used in the science of predicting volcanic eruptions. They can be used for mapping both old and new lava flows and for gathering data about the concentrations of gas in an area. As new technologies are advanced, scientists will probably be able to predict eruptions more accurately in the future.

Most of the work of a vulcanologist, a scientist who studies volcanoes, involves examining the remains of past volcanic eruptions and monitoring volcanoes that have the potential to erupt in the future.

What's the Point?

A volcano is a place on Earth's surface where material from the mantle escapes through the crust. When material escapes from the mantle and reaches Earth's surface, the event is called a volcanic eruption. The ejected material, including lava and volcanic particles, often falls back down or collects around the volcano's vent. Layers build up, sometimes quickly and sometimes over many years, forming a structure that is also called a volcano. The type of material that erupts from a volcano determines the size and shape of the resulting structure. The type of eruption and volcanic formation depends on the location and type of material that is ejected from it.

Some volcanoes erupt rather quietly, oozing out thin, runny lava. This type of lava forms broad, flat shield volcanoes. Other volcanoes erupt with a blast, ejecting thick lava, as well as ash, rock fragments, gases, and other debris. This material forms steep-sided stratovolcanoes made up of alternating layers of lava and rock particles. Volcanoes that erupt explosively and blast rock particles into the air are likely to form cinder cones.

EE 201

EVER-CHANGING EARTH

Among the instruments scientists use to predict volcanoes the most important are seismographs, which allow them to detect earthquakes and vibrations in the ground due to magma movement, and the instruments that detect the presence of sulfur dioxide. Sulfur dioxide—the gas that smells like rotten eggs—is the gas that farmers smelled when Parícutin opened up. Scientists also use instruments to detect swelling in the sides of volcanoes. They use satellites to map lava flows and gather data about gas concentrations in an area.

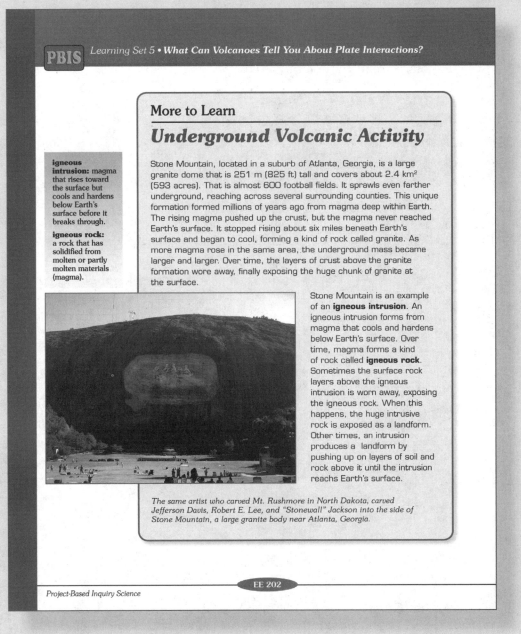

More to Learn

Underground Volcanic Activity

igneous intrusion: magma that rises toward the surface but cools and hardens below Earth's surface before it breaks through.

igneous rock: a rock that has solidified from molten or partly molten materials (magma).

Stone Mountain, located in a suburb of Atlanta, Georgia, is a large granite dome that is 251 m (825 ft) tall and covers about 2.4 km² (593 acres). That is almost 600 football fields. It sprawls even farther underground, reaching across several surrounding counties. This unique formation formed millions of years ago from magma deep within Earth. The rising magma pushed up the crust, but the magma never reached Earth's surface. It stopped rising about six miles beneath Earth's surface and began to cool, forming a kind of rock called granite. As more magma rose in the same area, the underground mass became larger and larger. Over time, the layers of crust above the granite formation wore away, finally exposing the huge chunk of granite at the surface.

Stone Mountain is an example of an **igneous intrusion**. An igneous intrusion forms from magma that cools and hardens below Earth's surface. Over time, magma forms a kind of rock called **igneous rock**. Sometimes the surface rock layers above the igneous intrusion is worn away, exposing the igneous rock. When this happens, the huge intrusive rock is exposed as a landform. Other times, an intrusion produces a landform by pushing up on layers of soil and rock above it until the intrusion reachs Earth's surface.

The same artist who carved Mt. Rushmore in North Dakota, carved Jefferson Davis, Robert E. Lee, and "Stonewall" Jackson into the side of Stone Mountain, a large granite body near Atlanta, Georgia.

EE 202

More to Learn: Underground Volcanic Activity

5 min

The class discusses igneous intrusions using the example of Stone Mountain.

△ Guide

Point out the photograph in the text. Tell students that it is a solid granite body, called Stone Mountain. Explain how it formed under the crust. Magma rising from the hot lower regions of Earth's mantle pushed on the crust, but never broke through. It stopped rising about six miles below the surface, where it began to cool, forming granite. Magma continued to rise in the area, so that the mass of granite became larger. Eventually, the ground above the granite wore away, so that the huge chunk of granite was exposed.

Tell students that this kind of formation is called an igneous intrusion. An igneous intrusion forms from magma that cools below Earth's surface. Rock that is formed from cooling magma is called igneous rock. The granite of Stone Mountain is a kind of igneous rock.

Assessment Options

Targeted Concepts, Skills, and Nature of Science	How do I know if students got it?
Scientists often work together and then share their findings. Sharing findings makes new information available and helps scientists refine their ideas and build on others' ideas. When another person or group's idea is used, credit needs to be given.	**ASK:** How did discussing your classification of volcanoes in your region with other pairs help you? **LISTEN:** Students should recognize that their discussions helped them to support their ideas or to revise them as necessary.
Scientists must keep clear, accurate, and descriptive records of what they do so they can share their work with others and consider what they did, why they did it, and what they want to do next.	**ASK:** Why was it important to update your *Region Project Board?* **LISTEN:** Students should recognize that it is important to record evidence that will help them work toward answering the *Big Question.*
Earthquake activity, volcanic activity, and topography are all evidence that Earth's crust is moving and changing.	**ASK:** In places where there are a lot of stratovolcanoes, what kind of plate interaction is probably occurring? In places where there are a lot of shield volcanoes, what kind of plate interaction is probably occurring? **LISTEN:** Students should recognize that stratovolcanoes are most likely to occur where plates collide, so plates are probably colliding where there are a lot of stratovolcanoes. Similarly, they should recognize that shield volcanoes are most likely to occur where plates are moving apart, so plates are probably moving apart in places where there are a lot of shield volcanoes.

486

Targeted Concepts, Skills, and Nature of Science	How do I know if students got it?
Interactions between Earth's crustal plates can result in mountain building, rift valleys, and geologic activities such as Earthquakes and volcanoes. Underwater volcanic activity may form underwater mountains, which can thrust above the ocean's surface to become islands.	**ASK:** What type of geologic activity can form chains of mountains on the ocean floor? **LISTEN:** Students should recall reading that ocean-floor spreading can create chains of mountains. They also read how chains of mountains can form on the ocean floor as plates in Earth's crust move over hot spots in the mantle, leading to a series of volcanoes.

Teacher Reflection Options

- What concepts did students have difficulty with? How can you help them with these concepts?

- Based on class discussions, what evidence do you have that students were able to make connections between volcano types, the volcanoes in their regions, and plate boundaries?

- How were you able to keep students focused on the task as they met with their partners and their region groups? What might you try next time?

NOTES

....

....

....

....

....

NOTES

5.4 Explore

What Can the Volcanoes in My Region Tell Me About How the Plates Are Moving?

◀ *1 class period*

A class period is considered to be one 40 to 50 minute class.

Overview

Students examine the types of volcanoes in their region and use what they know about volcano types to infer what directions the plates in and around their regions are moving. They begin by identifying the most common type of volcano in their region and identifying what kind of plate interaction is associated with that volcano type. They present their inferences to the class. The class discusses whether groups' inferences about plates in their regions are consistent with other groups' inferences. They identify inconsistencies they need to investigate further and record these investigative questions along with their new ideas on the *Project Board*.

Targeted Concepts, Skills, and Nature of Science	Performance Expectations
Scientists often work together and then share their findings. Sharing findings makes new information available and helps scientists refine their ideas and build on others' ideas. When another person or group's idea is used, credit needs to be given.	Students should work with their partners and region groups to infer the directions the plates are moving in and around their regions. They share their ideas with the class, and discuss how they are consistent or inconsistent with other groups' ideas and the class's science knowledge.
Scientists must keep clear, accurate, and descriptive records of what they do so they can share their work with others and consider what they did, why they did it, and what they want to do next.	Students should record their data and ideas on the *Big World Map*, their *Volcano Table* page, and the *Project Board*.
Scientists make claims (conclusions) based on evidence obtained (trends in data) from reliable investigations.	Students should infer the directions the plates are moving in and around their region, and support their ideas with data.

Targeted Concepts, Skills, and Nature of Science	Performance Expectations
New crust is formed at the mid-ocean ridge where the plates move apart. Oceanic crust is destroyed when it collides with continental crust and is subducted. In this way, Earth's crust is recycled.	Students should recognize that plates are moving away from some plate boundaries where new crust is being created.

Materials	
1 per student	*Three-page Map* (from *Section 5.1*) *Volcano Table* page *Project Board* page
1 per class	Class *Project Board* *Big World Map* with transparency layer
1 per region group	Poster sheets Green marker

Homework Options

Reflect

- **Science Process:** How were you able to infer the direction plates are moving from the types of volcanoes that occur at plate boundaries? What ideas do you have about why the types of some volcanoes at plate boundaries are inconsistent with the class's inferences? *(This question is meant to engage students in reflecting on the reasoning they used in this activity and on what they still need to learn.)*

NOTES

....

....

....

SECTION 5.4 IMPLEMENTATION

5.4 Explore

What Can the Volcanoes in My Region Tell Me About How the Plates Are Moving?

You have now identified what types of volcanoes are found in your region. You have also learned enough about each type of volcano to connect it to a specific location, plate boundary, or plate interaction. If you know the types of volcanoes in your region, you will be able to make an inference about how the plates in your region move and interact.

In this section, you will use data about the types of volcanoes in your region to make inferences about the plate boundaries in your region and the directions the plates might be moving. Remember that inferences are interpretations of observations. The types of volcanoes are your observations, and you will use knowledge you now have about what causes different types of volcanoes to make your inferences.

Procedure

1. Look at the types of volcanoes you marked on your *Three-page Map*. Remember that you marked shield volcanoes with a blue triangle, stratovolcanoes with a yellow square, and cinder cone volcanoes with a red circle. In the row on the *Volcano Table* page labeled *Location in our region*, record where each type of volcano is located. Record where each type of volcano is in relation to the earthquakes and plate boundaries in your region. Also record the pattern they make. For example, you might say that "shield volcanoes are in a line running parallel to the plate," or that "stratovolcanoes are in a cluster on the east side of the plate."

EE 203

EVER-CHANGING EARTH

5.4 Explore

What Can the Volcanoes in My Region Tell Me About How the Plates Are Moving?

5 min

Students are introduced to the activity.

○ **Engage**

Point out that students have found plate boundaries and they know that plates interact at plate boundaries. Ask them what they know about the directions plates move. They probably will not be able to say much at this point. Remind them that scientists have been able to learn about Earth's interior by making inferences from what they can observe at Earth's surface. Tell them that they will be using their data on volcanoes to make inferences about the directions plates move.

*A class period is considered to be one 40 to 50 minute class.

Procedure

10 min

*Students examine
the data on their
Three-page Maps and
Volcano Table pages.*

❝You have found plate boundaries, and you know some of the ways they interact and cause geologic activity. Can you say what direction the plates are moving? That's important, right? Just as scientists make inferences about Earth's interior, you will now use your data on volcanoes to make inferences about the directions plates move.**❞**

---

of volcanoes in your region, you will be able to make an inference about how the plates in your region move and interact.

In this section, you will use data about the types of volcanoes in your region to make inferences about the plate boundaries in your region and the directions the plates might be moving. Remember that inferences are interpretations of observations. The types of volcanoes are your observations, and you will use knowledge you now have about what causes different types of volcanoes to make your inferences.

Procedure

1. Look at the types of volcanoes you marked on your *Three-page Map*. Remember that you marked shield volcanoes with a blue triangle, stratovolcanoes with a yellow square, and cinder cone volcanoes with a red circle. In the row on the *Volcano Table* page labeled *Location in our region,* record where each type of volcano is located. Record where each type of volcano is in relation to the earthquakes and plate boundaries in your region. Also record the pattern they make. For example, you might say that "shield volcanoes are in a line running parallel to the plate," or that "stratovolcanoes are in a cluster on the east side of the plate."

	Shield Volcanoes	Stratovolcanoes	Cinder Cone Volcanoes	Volcanoes in my region
Common shape				
Type of eruption				
Materials that are ejected				
How the volcanoes form				
Where the volcanoes form				
Other information				
Location in our region				
Questions				

Volcano Table   5.3.1

EE 203

EVER-CHANGING EARTH

⬡ Get Going

Have students examine the types of volcanoes they recorded on their *Three-page Maps* in *Section 5.1*. In the *Location in our region* row of their *Volcano Table* page, have them record where each type of volcano is located. They should also record where the volcanoes are in relation to the earthquakes and plate boundaries in the region and what patterns they make.

△ Guide

As students examine the information on their *Three-page Maps,* monitor their progress. Ask them if they have identified any patterns, and if the patterns surprise them. Are the volcanoes near the earthquakes?

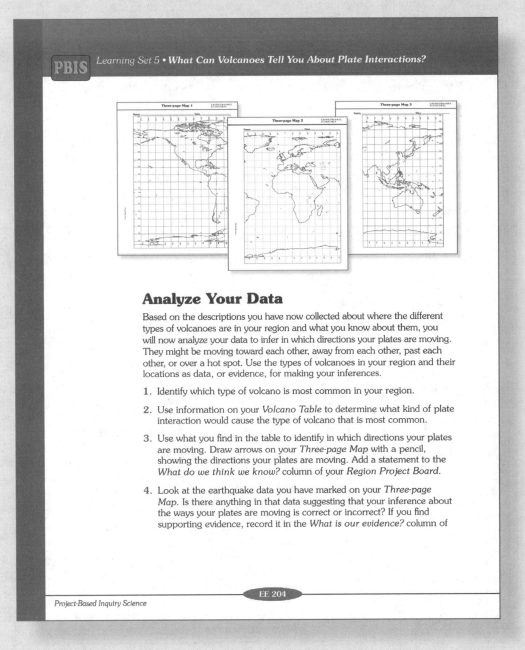

Analyze Your Data

Based on the descriptions you have now collected about where the different types of volcanoes are in your region and what you know about them, you will now analyze your data to infer in which directions your plates are moving. They might be moving toward each other, away from each other, past each other, or over a hot spot. Use the types of volcanoes in your region and their locations as data, or evidence, for making your inferences.

1. Identify which type of volcano is most common in your region.

2. Use information on your *Volcano Table* to determine what kind of plate interaction would cause the type of volcano that is most common.

3. Use what you find in the table to identify in which directions your plates are moving. Draw arrows on your *Three-page Map* with a pencil, showing the directions your plates are moving. Add a statement to the *What do we think we know?* column of your *Region Project Board*.

4. Look at the earthquake data you have marked on your *Three-page Map*. Is there anything in that data suggesting that your inference about the ways your plates are moving is correct or incorrect? If you find supporting evidence, record it in the *What is our evidence?* column of

EE 204

Project-Based Inquiry Science

Analyze Your Data

10 min

Students analyze their data to infer the direction of plate movement in their regions.

△ **Guide**

Tell students that they will analyze their data to infer which direction their plates are moving. Go over the steps in the student text with the class.

First, they should identify the type of volcano that is most common in their region. They should determine what kind of plate interaction would cause that kind of volcano. Based on the kind of plate interaction they determine is happening in their region, they should determine in which directions the plates in their region are moving. (e.g., if two plates are colliding, then students can conclude that they are moving toward each other.)

They should draw arrows on their *Three-page Map* to indicate the direction each plate is moving. They should also record claims about which direction each plate is moving in their *Region Project Board*.

Once they have recorded their inferences, they should evaluate whether the earthquake data for their region supports or conflicts with their inferences. If the data supports their inferences, they should record it in the *What is our evidence?* column of their *Region Project Board*. If it conflicts with their inferences, they should record it as an investigative question in their *Region Project Board*. They should review the data on their *Volcano Table* page and evaluate whether it supports or conflicts with their inferences. If any of the data conflicts with their inferences, they should put an investigative question on their *Region Project Board*.

Have students get started. Let them know that they will share their analyses with the class.

△ Guide and Assess

As students analyze their data, monitor their progress. Ask them what ideas they have discussed. When they have had a few minutes to make inferences, ask them how their earthquake and volcano data support or conflict with their inferences.

Using the following facts to assess students' progress:

Region	Inference of plate movement
Iceland	The Eurasian Plate and the North American Plate are moving away from each other.
Java Trench	The Indo-Australian Plate is moving north, towards the Eurasian Plate.
Mount Everest	The Indo-Australian Plate is moving north, towards the Eurasian Plate.
Mount Kilimanjaro	The African Plate is moving east, towards the Indo-Australian Plate.
Mount Fuji	The Eurasian Plate and the Pacific Plate are moving towards each other, the Eurasian Plate moving east and the Pacific Plate moving west. The Indo-Australian Plate is moving north, towards the Eurasian and Pacific Plates.
Baja Peninsula	The North American Plate and the Pacific Plate are moving alongside each other.
Mount Aconcagua	The Nazca Plate (along the coast of Chile) and the South American Plate are moving towards each other.

5.4 Explore

your *Region Project Board*. If anything in your earthquake data suggests that your inference is wrong, record it as a question on your *Region Project Board*. For example, you might write, "If my region's plates are moving apart, why do I see earthquakes happening in my plate boundary zone?"

5. Examine the data recorded in your *Volcano Table*. If you find anything there that suggests that your inference about the ways your plates are moving is incorrect, record it as a question, as well. For example, you might write, "If the plates in my region are moving toward each other, then why are there also shield volcanoes in my plate boundary zone?"

Conference

You will soon be sharing with your class your ideas about how your plates move. If another pair of students in your class is working on the same region as you, work with them to prepare for your presentation. Make sure you agree about the ways the plates are moving and the evidence you used to make that inference.

In preparation for sharing your ideas with the class, you will need to mark the *Big World Map* and prepare to report to the class the evidence you used to decide how your plates are moving.

1. Use a green marker to put arrows on the transparency layer of the *Big World Map* showing in which directions you think the plates in and around your region are moving.

2. Make a small poster showing the data and knowledge you used to decide how those plates are moving. Also include any questions you recorded that suggest why your inference may not be entirely accurate.

Communicate Your Ideas

Investigation Expo

Take turns reporting what you inferred about the plate movement in each region. When it is your group's turn, point to the *Big World Map* to show the class the types of volcanoes that are most common in your region. Then present your knowledge about the way plates interact to create those kinds of volcanoes. Next, point to the *Big World Map* again to show how you think your plates are moving. Then discuss the questions you have that suggest why your inference may not be entirely accurate.

EE 205

Conference

10 min

Pairs meet with other pairs assigned to the same region to prepare presentations.

△ Guide

When students have finished analyzing their data, have them meet with other students assigned to the same region to prepare presentations. Distribute green markers and poster sheets for students' presentations. Students should begin by discussing their conclusions and coming to an agreement on how the plates in their region move. When they have reached agreement, they should prepare their presentations.

Remind students what an *Investigation Expo* is. An *Investigation Expo* contains two parts—a presentation, including posters or other visual materials, and a discussion. Have the students use the green markers to put arrows on the transparency on the *Big World Map* to show which directions the plates are moving in and around their region. Then they should make small posters showing the data and science knowledge they used to infer how the plates are moving. Their posters should also show any questions they recorded about evidence or science knowledge that conflicted with their inferences.

Communicate Your Ideas: Investigation Expo

15 min

Region groups present their ideas and a class discussion follows.

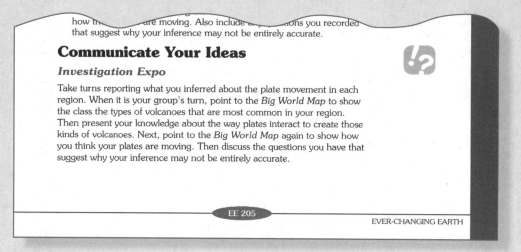

how th_____ are moving. Also include ____ons you recorded that suggest why your inference may not be entirely accurate.

Communicate Your Ideas

Investigation Expo

Take turns reporting what you inferred about the plate movement in each region. When it is your group's turn, point to the *Big World Map* to show the class the types of volcanoes that are most common in your region. Then present your knowledge about the way plates interact to create those kinds of volcanoes. Next, point to the *Big World Map* again to show how you think your plates are moving. Then discuss the questions you have that suggest why your inference may not be entirely accurate.

EE 205

EVER-CHANGING EARTH

△ Guide

When students have had time to prepare their presentations, have each group present. Each group should use the *Big World Map* to show the types of volcanoes that are most common in their region. They should share what they know about how plates interact to create those volcanoes. They should use their posters and the *Big World Map* to show how their plates are moving. Make sure the students discuss the questions they still have after each presentation.

NOTES

....

....

As you listen to the presentations of each group, use what you know about the different types of volcanoes to decide if you agree with their inferences about the ways the plates are moving. If you do not understand how they made their decisions, ask for clarification. If you disagree, tell them why you disagree, providing data and knowledge that you think they should have considered. Be sure to be respectful. Keep track of your disagreements. You will want to add them as questions to the class *Project Board*.

After all the groups have made their presentations, look at the *Big World Map* as a class to answer these questions.

1. Each plate boundary you have identified runs through at least two regions. Are the inferences the groups made about the directions the plates are moving consistent across both regions?

2. Look to see if the inferences you have made about the directions plates are moving are consistent with each other. For example, if one plate is moving toward another, is it marked as moving away from the plate on the other side? Is it consistent with what you know about that plate? Look for these kinds of consistencies in the way each plate moves.

3. Identify any plate movements you are still unsure of.

Update the *Project Board*

Now add to the class *Project Board* what you know about different kinds of volcanoes and the plate movements that cause them. Remember that any information added to the *What are we learning?* column should be supported with evidence in the *What is our evidence?* column

Also add questions you still need to answer to understand the plate movements in your region. Make sure the questions you wrote down as you analyzed your data are included on the class *Project Board*.

What's the Point?

Each type of volcano erupts as a result of different kinds of plate movement. Shield volcanoes form where plates are moving apart or where the crust is thin. Cinder cones usually occur where plates are moving apart. Stratovolcanoes are found where plates are moving together. Knowing the plate movements that cause different types of volcanoes allows you to infer how plates are moving in an area based on the volcanoes found there.

Emphasize that students should evaluate groups' ideas based on what they know about the different types of volcanoes. If they do not understand how a group arrived at their conclusions, they should ask questions to clarify. If they disagree with any of the group's conclusions, they should tell the group why they disagree, supporting their ideas with data and science knowledge. They should also keep track of their disagreements, so that they can record them as investigative questions on the class *Project Board*.

Once all groups have presented, lead a class discussion of the ideas presented, using the questions in the student text. Draw students' attention to the *Big World Map,* and ask them if groups with neighboring regions that share plate boundaries have recorded directions of plate movement that are consistent with each other. If a plate is shown moving toward a boundary in one group's region, but is shown moving away from the same boundary in another group's region, the two groups have made inconsistent conclusions. Ask students if the motion of the plates at different plate boundaries is consistent. If a plate is moving towards a boundary on one end, is it moving away from a boundary on the other end? They should keep in mind that one plate cannot move in opposite directions at the same time. Ask if there are any plate movements that they are unsure of, such as any directions of plate motion they inferred that were inconsistent for any plates.

Update the Project Board

10 min

The class has a discussion to update the Project Board.

Update the *Project Board*

Now add to the class *Project Board* what you know about different kinds of volcanoes and the plate movements that cause them. Remember that any information added to the *What are we learning?* column should be supported with evidence in the *What is our evidence?* column

Also add questions you still need to answer to understand the plate movements in your region. Make sure the questions you wrote down as you analyzed your data are included on the class *Project Board*.

△ Guide

As students discuss plate movements that they still need to investigate, draw their attention to the *Project Board*. Ask them what new information about the different kinds of volcanoes and about plate movements they can add to the *Project Board*. Record their answers in the *What are we learning?* column. Ask them what evidence they have for these ideas, and record their answers in the *What is our evidence?* column.

Ask them what questions they still need to investigate. Record their answers in the *What do we need to investigate?* column of the *Project Board*. Any disagreements they had about the directions plate move should be added to the *Project Board*.

NOTES

Assessment Options

Targeted Concepts, Skills, and Nature of Science	How do I know if students got it?
Scientists often work together and then share their findings. Sharing findings makes new information available and helps scientists refine their ideas and build on others' ideas. When another person or group's idea is used, credit needs to be given.	**ASK:** Why was it important to share your predictions about the direction of plate movements in and around your region with the class? **LISTEN:** Students should recognize that sharing their ideas about the direction of plate movements allowed them to identify inconsistencies in different groups' ideas, which allowed them to identify questions that they need to investigate.

Teacher Reflection Questions

- What inconsistencies did students identify in their conclusions? How were they able to formulate investigative questions to resolve the inconsistencies?

- What evidence do you have that students listened critically to presentations? What can you do to keep students engaged in presentations?

- How did you encourage students to participate in class discussion? What might you try next time?

NOTES

NOTES

Back to the Big Question

What Processes Within Earth Cause Geologic Activity?

◀ $1\frac{1}{2}$ *class periods*

A class period is considered to be one 40 to 50 minute class.

Overview

Students list the geologic terms they have learned in this *Learning Set* and make sketches to show the defining features of each term. They record connections between them, synthesizing the geologic ideas they have learned. Using data from their investigations and science knowledge from their reading, they revise their explanations of the geologic activity in their regions. They consider what information would help them better explain what causes geologic activity and changes in their Earth structure, and they update the *Project Board*. Then they learn about sedimentary, metamorphic, and igneous rock and how rocks can change from one type to another in the rock cycle.

Targeted Concepts, Skills, and Nature of Science	Performance Expectations
Scientists often work together and then share their findings. Sharing findings makes new information available and helps scientists refine their ideas and build on others' ideas. When another person's or group's idea is used, credit needs to be given.	Students should work together in small groups to revise their explanations. They should share their explanations with the class, discussing how different groups supported their claims.
Scientists must keep clear, accurate, and descriptive records of what they do so they can share their work with others and consider what they did, why they did it, and what they want to do next.	Students should keep clear, accurate, and descriptive records of the geologic concepts they have learned of and their claims with supporting evidence.
Scientists make claims (conclusions) based on evidence obtained (trends in data) from reliable investigations.	Students should revise their claims based on new science knowledge and data.

Targeted Concepts, Skills, and Nature of Science	Performance Expectations
Explanations are claims supported by evidence, accepted ideas, and facts.	Students should use their new science knowledge and new data to support their revised claims.
Earth's crust is constantly changing. These changes are usually a very slow process that is not immediately observable. Some changes are very rapid and are observable.	Students should describe volcanoes as evidence of changes in their region, and causes of changes in topography.
Earthquake activity, volcanic activity, and topography are all evidence that Earth's crust is moving and changing.	Students should include earthquake, volcano, and topographic data as evidence that Earth's crust is moving and changing.
Interactions between Earth's crustal plates can result in mountain building, rift valleys, and geologic activity such as earthquakes and volcanoes. Underwater volcanic activity may form underwater mountains, which can thrust above the ocean's surface to become islands.	Students should support claims about the directions of plate movement using patterns in volcanic activity as evidence. They should be able to describe the formation of islands from volcanic activity.
The rock cycle is driven by the constant destructive and constructive processes occurring in the materials that make up Earth's crust, including tectonic activity, mountain building, weathering and erosion, sedimentation, and the changing of rocks from one kind to another over long periods of time.	Students should be able to describe the rock cycle.

Materials

1 per class	Class *Project Board*
1 per student	*Project Board* page Pen pal letter *Create Your Explanation* page
1 per classroom	*Ever-Changing Earth Teacher Notes and Suggeted Data* table
1 per class	*Big World Map* with transparency layer

Homework Options

Reflection

- **Science Content:** How did you revise the claim(s) in your explanation? *(Students should have revised their claims to show how the heat of Earth's core and the convection currents in the mantle cause plate motion.)*

- **Science Content:** Describe the rock cycle. *(Students should describe the rock cycle in words or with a diagram similar to the one in the student text. Students should note that the cycle has no beginning or end and that the rock cycle has no definite sequence.)*

NOTES

....

....

....

....

....

....

....

....

....

....

....

NOTES

Learning Set 5

Back to the Big Question

What processes within Earth cause geologic activity?

You now know a lot about patterns of volcanoes in your region and around the world. You have inferred directions the plates might be moving in, though you are probably still unsure about how accurate your inferences are. You have seen that volcano and earthquake patterns are related to each other, but you are still wondering exactly why. In the next section, you will learn more that will help you answer that question. But before moving on, you will add to your *Picture Map* and use what you have been learning to revise your explanation of the processes within Earth that are shaping Earth's crust in your region.

Add to Your *Picture Map*

The goal of this *Learning Set* was to understand more about how Earth's plates move. To do that, you studied volcanoes—what they are, the ways they form, and the Earth structures they create. You learned many geologic terms in this *Learning Set*: *volcano, volcanic eruption, magma, lava, active volcano, dormant volcano, extinct volcano, magma chamber, vent, summit crater, caldera, shield volcano, stratovolcano, cinder cone volcano, volcanic ash,* and *hot spot*. As you have done in previous *Learning Sets*, you will create pictures to show what the words mean. Then, you will build a map to show how they relate to each other.

Write each term on a separate index card using large text so others will be able to read it from far away. Next to the term, or on the back of the card, draw a picture to show what the geologic term means. Make your picture as accurate as possible. Be sure to include features that would help someone else understand the geologic term.

Go back to the cards you made previously, and see if there is anything you want to add to or change on any of those.

Learning Set 5

Back to the Big Question

5 min

Students are introduced to the activity.

○ Engage

Remind students of the Unit's *Big Question: What processes within Earth cause geologic activity?* Tell them that they will now update their *Picture Maps* and use the new information and concepts they have learned to revise the explanations they created in *Learning Set 3.* Have the class *Project Board* on display. Let students know they may want to refer to their *Project Board* as they are revising their explanations.

*A class period is considered to be one 40 to 50 minute class.

Add to Your Picture Map

10 min

Students map the concepts they have learned using index cards.

Add to Your *Picture Map*

The goal of this *Learning Set* was to understand more about how Earth's plates move. To do that, you studied volcanoes—what they are, the ways they form, and the Earth structures they create. You learned many geologic terms in this *Learning Set*: volcano, volcanic eruption, magma, lava, active volcano, dormant volcano, extinct volcano, magma chamber, vent, summit crater, caldera, shield volcano, stratovolcano, cinder cone volcano, volcanic ash, and hot spot. As you have done in previous *Learning Sets*, you will create pictures to show what the words mean. Then, you will build a map to show how they relate to each other.

Write each term on a separate index card using large text so others will be able to read it from far away. Next to the term, or on the back of the card, draw a picture to show what the geologic term means. Make your picture as accurate as possible. Be sure to include features that would help someone else understand the geologic term.

Go back to the cards you made previously, and see if there is anything you want to add to or change on any of those.

△ Guide

Tell students that they will add to their *Picture Maps* by writing important terms on index cards, as they did in previous *Learning Sets*. They will draw a picture of each term to communicate what it means. Emphasize that their drawings should help people who are not familiar with the terms to understand what they mean. The student text mentions some of the words that may be new to students: volcano, volcanic eruption, magma, lava, active volcano, dormant volcano, extinct volcano, magma chamber, vent, summit crater, caldera, shield volcano, stratovolcano, cinder cone volcano, volcanic ash, and hot spot.

Students should also revise the cards they made in previous *Learning Sets*. Emphasize that they have learned more about these concepts and that their cards should show what they have learned.

⬡ Get Going

Distribute index cards and have students add to their *Picture Maps*. Emphasize that each student should create a set of cards illustrating the terms.

When students have completed their cards, have them share their cards with groups of students who were assigned to the same region. Each student should listen to other members' descriptions of the terms and think about information they can add to their own cards or changes they can make to their drawings.

Have students work with their groups to find how the terms go together, including the terms from *Learning Sets 1, 2, 3,* and *4*. They should arrange their cards on the table to show how the ideas connect. When they have agreed on how the ideas connect, they should record the connections on the back of the cards. If members of the group disagree about how the ideas connect, they should record their disagreement.

PBIS *Learning Set 5 • What Can Volcanoes Tell You About Plate Interactions?*

When you have completed your cards, share them with a group of classmates. Your teacher will tell you which group. Listen carefully as someone in your group describes each geologic term. For each card, notice if there is additional information or if there are changes you need to make to your drawing or definition.

Now, work with your group to create a map that shows how the geologic terms go together. Lay the new cards you made and old cards that you think connect to them on the table to show how each idea connects with another. For example, "vent connects to volcano, which connects to volcanic eruption." Record connections on all cards.

Discuss the connections with your group. If you cannot come to an agreement now, record your disagreement. As you learn more about the geologic terms, you will be better able to connect the ideas together. Then you can revise your cards and connections. Record the connections you made on the back of each card.

Project-Based Inquiry Science

EE 208

△ Guide and Assess

As students work on their *Picture Maps,* monitor their progress and assist them with any difficulties they encounter. If they need guidance as they create sketches to illustrate their geologic terms, have them imagine that they are trying to explain these ideas to someone using sketches. Ask them questions about the ideas to guide them towards statements that they can illustrate.

EVER-CHANGING EARTH

When students share their cards with their groups, listen to how they discuss differences in the information on their cards and how they discuss the best arrangement of their cards. Emphasize that students should ask questions and make comments constructively. If they have difficulty arranging their cards, ask them what the most important connections between the ideas they have illustrated are. For each idea, what other ideas do they have to use in an explanation?

NOTES

Revise Your Explanation

Now it is time to revise your explanation of the geologic activity in your region. Working with your partner, review the explanation of geologic activity in your region that you made at the end of *Learning Set 3*. Use what you now know about volcanoes and their causes to check the accuracy of what is in your old explanation and to decide how to update it. You have learned a lot more since you made that explanation, so you will probably want to revise it. Use a new *Create Your Explanation* page for your revised explanation. Remember that a good explanation has several parts to it:

- **your claim:** a statement of what you understand or a conclusion you've reached

- **your evidence:** data collected from investigations that support your claim

- **your science knowledge:** knowledge about how things work that supports your claim

- **your explanation itself:** a logical statement connecting your evidence and science knowledge to your claim in a way that can convince someone that your claim is valid. Good explanations tell what is happening that makes the claim valid.

Your claim will be your best statement about the processes beneath Earth's surface that are causing the geologic activity in your region. Your evidence comes from the drawings you have made and the data you have collected about volcanoes in your region. Your science knowledge comes from your reading.

Work with your partner to create the best explanation you can. You will have one more chance later in the Unit to revise your explanation. For now, do the best you can based on what you have learned so far. It may be easier to express your explanation by attaching phrases to sketches than to simply use words. Feel free to combine sketches and words in your explanation.

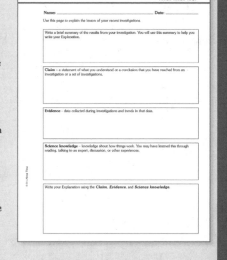

Revise Your Explanation

10 min

Students revise their explanations of geologic activity in their regions.

△ Guide

Begin by distributing new *Create Your Explanation* pages. Let students know they will work with their partners to revise their explanations of the ways that movements of Earth's layers cause changes in their regions. They will use evidence from their drawings and models, and they will use science knowledge from their reading.

Review the parts of a good explanation with the class (the claim, the evidence, the science knowledge, and the explanation connecting the evidence and the science knowledge to the claim.) They should revise their claims to connect plate motion to volcano formation. They should include what they have learned about how volcanoes form, the different types of volcanoes, and how the different types of plate interaction cause different types of volcanoes.

☐ Assess

As pairs work on their explanations, monitor their progress and help them with any difficulties they are having. Ask them what evidence and science knowledge they are using to support their claims. Use the *Ever-Changing Earth Teacher Notes and Suggested Data* table in the Appendix to assess the accuracy of students' explanations.

Note the similarities and differences among pairs' claims. During presentations, you might consider having two pairs with very similar claims present one after the other so that students can compare how they supported their claims.

NOTES

_____

_____

_____

_____

_____

_____

_____

_____

_____

Conference

At the end of *Learning Set 3,* you met with other pairs who where also assigned your region. Meet with this group again to share the explanations you have developed about the geologic activity in your region. Listen and watch for ways others have explained the data patterns. Look for different ways other teams expressed their explanations. Think about ways you can improve your explanation. Revise your explanation based on what you learn from your peers.

As a group, develop an explanation you think best explains the geologic activity in your region. You will share this explanation with the rest of the class.

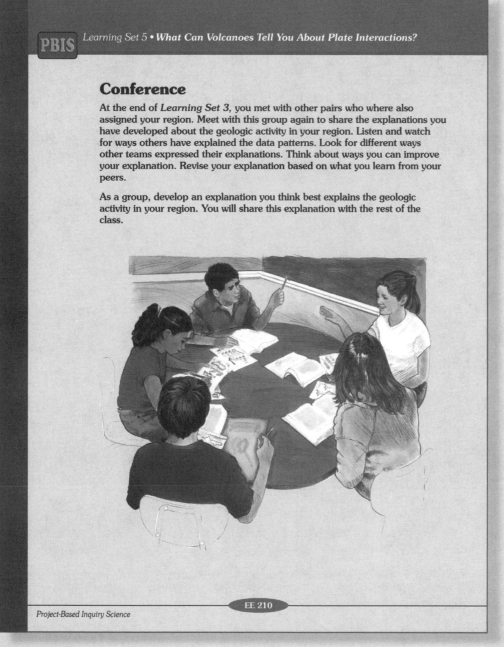

EE 210

Project-Based Inquiry Science

Conference
10 min

Pairs share their explanations with other students assigned to the same region.

△ Guide

When students have revised their explanations, have pairs meet with other pairs who studied the same region to share their explanations. As each pair presents their explanation, the other students in the group should listen and think about ways they can improve their explanations.

When all pairs in a group have presented, each pair should independently revise their explanation. If other pairs in the group used evidence that they did not use, they should include this evidence. If they realized that their interpretation of the data could be improved, they should revise their claims accordingly.

When pairs have revised their explanations, they should briefly share their revisions with the group. The group should discuss the explanations presented and choose the one that they think is best. The group will present this explanation to the class.

NOTES

....

....

....

....

....

....

....

....

....

....

....

....

Communicate

Share your Explanation

Present your explanation to the class. As you listen to the explanations of others, notice how well each explanation connects what is happening in Earth's layers to the geologic activity in each region. As you are listening, watch for ways others have explained patterns similar to yours.

Reflect

With your partner, answer the following questions.

1. Did you revise your explanation after group discussion? If so, how and why?

2. How trustworthy and complete do you think your explanation is? To figure that out, think about how well it explains the volcano activity in your region, as well as in other similar regions.

3. What else do you need to investigate to make a better explanation of the processes causing geologic activity in your region?

Update the *Project Board*

You have collected a lot of information about the geologic activity in your region and around your Earth structure. You have discovered differences and similarities in earthquake and volcano data patterns. This is all important for addressing the *Big Question* for this Unit, *What processes within Earth cause geologic activity?* You may want to add more to the *Project Board* about the geologic activity that causes volcanoes. Remember that any information added to the *What are we learning?* column should be supported with evidence in the *What is our evidence?* column.

After filling in the *What are we learning?* and *What is our evidence?* columns, add any new questions you have identified to the *What do we need to investigate?* column. Add questions you need answered to help you better explain how processes within Earth affect geologic activity and questions you need answered to better explain the geologic activity in your region.

EE 211

EVER-CHANGING EARTH

Communicate: Share Your Explanation

15 min

Groups present their explanations.

△ Guide

When groups have discussed their explanations, have them present the explanation they chose to the class. With the class, review the explanation, and ask the class to identify the parts of the explanation. Encourage the class to suggest any different ideas they have for the explanations presented. Ask groups with similar interpretations if they used any different evidence or science knowledge to support their claims.

☐ **Assess**

As the class discusses the presentations and the final class recommendation, listen to how students discuss their ideas. Do students ask each other about things that are not clear? Do they give constructive feedback?

Reflect

10 min

Pairs answer the Reflect *questions and participate in a class discussion.*

watch fo. ~~~~have explained pa. ~~~~o yours.

Reflect

With your partner, answer the following questions.

1. Did you revise your explanation after group discussion? If so, how and why?

2. How trustworthy and complete do you think your explanation is? To figure that out, think about how well it explains the volcano activity in your region, as well as in other similar regions.

3. What else do you need to investigate to make a better explanation of the processes causing geologic activity in your region?

△ Guide

Once groups have presented their explanations to the class, have students answer the *Reflect* questions with their partners. Emphasize that they should be prepared to share their answers with the class.

△ Guide and Assess

When students have had time to answer the *Reflect* questions, lead a class discussion of their responses. Listen for the following in students' answers:

1. Students should specify the changes they made to their explanations. If their original explanations were supported by too little evidence, or if their claims did not match the evidence, they should have revised their explanations to use more data or to interpret the evidence better.

2. Students should honestly evaluate how well they have explained earthquake patterns in their regions, and how well their explanations can be applied to regions with similar Earth structures.

3. This question is meant to engage students in thinking about what they need to investigate. Students should have questions about what causes plates to move, what patterns they can find in volcanic activity, what causes volcanic activity, what they can learn from depth data, and why some earthquakes occur in the middle of plates.

Update the *Project Board*

You have collected a lot of information about the geologic activity in your region and around your Earth structure. You have discovered differences and similarities in earthquake and volcano data patterns. This is all important for addressing the *Big Question* for this Unit, *What processes within Earth cause geologic activity?* You may want to add more to the *Project Board* about the geologic activity that causes volcanoes. Remember that any information added to the *What are we learning?* column should be supported with evidence in the *What is our evidence?* column.

After filling in the *What are we learning?* and *What is our evidence?* columns, add any new questions you have identified to the *What do we need to investigate?* column. Add questions you need answered to help you better explain how processes within Earth affect geologic activity and questions you need answered to better explain the geologic activity in your region.

Update the Project Board

10 min

The class has a discussion to update the Project Board.

△ Guide

Now update the *Project Board* with the class. Ask students what they have learned since they last updated the *Project Board*. Record their answers in the *What are we learning?* column. This should include claims from groups' explanations. For everything that students put in the *What are we learning?* column, ask them what evidence they have. Record the evidence in the *What is our evidence?* column. Finally, ask students what they still need to investigate, and record their answers in the *What do we need to investigate?* column. Students should record the questions they identified in the *Reflect* discussion.

NOTES

More to Learn:
The Rock Cycle

10 min

The class discusses the rock cycle.

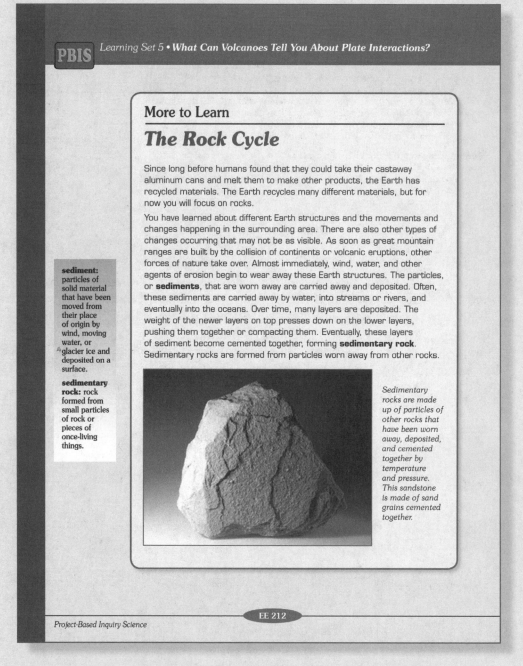

More to Learn

The Rock Cycle

Since long before humans found that they could take their castaway aluminum cans and melt them to make other products, the Earth has recycled materials. The Earth recycles many different materials, but for now you will focus on rocks.

You have learned about different Earth structures and the movements and changes happening in the surrounding area. There are also other types of changes occurring that may not be as visible. As soon as great mountain ranges are built by the collision of continents or volcanic eruptions, other forces of nature take over. Almost immediately, wind, water, and other agents of erosion begin to wear away these Earth structures. The particles, or **sediments**, that are worn away are carried away and deposited. Often, these sediments are carried away by water, into streams or rivers, and eventually into the oceans. Over time, many layers are deposited. The weight of the newer layers on top presses down on the lower layers, pushing them together or compacting them. Eventually, these layers of sediment become cemented together, forming **sedimentary rock**. Sedimentary rocks are formed from particles worn away from other rocks.

sediment: particles of solid material that have been moved from their place of origin by wind, moving water, or glacier ice and deposited on a surface.

sedimentary rock: rock formed from small particles of rock or pieces of once-living things.

Sedimentary rocks are made up of particles of other rocks that have been worn away, deposited, and cemented together by temperature and pressure. This sandstone is made of sand grains cemented together.

EE 212

△ Guide

Begin by introducing the idea that rocks change. Tell them there are three major types of rock, and a rock's type can change due to geologic processes. Then elicit and record their ideas about the types of rocks.

TEACHER TALK

"The Earth's crust is composed of many different substances that are recycled. There are many different types of rocks in the crust. The three main categories are igneous rocks, metamorphic rocks, and sedimentary rocks. The rocks are also recycled continuously. What do you think you know about these types of rocks?"

META NOTES

Consider having students take turns reading aloud or reading independently and then having different students summarize each paragraph.

△ Guide

Introduce the idea of erosion. Let students know that weathering and erosion break apart Earth's materials, such as rocks, and carry them from one place to another. Discuss how wind, water, and ice all can move particles of Earth. Discuss how rivers carry sediments and, over time, many layers of these sediments build up. The pressure from the layers pushing down causes them to become cemented together. These are then called sedimentary rocks. Limestone is an example of this type of rock.

NOTES

....

....

....

....

....

....

....

....

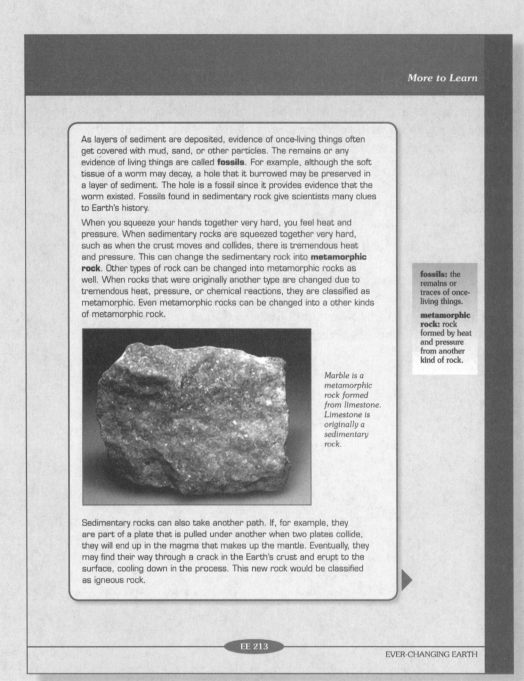

As layers of sediment are deposited, evidence of once-living things often get covered with mud, sand, or other particles. The remains or any evidence of living things are called **fossils**. For example, although the soft tissue of a worm may decay, a hole that it burrowed may be preserved in a layer of sediment. The hole is a fossil since it provides evidence that the worm existed. Fossils found in sedimentary rock give scientists many clues to Earth's history.

When you squeeze your hands together very hard, you feel heat and pressure. When sedimentary rocks are squeezed together very hard, such as when the crust moves and collides, there is tremendous heat and pressure. This can change the sedimentary rock into **metamorphic rock**. Other types of rock can be changed into metamorphic rocks as well. When rocks that were originally another type are changed due to tremendous heat, pressure, or chemical reactions, they are classified as metamorphic. Even metamorphic rocks can be changed into a other kinds of metamorphic rock.

fossils: the remains or traces of once-living things.

metamorphic rock: rock formed by heat and pressure from another kind of rock.

Marble is a metamorphic rock formed from limestone. Limestone is originally a sedimentary rock.

Sedimentary rocks can also take another path. If, for example, they are part of a plate that is pulled under another when two plates collide, they will end up in the magma that makes up the mantle. Eventually, they may find their way through a crack in the Earth's crust and erupt to the surface, cooling down in the process. This new rock would be classified as igneous rock.

EE 213

EVER-CHANGING EARTH

Discuss fossils (natural records of once-living things preserved in stone). The rock cycle and fossils are briefly discussed in the student text. Fossils are described as remains or evidence of living things. You may want to discuss fossils further with your students. Fossils usually form when many layers of sand and mud cover a plant or animal. When the pressure becomes high enough, the sand and mud become sedimentary rock. Then minerals seep into the remains of the plant or animal object, replacing the organic matter and creating a stone replica.

Discuss how sedimentary rock, under high temperatures and pressure, can undergo a chemical change and turn into a metamorphic rock, such as marble. Point out the image of marble in the student text.

NOTES

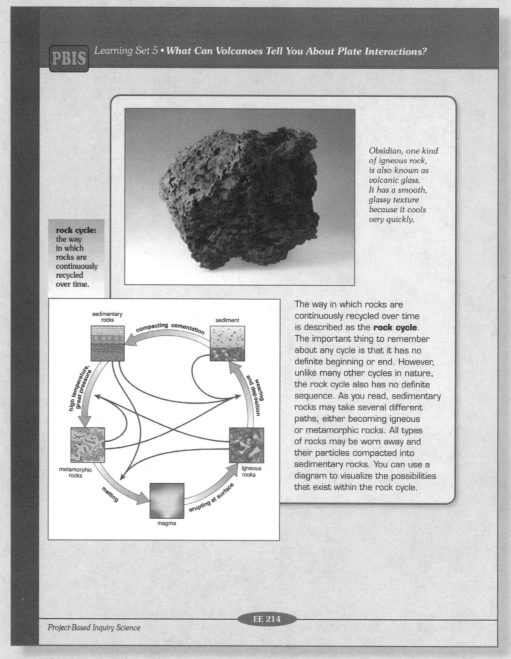

Obsidian, one kind of igneous rock, is also known as volcanic glass. It has a smooth, glassy texture because it cools very quickly.

rock cycle: the way in which rocks are continuously recycled over time.

The way in which rocks are continuously recycled over time is described as the **rock cycle**. The important thing to remember about any cycle is that it has no definite beginning or end. However, unlike many other cycles in nature, the rock cycle also has no definite sequence. As you read, sedimentary rocks may take several different paths, either becoming igneous or metamorphic rocks. All types of rocks may be worn away and their particles compacted into sedimentary rocks. You can use a diagram to visualize the possibilities that exist within the rock cycle.

Describe how rock in the crust—including sedimentary and metamorphic rock—melts into the magma of the mantle at places where a plate is pulled into the mantle. This molten rock can rise to the surface again as lava. When this lava cools and solidifies, it forms a type of rock known as igneous rock. An example of igneous rock is obsidian.

Point out that rock can be changed from igneous to sedimentary to metamorphic. Rock may undergo these changes in any order. The cycle of rock through these types is called the rock cycle.

Assessment Options

Targeted Concepts, Skills, and Nature of Science	How do I know if students got it?
Scientists often work together and then share their findings. Sharing findings makes new information available and helps scientists refine their ideas and build on others' ideas. When another person's or group's idea is used, credit needs to be given.	**ASK:** How did comparing your revised explanations to the explanations of other students assigned to your region help you? **LISTEN:** Students should recognize that by sharing explanations, they make their ideas available to compare with those of others, and they can identify claims and reasoning in their explanations that need revision.
Scientists make claims (conclusions) based on evidence obtained (trends in data) from reliable investigations.	**ASK:** What was the basis for the claims you made in your explanations? Why is this important? **LISTEN:** Students should have based their claims on the data they have gathered. They should realize that this is important because an explanation without evidence (or data) is simply an opinion.
Earth's crust is constantly changing. These changes are usually a very slow process that is not immediately observable. Some changes are very rapid and are observable.	**ASK:** Why is there a chain of islands in Hawaii? Why not just one volcanic island? What other evidence do you have that plates are continually moving? **LISTEN:** Students should recognize that the Hawaiian Islands form a chain because the plate they are on has continually moved over a hot spot in the mantle. They may have various ideas about evidence that suggests that plates are continuously moving, such as the volcanoes along the mid-ocean ridge that often have very long, continuous eruptions.

Targeted Concepts, Skills, and Nature of Science	How do I know if students got it?
The rock cycle is driven by the constant destructive and constructive processes occurring in the materials that make up Earth's crust, including tectonic activity, mountain-building, weathering and erosion, sedimentation, and the changing of rocks from one kind to another over long periods of time.	**ASK:** What part do volcanoes play in the rock cycle? **LISTEN:** Students should describe how lava emitted from volcanoes cools and solidifies into igneous rock.

Teacher Reflection Questions

- What concepts in this *Learning Set* were difficult for students? How can you help them master these concepts?

- How have you been able to evaluate students' progress as they learn about geologic activity and Earth structures?

- How were you able to engage students in class discussion? How can you encourage students to take responsibility for the progress made in class discussions?

Learning Set 6

What Geologic Activity Happens at Plate Boundaries?

◀ $6\frac{1}{4}$ *class periods*

A class period is considered to be one 40 to 50 minute class.

Overview

Students observe types of plate interactions in animations and simulate the types of interactions by making flip books. They discuss the correct order of events in the flip books with their group, and present their plate interactions to the class. The class considers how they can apply their observations to understanding the relationship of earthquake patterns to volcanos patterns. Students read descriptions of the plate interactions they simulated and identify regions where they think each type of plate interaction is occurring. They revise their flip books and present what they have learned to the class. They reflect on what they have learned and update their *Region Project Boards*. Then they work with their partners to decide what data they still need to determine the type of plate interaction that occurs in their region and the directions those plates are moving. They use *My World* to gather this data. Then they share their conclusions with other students assigned to the same region. When the region groups arrive at agreement, they share their conclusions with the class. The class discusses whether different groups' conclusions are compatible and how well their conclusions are supported by their data.

Targeted Concepts, Skills, and Nature of Science	Section
Scientists often work together and then share their findings. Sharing findings makes new information available and helps scientists refine their ideas and build on others' ideas. When another person's or group's idea is used, credit needs to be given.	6.1, 6.2, 6.3, 6.BBQ
Scientists must keep clear, accurate, and descriptive records of what they do so they can share their work with others and consider what they did, why they did it, and what they want to do next.	6.2, 6.3, 6.BBQ

Targeted Concepts, Skills, and Nature of Science	Section
Scientists make claims (conclusions) based on evidence obtained (trends in data) from reliable investigations.	6.3, 6.BBQ
Explanations are claims supported by evidence, accepted ideas, and facts.	6.BBQ
Graphs and tables are an effective way to analyze and communicate results of scientific investigation.	6.1
Scientists use models and tools, such as Geographic Information Systems, and a variety of maps to develop claims and explanations from evidence in the data.	6.1, 6.2, 6.3
Earthquake activity, volcanic activity, and topography are all evidence that Earth's crust is moving and changing.	6.BBQ
Interactions between Earth's crustal plates can result in mountain building, rift valleys, and geologic activity such as earthquakes and volcanoes. Underwater volcanic activity may form underwater mountains, which can thrust above the ocean's surface to become islands.	6.1, 6.2, 6.BBQ
Earth is a system made up of different layers, each with a distinctive composition and set of characteristics. These layers interact, driving the processes that shape Earth.	6.1, 6.2, 6.3
The way in which plates collide depends on the density of the interacting plates. Continental crust is less dense than oceanic crust and, therefore, has greater buoyancy. This causes continental crust to float over the denser oceanic crust when these plates converge.	6.1, 6.2
New crust is formed at the mid-ocean ridge where the plates move apart. Oceanic crust is destroyed when it collides with continental crust and is subducted. In this way, Earth's crust is recycled.	6.1, 6.2, 6.3
Plate interactions may be classified into zones, including rift zones, subduction zones, buckling zones, and transform zones. Patterns in earthquake and volcano data help scientists identify these zones.	6.1, 6.2, 6.3

Understanding for Teachers

Volcanoes occur where magma is able to breach Earth's crust. When magma reaches Earth's surface it is called lava. This lava adds to Earth's crust.

Magma and Lava Types

There are various types of magma. Common types are basaltic, andesitic, dacitic, and rhyolitic. Different lava types have different lava flows.

Basaltic magma has the lowest silica content, the least viscosity, and flows at approximately 30 to 60 km/h as lava. Andesitic has more silica and higher viscosity than basaltic and a lower silica content and viscosity than rhyolitic lava. Andesitic lava flows about 10 km/h. Rhyolitic magma has the highest silica content and the highest viscosity. Rhyolitic lava flows about 1 km/h. Dacitic magma contains about five percent less silica than rhyolitic lava and hence is a little less viscous and moves a little faster than rhyolitic lava. As the silica content increases, the viscosity increases. When these types of lava cool and solidify, they form igneous rock of the same name.

Balsatic lava erupts from shield volcanoes. Basaltic lava forms a'a and pahoehoe lava, commonly found in Hawaii. A'a lava surfaces are fragmented and rough. Pahoehoe surfaces can be smooth, like rope, or billowy.

Andesitic lava produces angular fragments, or blocks, which are not splintery and do not have cavities formed by gas. This contributes to the higher viscosity of andesitic lava. Some andesitic lavas form lava domes and are common to eruptions from stratovolcanoes. The tops of andesite flows have detached blocks, but the interior is composed of large volumes of lava that flow downward in a fragmented base layer. The front of the flow contains rubble, which is overridden by the massive flow.

Dacitic and rhyolitic lavas usually erupt from stratovolcanoes, and are not as abundant as andesitic lava. They occur in more explosive eruptions and are associated with a high gas content and high viscosity. During the initial eruptions, a pyroclastic flow may occur. The pyroclastic flow is a mixture of solid to semi-solid fragments and hot, expanding gases that can move like an avalanche down the cone at speeds over 100 km/hr.

Another type of pyroclastic flow is a nuée ardente. This flow type contains dense lava fragments from the collapse of a growing lava dome.

After an explosive eruption, de-gassed lava may flow as dacitic or rhyolitic lava. These types of lava often flow down one side of the cone to form lava domes. In some cases, thick rhyolitic lavas will cool as glassy obsidian flows.

All lava contains gases. The less viscous the lava type, the more easily it dissipates these gases.

NOTES

LEARNING SET 6 IMPLEMENTATION

◄ $6\frac{1}{4}$ *class periods* *

Learning Set 6

What Geologic Activity Happens at Plate Boundaries?

Earthquakes and volcanoes occurring in the regions of plate boundaries are evidence of plates moving away from one another, toward one another, and past one another. You have made some inferences about the direction the plates in your region are moving. However, you may not be completely confident about these inferences. And you still do not know enough about what is happening at the plate boundaries to know how the volcano and earthquake patterns you have observed are related to each other. In this *Learning Set,* you will learn more about plate interactions and what occurs at the plate boundaries that causes geologic activity. When you are finished, you will be better able to explain how your plates are moving and the effects of that movement. You will then be ready to answer the *Big Question, What processes within Earth cause geologic activity?*

Geologists estimate that the Southern Alps in New Zealand are rising as much as 1 centimeter (about a half inch) per year.

EE 215

EVER-CHANGING EARTH

Learning Set 6

What Geologic Activity Happens at Plate Boundaries?

5 min

Students are introduced to the question of the Learning Set.

○ **Engage**

Remind students of the *Big Question: What processes within Earth cause geologic activity?* Briefly discuss how students made inferences about plate interactions and movements in their regions. They may have recognized and started thinking about the relationships between patterns of earthquakes and patterns of volcanoes. Emphasize that to be confident of their inferences and to understand the relationship between earthquakes and volcanoes, they need to learn more about plate interactions. Tell them they will learn more about plate interactions and will then be able to answer the *Big Question*.

*A class period is considered to be one 40 to 50 minute class.

NOTES

SECTION 6.1 INTRODUCTION

6.1 Understand the Question

Think About What Geologic Activity Happens at Plate Boundaries

◀ *2 class periods*

A class period is considered to be one 40 to 50 minute class.

Overview

Students use animations of plate interactions to observe how the plates involved and the movement of the plates affect the geologic activity that occurs at the plates' edges. They work with their partners to describe what they observed for each type of interaction. Each pair of students makes a flip book showing what happens during the plate interaction types. They meet with other students assigned to the same plate interaction, and agree on a sequence of events for the flip books, and present their flip books to the class. In a class discussion, they consider how they can apply their observations of plate interactions to understanding the relationship of earthquakes and volcanoes at plate boundaries.

Targeted Concepts, Skills, and Nature of Science	Performance Expectations
Scientists often work together and then share their findings. Sharing findings makes new information available and helps scientists refine their ideas and build on others' ideas. When another person's or group's idea is used, credit needs to be given.	Students should collaborate to develop accurate representations of different types of plate interaction. Then they share their representations with the class.
Graphs and tables are an effective way to analyze and communicate results of scientific investigation.	Students should organize their observations on their *Plate Interactions: Animations* pages.
Scientists use models and tools, such as Geographic Information Systems, and a variety of maps to develop claims and explanations from evidence in the data.	Students should simulate plate interaction using their flip books.

Targeted Concepts, Skills, and Nature of Science	Performance Expectations
Earth is a system made up of different layers, each with a distinctive composition and set of characteristics. These layers interact, driving the processes that shape Earth.	Students should recognize that interactions between plates are driven by convection currents in Earth's mantle. They should also recognize that magma in the mantle interacts with the crust at plate boundaries. At oceanic-oceanic divergent boundaries, magma rises through the gap between plates and adds to the crust. At oceanic-continental convergent boundaries, magma melts the oceanic crust as it sinks under the continental crust.
Interactions between Earth's crustal plates can result in mountain building, rift valleys, and geologic activity such as earthquakes and volcanoes. Underwater volcanic activity may form underwater mountains, which can thrust above the ocean's surface to become islands.	Students should be able to describe how convergent and divergent plate interactions can lead to mountain building.
The way in which plates collide depends on the density of the interacting plates. Continental crust is less dense than oceanic crust and, therefore, has greater buoyancy. This causes continental crust to float over the denser oceanic crust when these plates converge.	Students should recognize that the greater density of oceanic crust usually makes it sink under the continental crust at oceanic-continental convergent boundaries.
New crust is formed at the mid-ocean ridge where the plates move apart. Oceanic crust is destroyed when it collides with continental crust and is subducted. In this way, Earth's crust is recycled.	Students should understand how plates move apart at the mid-ocean ridge, and magma rises into the gap, creating new crust.
Plate interactions may be classified into zones, including rift zones, subduction zones, buckling zones, and transform zones. Patterns in Earthquake and volcano data help scientists identify these zones.	Students should understand how the four different types of plate interaction they saw in their animations are distinct from each other.

Materials	
1 per class	DVD player and television or monitor *Earth Science Content* DVD
1 per student	*Plate Interactions: Animations* page
1 per pair	Plate interaction flip book
1 per class	Class *Project Board*

Homework Options

Reflection

- **Science Content:** What observations from the animations gave you information about the relationship between earthquakes and volcanoes? How could you find out more about the relationship between earthquakes and volcanoes? *(This question is meant to engage students in thinking about how to best learn from observations.)*

Preparation for 6.2

- **Science Content:** How are oceanic-continental convergent plate interactions different from continental-continental convergent plate interactions? Where do you think volcanoes are more likely to occur, why? *(Students should describe how in oceanic-continental convergent plate interactions, the oceanic crust—which is denser—typically passes under the continental crust and sinks into the mantle. In continental-continental convergent plate movements, both plates are typically pushed up at the boundary. Volcanoes are more likely to occur at oceanic-continental convergent plate boundaries. At these boundaries, the oceanic plate sinks into the mantle and melts, creating pockets of magma beneath the continental plate. These pockets of magma often become volcanoes. Students do not need to be able to explain this yet— they will read about it in the next section— but they should begin to think about it.)*

NOTES

SECTION 6.1 IMPLEMENTATION

6.1 Understand the Question

Think About What Geologic Activity Happens at Plate Boundaries

The earthquake data patterns you analyzed gave you enough information to determine the locations of plate boundaries. The types of volcanoes in your region provided more information about the directions your plates are moving and the geologic activity occurring in your region. To fully explain the processes within Earth that are causing this geologic activity, you need to know more about what is actually happening at the plate boundaries. This section will focus on the different ways plates interact at their boundaries and the resulting geologic activity. This will help you understand how volcanoes and earthquakes are related to each other and allow you to more fully explain what is causing the geologic activity in your region.

The Aleutian Islands are a chain of more than 300 small volcanic islands in the Northern Pacific Ocean, occupying an area of 17,666 km² (6821 mi²).

Get Started

You will watch four animations showing the different ways plates interact with one another. One animation will show what can happen when two plates move away from each other. Two animations will show what can happen when two plates collide. The last animation will show what can happen when two plates slide past each other.

EE 216

Project-Based Inquiry Science

6.1 Understand the Question

Think About What Geologic Activity Happens at Plate Boundaries

5 min

Students are introduced to the activity.

○ Engage

Begin by asking students what they would need to investigate to determine what the relationship between earthquakes and volcanoes is. Ask them what they need to investigate to better understand how plate movement contributes to geologic activity.

Tell students they will investigate the different ways plates interact at their boundaries. This will help them understand how volcanoes and earthquakes are related and will allow them to better explain what is causing geologic activity in their regions.

*A class period is considered to be one 40 to 50 minute class.

"You have determined where the plate boundaries are, and you know where earthquakes and volcanoes are. You may also have ideas about the relationship between earthquake activity and volcanoes. What would you need to investigate to learn more about the relationship of earthquake activity and volcanoes? What would you need to investigate to better understand how the movements of plates affect geologic activity?

In this section, you will investigate the different ways plates interact at their boundaries. This will help you to understand how volcanoes and earthquakes are related. It will also help you better explain what is causing geologic activity in your region."

Get Started

10 min

The class watches the plate-interaction animations.

Get Started

You will watch four animations showing the different ways plates interact with one another. One animation will show what can happen when two plates move away from each other. Two animations will show what can happen when two plates collide. The last animation will show what can happen when two plates slide past each other.

△ Guide

Let students know they will observe what happens when plates interact by watching animations of plates interacting in four different ways. One animation shows what happens when plates move away from each other, two animations show the different ways plates can converge, and the last animation shows what happens when plates slide past each other.

Emphasize that students should pay attention to the types of crust involved in the plate interactions. Remind students that some crust is denser than other crust. Crust on the ocean floor tends to be denser and thinner than continental crust. As they watch, they should think about how the types of crust involved in the plate interactions affect the resulting geologic activity.

Show the animations. Ask students if they have any questions about what the animations show. Show them again so students can more closely observe what happens.

You will see that the plates can interact several different ways depending on the type of crust involved. Remember that crust making up the ocean floor is thinner, but denser than continental crust. Although continental crust can be very thick, it is made up of rock that is less dense than that found in oceanic crust. As you watch the animations, pay attention to the different types of crust involved and how those differences affect geologic activity.

Conference

Work with your partner to complete the *Plate Interactions: Animations* page. For each animation, answer the following questions. If you cannot answer a question, make a note about what information you need to answer it. You may ask your teacher to replay the animations if you need to see them again.

- If more than one plate was involved, were the plates moving away from one another, toward one another, or sliding past one another? Record your observations in the row labeled *How the Plates Move*.

EE 217

Conference

15 min

Students think about their observations of the animations.

△ Guide

Once students have watched the animations, distribute the *Plate Interactions: Animations* pages and have students work with their partners to record what they observed. For each type of interaction, they should answer the bulleted questions in the student text and record their answers in the corresponding rows of the *Plate Interactions: Animations* page. Emphasize that if students cannot agree on something they observed in an animation, or if they are in doubt about what they observed, they should ask you to replay it.

△ Guide and Evaluate

As students discuss what they observed, note how different pairs are answering the questions. If any pairs record observations that are clearly mistaken, replay the animations for the class, emphasizing that they should check their answers to the questions as they watch the animations. Their completed tables should have the information given below.

	Animation 1: Plates move apart	Animation 2: Plates come together (continental-continental crust)	Animation 3: Plates come together (oceanic-continental crust)	Animation 4: Plates slide past each other
How the plates move	Plates move away from each other.	Plate move toward each other.	Plates move toward each other.	Plates slide past one another.
Action at the edges	Plates move apart, forming a gap between them.	One plate seems to bend upward, the other seems to break apart, the denser part sinks into the mantle and the less-dense part lifts up.	One plate bends down and sinks into the mantle, the other breaks apart and becomes mountainous, but remains nearly stationary.	Plates move past each other, possibly breaking up the edges.
Type of crust	The crust near the boundary lies under the ocean. Therefore, it is oceanic on both sides of the boundary, or oceanic-oceanic.	The surface of the crust near the boundary is dry land. Therefore, it is continental on both sides of the boundary, or continental-continental.	One plate lies under the ocean, and is therefore oceanic. The other is above the ocean, and is continental. The plates at the boundary are oceanic-continental.	The surface of the crust near the boundary is dry land. Therefore, it is continental on both sides of the boundary, or continental-continental.
How magma reaches the surface	Magma flows up in the gap formed where the plates pull apart.	No magma reaches the surface in the animation.	As the continental crust breaks, vents form in the fractures. Magma rises through these vents.	No magma reaches the surface in the animation.

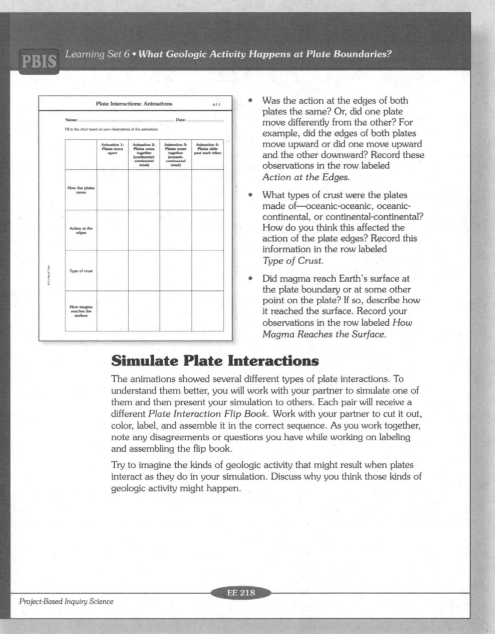

Plate Interactions: Animations   6.1.1

Name: _____   Date: _____

Fill in the chart based on your observations of the animations.

	Animation 1: Plates move apart	Animation 2: Plates come together (continental-continental crust)	Animation 3: Plates come together (oceanic-continental crust)	Animation 4: Plates slide past each other
How the plates move				
Action at the edges				
Type of crust				
How magma reaches the surface				

- Was the action at the edges of both plates the same? Or, did one plate move differently from the other? For example, did the edges of both plates move upward or did one move upward and the other downward? Record these observations in the row labeled *Action at the Edges.*

- What types of crust were the plates made of—oceanic-oceanic, oceanic-continental, or continental-continental? How do you think this affected the action of the plate edges? Record this information in the row labeled *Type of Crust.*

- Did magma reach Earth's surface at the plate boundary or at some other point on the plate? If so, describe how it reached the surface. Record your observations in the row labeled *How Magma Reaches the Surface.*

Simulate Plate Interactions

The animations showed several different types of plate interactions. To understand them better, you will work with your partner to simulate one of them and then present your simulation to others. Each pair will receive a different *Plate Interaction Flip Book*. Work with your partner to cut it out, color, label, and assemble it in the correct sequence. As you work together, note any disagreements or questions you have while working on labeling and assembling the flip book.

Try to imagine the kinds of geologic activity that might result when plates interact as they do in your simulation. Discuss why you think those kinds of geologic activity might happen.

Simulate Plate Interactions

10 min

Students assemble t heir flip books.

△ Guide

Let students know they will work with their partners to create a simulation of one of the types of plate interaction. To do this, they will assemble a flip book showing the sequence of events when two plates interact. When they are done, they will present their flip books to the class.

Distribute the flip books. Try to assign about the same number of pairs to each plate interaction type. For instance, if your class has 30 students, you can assign 4 pairs to divergent plate movement, 4 pairs to continental-continental convergent plate movement, 4 pairs to oceanic-continental convergent plate movement, and 3 pairs to transform plate movement.

Tell students that each pair should use the information in their *Plate Interactions: Animations* page to color, label, and assemble their flip book. They should label the mantle, the continental and oceanic crust, the magma, water, and any vents present in each page. Then they should observe the differences between the pages, and arrange the pages in the correct chronological order. When they have arranged the pages correctly, have students assemble the flip books. Emphasize that they should record any disagreements they have as they work on their flip books. These will be included in their presentations.

△ Guide and Assess

As students work on the flip books, monitor their progress and ask them how they are choosing the order of the pages in their flip books. They should be using signs of progressive geologic formation, such as spreading vents, and signs of plate movement.

NOTES

Be prepared to share how you colored in and assembled the book, the types of geologic activity you think might result from these interactions and the reasons why and any disagreements or questions you had while working together.

Conference

Now get together with the other pairs that assembled the same flip book, and prepare to make a presentation to the class.

Share your flip books. Try to come to an agreement about the sequence. Identify any disagreements you have as you work together. Prepare to show the sequence of events you agree on. Come to an agreement about the type of geologic activity that is likely to result from your type of plate interaction. If you cannot come to an agreement, prepare to share any disagreements with the class, along with evidence that supports the different opinions.

Communicate

Share Your Simulations and Ideas

You will take turns presenting your flip books to the class. When your group presents, first describe the kind of interaction you are showing. One person should turn the pages of the flip book, while others describe the sequence of events. Be sure to include in your description the actions at the edges of the plates, the types of crust interacting, and any presence and movement of magma. Finally, present your ideas about the kinds of earthquake and volcanic activity that might result from this kind of interaction.

As other groups prepare to present, examine your *Plate Interactions: Animations* page to identify what you expect to see in their simulation. Think about the kinds of geologic activity that might result from the type of interaction they are presenting. If a group presents information about a plate interaction that differs from what is on your chart, then you must make a decision. Ask yourself if you now have a better understanding of the plate interaction and should change your chart, or if there are inaccuracies in the group's presentation. Ask questions to clarify, or share your disagreements. Remember to be respectful when you disagree. If you cannot come to an agreement through class discussion, develop a question for the *Project Board*.

EE 219

EVER-CHANGING EARTH

Conference
10 min

Pairs prepare presentations with other pairs assigned to the same plate-interaction type.

△ Guide

When pairs have assembled their flip books, have them meet with other pairs who had the same plate interaction type to prepare to present their work. First, each pair should share their flip book. They should discuss the reasons they chose their sequence, and the group should come to agreement about what the correct sequence is. They should also discuss what kind of geologic activity they think will result from the plate interaction, and try to come to an agreement. This will be part of their presentation. If they cannot reach agreement, they should record what they disagree about and the reasons for their disagreement to share in their presentation. Provide new flip books if groups feel they need to start over.

☐ Assess

As students work with their groups, ask them what ideas they discussed. As they begin to arrange the pages of their flip books, ask different members of each group if they agree with the order the group has chosen, and have them give reasons why they agree or disagree.

Communicate: Share Your Simulations and Ideas

15 min

Groups present their flip books to the class.

with the cl... ...g with evidence that supp... ...nt opinions.

Communicate

Share Your Simulations and Ideas

You will take turns presenting your flip books to the class. When your group presents, first describe the kind of interaction you are showing. One person should turn the pages of the flip book, while others describe the sequence of events. Be sure to include in your description the actions at the edges of the plates, the types of crust interacting, and any presence and movement of magma. Finally, present your ideas about the kinds of earthquake and volcanic activity that might result from this kind of interaction.

As other groups prepare to present, examine your *Plate Interactions: Animations* page to identify what you expect to see in their simulation. Think about the kinds of geologic activity that might result from the type of interaction they are presenting. If a group presents information about a plate interaction that differs from what is on your chart, then you must make a decision. Ask yourself if you now have a better understanding of the plate interaction and should change your chart, or if there are inaccuracies in the group's presentation. Ask questions to clarify, or share your disagreements. Remember to be respectful when you disagree. If you cannot come to an agreement through class discussion, develop a question for the *Project Board*.

△ Guide

Now have groups present their flip books to the class. They should begin by describing the type of interaction shown in their flip book. One student should turn the pages of their flip book, while other members of the group describe the sequence of events. They should describe what happens at the edges of the plates, what type of crust is involved, and what role, if any, magma plays in the interaction. They should give reasons why they chose the sequence and describe any disagreements they had.

Emphasize that as each group presents, students in the audience should think about how the information in their *Plate Interactions: Animations* page compares to the information in the group's flip book. If there are differences, students will have to decide whether the information on their *Plate Interactions: Animations* page is correct. If they think there is an inaccuracy in the flip book, they should offer constructive comments. If anything is unclear, they should ask questions. Emphasize that it is important to be polite.

If the class cannot come to agreement about one of the plate interaction types, note this to record later as a question in the *What do we need to investigate?* column of the *Project Board*.

Reflect

1. Describe how differences in the type of crust can affect how two plates interact.

2. How do you think the type of interaction at one plate boundary might affect the type of interaction found at another plate boundary?

3. What do you now understand better about the relationship between earthquakes and volcanoes?

4. What else do you need to learn to understand better what is happening at different plate boundaries?

5. What else do you need to learn to understand better how earthquakes and volcanoes are related?

Update the *Project Board*

As a class, update the *Project Board*. List what you think you know about plate boundaries and how different types of interactions relate to geologic activity in the *What do we think we know?* column. Use questions developed during presentations and discussions to help determine what you need to investigate further. Any questions that remain about the relationship between earthquakes and volcanoes should be added to the *What do we need to investigate?* column.

What's the Point?

You saw in the animations what happens at different plate boundaries when they interact. The ways that the plates interact and the resulting geologic activity depend on several factors, including how the plates are moving and the type of crust involved. You are beginning to see the relationship between earthquakes and volcanoes. As you explore more about the different types of plate boundaries and the interactions that occur, you will be able to connect them to the patterns of geologic activity you have identified in your regions. In this *Learning Set,* you will learn about other factors that determine what happens at each type of plate boundary. With this information, you will be able to determine the processes within Earth that cause geologic activity and understand the resulting changes to Earth's crust.

EE 220

Project-Based Inquiry Science

Reflect

20 min

Students answer the Reflect *questions, followed by a class discussion.*

△ Guide

When all groups have presented, have students answer the *Reflect* questions. Emphasize that they will discuss their answers with the class.

☐ Assess

As pairs discuss the *Reflect* questions, ask them what ideas they discussed and whether they had any disagreements. Notice how students are contributing to the discussions.

△ Guide and Evaluate

When students have answered the *Reflect* questions, lead a class discussion of their responses. As the class discusses, encourage them to support their ideas with information from the flip books and observations from the animations. Encourage students to comment on each other's ideas. If students disagree with an idea, they should politely explain why.

As students discuss their ideas, use the following guidelines to evaluate their ideas:

1. Students should recognize that the greater density of oceanic crust will generally make it sink under continental crust when there is convergent plate interaction between the two types. By contrast, in a continental-continental convergent plate interaction, both plates are likely to partially push up, forming mountainous surface.

2. Students should recognize that if a plate is converging with another plate on one side, it must be pulling away from a plate on the other side. For instance, if a plate is involved in oceanic-continental convergent plate movement on its western edge, it is probably involved in divergent plate movement on its eastern edge. It may also be involved in transform plate movement at its northern and southern edges.

3. Students should now be able to describe how specific types of plate interaction cause earthquakes and volcanoes and how the different types of plate interaction are more or less likely to cause earthquakes or volcanoes.

4. This question is meant to engage students in thinking about what they need to learn about how plates interact. Students may suggest that they need more data on geologic activity at specific plate boundaries. They may want to know if all divergent boundaries are oceanic-oceanic divergent boundaries, or if some occur in continental crust. They may also want to know if different materials in the crust or different types of magma affect the way plates interact.

NOTES

....

....

5. This question is meant to help students reflect on what they know about the relationship between earthquakes and volcanoes and what they need to learn. They may want to know if volcanoes ever occur at transform boundaries and continental-continental convergent boundaries. They may also want to know if volcanic activity and earthquake activity at a plate boundary can affect each other. They might suspect that earthquakes create fissures that become volcanic vents, or that volcanoes cause earthquakes as magma and gas moving through the crust put pressure on parts of the crust.

What else do you ~~understand~~ ~~types~~ and volcanoes are related?

Update the *Project Board*

As a class, update the *Project Board*. List what you think you know about plate boundaries and how different types of interactions relate to geologic activity in the *What do we think we know?* column. Use questions developed during presentations and discussions to help determine what you need to investigate further. Any questions that remain about the relationship between earthquakes and volcanoes should be added to the *What do we need to investigate?* column.

What's the Point?

Update the Project Board

10 min

The class has a discussion to update the Project Board.

△ **Guide**

Lead a class discussion of what new knowledge the class can put on the *Project Board*. Ask them what ideas about how different types of plate interactions relate to geologic activity they can put on the *Project Board*. Record their answers in the *What do we think we know?* column. Students may have observed that volcanoes are most likely to occur where divergent and oceanic-continental continental plate movements occur. They may also have observed that earthquakes are most likely to occur where either type of convergent plate movement occurs.

Ask them what they need to investigate. Any disagreements they had about the animations or flip books should be addressed with investigative questions. Record their investigative questions in the *What do we need to investigate?* column.

NOTES

....

....

Assessment Options

Targeted Concepts, Skills, and Nature of Science	How do I know if students got it?
Scientists often work together and then share their findings. Sharing findings makes new information available and helps scientists refine their ideas and build on others' ideas. When another person's or group's idea is used, credit needs to be given.	**ASK:** How did sharing your flip books with other students working on the same plate interactions help you improve your flip books? **LISTEN:** Students should have either reinforced their choices when they discussed them, or they should have identified and addressed weaknesses.
Scientists use models and tools, such as Geographic Information Systems, and a variety of maps to develop claims and explanations from evidence in the data.	**ASK:** How did simulating plate interactions with flip books help you understand how plates interact? **LISTEN:** Students should have used their flipbooks to explore what sequence of events in plate interactions was possible. Students should realize that because plate interactions take place on a large scale, they would not have been able to observe this directly.

NOTES

....

....

....

....

....

Targeted Concepts, Skills, and Nature of Science	How do I know if students got it?
Earth is a system made up of different layers, each with a distinctive composition and set of characteristics. These layers interact, driving the processes that shape Earth.	**ASK:** How does the mantle interact with the crust in divergent plate movement? How does it interact with the crust in oceanic-continental convergent movement? **LISTEN:** Students should recognize that convection currents carry oceanic plates away from each other. Magma from the mantle rises into the gap between the plates, and creates new crust. They should recognize that convection currents also drive oceanic plates into continental plates at convergent boundaries. At these boundaries, the mantle melts and destroys oceanic crust as it sinks below continental crust.
Interactions between Earth's crustal plates can result in mountain building, rift valleys, and geologic activity such as earthquakes and volcanoes. Underwater volcanic activity may form underwater mountains, which can thrust above the ocean's surface to become islands.	**ASK:** How do mountains form due to continental-continental convergent movement? How do mountains form due to oceanic-oceanic divergent motion? **LISTEN:** Students should describe how two continental plates come together and push upwards. They should also describe how two oceanic plates move apart, and magma flows up to form mountains.

NOTES

....

....

Targeted Concepts, Skills, and Nature of Science	How do I know if students got it?
The way in which plates collide depends on the density of the interacting plates. Continental crust is less dense than oceanic crust and, therefore, has greater buoyancy. This causes continental crust to float over the denser oceanic crust when these plates converge.	**ASK:** Why does oceanic crust move under continental crust where they come together? **LISTEN:** Students should explain that oceanic crust is denser than continental crust, and its greater density causes it to move under the continental crust.
New crust is formed at the mid-ocean ridge where the plates move apart. Oceanic crust is destroyed when it collides with continental crust and is subducted. In this way, Earth's crust is recycled.	**ASK:** How is crust added at the mid-ocean ridge? What happens to crust where there are oceanic-continental convergent movements? **LISTEN:** Students should be able to describe how magma rising in the gap where plates move apart builds mountains. They should also be able to describe how oceanic crust moves into the mantle at oceanic-continental convergent boundaries.

Teacher Reflection Questions

- What investigative questions did students record? How will they answer these questions?

- What evidence do you have that students are applying what they have observed to understanding the relationship between earthquakes and volcanoes? What can you do to engage students in learning about earthquakes and volcanoes?

- What management issues came up during group meetings and presentations? What can you do to address these issues in the future?

6.2 Read

How Do Scientist Describe the Interactions Between Moving Plates?

◀ *1 class period*

A class period is considered to be one 40 to 50 minute class.

Overview

Students are introduced to the basic terms and concepts used to describe plate boundary interactions. They work with their partners to read descriptions of the plate interactions they simulated, and record any new information in a table. They meet with the groups they completed their flip books with and share the information they recorded from their reading. They identify regions they think have the type of plate boundary interactions they have read about. The groups revise their flip books and prepare presentations to share what they have learned with the class. The class discusses which regions have which type of plate interaction. After the discussion, pairs reflect on what they have learned and update their *Region Project Boards*. In the *More to Learn* segment, they read about basaltic and andesitic magma.

Targeted Concepts, Skills, and Nature of Science	Performance Expectations
Scientists often work together and then share their findings. Sharing findings makes new information available and helps scientists refine their ideas and build on others' ideas. When another person's or group's idea is used, credit needs to be given.	Students should identify regions with the type of plate interactions they are studying and develop presentations with their groups. They should present what they learned to the class, and discuss which regions have which types of plate interactions.
Scientists must keep clear, accurate, and descriptive records of what they do so they can share their work with others and consider what they did, why they did it, and what they want to do next.	Students should record new information about plate interactions on their *Plate Interactions: Boundaries and Zones* pages.

Targeted Concepts, Skills, and Nature of Science	Performance Expectations
Earth is a system made up of different layers, each with a distinctive composition and set of characteristics. These layers interact, driving the processes that shape Earth.	Students should be able to describe the role the mantle plays in the types of plate interaction they read about, and in the production of different types of magma.
Scientists use models and tools, such as Geographic Information Systems, and a variety of maps to develop claims and explanations from evidence in the data.	Students should revise their flip books to represent the new information they have learned.
Interactions between Earth's crustal plates can result in mountain building, rift valleys, and geologic activity such as earthquakes and volcanoes. Underwater volcanic activity may form underwater mountains, which can thrust above the ocean's surface to become islands.	Students should be able to describe how subduction zones, buckling zones, divergent boundaries, and rift zones cause mountain building, rift valleys, islands, and geologic activities such as earthquakes and volcanoes.
The way in which plates collide depends on the density of the interacting plates. Continental crust is less dense than oceanic crust and, therefore, has greater buoyancy. This causes continental crust to float over the denser oceanic crust when these plates converge.	Students should be able to describe how the density of plates that converge affects the type of movement zone that results.
New crust is formed at the mid-ocean ridge where the plates move apart. Oceanic crust is destroyed when it collides with continental crust and is subducted. In this way, Earth's crust is recycled.	Students should be able to describe how new crust is added at divergent boundaries and how ridges form. Students may be able to identify converging plates at opposite sides of a divergent boundary and the recycling of Earth's crust.
Plate interactions may be classified into zones including rift zones, subduction zones, buckling zones, and transform zones. Patterns in Earthquake and volcano data help scientists identify these zones.	Students should be able to describe the different plate interactions and how they are classified into different zones based on the patterns found in earthquake, volcano, and topographic data.

Materials	
1 per student	*Plate Interactions: Boundaries and Zones* page *Region Project Board* page
1 per pair	Plate interaction flip books (made in *Section 6.1*)
1 per group	Poster pages

Homework Options

Reflection

- **Science Content:** Describe what happens to the magma in buckling zones, subduction zones, and rift zones? *(Students should describe the convection currents of the magma to show how plates move to create a given type of zone, and they should discuss the formation of volcanoes.)*

NOTES

....

....

....

....

....

....

....

NOTES

SECTION 6.2 IMPLEMENTATION

◄ 1 class period*

6.2 Read

How Do Scientists Describe the Interactions Between Moving Plates?

You just observed in the animations that different types of plate interactions result in different types of geologic activity. In this section, you will learn more about the ways plates interact. This will help you better explain the geologic activity in your region. After learning how scientists describe plate interactions, you will read to find out more detail about one of the ways plates interact. You will then report what you have learned to the class.

EE 221

EVER-CHANGING EARTH

6.2 Read

How Do Scientists Describe the Interactions Between Moving Plates?

5 min

Students are introduced to the activity.

○ Engage

Ask students what questions they still have about how plates interact. Review the investigative questions on the *Project Board* if necessary. Tell students they will now learn more about how plates interact. Emphasize that learning about how plates interact will help them explain the geologic activity in their regions.

*A class period is considered to be one 40 to 50 minute class.

How Scientists Describe Plate Interactions

10 min

Students discuss the basic terms used to describe plate interactions.

How Scientists Describe Plate Interactions

convergent boundary: a plate boundary where two plates are moving toward each other.

converge: to move together, toward each other.

subduction zone: an area where the edge of one plate moves under another plate at a convergent boundary.

buckling zone: an area where plates push against each other making large folds in the rock.

divergent boundary: a boundary where two plates are moving away from each other.

diverge: to move away from each other.

rift zone: a valley that is caused as two continental plates diverge.

transform boundary: a boundary where two plates are moving sideways along each other's edge.

Scientists use specific terms when talking about plate movements and interactions. Understanding the meaning of these terms can help you learn about what scientists think happen at places where Earth's plates meet.

In some places where Earth's plates meet, they are moving toward each other. When plates are moving toward each other, scientists call the place where they meet a **convergent boundary**. To **converge** means two things have moved toward each other. As you saw in the animations, in some areas where plates converge, the edge of one plate moves under another one. Scientists call an area where one plate moves under another a **subduction zone**. In other areas where plates converge, they push against each other. If there is enough force pushing the plates together, the edge of one or both plates will crumple, forming large folds in the rock. An area where plates push against each other making large folds in the rock is called a **buckling zone.**

Scientists refer to a boundary where two plates are moving away from each other as a **divergent boundary**. To **diverge** means to move away from each other. When there is a divergent boundary between two plates of continental crust, a valley can begin to form in the gap that grows between the plates. As this valley grows wider, it takes on a characteristic form. Often there are faults along the valley, and rivers can flow into the valley, filling it with water. This sort of valley that is caused as two continental plates diverge is called a **rift zone**.

Plates can also slide sideways past another plate. Or, two plates may slide in opposite directions past each other. A boundary where two plates are moving sideways along each other's edge is called a **transform boundary**. The movement between plates is sideways at a transform boundary. Since the plates do not move toward each other or away from each other at a transform boundary, no crust is created or destroyed. However, a transform boundary can still cause many changes to Earth's crust. Most transform boundaries occur between two plates under an ocean, but a few occur on land, between plates of continental crust.

EE 222

△ Guide

Introduce the basic terms that students will be using to learn about and describe plate interactions. You may wish to use the students' completed flip books or the animations to demonstrate what each of the terms refers to.

First introduce the term convergent boundary. You can hold up flip books that simulate interactions at convergent boundaries. Tell students that at a convergent boundary, plates are moving toward each other. The word converge means two things moves toward each other.

Then discuss the two types of convergent boundaries. When the edge of one plate moves under the other, the boundary is called a subduction zone. Students saw an example of this in the oceanic-continental convergent plate movement animation. Let them know when the edges of two plates push against each other and crumple, the boundary is called a buckling zone. Students saw an example of this in the continental-continental convergent plate movement animation.

Introduce the term divergent boundary. You can hold up flip books that simulate interactions at divergent boundaries. Tell students that a divergent boundary is a boundary where plates are moving away from each other. The word diverge means two things are moving away from each other.

Discuss what happens when there is a divergent boundary between two plates of continental crust. A valley can form in the gap between the two plates, often with faults along it and rivers flowing into it. This type of valley is known as a rift zone.

Introduce the term transform boundary. A transform boundary is a boundary where two plates slide past each other. Crust is not made nor destroyed at transform boundaries, but many changes can take place on Earth's surface above a transform boundary.

NOTES

....

....

....

....

....

....

....

....

Procedure

10 min

Students read descriptions of the plate interactions they simulated and record new information.

Procedure

On the following pages are four descriptions of the different way plates interact at their edges. You will read the description of the plate interaction you simulated with your flip book. Then you will share what you have learned with the class. Through sharing, everyone in the class will have the opportunity to learn about all of the different types of boundaries and interactions.

Work with your partner to read and understand the description of the plate interaction you are assigned. While you are reading, think about the following questions, and record answers to them in the appropriate column of a *Plate Interactions: Boundaries and Zones* page.

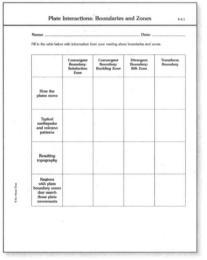

- How are the plates moving in this kind of zone?

- What earthquake and volcano patterns are associated with this type of plate interaction?

- What Earth structures and topography result from this type of plate interaction?

- Which regions do you think have this type of plate interactions?

- How can you make the simulation in your flip book more accurate?

When you finish reading the description and answering the questions, re-label your flip book, if needed, to make it more accurate.

EE 223

EVER-CHANGING EARTH

△ Guide

Tell students they will read a description of the plate interaction that they simulated with their flip book. Then they will present what they have learned to the class.

Distribute *Plate Interactions: Boundaries and Zones* pages and go over the bulleted questions in student text. They should record answers to the first four questions in the corresponding row of their *Plate Interactions: Boundaries and Zones* page. Emphasize that they should be thinking about the fifth question *How can you make the simulation in your flip book more accurate?* as they work.

Have students work with their partners to read the description of their plate interaction and answer the questions. Tell them that they should revise their flip books if they think they are not completely accurate.

△ Guide and Assess

As students read descriptions of their plate interactions, assess how they are identifying and using new information. Ask them what ideas they are recording in their *Plate Interactions: Boundaries and Zones* pages and whether they need to revise their flip books.

NOTES

Subduction Zones

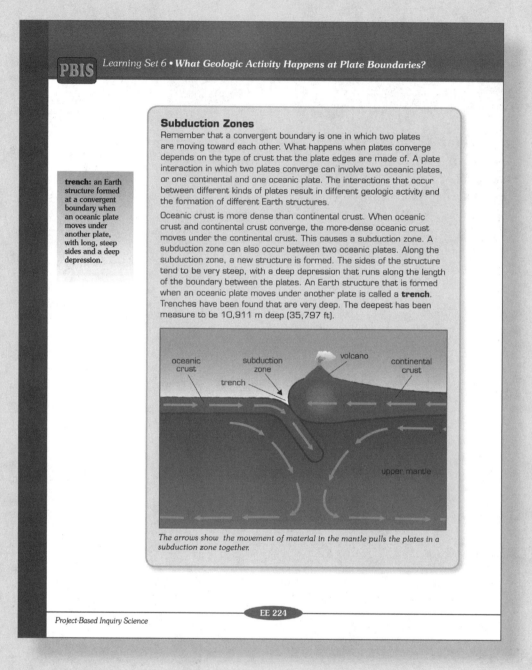

Subduction Zones

Remember that a convergent boundary is one in which two plates are moving toward each other. What happens when plates converge depends on the type of crust that the plate edges are made of. A plate interaction in which two plates converge can involve two oceanic plates, or one continental and one oceanic plate. The interactions that occur between different kinds of plates result in different geologic activity and the formation of different Earth structures.

Oceanic crust is more dense than continental crust. When oceanic crust and continental crust converge, the more-dense oceanic crust moves under the continental crust. This causes a subduction zone. A subduction zone can also occur between two oceanic plates. Along the subduction zone, a new structure is formed. The sides of the structure tend to be very steep, with a deep depression that runs along the length of the boundary between the plates. An Earth structure that is formed when an oceanic plate moves under another plate is called a **trench**. Trenches have been found that are very deep. The deepest has been measure to be 10,911 m deep (35,797 ft).

trench: an Earth structure formed at a convergent boundary when an oceanic plate moves under another plate, with long, steep sides and a deep depression.

The arrows show the movement of material in the mantle pulls the plates in a subduction zone together.

△ Guide and Assess

Pairs working on subduction zones should record information about trenches and consider how this information changes their understanding of geologic processes at subduction zones.

Thinking about what happens to the sinking plate can help explain the geologic activity that happens in subduction zones. As the edge of the sinking plate moves down toward the mantle, it becomes hotter and hotter. Eventually it is destroyed as the edges of the plate melt from the high temperatures in the mantle and form magma. This creates pockets of magma beneath the upper plate. This magma rises because it is hotter and, therefore, less dense than the surrounding mantle material. As the magma makes its way back toward the crust, it melts its way through rocks of the crust. This melted crust mixes with the rising magma, changing its composition. If it makes its way to the surface, it breaks through as a volcanic eruption, forming a volcanic mountain or island.

Since oceanic crust is denser than continental crust, oceanic crust always sinks when continental crust and oceanic crust collide. If the two converging plates are both oceanic, then the older, denser ocean plate will be the one to sink. Oceanic crust includes rocks and sediments that contain large numbers of water molecules. This means that huge amounts of water are carried deep within Earth. As it moves towards the mantle, the water turns to steam. This sets up conditions for very explosive volcanic eruptions.

There can be earthquakes in subduction zones also. Friction between the top of the sinking plate and bottom of the floating plate can cause earthquakes as far as 700 km (435 mi) below the surface of Earth. These earthquakes, which may create new cracks in the crust, can also contribute to volcanic activity.

Mount St. Helens is located in a subduction zone. The denser Juan de Fuca oceanic plate is pushed beneath the North American plate made up of rocks with lower densities. As you can see, the eruption of Mount St. Helens in 1980 was very explosive. Volcanoes along subduction zones eject slow-moving lava and various sizes of volcanic particles.

NOTES

....

....

....

△ Guide and Assess

Below are sample answers to the bulleted questions in the student text.

Subduction Boundaries

How are the plates moving in this kind of zone?	*The plates converge. The denser plate moves under the less-dense plate. If one plate is oceanic and one plate is continental, the oceanic plate moves under the continental plate. If both plates are oceanic, the older, denser plate moves under the newer plate.*
What earthquake and volcano patterns are associated with this type of plate interaction?	*Earthquakes happen in a narrow band. They usually happen deep below the surface. Volcanoes happen in a narrow line right next to the earthquakes.*
What Earth structures and topography result from this type of plate interaction?	*Trenches. A trench is a deep depression with steep sides.*
Which regions do you think have this type of plate interaction?	*Java Trench, Mount Fuji or the Japan Trench, the Andes or the Baja Peninsula*

NOTE: Students will discuss which regions have this type of plate interaction with the class later, and it is not necessary for them to identify all of the regions accurately at this point.

Ask students working on subduction zones what ideas they have for revising their flip books. The pictures of how to illustrate plate interactions at subduction zones in their text may give them ideas.

NOTES

....

....

....

....

....

Subduction Zones

To illustrate a subduction zone: Use your two hands to represent two plates next to each other, sliding the edge of one hand under the other. This is subduction. The edge on the top hand gets pushed up as the bottom hand pushes under.

Label subduction zones:

Mark each subduction zone with this symbol:

Draw arrows to show that the two plates are moving together:

What Does the Geologic Activity at a Subduction Zone Look Like?

- Earthquakes happen in a narrow band.
- Volcanoes happen in a narrow line right next to the line of earthquakes.
- Earthquakes generally happen deep below the surface as one plate sinks beneath the other.
- A deep trench is next to a line of steep volcanic mountains.

NOTES

....

....

Buckling Zones

Buckling Zones

Remember that a convergent boundary is one in which two plates are moving toward each other. What happens when plates converge depends on the type of curst that the plate edges are made of. A convergent plate interaction can involve two oceanic plates or one continental and one oceanic plate. The interactions that occur between different kinds of plates result in different geologic activity and the formation of different Earth structures. Buckling zones are regions along convergent plate boundaries where two continental plates of equal density converge. As the two plates slowly collide, the enormous force causes rocks at the edges of the plates to buckle. The edges of these plates thicken and push upward, forming large, folded mountain ranges. Some of the largest and highest mountain ranges in the world were created in this way. Some mountain ranges, such as the Himalayas, are still being pushed up today as the plates involved continue to collide.

The movement of material in the mantle pulls the plates in a buckling zone together. Because these two plates are of equal density, the two plates push up together to form large mountain ranges such as the Himalayas.

To visualize what happens in a buckling zone, think about what might happen if you pushed two graham crackers together. Graham crackers are thick and crumbly, similar to continental crust. Two graham crackers also have the same density. When you push the two crackers into each other, the edges crumble and create smaller bits. Imagine those small bits as giant rocks that push up, forming a mountain range.

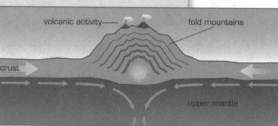

When two plates push against each other with enough force to fold the rocks at the edges, they create a lot of heat. The heat causes some of the continental crust on the edges to melt. The crust that melts mixes with mantle material beneath the plates to create magma. This melting could cause volcanoes, but usually the crust is so thick at a buckling zone that the magma remains underground. When volcanic eruptions occur in buckling zones, they usually eject hot rock, ash, and slow-moving lava.

The Appalachian Mountains, extending from Maine to Georgia, are among the oldest mountains on Earth. Their formation began over a billion years ago through a series of collisions between plates of continental crust. As the continents collided, their edges buckled to form the majestic Appalachian range.

EE 227

EVER-CHANGING EARTH

△ Guide and Assess

Pairs working on buckling zones should record information about folded mountain ranges and consider how this information changes their understanding of geologic processes at buckling zones.

Below are sample answers to the bulleted questions in the student text.

Buckling Zones	
How are the plates moving in this kind of zone?	*The plates are converging. Because they are of equal density, neither plate sinks under the other. Instead, they buckle and plates rise up at their edges.*
What earthquake and volcano patterns are associated with this type of plate interaction?	*The earthquakes are scattered, and they occur near the surface. There are few volcanoes. They are scattered, and their eruptions eject rock, ash, and slow-flowing lava.*
What Earth structures and topography result from this type of plate interaction?	*A buckling zone will have a large, folded mountain range.*
Which regions do you think have this type of plate interaction?	*Himalayas or Mount Everest*

NOTE: Students will discuss which regions have this type of plate interaction with the class later, and it is not necessary for them to identify all of the regions accurately at this point.

Ask students working on buckling zones what ideas they have for revising their flip books. The pictures of how to illustrate plate interactions at buckling zones in their text may give them ideas.

NOTES

....

....

....

....

Buckling Zones

To illustrate a buckling zone:
Use your two hands to represent two plates next to each other. Push your two hands against each other, with the touching edges rising up together like a mountain. This is buckling.

Label buckling zones:

Mark each buckling zone with this symbol:	Draw arrows to show that the two plates are moving together:

What Does the Geologic Activity at a Buckling Zone Look Like?

- Earthquakes happen in a scattered pattern.
- Volcanoes are few and scattered.
- Earthquakes generally happen near the surface.
- A large, folded mountain range sits on continental crust.

NOTES

....

....

....

Divergent Boundaries and Rift Zones

A divergent boundary is a region where two plates are spreading away from each other. Diverging plates move away from each other very slowly as a result of the movement of mantle material underneath. As plates move apart, magma rises from the mantle. It pushes up the crust at the edges of the plates, eventually breaking through the plate boundary and creating new crust at the point where the plates pulled apart. The Mid-Atlantic Ridge is an underwater mountain range created at this type of plate boundary.

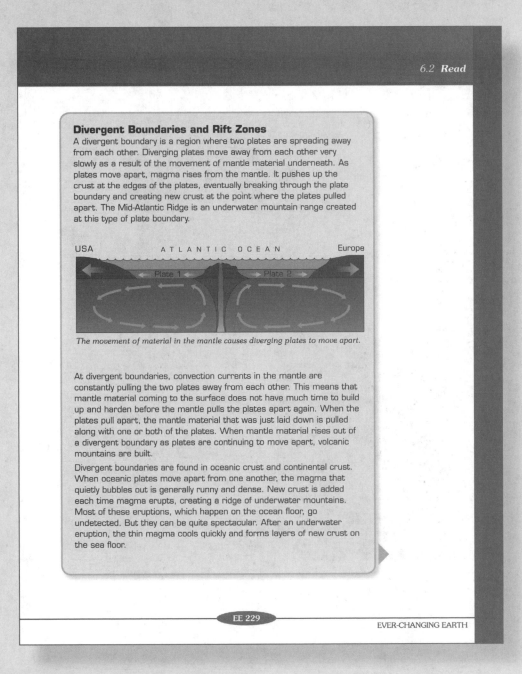

The movement of material in the mantle causes diverging plates to move apart.

At divergent boundaries, convection currents in the mantle are constantly pulling the two plates away from each other. This means that mantle material coming to the surface does not have much time to build up and harden before the mantle pulls the plates apart again. When the plates pull apart, the mantle material that was just laid down is pulled along with one or both of the plates. When mantle material rises out of a divergent boundary as plates are continuing to move apart, volcanic mountains are built.

Divergent boundaries are found in oceanic crust and continental crust. When oceanic plates move apart from one another, the magma that quietly bubbles out is generally runny and dense. New crust is added each time magma erupts, creating a ridge of underwater mountains. Most of these eruptions, which happen on the ocean floor, go undetected. But they can be quite spectacular. After an underwater eruption, the thin magma cools quickly and forms layers of new crust on the sea floor.

Divergent Boundaries and Rift Zones

△ Guide and Assess

Pairs working on divergent boundaries and rift zones should record information about folded mountain ranges and consider how this information changes their understanding of geologic processes at divergent boundaries and rift zones.

rifting: surface cracking that occurs at a divergent boundary beneath continental crust.

rift valley: a valley formed when the thin crust between spreading plates sinks.

The Great Rift Valley, located in Kenya, Africa, is a large rift in Earth's crust that literally tears Kenya down the length of the country for thousands of kilometers.

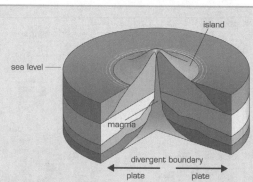

Sometimes the underwater mountains that are formed at divergent boundaries surface above the water and become islands. The island of Surtsey in the North Atlantic Ocean was formed by this process.

When a divergent boundary occurs beneath continental crust, **rifting**, or surface cracking, occurs. Rifting begins as hotter than normal magma causes thick continental crust to bulge. As the crust continues to bulge, it is stretched thin and cracks occur. To understand this better, think of a cake baking in the oven. As it rises, it stretches the outer crust until cracks form in the top of the cake.

In Earth's crust, the diverging plates are pulled apart by convection in the mantle, eventually causing a tear. Faults form on either side of the tear and the thin crust between the spreading plates sinks to form a valley between two mountain ranges. These are called **rift valleys**. Over millions of years, as the two plates continue to diverge, a rift valley can sink so low that it is below sea level. As sea water moves in, new oceans are formed.

NOTES

....

....

....

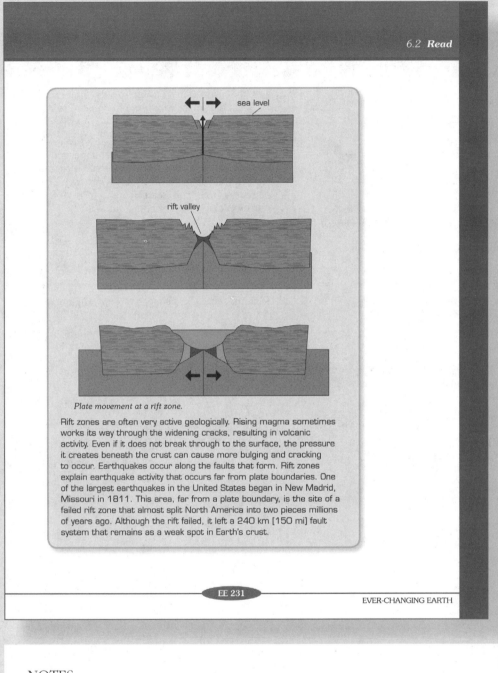

Plate movement at a rift zone.

Rift zones are often very active geologically. Rising magma sometimes works its way through the widening cracks, resulting in volcanic activity. Even if it does not break through to the surface, the pressure it creates beneath the crust can cause more bulging and cracking to occur. Earthquakes occur along the faults that form. Rift zones explain earthquake activity that occurs far from plate boundaries. One of the largest earthquakes in the United States began in New Madrid, Missouri in 1811. This area, far from a plate boundary, is the site of a failed rift zone that almost split North America into two pieces millions of years ago. Although the rift failed, it left a 240 km [150 mi] fault system that remains as a weak spot in Earth's crust.

NOTES

....

....

....

Below are sample answers to the bulleted questions in the student text.

Divergent Boundaries and Rift Zones

How are the plates moving in this kind of zone?	*The plates are moving away from each other. Magma rises up in the gap, forming new crust.*
What earthquake and volcano patterns are associated with this type of plate interaction?	*Divergent boundaries typically have narrow bands of earthquakes. When the boundary is underwater, there are a few scattered volcanoes around the line of earthquakes. When the boundary is on land, the volcanoes form a narrow band.*
What Earth structures and topography result from this type of plate interaction?	*A narrow ridge of volcanic mountains or narrow ridges of mountains with a valley between them is typically formed in this interaction.*
Which regions do you think have this type of plate interaction?	*Iceland, Great Rift Valley, or Mount Kilimanjaro*

NOTE: Students will discuss which regions have this type of plate interaction with the class later, and it is not necessary for them to identify all of the regions accurately at this point.

Ask students working on divergent boundaries and rift zones what ideas they have for revising their flip books. The pictures of how to illustrate plate interactions at divergent boundaries and rift zones in their text may give them ideas.

NOTES

Divergent Boundaries

To illustrate a divergent boundary: Use your two hands to represent two plates next to each other. Have a partner push his or her hands up, in between your hands, representing the rising magma as the plates move apart.

Label divergent boundaries:

Mark each rift zone with this symbol:

Draw arrows to show that the two plates are moving apart:

What Does the Geologic Activity at a Divergent Boundary Look Like?

- Earthquakes are shallow and small. The data pattern forms a narrow band or line of earthquakes.

- If volcanoes are under water, there are a few scattered volcanoes near the line of earthquakes. If volcanoes are on land, they appear as a narrow band.

- There is a narrow ridge of volcanic mountains or a narrow ridge of mountains with a valley in between.

NOTES

....

....

....

What Is a Transform Boundary?

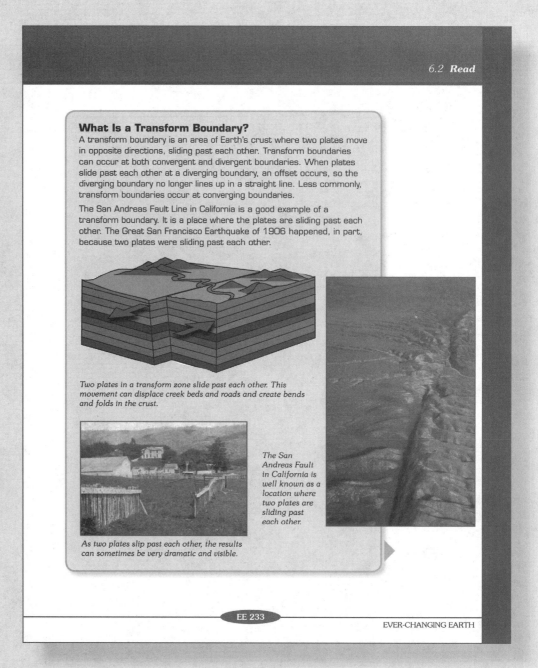

What Is a Transform Boundary?

A transform boundary is an area of Earth's crust where two plates move in opposite directions, sliding past each other. Transform boundaries can occur at both convergent and divergent boundaries. When plates slide past each other at a diverging boundary, an offset occurs, so the diverging boundary no longer lines up in a straight line. Less commonly, transform boundaries occur at converging boundaries.

The San Andreas Fault Line in California is a good example of a transform boundary. It is a place where the plates are sliding past each other. The Great San Francisco Earthquake of 1906 happened, in part, because two plates were sliding past each other.

Two plates in a transform zone slide past each other. This movement can displace creek beds and roads and create bends and folds in the crust.

The San Andreas Fault in California is well known as a location where two plates are sliding past each other.

As two plates slip past each other, the results can sometimes be very dramatic and visible.

EE 233

EVER-CHANGING EARTH

Pairs working on transform boundaries should record information about faults and consider how this information changes their understanding of geologic processes at divergent boundaries and rift zones.

Below are sample answers to the bulleted questions in the student text.

Transform Boundaries

How are the plates moving in this kind of zone?	*The plates may be convergent or divergent, but at transform boundaries, they slide past each other.*
What earthquake and volcano patterns are associated with this type of plate interaction?	*There are typically a lot of earthquakes in various patterns at these boundaries. Volcanoes are not explicitly addressed in the reading, but transform boundaries are not associated with volcanoes.*
What Earth structures and topography result from this type of plate interaction?	*Large faults form at transform boundaries.*
Which regions do you think have this type of plate interaction?	*San Andreas Fault*

NOTE: Students will discuss which regions have this type of plate interaction with the class later, and it is not necessary for them to identify all of the regions accurately at this point.

Ask students working on transform boundaries what ideas they have for revising their flip books. The pictures of how to illustrate plate interactions at transform boundaries in their text may give them ideas.

NOTES

Transform Boundaries

To illustrate a transform boundary: Use your two hands to represent two plates next to each other. Keeping the edges of your hands touching, move both hands, sliding one past the other.

Label transform boundaries:

Mark each transform zone with this symbol:	Draw arrows to show that the two plates are sliding past each other:

What Does the Geologic Activity at a Transform Boundary Look Like?

Transform boundaries are difficult to identify from earthquake and volcano data. You can identify all other plate boundary predictions and then try to predict which remaining boundaries must be transform boundaries.

- Lots of earthquakes.
- Volcanoes occur in a variety of patterns.

NOTES

....

....

....

6.2 Read

Conference

After you have read your article, get together with the same small group you worked with on the flip book. Review and revise your flip book, making sure it reflects what you read in the section about the plate boundary. Share the notes on your *Plate Interactions* pages. If you disagree with others, review the article and see if that helps you come to an agreement. If you cannot agree, make a note of it so you can investigate it further.

Together, prepare a poster summarizing what you learned about your type of plate interaction. Your poster should include your type of plate boundary or zone, the data patterns associated with it, a description of how plates move in these regions, the resulting changes in the topography, and the Earth structures your class has been investigating that you think resulted from each type of interaction. Make sure your poster has all the information your classmates need to understand your kind of boundary or zone and its interactions. Make the poster neat and organized enough so your classmates will be able to find information they need.

Decide how you are going to make your presentation. Everybody in the group should have a chance to be part of the presentation. You may use a drawing describing your boundary type or zone, your poster, and your flip books in your presentation. Use these visuals to help you clearly present the way the plates are moving, the earthquake and volcano patterns those kinds of movements create, and the kinds of landforms that are created by your type of plate interaction. Two people should use their hands to model the plate boundary or zone that is being presented. At the end of your presentation, be prepared to share your ideas about the regions with geologic activity that matches your type of zone.

EE 235

EVER-CHANGING EARTH

Conference
10 min

Students meet with their groups to prepare presentations.

△ Guide

When students have finished reading about their type of plate interactions, have them meet with the groups they made their flip books with. Tell them they will begin by reviewing their flip books and sharing ideas they have for revising them. They will work together to revise their flip books. Tell them they will also share notes on their *Plate Interactions* pages. If they disagree about any of their notes, they should review the article in the student text and try to come to an agreement. If they cannot come to an agreement, they should note their disagreement for further investigation.

⬡ Get Going

Distribute poster materials and tell students they will prepare posters summarizing what they learned about their types of plate interaction. Tell them what information should be included in their posters—the type of plate boundary or zone, the earthquake and volcano patterns associated with it, a description of how plates move in the region, the resulting topography, and Earth structures the class has been studying that could result from the type of interaction. Emphasize that rest of the class will be learning from their presentations, so their posters need to clearly communicate what they learned about the plate interaction.

Emphasize that students should think about how they will present what they learned. They should ensure that everyone in the group will take part in the presentation. Together, they need to clearly show the way the plates are moving, what earthquake and volcano patterns are caused by their type of plate interactions, and what Earth structures and topography are created by their type of plate interaction. Two people in the group should use their hands to model the plate boundary or zone. They may also use drawings, their poster, and their flip books to aid their presentation.

NOTES

Communicate

Investigation Expo

When it is your turn to share with the class what you have read, begin by naming the type of boundary or zone you have read about. Then use the drawing describing your zone, your poster, and your flip books to teach the class about your boundary or zone type.

Plate Interactions: Boundaries and Zones   6.2.1

Name: _____   Date: _____

Fill in the table below with information from your reading about boundaries and zones.

	Convergent Boundary: Subduction Zone	Convergent Boundary: Buckling Zone	Divergent Boundary: Rift Zone	Transform Boundary
How the plates move				
Typical earthquake and volcano patterns				
Resulting topography				
Regions with plate boundary zones that match these plate movements				

As you listen to others, record what you are learning about each plate boundary in your *Plate Interactions: Boundaries and Zones* page. If you do not understand something that is presented, ask clarification questions. You may find that you disagree about the examples of each boundary or zone type. Save discussion of these disagreements for after everybody has presented.

After all the groups have presented, spend some time as a class discussing which Earth structures you think developed from which kinds of plate interactions. Be sure to provide evidence when you present your ideas. Your class will probably have disagreements. And for some of the regions, you may think that none of the plate interactions match. You may want to add questions to the *Project Board*.

Communicate: Investigation Expo

15 min

Groups present and the class discusses which regions and Earth structures resulted from these plate interactions.

⬡ Get Going

Have groups present. Emphasize that students in the audience should record what they are learning in their *Plate Interactions: Boundaries and Zones* pages as they listen. Remind students to ask questions if anything is unclear. If they disagree with the examples of regions where a type of plate interaction occurs that a group identified, they should wait until after all groups have presented to discuss their disagreement.

△ Guide and Assess

After all groups have presented, lead a class discussion determining which Earth structures developed from which kinds of plate interactions. Emphasize that students should support their ideas with evidence.

Students' ideas about which type of plate interactions occur at certain regions will be educated guesses in some cases, rather than positive identifications. They should understand that scientists, too, can often only make hypotheses about what happens below Earth's surface.

META NOTES

For ease of discussion, students will try to identify regions with types of plate interactions. However, in some cases there will be more than one type of plate interaction in a region. There may be more than one plate boundary in a region, and a single plate may have more than one type of boundary in close proximity. If students begin to talk about specific plate boundaries instead of regions, point out that this is a more accurate way to discuss plate interactions.

NOTES

6.2 Read

Reflect

Working with your partner, answer these questions. Some are about your region and Earth structure.

1. Use the chart you made to answer the following questions:

   • At which types of boundaries or in which types of zones is material being added to the crust?

   • At which types of boundaries or in which types of zones is crust being destroyed?

   • What causes one plate to slip beneath another plate?

   • Most earthquakes happen near the surface in thin crust. At which types of boundaries or in which types of zones do earthquakes happen deep below the surface? Why?

2. You now know the patterns of geologic activity that are usually associated with each type of plate interaction and boundary zone. Which pattern matches the pattern of earthquakes and volcanoes you observed in your region? What does that tell you about the type of boundary and zone in your region?

3. Now that you know what kind of boundary and zone you have in your region, you might want to revise your prediction about how the plates are moving. How do you think the plates are moving in your region? Add your ideas to the *What do we think we know?* column of your Region *Project Board.*

What's the Point?

Convergent boundaries occur where two plates are moving toward each other. If the two plates have different densities, the plate with greater density will slip beneath the plate with lower density. The denser plate then sinks into the mantle, and its edges melt and combine with mantle material to make magma. This magma then works its way toward the crust, resulting in volcanic activity. Regions where this is happening are called subduction zones. The interaction of plates in a subduction zone also causes earthquakes deep within the Earth.

EE 237

Reflect

10 min

Students answer the Reflect *questions with their partners.*

△ Guide and Assess

Have students work with their partners to answer the *Reflect* questions.

As pairs answer the *Reflect* questions, monitor their progress and assess their understanding. Use the following to assess students' responses to the *Reflect* questions:

1. Students should use their *Plate Interactions: Boundaries and Zones* pages to support their answers.

   - Students should identify that material is being added to the crust at divergent boundaries.

   - Students should discuss convergent boundaries. They should identify subduction zones as places where crust is destroyed. At subduction zones, crust is melted into the mantle.

   - Students should describe how when a plate is denser than the plate it is converging with, it slips beneath the other plate.

   - Students should discuss subduction zones. They should describe how earthquakes at subduction zones occur where the sinking plate rubs against the plate above it. This means that the earthquake occurs at the bottom of the upper plate. Since plates are very thick, the earthquake is very deep.

2. Students should use evidence from their *Three-page Maps* and *Volcano Tables,* as well as what they have just learned about patterns of geologic activity associated with each type of plate interaction to identify what type of boundary and zone is in their region.

3. Students should review their predictions on their *Region Project Boards* and revise them as necessary.

NOTES

....

....

....

....

....

....

If the plates at a convergent boundary are of equal density, then the results are different. The edges of the plates crumble and push upward, forming mountain ranges. This kind of region is called a buckling zone.

Diverging boundaries occur where two plates are moving away from each other. When thinner, oceanic plates move away from each other, magma quietly reaches the surface in the gap created by the separation of the two plates, and new crust is formed. This creates a ridge of mountains. As new crust is added at the divergent boundary, older crust moves away from the plate boundary.

Transform boundaries occur where two plates are sliding past each other. This action produces a great deal of stress as the rugged edges of the plates grind past each other. The stress is released as earthquakes.

As you begin to apply this information to your region, you will see how the plate movements and type of crust involved determine the geologic activity in the area.

The stress caused by plates moving past one another at transform boundaries cause earthquakes that can lead to extensive property damage.

Project-Based Inquiry Science

NOTES

....

....

....

More to Learn: Magma

10 min

The class discusses basaltic and andesitic magmas and how they affect volcanic eruptions.

More to Learn

Magma

You have read about magma many times throughout this Unit. Magma has been associated with both earthquakes and volcanoes. But different types of magma form at different plate boundaries. The type of magma determines how volcanoes in the region will erupt. To understand what is happening geographically, you need to know about the type of magma in your region.

Why Do Some Volcanoes Erupt Quietly and Other Explosively?
You know that the way a volcano erupts depends on the composition of the magma. Thinner, runnier magma allows more trapped gases to escape. Without these trapped gases to build pressure, the magma erupts quietly. Thicker magma does not allow trapped gases to escape so easily, resulting in more explosive eruptions.

You have identified the types of volcanoes in your region. From earlier readings, you know which types erupt more explosively and which erupt more quietly. You may then be wondering about the type, or composition, of magma in your region. All magmas come from Earth's mantle. However, magma is formed from different types of rocks and in different environments. For example, the temperature and amount of water in the ground vary in different places. Magmas with higher temperatures are more fluid, or runnier, than magmas with lower temperatures. All magma also contains silica, a combination of silicon and oxygen. Magmas with higher amounts of silica are less fluid than magmas with lower amounts of silica.

There are several types of magmas. Two types of magma important to your work are **basaltic** and **andesitic** magmas.

Basaltic Magma
Compared to other types of magma, basaltic magma has low silica content and high temperatures. It erupts as thin, runny lava from

basaltic magma: a type of magma with low silica content and high temperatures that erupts as thin, runny lava flows and cools to form hard, black volcanic rock.

andesitic magma: a type of magma with high silica content and low temperatures that erupts as thicker, slow-moving lava and cools to form gray to black volcanic rocks.

Pahoehoe is a type of lava that hardens into smooth, rope-like wrinkles.

○ **Engage**

Tell students that different kinds of magma form at different plate boundaries. Ask students if they have any ideas about how different kinds of magma might affect the geologic activity at a plate boundary.

△ Guide

Ask students why they think some volcanoes erupt quietly and others explosively. Students may already have some ideas about this from their reading. They already learned that thin lava allows gases to escape easily, leading to quiet eruptions. Thicker lava traps gases, and leads to explosive eruptions.

Discuss how there are variations in the types of magma in different places. All magmas come from Earth's mantle. All magmas contain silica, a combination of silicon and oxygen. But the amount of silica and temperatures of magmas vary from place to place, as do the amount of water in the ground.

Let students know the two types of magma that will be important for their work are basaltic and andesitic magma.

NOTES

beneath oceanic crust at mid-ocean ridges or shield volcanoes. Most oceanic crust is made of basalt, or rock formed from basaltic magma. Since oceanic crust is thin, the erupting magma does not pass through layers of other rocks that could change its composition. When the lava cools and hardens, it forms hard, black volcanic rock.

Andesitic Magma

Andesitic magma has higher silica content and lower temperatures than basaltic magma. These magmas erupt above areas where two plates come together, one with oceanic crust and the other with continental crust. The denser oceanic crust slips beneath the continental crust and sinks into the mantle. Rocks in the upper part of the oceanic crust contain water. When these rocks sink into the mantle, they take a lot of water with them. As the water is heated, it turns to steam. This adds to the gas content of the magma.

Mount St. Helens is a stratovolcano that erupts very explosively. The magma that erupts from this volcano is andesitic, very thick, and high in silica content.

Recall that oceanic crust is made of basalt. The crust that sinks and melts is basalt. However, this magma travels through thick continental crust to reach Earth's surface. As it does, the magma can mix with silica contained in the continental crust, raising its silica content. It also mixes with other minerals. This changes its composition to that of andesitic magma.

Andesitic magma usually erupts from stratovolcanoes. The thick lava cools to form gray to black volcanic rocks. Due to the explosive nature of these eruptions, these rocks may be blasted into different-sized particles.

Scientists look at eruption patterns and the type of magma produced to try to explain how and why volcanoes work. The type of magma can reveal a lot about what lies beneath Earth's surface. These are significant indirect observations that scientists can use to learn more about Earth's interior.

Discuss the distinguishing features of basaltic magma. It has a relatively low silica content and high temperatures. It erupts as thin, runny lava from beneath oceanic crust at mid-ocean ridges or shield volcanoes. When it cools and hardens it forms hard, black volcanic rock. Most oceanic crust is made of basalt, formed from basaltic magma.

Discuss the distinguishing features of andesitic magma. Andesitic magma has a higher silica content and lower temperatures than basaltic magma. These magmas are found near oceanic-continental subduction zones. Oceanic crust is primarily composed of basalt. This means that it has a relatively low silica content. However, as magma formed from basalt at a subduction zone travels to the surface, it can gain silica and other minerals from the continental crust. This gives it the composition characteristic of andesitic magma. The upper part of the oceanic crust also contains water, which turns into steam as the crust melts into the mantle. This adds gas to the andesitic magma.

Andesitic lava usually erupts from stratovolcanoes. When it cools and hardens, it forms gray to black volcanic rocks. Because stratovolcano eruptions can be very explosive, these rocks are often blasted into smaller particles.

Assessment Options

Targeted Concepts, Skills, and Nature of Science	How do I know if students got it?
Scientists often work together and then share their findings. Sharing findings makes new information available and helps scientists refine their ideas and build on others' ideas. When another person's or group's idea is used, credit needs to be given.	**ASK:** Why was discussing which regions have which types of plate interaction with the class important? **LISTEN:** Students should recognize that each group in the class was able to contribute different ideas and knowledge to the discussion, allowing the class to make decisions based on all of their ideas.
Scientists must keep clear, accurate, and descriptive records of what they do so they can share their work with others and consider what they did, why they did it, and what they want to do next.	**ASK:** Why was it important to update your *Region Project Board*? **LISTEN:** Students should recognize that recording their latest ideas and questions on their *Region Project Board* helped them to track what they have done and to think about what they still need to do.

Targeted Concepts, Skills, and Nature of Science	How do I know if students got it?
Earth is a system made up of different layers, each with a distinctive composition and set of characteristics. These layers interact, driving the processes that shape Earth.	**ASK:** What role does the mantle play in the types of plate interaction? **LISTEN:** Students should recognize that convection currents cause the plates to interact. They should also recognize that the mantle supplies the magma that rises to fill the gaps in divergent boundaries and creates new crust, and destroys old crust at subduction zones.
Interactions between Earth's crustal plates can result in mountain building, rift valleys, and geologic activity such as earthquakes and volcanoes. Underwater volcanic activity may form underwater mountains, which can thrust above the ocean's surface to become islands.	**ASK:** What geologic formations result from plate interactions at subduction zones, buckling zones, divergent boundaries, and rift zones? **LISTEN:** Students should be able to describe how mountain ranges are pushed up at buckling zones and, to a lesser extent at subduction zones. They should describe how mountain ranges, volcanoes, and volcanic islands form at divergent boundaries. They should also describe how valleys, mountains, and volcanoes form at rift zones.

NOTES

....

....

....

....

Targeted Concepts, Skills, and Nature of Science	How do I know if students got it?
The way in which plates collide depends on the density of the interacting plates. Continental crust is less dense than oceanic crust and, therefore, has greater buoyancy. This causes continental crust to float over the denser oceanic crust when these plates converge.	**ASK:** Why is the geologic activity at subduction zones different from the geologic activity at buckling zones? **LISTEN:** Students should explain how the plates at subduction zones have unequal density, while the plates at buckling zones have roughly equal density. This means that at subduction zones, the denser plate moves under the less-dense plate, leading to the earthquakes and volcanoes characteristic of subduction zones; while at buckling zones, the plates push each other up at the edges, leading to the characteristic mountain ranges of buckling zones.
New crust is formed at the mid-ocean ridge where the plates move apart. Oceanic crust is destroyed when it collides with continental crust and is subducted. In this way, Earth's crust is recycled.	**ASK:** How is new crust created at the mid-ocean ridge? How is crust destroyed at subduction zones? **LISTEN:** Students should describe how magma rises in the gaps at divergent boundaries and hardens into new crust. They should also be able to describe how oceanic crust moves into the mantle and melts at subduction zones.

NOTES

Teacher Reflection Options

- What difficulties did students have finding Earth structure regions that fit into each type of zone described?

- How were you able to engage students in presenting what they learned and learning from other students? What might you try next time?

- What difficulties arose as students read with their partners and discussed their ideas with their groups? What could you try next time?

NOTES

6.3 Investigate

What Type of Plate Boundaries and Interactions Are Found in Your Region?

◀ $1\frac{1}{4}$ *class periods*

A class period is
considered to be one
40 to 50 minute class.

Overview

Students begin by considering the plate movement and interaction in the region of the Galapagos Islands. Based on topographic features, volcanic activity, and earthquake activity, they determine what direction each plate in the region is moving and how the plates interact. They work with their partners to identify what types of data they still need to identify how plates are moving and interacting in their regions. Pairs use *My World* to collect this data. They use this data to support or revise their previous inferences about how the plates move and interact in their regions. They discuss their conclusions with other students assigned to the same region and come to an agreement about how plates move and interact. They share their conclusions with the class, and the class reviews and evaluates how compatible their conclusions are and how well they are supported by the data.

Targeted Concepts, Skills, and Nature of Science	Performance Expectations
Scientists often work together and then share their findings. Sharing findings makes new information available and helps scientists refine their ideas and build on others' ideas. When another person or group's idea is used, credit needs to be given.	Students should gather data with their partners, discuss their conclusions with their groups, and discuss how groups' conclusions work together with the class.
Scientists must keep clear, accurate, and descriptive records of what they do so they can share their work with others and consider what they did, why they did it, and what they want to do next.	Students should refer to their records from previous investigations, and revise and refine them as they gather new information.

Targeted Concepts, Skills, and Nature of Science	Performance Expectations
Scientists make claims (conclusions) based on evidence obtained (trends in data) from reliable investigations.	Students should better support or refine their claims about plate movement and interaction in their regions based on evidence obtained using *My World*.
Scientists use models and tools, such as Geographic Information Systems, and a variety of maps to develop claims and explanations from evidence in the data.	Students should gather information from *My World* and use their *Three-page Maps* and the *Big World Map* to organize information.
Earth is a system made up of different layers, each with a distinctive composition and set of characteristics. These layers interact, driving the processes that shape Earth.	Students should determine what evidence indicates the types of plate interactions.
New crust is formed at the mid-ocean ridge where the plates move apart. Oceanic crust is destroyed when it collides with continental crust and is subducted. In this way, Earth's crust is recycled.	Students should be able to identify regions where new crust is being created and regions where old crust is being destroyed.
Plate interactions may be classified into zones including rift zones, subduction zones, buckling zones, and transform zones. Patterns in Earthquake and volcano data help scientists identify these zones.	Students should be able to describe and identify the different zones and types of plate interaction.

NOTES

Materials	
1 per pair	Computer with *My World*
1 per student	*Three-page Map* *Region Project Board* page
1 per class	*Big World Map*

Homework Options

Reflection

- **Science Content:** Which type of volcanoes do you have in your Earth structure region and how does this fit with the movement zones you have found in the region? *(The purpose of this question is for students to consider the connections between volcano types and the type of plate movement.)*

- **Science Content:** Which conclusion do you feel most confident about? Which conclusion do you feel least confident about? Do you have any ideas about what data could make you more confident of these conclusions? Is it possible to be certain of your conclusions given the data available? *(This question is meant to engage students in evaluating their conclusions and supporting evidence. Students should also understand that in some cases scientists can only propose tentative hypotheses.)*

NOTES

....

....

....

....

....

NOTES

SECTION 6.3 IMPLEMENTATION

6.3 Investigate

What Type of Plate Boundaries and Interactions Are Found in Your Region?

You have made some inferences about the types of plate boundaries and plate interactions in your region. In this section, you will have a final opportunity to gather additional data to support those inferences. First, you will look at the example below with your class. As a class, you will try to identify the type of plate boundary and the interactions between the plates in the Galapagos Islands region. Then you will use *My World* to collect data that will help you better identify the plate interactions in and near your region.

Plate Boundaries in the Galapagos Region

Jennifer and Aiden were working with the Galapagos Islands region. The islands are circled in red. They had already determined that there is a plate off the west coast of South America. They identified it as the Nazca Plate. Now they are trying to decide how the plates are moving in the region of the Galapagos Islands. Look at the two data maps below. Volcanoes and three years of medium earthquakes are plotted on the map on the left, and elevation and depth are plotted on the other.

 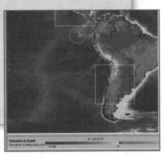

EE 241

EVER-CHANGING EARTH

6.3 Investigate

What Type of Plate Boundaries and Interactions Are Found in Your Region?

5 min

Students are introduced to the activity.

△ Guide

Begin by reminding students that they inferred what types of plate boundaries and plate interactions were present in their regions in *Learning Set 5*. Tell students that in this section they will gather additional data and use what they have learned about zones to support, or revise, those inferences.

*A class period is considered to be one 40 to 50 minute class.

"You have already inferred what types of plate boundaries and plate interactions you have in your region. Now that you know more about the ways plates can interact, you will find more evidence to help you better support your inferences or to revise them."

Plate Boundaries in the Galapagos Region

5 min

Students are introduced to plate motion and interaction in the Galapagos region.

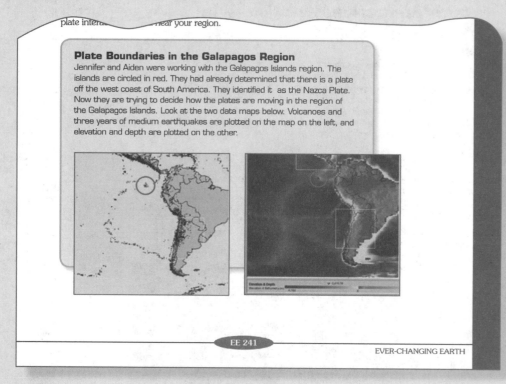

plate intera... ...near your region.

Plate Boundaries in the Galapagos Region

Jennifer and Aiden were working with the Galapagos Islands region. The islands are circled in red. They had already determined that there is a plate off the west coast of South America. They identified it as the Nazca Plate. Now they are trying to decide how the plates are moving in the region of the Galapagos Islands. Look at the two data maps below. Volcanoes and three years of medium earthquakes are plotted on the map on the left, and elevation and depth are plotted on the other.

EE 241

EVER-CHANGING EARTH

△ Guide

Discuss the example of the Galapagos Islands. Describe the scenario: two students, Jennifer and Aiden, were investigating the Galapagos Islands region. Point out that these islands are shown circled in red in the images in student text. Jennifer and Aiden determined that there is a plate off the west coast of South America, which they identified as the Nazca Plate. Now they are trying to determine how the plates are moving in the Galapagos Islands region using the data in the data maps. Ask students how they would determine how the plates are moving in the region using the data maps.

Stop and Think

As a class, answer these questions.

1. What type of plate boundary is in the region of the Galapagos Islands? How do you know?
2. There are other types of plate boundaries around the Nazca Plate. See if you can identify them.
3. In what direction do you think each of the plates is moving?
4. How do you think these plates interact with each other? Why?

Investigate

You will be using *My World* to collect any data you still need to identify the type of plate boundary in your region and the ways your plates are moving. This time, you will not have instructions about exactly what to look for in *My World*. Instead, you will have to figure out which data you need so that you have enough evidence to support a claim about the ways the plates are moving and interacting. For reminders about using *My World*, see *Using My World* at the end of the book.

You have already made inferences about the ways your plates are moving and interacting. *My World* can now be used to find supporting evidence for the inferences you made. You might begin by looking at the patterns of earthquakes and volcanoes near your plate boundary. You might follow up by comparing these patterns to the typical data patterns for each type of boundary or zone.

You should also check if the data patterns in your region match those for any other type of boundary or zone. If so, you may need to collect more data to make a final determination.

Procedure

1. Working with your partner, use *My World* to analyze earthquake and volcano data for the boundaries around your plate. Use the following steps to capture data that you will add to your *Three-page Map*.
   a. **Open the *My World* project file *ESInquiry*.** This is a project file that has information about elevation and depth, earthquakes, and volcanoes.
   b. **Show the volcano layer** and select three years of medium earthquakes.

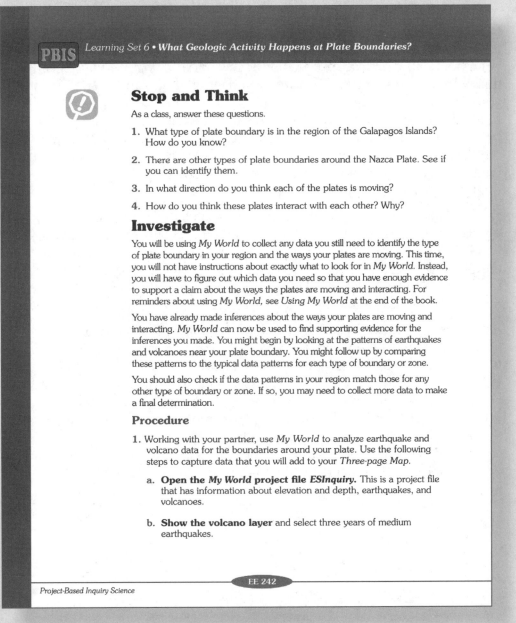

Stop and Think

5 min

The class has a discussion of the Stop and Think *questions.*

△ Guide

As students discuss how they would determine how the plates are moving in the region, draw their attention to the *Stop and Think* questions. Ask students what type of plate boundary is in the region. Based on the elevated ridge on the ocean floor running through the Galapagos Islands and the narrow lines of volcanic and earthquake activity along the ridge, they should identify this as a divergent boundary. They should also be able to explain how the evidence in the maps (the lines of volcanic and earthquake activity and the elevated ridge) support their identification.

Ask students if there are other types of plate boundaries in the region of the Nazca Plate. Can they identify the types? To the east of the Nazca Plate is the South American continent. Along the coast of this continent is a plate boundary with Nazca Plate. Students should recognize that, because this is an oceanic-continental plate boundary, it is probably a subduction zone. The thick bands of earthquakes and volcanoes along the west coast of South America are evidence that this inference is correct. The southern boundary of Nazca is also visible as a ridge and a string of earthquakes in the Pacific. Similar to the northern boundary of Nazca, this is distinguished by an elevated ridge and a narrow line of earthquakes, so it is probably a divergent boundary.

Ask students what direction they think the plates in the region of the Galapagos Islands are moving. Students should recognize that both plates involved in the subduction zone are moving toward each other. In addition, the plates that share divergent boundaries are moving away from each other. This suggests that the Nazca Plate is moving to the east, while the South American Plate and the Pacific Plate are moving west.

Ask students how they think these plates interact with each other. They should apply what they learned from observing animations and creating flip books to answering this question. The boundary between the Nazca Plate and the South American Plate is a subduction zone, so the Nazca Plate is moving under the South American Plate, leading to mountain building, volcanic activity, and earthquakes along the west coast of South America. The oceanic boundaries of the Nazca Plate are both divergent boundaries, so Nazca is moving away from these plates, leading to ocean-floor ridges and volcanoes where magma rises up in the gaps between the plates.

NOTES

....

....

....

....

....

....

Investigate

You will be using *My World* to collect any data you still need to identify the type of plate boundary in your region and the ways your plates are moving. This time, you will not have instructions about exactly what to look for in *My World*. Instead, you will have to figure out which data you need so that you have enough evidence to support a claim about the ways the plates are moving and interacting. For reminders about using *My World,* see *Using My World* at the end of the book.

You have already made inferences about the ways your plates are moving and interacting. *My World* can now be used to find supporting evidence for the inferences you made. You might begin by looking at the patterns of earthquakes and volcanoes near your plate boundary. You might follow up by comparing these patterns to the typical data patterns for each type of boundary or zone.

You should also check if the data patterns in your region match those for any other type of boundary or zone. If so, you may need to collect more data to make a final determination.

Procedure

1. Working with your partner, use *My World* to analyze earthquake and volcano data for the boundaries around your plate. Use the following steps to capture data that you will add to your *Three-page Map.*

   a. **Open the *My World* project file *ESInquiry*.** This is a project file that has information about elevation and depth, earthquakes, and volcanoes.

   b. **Show the volcano layer** and select three years of medium earthquakes.

Project-Based Inquiry Science

Investigate

10 min

Students collect any remaining data they need for identifying the type of plate boundary and plate movements in their region.

△ Guide

Let students know that now that they better understand how plates move and what affects geologic activity at plate boundaries, they will use *My World* to collect data to identify the type of plate boundary in their region and the ways their plates are moving. Emphasize that previously when students gathered data, they followed specific instructions. Now they will rely on their own understanding of plate interaction to determine what data they need.

Point out that students have already made inferences about the ways their plates are moving and interacting. Now they should determine how they can better support their inferences and what data they need to do so, or whether they need to revise their inferences.

○ Get Going

Have pairs start *My World* at their computer stations. Review how to use *My World* as necessary. The student text provides instructions on setting up their *My World* interface for this investigation. First, they should select the *Earth Structures and Processes* library and the *ESInquiry* project file. Then they should turn on the volcano layer and the medium earthquakes layer, selecting *3 years* from the layer menu. Then they should navigate to their region in the *My World* map using the zoom tool.

c. **Re-center the map** and/or zoom in to view your region. Use your *Three-page Map* as a guide for where to look.

d. **Observe and record data about your zone** that you need to identify the types of plate boundaries in your region and the directions your plates are moving.

2. Label the types of plate boundaries in your region on the *Three-page Map* you created earlier. Use the symbols recommended in the plate boundary and zone descriptions to record the types of boundaries in your region.

3. Based on the symbols you drew on your map and using what you have read about plate movement, determine how your plates are moving. Draw arrows on your *Three-page Map* to show if the plates are moving toward each other, away from each other, or sliding past each other. If only one plate is involved, show the direction that this plate is moving.

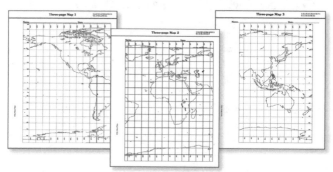

Conference

Working with other pairs who are assigned the same region, come to an agreement about the directions the plates are moving, the type of boundary, and the data that supports your ideas. When you have come to an agreement, update the *What are we learning?* column of your *Region Project Board*. Then draw boundary markers and arrows on the transparency overlay of the *Big World Map* to share with the class.

EE 243

EVER-CHANGING EARTH

META NOTES

While students should be allowed to determine what data they need on their own, they may need reminders about how to use *My World* to find some data. For instance, they may realize that they need depth data for earthquakes in their region, but may not remember how to retrieve depth data, or they may not remember how to see the elevations of topographic features. Assist them as necessary. Remind them that they can refer to *Using My World* in their texts.

In order to judge the depth of the earthquakes in their regions, students may find it easier to look at the depths of earthquakes globally in the *Big Data Map* than to navigate to different regions in *My World*. They can also ask students working in other regions.

Tell students they need to record the types of plate boundaries in their regions on their *Three-page Map* using the symbols given in the plate boundary descriptions in their text. They should draw arrows on their *Three-page Map* to show how the plates are moving.

△ Guide and Assess

As students gather data using *My World,* assist them with any difficulties that come up. Ask them what data they need in order to be sure of the type of plate boundary in their region and of how plates are moving. How will this data help them support their inference or make their final identification?

Students who are investigating Hawaii should identify the direction of the Pacific Plate and how the Pacific Plate interacts with neighboring plates to the east.

Students who are investigating Iceland may have difficulty reconciling the volcanic and earthquake activity on the island of Iceland with the patterns of earthquake and volcanic activity elsewhere on the plate boundary. You can remind students that their objective is to identify the type of plate boundary and how the plates are moving, so the pattern of earthquake and volcanic activity along the plate boundary should be their starting point. They may also have hypotheses about why geologic activity on the island differs from surrounding activity. A widely accepted hypothesis is that Iceland lies above a plume in the mantle, just as Hawaii lies above a plume. Unlike Hawaii, Iceland is on a plate boundary, so the plume rises between the divergent plates rather than melting through a plate.

△ Guide

When pairs have had time to record their data, have them meet with other pairs assigned to the same region and share their data and conclusions about the directions the plates are moving and what types of plate boundaries are in their region. They should have a brief discussion to come to agreement about the directions, boundary types, and what data supports their ideas. Then they should update the *What are we learning?* column of their *Region Project Boards* and draw boundary markers and arrows on the transparency overlay of the *Big World Map* to share with the class. Let them know that they will report their conclusions to the class.

☐ Assess

As students discuss their conclusions, monitor their progress, and assess how well they can support their conclusions.

Conference

10 min

Students discuss their conclusions and update their Region Project Boards *with their region groups.*

NOTES

....

....

....

....

Communicate: Share Your Ideas

10 min

Region groups present their conclusions.

Communicate

Share Your Ideas

When it is your group's turn, report what you have decided about the boundaries in your region and the directions in which the plates are moving. Share the data that supports your ideas. If your group had disagreements, report these, and report how you came to an agreement. Each pair should also report the differences between their current ideas and earlier ideas about how their plates are moving.

Analyze Your Data

As a class, look at all the movement arrows drawn on the class map, and try to answer these questions. Go back to the data to verify and discuss patterns in the data or if you are having disagreements.

- For each plate you have identified, how is it moving?

- Where each plate meets other plates, how are the plates interacting?

- How well do all the predicted movements work together?

Reflect

1. At the beginning of *Section 6.2,* you made a prediction about how the plates in your region were interacting. Based on what you have learned since then, revise this prediction and describe the plate boundaries and interactions in your region. Draw a diagram describing the movement and interactions happening in your region and the resulting landforms. Include any supporting evidence to your diagram.

2. Identify the types of data you used to make decisions about the ways your plates are moving and interacting.

3. Identify what you are sure about and what you are still unsure about.

What's the Point?

In this section, you had the opportunity to apply what you learned about different types of plate boundaries to identify the directions plates in your region are moving. You are connecting all of the things you have learned, which is important as you come close to answering the *Big Question* for this Unit *What processes within Earth cause geologic activity?*

EE 244

Project-Based Inquiry Science

△ Guide

When each group has come to an agreement about the plate boundaries and plate motions in their region, have them report their conclusions to the class. Groups should point out the boundary types and direction arrows they marked on the *Big World Map* transparency overlay, and they should tell the class what decisions they made about the plate boundaries and motions. They should tell the class what data supports their decisions. If they had any disagreements, they should tell the class what the disagreements were and how they came to agreement. They should also report any differences between their current ideas and earlier ideas.

Students will have a chance to discuss whether the boundary types and motions of the plates that different groups identified are compatible and whether the data supports their ideas. For now, they should try to understand the conclusions groups present and how they used their data to reach these conclusions. Emphasize that they should ask questions to clarify if anything seems unclear.

△ Guide

Once all groups have reported their conclusions, ask the class to look at all the arrows drawn on the plate boundary overlay on the *Big World Map,* and to think about whether all the plate movements make sense.

Analyze Your Data
10 min

The class has a discussion of the questions.

> **TEACHER TALK**
>
> ❝Look at all the movement arrows drawn on the class's *Big World Map* overlay. Think about how the plates move. Do all the predicted movements work together? ❞

Lead a class discussion of the bulleted questions in the student text.

- If groups' conclusions were compatible, they should be able to state the direction of each plate by looking at the arrows on the plate. If there are contradictory directions indicated for any plates on the *Big World Map,* ask students how they can resolve the discrepancy. They may need to revisit the types of plate interactions at the boundaries they identified.

- Again, students should be able to state the type of plate interaction at each boundary by looking at the *Big World Map.* However, if the directions of plate movement they identified are not compatible, they may consider revising one or more of the plate interaction types.

- As students review the plate movements and interaction types on the *Big World Map,* they should make sure that all of the movements and interaction types work together.

◇ Evaluate

During this discussion, ensure that students identify any mistakes in their conclusions. If any of the plates' directions or plate interactions are incorrect, ask students if these directions or interactions fit with the rest of the map and if they are supported by the data. You can use the map of plate boundaries and movements on the following page to check students' work.

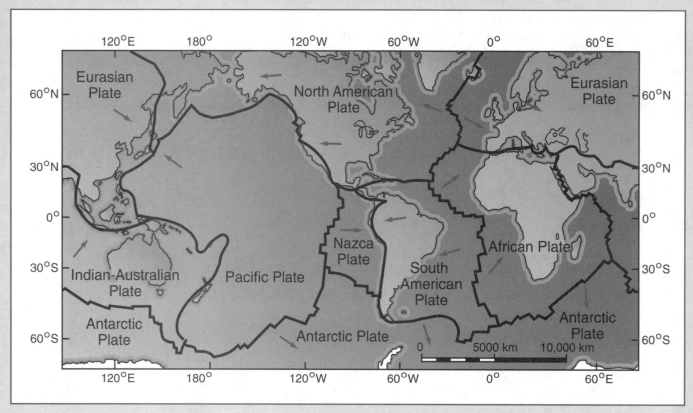

Reflect

15 min

Students work with their partners to answer the Reflect *questions.*

• How well do all the predicted movements work together?

Reflect

1. At the beginning of *Section 6.2*, you made a prediction about how the plates in your region were interacting. Based on what you have learned since then, revise this prediction and describe the plate boundaries and interactions in your region. Draw a diagram describing the movement and interactions happening in your region and the resulting landforms. Include any supporting evidence to your diagram.

2. Identify the types of data you used to make decisions about the ways your plates are moving and interacting.

3. Identify what you are sure about and what you are still unsure about.

What's the Point?

△ Guide

Have students work with their partners to answer the *Reflect* questions. Emphasize that students should use whatever evidence from the Unit they think will best support their answers.

☐ Assess

As students work with their partners, monitor their progress and assess their work. They should now draw on all that they have done in this Unit to make final evaluations of what predictions they can make about plate boundaries and interactions in their regions, what data they can use to make these predictions, and how confident they can be of their predictions.

You can use the following guidelines to assess students' answers to each question:

1. Students should use what they have learned about subduction zones, buckling zones, divergent boundaries, and rift zones and what they have learned from their classmates' work on their regions to revise their predictions. Their diagrams should show the directions plates in their regions are moving, whether boundaries are convergent or divergent, and if they are subduction zones, buckling zones, or rift zones. They should also show how the plate interactions in the region lead to landforms on the surface.

2. Students should record any types of data—including patterns of earthquakes, earthquake depth and magnitude, patterns of volcanoes, and types of volcanoes—they used to identify types of plate interaction and to infer plate movements.

3. Students should consider how well their data support their conclusions and whether there are other ways to interpret their data. Some regions, such as the Baja Peninsula and Iceland, have complicated geologic activity, and the data for these regions may be difficult to interpret with confidence.

Assessment Options

Targeted Concepts, Skills, and Nature of Science	How do I know if students got it?
Scientists often work together and then share their findings. Sharing findings makes new information available and helps scientists refine their ideas and build on others' ideas. When another person or group's idea is used, credit needs to be given.	**ASK:** How did discussions with your region groups help you refine your conclusions? How was it helpful to discuss your conclusions with the class? **LISTEN:** Students should have been able to identify problems with their conclusions or gain confirmation of their conclusions from their group discussions. They should have been able to identify conclusions that were incompatible with other groups', or to confirm that the conclusions were compatible, during the class discussion.

Targeted Concepts, Skills, and Nature of Science	How do I know if students got it?
Scientists make claims (conclusions) based on evidence obtained (trends in data) from reliable investigations.	**ASK:** What were your final claims about plate movements and interactions in your region? What evidence did you use to support your claims? **LISTEN:** Students should recognize that the arrows they drew indicating the movement of plates and the boundary types they recorded were claims. They should specify the data that they used as evidence to support their claims.
Scientists use models and tools, such as Geographic Information Systems, and a variety of maps to develop claims and explanations from evidence in the data.	**ASK:** What were some ways you used maps to help you develop ideas about how plates move and interact in your region and around the world? **LISTEN:** Students should say that they used *My World* to get data, that they recorded the directions of plate movements visually on the *Big World Map* transparency, and that they recorded their work on the *Three-page Map*.

Teacher Reflection Questions

- In which regions were plate boundaries and plate movements most difficult for students to identify? How can you support students working in those regions next time?

- How did the small group and class discussions assist students with the content?

- What difficulties came up as students worked with different groups? How can you address those difficulties next time?

Back to the Big Question

What Processes Within Earth Cause Geologic Activity?

◀ *1 class period*

A class period is considered to be one 40 to 50 minute class.

Overview

Students list the geologic terms they have learned in this *Learning Set* and make sketches to show the defining features of each term. They record connections between them, synthesizing the geologic ideas they have learned. Using data from their investigations and science knowledge from their reading, they revise their explanations of the geologic activity in their regions. They consider what information would help them better explain what causes geologic activity and changes in their Earth structure, and they update the *Project Board*.

Targeted Concepts, Skills, and Nature of Science	Performance Expectations
Scientists often work together and then share their findings. Sharing findings makes new information available and helps scientists refine their ideas and build on others' ideas. When another person's or group's idea is used, credit needs to be given.	Students should work with their partners to revise their explanations. They should share their explanations with the class, discussing how different groups supported their claims.
Scientists must keep clear, accurate, and descriptive records of what they do so they can share their work with others and consider what they did, why they did it, and what they want to do next.	Students should keep clear, accurate, and descriptive records of the geologic concepts they have learned and of their claims and supporting evidence.
Scientists make claims (conclusions) based on evidence obtained (trends in data) from reliable investigations.	Students should revise their claims based on new science knowledge and data.
Explanations are claims supported by evidence, accepted ideas, and facts.	Students should use the new science knowledge and new data to support their revised claims.

Targeted Concepts, Skills, and Nature of Science	Performance Expectations
Earthquake activity, volcanic activity, and topography are all evidence that Earth's crust is moving and changing.	Students should include earthquake, volcano, and topographic data as evidence that Earth's crust is moving and changing.
Interactions between Earth's crustal plates can result in mountain-building, rift valleys, and geologic activity such as Earthquakes and volcanoes. Underwater volcanic activity may form underwater mountains, which can thrust above the ocean's surface to become islands.	Students should support claims about the directions of plate movement using patterns in volcanic activity as evidence. They should be able to describe the formation of islands from volcanic activity.

Materials	
1 per class	Class *Project Board*
1 per student	*Project Board* page Pen pal letter *Create Your Explanation* page
1 per classroom	*Ever-Changing Earth Teacher Notes and Suggested Data* table
1 per class	*Big World Map* with the plate boundary transparencies

Homework Options

Reflection

- **Science Content:** How did you revise the claim(s) in your explanation? *(Students should have revised their claims to show how the heat of Earth's core and the convection currents in the mantle cause plate motion.)*

Learning Set 6

Back to the Big Question

What processes within Earth cause geologic activity?

You now have created a full map of Earth's plates and have identified the direction the plates are moving. You have also identified different ways plates are interacting to cause the geologic activity in your region. Before addressing the *Big Question*, you will complete your explanation of the geologic activity in your region. As you have done at the end of other *Learning Sets*, you will also work on your Picture Map.

Add to Your *Picture Map*

The goal of this *Learning Set* was to understand more about what is happening where plates interact with each other. You learned many geologic terms in this *Learning Set*: *convergent boundary, converge, divergent boundary, diverge, rift zone, buckling zone, subduction zone,* and *transform zone*. Feel free to add any other terms you think are important. As you have done in previous *Learning Sets*, you will create pictures to show what the words mean and then build a map to show how they relate to each other.

Write each term on a separate index card using large text so others will be able to read it from far away. Then, next to the term or on the back of the card, draw a picture to show what the geologic term means. Make your picture as accurate as possible. Be sure to include features that would help someone else understand the geologic term. Then go back to the cards you made previously, and see if there is anything you want to add to or change on any of those.

When you have completed your cards, share them with a group of classmates. Your teacher will tell you which group. Listen carefully as someone in your group describes each geologic term. For each card, you should add additional information or make necessary changes to your drawing or definition.

EE 245

EVER-CHANGING EARTH

Learning Set 6

Back to the Big Question

5 min

Students are introduced to the activity.

○ Engage

Remind students of the *Big Question: What processes within Earth cause geologic activity?* Tell them they will now update their *Picture Maps* and use the new information and concepts they have learned to revise the explanations they created in *Learning Set 3*. Have the class *Project Board* on display. Tell students they may want to refer to their own *Project Board* pages as they are revising their explanations.

*A class period is considered to be one 40 to 50 minute class.

Add to Your Picture Map

10 min

Students map the concepts they have learned using index cards.

---

in your ... have done at the ... ing ... also work on your Picture Map.

Add to Your *Picture Map*

The goal of this *Learning Set* was to understand more about what is happening where plates interact with each other. You learned many geologic terms in this *Learning Set*: **convergent boundary, converge, divergent boundary, diverge, rift zone, buckling zone, subduction zone,** and **transform zone.** Feel free to add any other terms you think are important. As you have done in previous *Learning Sets*, you will create pictures to show what the words mean and then build a map to show how they relate to each other.

Write each term on a separate index card using large text so others will be able to read it from far away. Then, next to the term or on the back of the card, draw a picture to show what the geologic term means. Make your picture as accurate as possible. Be sure to include features that would help someone else understand the geologic term. Then go back to the cards you made previously, and see if there is anything you want to add to or change on any of those.

When you have completed your cards, share them with a group of classmates. Your teacher will tell you which group. Listen carefully as someone in your group describes each geologic term. For each card, you should add additional information or make necessary changes to your drawing or definition.

△ Guide

Tell students that they will add to their *Picture Maps* by writing important terms on index cards, as they did in previous *Learning Sets*. They will draw a picture of each term to communicate what it means. Emphasize that their drawings should help people who are not familiar with the terms understand what they mean. The student text mentions some of the words that may be new to students: convergent boundary, converge, divergent boundary, diverge, rift zone, buckling zone, subduction zone, and transform zone. Students should also revise the cards they made in previous *Learning Sets*. Emphasize that they have learned more about these concepts and that their cards should show what they have learned.

⬡ Get Going

Distribute index cards and have students add to their *Picture Maps*. Emphasize that each student should create a set of cards illustrating the terms.

When students have completed their cards, have them share their cards with groups of students who were assigned to the same region. Each student should listen to other members' descriptions of the terms and think about information they can add to their own cards or changes they can make to their drawings.

Have students work with their groups to find how the terms go together, including the terms from *Learning Sets 1, 2, 3, 4,* and *5.* They should arrange their cards on the table to show how the ideas connect. When they have agreed on how the ideas connect, they should record the connections on the back of the cards. If members of the group disagree about how the ideas connect, they should record their disagreement.

△ Guide and Assess

As students work on their *Picture Maps,* monitor their progress and assist them with any difficulties they encounter. If they need guidance as they create sketches to illustrate their geologic terms, have them imagine that they are trying to explain these ideas to someone using sketches. Ask them questions about the ideas to guide them towards statements they can illustrate.

When students share their cards with their groups, listen to how they discuss differences in the information on their cards and how they discuss the best arrangement of their cards. Emphasize that students should ask questions and make comments constructively. If they have difficulty arranging their cards, ask them what the most important connections between the ideas they have illustrated are. For each idea, what other ideas do they have to use in an explanation?

NOTES

....

....

....

....

....

....

Revise Your Explanation

10 min

Students revise their explanations of geologic activity in their regions.

Work with your group to create a map that shows how the geologic terms go together. Lay the new cards you made and old cards that you think connect to them on the table. Look for different ways the ideas, both old and new, connect. On each card, record the connections you made. Also record any disagreements your group had about connections, and mark any connections you do not understand. You are probably finding that you understand a lot more than you did earlier in the Unit.

Revise Your Explanation

Now you will revise your explanation of the geologic activity in your region one last time. You will be using this explanation as a basis for answering the *Big Question* for this Unit, *What processes within Earth cause geologic activity?* It is important to be accurate and complete.

Working with your partner, examine the explanation of geologic activity in your region you made at the end of *Learning Set 5*. Use what you now know about how plates interact to decide how accurate your explanation was. You have learned a lot more since then, so you will probably want to revise it. Use a new *Create Your Explanation* page for your revised explanation. Remember that a good explanation has several parts to it.

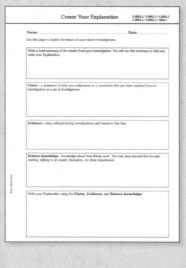

Review your claim to see if this final statement about geologic activity in your region accurately reflects all that you now understand. Make any changes necessary to include what you have just learned about plate interactions and the geologic activity associated with each of them. Bring together the supporting evidence for your claim. This includes your maps, data, charts, and notes. Be sure to include supporting science knowledge you learned during this *Learning Set*. You will be using all of this to support your final explanation.

Then develop an explanation statement that brings your claim, evidence, and science knowledge together. It should help someone to understand what is happening within Earth to cause changes in your region. It should also help someone understand what causes the geologic processes that cause changes in your region.

EE 246

Project-Based Inquiry Science

△ Guide

Distribute new *Create Your Explanation* pages to students and let them know they will work with their partners to revise their explanations of the ways that movements of Earth's layers cause changes in their regions. They should use evidence from their drawings and models, and science knowledge from their reading.

Review the parts of a good explanation with the class—the claim, the evidence, the science knowledge, and the explanation connecting the evidence and the science knowledge to the claim. They should revise their claims to connect plate motion to volcano formation. They should include what they have learned about how volcanoes form, the different types of volcanoes, and how the different types of plate interaction cause different types of volcanoes.

☐ Assess

As pairs work on their explanations, monitor their progress and help them with any difficulties they are having. Ask them what evidence and science knowledge they are using to support their claims.

Note the similarities and differences among pairs' claims. During presentations, you might consider having two pairs with similar claims present one after the other so students can compare how they supported their claims.

NOTES

Communicate: Share Your Explanation

15 min

Groups present their explanations.

Communicate

Share Your Explanation

It is now time to present your full explanation of how processes within Earth cause geologic activity. Make a poster that shows your claim, evidence, supporting science knowledge, and explanation statement. You will now organize and present your final explanation of your region's geological activity. Make a poster that includes all of the following:

- a description of your region, including the type of plate boundaries found there and the interactions between these plate boundaries

- the patterns of earthquake and volcanic activity in your region and how they compare to other regions

- the evidence you used to decide how the plates in your region move and interact

- the science knowledge you used to explain the geologic activity in your region

Present your explanation to the class. Make sure you describe everything that is in your evidence and how it supports your explanation. For example, you may want to point out data patterns in your maps and show how they match the geologic activity for the type of plate interaction you think is happening in your region.

As you listen to the explanations of others, notice how well each explanation connects the evidence or science knowledge to the geologic activity in each region. As you are listening, watch for ways others have explained patterns similar to the ones in your region. Decide, for each explanation you hear, if you are convinced. Did the group connect all the data and science knowledge to their claim? Did their explanation statement tell you everything you need to know to understand why the geologic activity in their region is happening?

Reflect

With your partner, answer the following questions.

1. How trustworthy and complete do you think your explanation is? To figure that out, think about how well it explains the geologic activity in other, similar regions.

△ Guide

When pairs have completed their explanations, have them present to the class. With the class, review the explanation, and ask the class to identify the parts of the explanation. Encourage the class to suggest any different ideas they have for the explanations presented. Ask pairs with similar interpretations if they used any different evidence or science knowledge to support their claims.

☐ Assess

As the class discusses the presentations and the final class recommendation, listen to how students discuss their ideas. Do students ask each other about things that are not clear? Do they give constructive feedback?

△ Guide and Assess

Once groups have presented their explanations to the class, have students answer the *Reflect* questions with their partners. Emphasize that they should be prepared to share their answers with the class.

When students have had time to answer the *Reflect* questions, lead a class discussion of their responses. Listen for the following in students' answers:

1. Students should honestly evaluate how well they have explained earthquake patterns in their regions, and how well their explanations can be applied to regions with similar Earth structures.

2. This question is meant to engage students in thinking about what they need to investigate. Students should have questions about what causes plates to move, what patterns they can find in volcanic activity, what causes volcanic activity, what they can learn from depth data, and why some earthquakes occur in the middle of plates.

Reflect

10 min

Pairs answer the Reflect *questions and then have a class discussion.*

NOTES

....

....

....

....

....

....

....

Update the Project Board

10 min

The class has a discussion to update the *Project Board*.

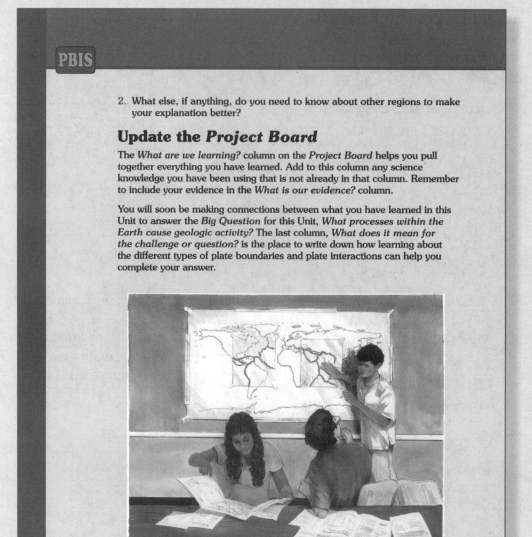

2. What else, if anything, do you need to know about other regions to make your explanation better?

Update the *Project Board*

The *What are we learning?* column on the *Project Board* helps you pull together everything you have learned. Add to this column any science knowledge you have been using that is not already in that column. Remember to include your evidence in the *What is our evidence?* column.

You will soon be making connections between what you have learned in this Unit to answer the *Big Question* for this Unit, *What processes within the Earth cause geologic activity?* The last column, *What does it mean for the challenge or question?* is the place to write down how learning about the different types of plate boundaries and plate interactions can help you complete your answer.

EE 248

Project-Based Inquiry Science

△ Guide

Now update the *Project Board* with the class. Ask students what they have learned since they last updated the *Project Board*. Record their answers in the *What are we learning?* column. This should include claims from groups' explanations. For everything that students put in the *What are we learning?* column, ask them what evidence they have. Record the evidence in the *What is our evidence?* column. Finally, ask students what they still need to investigate, and record their answers in the *What do we need to investigate?*

column. Students should also record the questions they identified in the *Reflect* discussion.

Teacher Reflection Questions

- What concepts in this *Learning Set* were difficult for students? How can you help them master these concepts?

- How have you been able to evaluate students' progress as they learn about geologic activity and Earth structures?

- What kind of discussions did the class have as you updated the *Project Board?* How were you able to keep discussions constructive?

NOTES

NOTES

Answer the Big Question

What Processes Within Earth Cause Geologic Activity?

◀ *1 class period*

A class period is considered to be one 40 to 50 minute class.

Overview

Students revise their explanations of the ways that processes in Earth cause geologic activity. They use the data they collected, the models they made, and the science knowledge they learned to support their claims, synthesizing everything they have learned. They share their explanations with the class, and the class chooses two or three explanations they think best answers the *Big Question,* evaluating the claims and evidence the class has developed. Then the class learns about how scientists answer the *Big Question.* They are introduced to the theory of plate tectonics, as well as the contributory theories of continental drift and ocean-floor spreading. Then they use what they have learned to revise the class explanation a final time.

Materials	
1 per class	Class *Project Board* *Big World Map* with the plate boundary transparencies
1 per student	*Project Board* page *Create Your Explanation* page
1 per classroom	*Ever-Changing Earth Teacher Notes and Suggested Data* table

Activity Setup and Preparation

Consider having a computer with *My World* available for students to use if needed. They may need to double-check some of their data or they may want to use it to project a map during their presentation. Students should be able to project or display their data maps for the class to see.

Homework Options

Reflection

- **Science Process:** Describe the process you went through to create your explanation. *(This question is meant to help students reflect on what they did that was successful or unsuccessful as they created explanations.)*

NOTES

Answer the Big Question

What Processes Within Earth Cause Geologic Activity?

Throughout this Unit, you have been collecting and analyzing data that shows the geologic activity in the region of your Earth structure. Using this evidence, along with science knowledge gained throughout the Unit, you have also created explanations that begin to answer the *Big Question* on a smaller scale, at the level of your region. By sharing information and listening to the explanations of others, you have also learned about other regions around the world. Now you will take what you learned and apply it to the *Big Question: What processes within Earth cause geologic activity?*

Revise Your Explanation

Working with your partner, examine the explanation you made at the end of *Learning Set 4.* You attempted then to answer the *Big Question,* but you did not know enough to answer it completely. You should be able to answer it more completely now. Use a new *Create Your Explanation* page for your revised explanation. Remember that a good explanation has several parts to it:

- **your claim:** a statement of what you understand or a conclusion you have reached

- **your evidence:** data collected from investigations that support your claim

- **your science knowledge:** knowledge about how things work that supports your claim

- **your explanation:** a logical statement connecting your evidence and science knowledge to your claim in a way that can convince someone that your claim is valid. Good explanations tell what is happening that makes the claim valid.

EE 249

EVER-CHANGING EARTH

○ Engage

Remind students of the *Big Question: What processes within Earth cause geologic activity?* Emphasize that students have been addressing the *Big Question* on a small scale, when they created explanations of geologic activity in their regions. Tell them that now they will apply what they learned directly to the *Big Question.*

*A class period is considered to be one 40 to 50 minute class.

TEACHER TALK

"The *Big Question* that you have been developing an answer to is *What processes within Earth cause geologic activity?* You have taken steps toward answering this question by creating explanations of geologic activity in your regions. Now you will apply what you have learned to answering the *Big Question* directly.**"**

Revise Your Explanation

5 min

Students work with their partners to revise their explanations.

What processes within Earth cause geologic activity?

Revise Your Explanation

Working with your partner, examine the explanation you made at the end of *Learning Set 4*. You attempted then to answer the *Big Question*, but you did not know enough to answer it completely. You should be able to answer it more completely now. Use a new *Create Your Explanation* page for your revised explanation. Remember that a good explanation has several parts to it:

- **your claim:** a statement of what you understand or a conclusion you have reached

- **your evidence:** data collected from investigations that support your claim

- **your science knowledge:** knowledge about how things work that supports your claim

- **your explanation:** a logical statement connecting your evidence and science knowledge to your claim in a way that can convince someone that your claim is valid. Good explanations tell what is happening that makes the claim valid.

△ Guide

Tell students they will now revise the explanations they created at the end of *Learning Set 4*. Emphasize that in these explanations, they tried to answer the *Big Question*. They know more now, and are better able to answer the *Big Question*.

Distribute *Create Your Explanation* pages. Briefly review the parts of a good explanation. These are the claim, the evidence, the science knowledge, and the explanation connecting the evidence and the science knowledge to the claim. Tell students that they will use the drawings and models they have made, the data they have collected, and the science knowledge they have learned to support claims about what processes within Earth cause geologic activity. Then have students work with their partners to revise their explanations.

☐ Assess

As groups work on their explanations, monitor their progress and help them with any difficulties they are having. Ask them what evidence and science knowledge they are using to support their claims.

Also note the similarities and differences among groups' claims. During presentations, you might consider having two groups with very similar claims present one after the other so that students can compare how they supported their claims.

PBIS

Your claim will be your best statement about the processes beneath Earth's surface that are causing geologic activity around the world. Your evidence comes from the drawings you have made, the modeling you have done, and the data you have collected throughout this Unit. You should also use evidence presented by other groups in their presentations. Your science knowledge comes from your reading. Work with your partner to create the best explanation you can about how processes beneath Earth's surface cause geologic activity. It may be easier to express your explanation by attaching phrases to sketches than to simply use words. Feel free to combine sketches and words in your explanation.

Communicate

Share Your Explanation

As you participate in this *Communicate*, you will be both audience and presenter. Be prepared to answer and ask other groups the following questions:

- Do you think each group developed a convincing explanation, well supported by data and science knowledge?

- What else could be included in each presentation to make the explanation more convincing?

- How did the evidence you used compare with others? Why do you think there were differences?

- How did answers to the *Big Question* for this Unit compare between groups? Why do you think there were differences? Which explanation do you think is best? Why?

Revise Your Explanation

Now work with your class to develop a single explanation. Think about the explanations presented by other groups, as well as the evidence and science knowledge they used to support it. As a class, narrow down the explanations to the two or three that you think best answered the *Big Question* and had the best supporting evidence. Look to see how they are similar and how they are different. Discuss those differences and try to resolve them using other types of evidence. When you are finished, you will read about how scientists answer the *Big Question*. You will have a chance to work as a class to revise your explanations one more time.

EE 250

Project-Based Inquiry Science

Communicate: Share Your Explanation

15 min

Groups present their revised explanations.

△ Guide

Display the *Big World Map* with the plates transparencies for students to use during their presentations. Remind students that they can use this, their *Three-page Maps,* and other records to visually demonstrate the evidence that supports their claims.

Emphasize that the class should be thinking about the bulleted questions in the student text as they listen to presentations, so groups should consider these as they prepare their presentations. Give students a few minutes to prepare.

When groups are ready, have them present their revised explanations. Emphasize that students should think about how they could answer the questions in the student text as they listen to presentations. Consider having students record the answers.

◇ Evaluate

As each group presents, use the *Ever-Changing Earth Teacher Notes and Suggested Data* table to make sure that students have accurately described and explained the geologic activity in their regions.

△ Guide

After each presentation, hold a brief class discussion. Ask the class if the data was presented accurately. Did it support the claims the group made? Were there any contradictions in the group's explanation? Was the explanation consistent with other groups' explanations?

Revise Your Explanation

10 min

The class has a discussion to develop a single explanation.

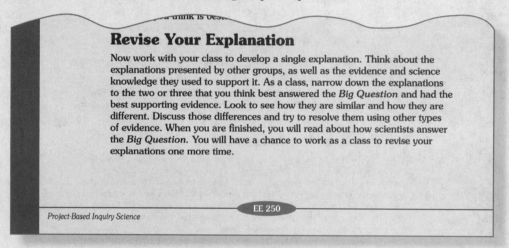

Revise Your Explanation

Now work with your class to develop a single explanation. Think about the explanations presented by other groups, as well as the evidence and science knowledge they used to support it. As a class, narrow down the explanations to the two or three that you think best answered the *Big Question* and had the best supporting evidence. Look to see how they are similar and how they are different. Discuss those differences and try to resolve them using other types of evidence. When you are finished, you will read about how scientists answer the *Big Question*. You will have a chance to work as a class to revise your explanations one more time.

Project-Based Inquiry Science   EE 250

△ Guide

Have the class choose two or three explanations they think best answers the *Big Question* and are best supported by evidence. Lead a discussion to compare these explanations and to resolve the differences between them. Record their revised explanation on the board or on a transparency. Tell the class that they will have one more chance to revise their explanation after they read about how scientists explain geologic activity.

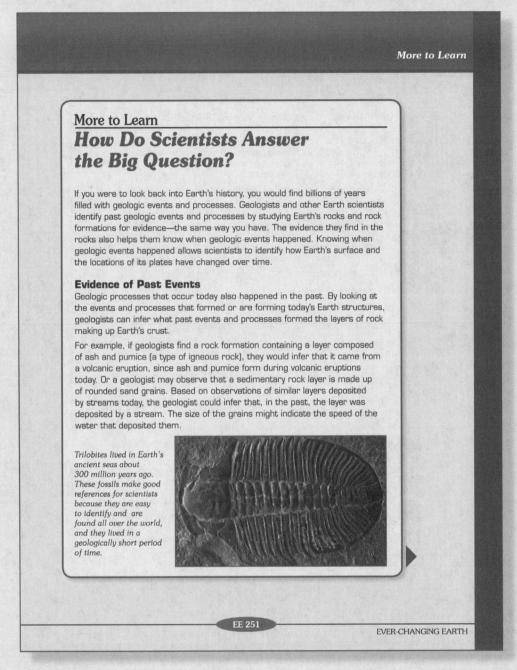

More to Learn
How Do Scientists Answer the Big Question?

If you were to look back into Earth's history, you would find billions of years filled with geologic events and processes. Geologists and other Earth scientists identify past geologic events and processes by studying Earth's rocks and rock formations for evidence—the same way you have. The evidence they find in the rocks also helps them know when geologic events happened. Knowing when geologic events happened allows scientists to identify how Earth's surface and the locations of its plates have changed over time.

Evidence of Past Events

Geologic processes that occur today also happened in the past. By looking at the events and processes that formed or are forming today's Earth structures, geologists can infer what past events and processes formed the layers of rock making up Earth's crust.

For example, if geologists find a rock formation containing a layer composed of ash and pumice (a type of igneous rock), they would infer that it came from a volcanic eruption, since ash and pumice form during volcanic eruptions today. Or a geologist may observe that a sedimentary rock layer is made up of rounded sand grains. Based on observations of similar layers deposited by streams today, the geologist could infer that, in the past, the layer was deposited by a stream. The size of the grains might indicate the speed of the water that deposited them.

Trilobites lived in Earth's ancient seas about 300 million years ago. These fossils make good references for scientists because they are easy to identify and are found all over the world, and they lived in a geologically short period of time.

EE 251

EVER-CHANGING EARTH

More to Learn: How Do Scientists Answer the Big Question?

15 min

The class discusses how scientists answer the Big Question.

△ Guide

Begin by telling students that scientists take the same approach to answering the *Big Question* as students have taken. They use evidence from Earth's surface and other data to identify past geologic events and processes. They get the evidence from examining Earth's rocks and surface. Students will now learn more about how scientists determine Earth's history.

If the rock layer also contains shells, the type of shell could indicate that the rock formed in water. The type of living thing that made the shells could also provide clues to the depth and temperature of the water. Microscopic pollen grains in the rock could identify plants living near the water when the rock formed. Still other rock layers may contain evidence of glaciers, wind-blown deserts, or even asteroid collisions.

The structure of rock layers also provides evidence of past events. Sediments and some types of lava flow usually form in horizontal layers. Based on these observations, geologists infer that most sedimentary rocks and certain types of igneous rocks originally formed in horizontal layers. When they find rock layers that are not horizontal, they infer that there was a past geologic event. For example, tilted or folded rock layers in a mountain range are evidence of uplift and mountain building. Rock layers broken and shifted along a fault are evidence of earthquake activity.

relative age: the age of one object or event compared to another.

absolute age: the number of years an object has existed.

Evidence of Age

To determine when geologic events happened, geologists determine the ages of the rocks in the area of the geologic event. There are two ways to express the age of rock—**relative age** and **absolute age**.

Relative age is the age of one object or event compared to another. Over millions of years, sediments build up, and each layer forms on top of one that was already there. This means each layer is younger than the one under it and older than the one on top of it. In a series of sedimentary layers, the bottom layer is oldest and the top layer is youngest, unless some other factors, such as mountain building or earthquakes, have changed the order of the layers.

Layers can also show evidence of the long history of life on Earth. Fossilized remains in each layer show which kinds of animals and plants lived in different ages. These fossils can show how life and environmental conditions changed over billions of years.

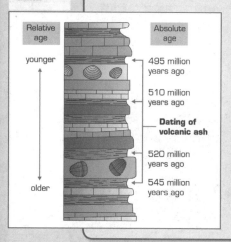

Relative age

younger

older

Absolute age

495 million years ago

510 million years ago

Dating of volcanic ash

520 million years ago

545 million years ago

NOTES

△ Guide

Discuss how scientists use geologic events and processes happening today to infer what events and processes formed the layers of rock in Earth's crust. The geologic events and processes happening today also happened in the past, and the geologic formations that result are similar to the geologic formations that resulted from past events. Therefore, when scientists find a very old geologic formation they can make inferences about what kind of event happened in the past to create the formation.

The student text gives several examples of how scientists can infer past geologic events. Discuss each of these examples.

The student text begins with an example of a rock formation containing a layer composed of ash and pumice. Because ash and pumice form during volcanic eruptions today, scientists would infer that such a layer was formed by a volcanic eruption in the past.

The text also gives the example of sedimentary rock. If scientists observe a sedimentary rock layer composed of rounded sand grains, they can use observations of similar layers deposited by streams today to infer that the layer of sedimentary rock was deposited by a stream.

Also discuss the example of rock layers containing shells. Shells from sea life could indicate that the rock layer formed in water. The type of sea life could also provide clues to the depth and temperature of the water.

Discuss how the structure of rock layers can provide evidence of past events. Many rock layers, including sedimentary layers and some types of lava flows, form as horizontal layers. When scientists find layers of these types that are not horizontal, they infer that a past geologic event changed the disposition of the layer. For example, tilted or folded rock layers in a mountain range are evidence of uplift and mountain building.

△ Guide

Discuss how geologists use the age of rocks to determine when geologic events occurred. The age of rocks can be expressed as relative age and as absolute age. Tell students that the relative age of an object is its age compared with the age of another object. The student text explains a common way of finding the relative age of rocks and other objects in Earth—by examining the layers that lie above and below the object. Over time, layers form on top of older layers as sediment settles. This means that lower layers are older than layers near the surface. Point out the illustration in the student text. Objects found in the lower layers are usually older than objects found in the upper layers. Exceptions may occur when mountain formation or earthquakes disrupt the order of the layers.

Evidence of Past Events

Evidence of Age

Absolute age is the number of years an object has existed. Scientists can determine this through a process called **radioactive dating**. The minerals in certain kinds of rock contain atoms of unstable **radioactive elements,** chemical elements whose atoms occasionally change into atoms of other chemical elements, giving off energy in the process, such as uranium. After a complex series of steps, atoms of a new stable element are formed. The decay occurs at a steady, constant rate, so it can be used as a "clock" to determine the actual age of the rock. Knowing the decay rate, a scientist can calculate how many years decay has been going on since the rock formed by measuring how much of a radioactive element in a rock has changed into a new stable element. This tells the scientists the rock's age.

The Geologic Time Scale

Geologists have divided Earth's history into arrangements of geologic events in the order they happened, called the **geologic time scale**. The geologic time scale is based on the fossil record and order in which rocks are found.

radioactive dating: measuring the steady, constant rate of decay of radioactive elements in rock to determine the absolute age of the rock.

radioactive elements: a chemical element whose atoms occasionally change into atoms of other chemical elements, giving off energy in the process.

geologic time scale: the arrangement of geologic events in the order they happened, based on the fossil record and the order in which rocks are found.

Major Divisions of Geologic Time
(boundaries in millions of years before present)

Era	Period	Event	
Cenozoic	Quaternary	modern humans	
Cenozoic	Tertiary	abundant mammals	1.8
Mesozoic	Cretaceous	flowering plants; dinosaur extinction	65
Mesozoic	Jurassic	first birds and mammals; abundant dinosaurs	145
Mesozoic	Triassic	abundant coniferous trees	213
Paleozoic	Permian	extinction of trilobites and other marine animals	248
Paleozoic	Pennsylvanian	fern forests; abundant insects; first reptiles	286
Paleozoic	Mississippian	sharks; large primitive trees	325
Paleozoic	Devonian	amphibians and fish-like animals	360
Paleozoic	Silurian	early plants and animals on land	410
Paleozoic	Ordovician	first fish	440
Paleozoic	Cambrian	abundant marine invertebrates; trilobites dominant	505
			544
Proterozoic		primitive aquatic plants	
			2500
Archean		oldest fossils; bacteria and algae	

EVER-CHANGING EARTH

NOTES

....

....

Then tell students that absolute age is the number of years an object has existed. The student text explains how scientists use radioactive dating to determine the absolute age of objects. Radioactive dating relies on the decay of unstable radioactive elements in an object. Atoms in these elements occasionally change into atoms of other chemical elements, giving off energy in the process. This decay happens at a constant rate, so the amount of decay that has occurred in an object can be used to estimate its absolute age. Scientists can measure how much of the radioactive element has changed to a new element in the object to determine the amount of decay that has occurred.

△ Guide

Discuss how geologists have divided Earth's history into time periods on the geologic time scale. Point out the table showing the divisions of geologic time in student text. The table shows significant events that occurred in each of the periods. The Cambrian period is distinctive for the abundance of marine invertebrates. The Silurian period is distinctive for the appearance of animals on land. Much later, the Quaternary period is marked by the rise of human beings.

The Geologic Time Scale

NOTES

The History of the Plate Tectonic Theory

In the letter from Benny, you read about his cracked-egg model of how large pieces of Earth's crust, called plates, move about on the mantle. The explanations you have developed about Earth's structures and processes are based on a scientific theory called **plate tectonics** that is very similar to Benny's theory. According to the theory of plate tectonics, Earth's lithosphere is divided into a number of plates that move and interact with one another. The lithosphere includes Earth's crust and the outermost parts of the mantle.

You have examined some evidence of plate tectonics while working on this Unit. Scientists used evidence very similar to the evidence you used to develop the theory of plate tectonics.

The plate tectonics theory developed gradually through the work of many scientists, from Alfred Wegener's publications in 1915 to Brent Dalrymple's presentation at a meeting of the Geological Society of America in 1965.

Before Dalrymple brought together the work of the previous fifty years, scientists explained Earth's processes and structures using two other theories: *continental drift* and *ocean-floor spreading*. Both of those theories were supported by evidence, but neither could completely explain what was happening to cause geologic activity. It was very exciting to scientists when Dalrymple provided evidence showing that the theory of plate tectonics unified both previous theories.

Continental Drift

In 1912, Alfred Wegener, a German meteorologist, proposed a theory that all of the continents were once a single landmass. He suggested that this landmass, known as Pangaea (pan-jee-uh), split into continents millions of years ago. Over time, the continents drifted to their present positions. Wegener's theory was known as continental drift.

Much of Wegener's evidence came from studying the coastlines of the continents. Looking at the coastlines, he could see that if the coastlines are brought together, the edges would almost match. He then did research to see if he could support his theory with evidence. He found that many rock formations, plant and animal fossils, and living organisms were the same across continents. He also found that the past climates of the different continents were similar. All of this was evidence that the continents might have been connected at some time.

plate tectonics: the theory that the lithosphere is divided into a number of plates, and the study of how the plates move and interact with one another.

NOTES

△ Guide

Tell students that the explanations they developed are based on plate tectonic theory. Explain that the theory of plate tectonics says that Earth's lithosphere is divided into a number of plates that move and interact with one another. (The lithosphere comprises Earth's crust and part of the mantle.) Emphasize that the evidence students used to support their explanations is very similar to the evidence scientists use to support the theory of plate tectonics.

Discuss the history of the theory of plate tectonics. As presented by Brent Dalrymple at a meeting of the Geological Society of America in 1965, the theory combined two older theories—continental drift and ocean-floor spreading.

△ Guide

The theory of continental drift was proposed by Alfred Wegener, a German meteorologist, in 1912. This theory proposed that all of the continents were once a single landmass, which has been named Pangaea. This landmass separated into continents, which drifted to their present positions over millions of years. The truth of this theory was suggested by the similarity of the coastlines that would once have been joined.

The History of Plate Tectonic Theory

Continental Drift

NOTES

....

....

....

....

....

....

....

Wegener saw that many of the same fossil types were found on different continents. This indicated that the land on which these animals and plants lived was once a single landmass. Matching rock formations and living organisms also provided evidence of a single landmass.

Wegener also found evidence for this theory in the structure of Earth's crust. As you read earlier in the Unit, Earth's crust is made up of continental and oceanic crust. The continents are higher than the oceans because they are less dense—they will not sink as deeply in the more fluid mantle below. Wegener thought the continents could "drift" by simply moving sideways. However, Wegener's theory could not explain exactly what forces could have caused continents to move sideways.

Ocean-floor Spreading

By the 1950s, oceanographic research vessels could accurately survey the ocean floor. Scientists discovered that underwater mountain chains run down the center of almost every ocean in the world. These underwater mountain chains are split by deep rifts.

The rifts are associated with volcanic activity, and there are many faults in the surface around them. This activity suggested that movement was occurring on the ocean floors.

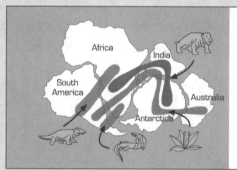

Fossil Evidence

- Fossil remains of the Triassic land reptile *Cynognathus*

- Fossil evidence of the Triassic land reptile *Lystrosaurus*

- Fossil of the fern *Glossopteris*

- Fossil remains of the freshwater reptile *Mesosaurus*

The distribution of the fossil remains of plants and animals suggest that the continents were once connected to one another.

NOTES

....

....

Wegener also found geologic evidence to support his theory. The fossils of some species could be found on multiple continents, suggesting that they once roamed freely across these continents. Some rock formations were also found on several continents.

△ Guide

Ocean-floor Spreading

Discuss the development of understanding of ocean-floor spreading. Tell students that by the 1950s, scientists were able to map the ocean floor, developing an accurate picture of formations on the ocean floor. This revealed underwater mountain chains that run along the center of almost every ocean. The mountain chains were split by rifts. Geologic activity in the rifts, including volcanoes and faults, suggested that movement was occurring. Scientists also discovered that ocean-floor rocks were younger than the rocks of continents and rocks farther from mid-ocean ridges were older than rocks near the ridges. You may want to sketch this on the board or a transparency to help students see the implications of it. Students should see that this suggests that new rock was forming at the ridges and then moving out.

NOTES

....

....

....

....

....

....

....

....

....

EVER-CHANGING EARTH

Scientists found that ocean-floor rocks were younger than the rocks of the continents. In addition, they found that the ocean-floor rocks farther from the mid-ocean ridges were older than those close to the ridges. This suggested that rocks were forming at the ridges and then moving sideways, away from the ridges.

Scientists proposed a theory of ocean-floor spreading, proposing that the ocean floor was spreading sideways, away from the mid-ocean ridges. In this process, new ocean floor is constantly being formed, and the floor on either side of the ridge is constantly pushed sideways. This theory explained the missing piece from Wegener's theory of continental drift. The theory of ocean-floor spreading provided the forces that cause the plates to move sideways, causing the continents to "drift" apart.

But by itself, this theory could not explain all of Earth's geologic activity. Scientists wondered: If new ocean floor is constantly forming, why isn't Earth's crust getting larger? The theory of ocean-floor spreading could not explain that.

The answer was found in deep trenches discovered in the ocean floor. Trenches are crevices where the ocean floor bends downward sharply. Evidence shows that the ocean floor is plunging downward into the trenches and being pushed into the mantle, where it melts. While new rock is constantly being formed at the ridges, older rock is being destroyed in the trenches.

Plate Tectonics

By the 1960s, scientists had collected evidence that continents and ocean floors were moving. They developed a single theory—plate tectonics—to explain these processes. Continental drift and ocean-floor spreading are two key elements of plate tectonic theory. Plate tectonic theory states that Earth's outermost layer is broken into large, rigid pieces called plates. These plates float on the mantle and are all moving in different directions and at different speeds in relation to each other. Each moves from 2 cm to 10 cm per year. That is about the speed at which your fingernails grow. The plates also move around like bumper cars. They sometimes crash together, pull apart, or sideswipe each other. The zone where two plates meet is called a plate boundary.

The inspiration for plate tectonic theory began in 1912 with Alfred Wegener, who noted how the east coast of South America and the west coast of Africa looked as if they were once attached. Many others, mostly mapmakers and scientists, had noted the same similarity as early as the 1500s. However, Wegener was the first to provide fossil evidence.

NOTES

Tell students that scientists proposed a theory of ocean-floor spreading, which stated that the ocean floor was spreading away from the ridges. This theory helped to explain why the continents were drifting apart, as Wegener had proposed. Deep trenches in the ocean floor offered an explanation of what happened to older crust. Based on evidence, it appears that older crust is plunging through the trenches into the mantle, where it melts.

△ Guide

Discuss how scientists had enough evidence by the 1960s to develop a single theory to explain these processes, called plate tectonics. The theory states that Earth's outermost layer—the lithosphere—is broken into large pieces, called plates. The plates float on the mantle, and move independently of each other. They move about 2 cm to 10 cm per year.

Plate Tectonics

NOTES

Brent Dalrymple, an American geologist, took the work of Wegener and many others, and he built upon it, adding evidence based on his research of Earth's magnetic fields. The modern theory of plate tectonics was born in 1965. It was an important moment in Earth science.

The theory of plate tectonics is a powerful theory. Scientists call a theory powerful when it helps them to answer the questions "How?" and "Why?"

The theory of plate tectonics helped scientists answer questions like:

- How can fossil shells of marine animals exist at the tops of mountains or fossil fish exist in the middle of a desert?
- How did the Himalayan mountain chain form, or the Great Rift Valley in Africa?
- How can organisms from different continents have common ancestors?

The theory of plate tectonics provided geology with a grand theory of "how Earth works." Mysteries were no longer mysteries. This powerful theory has helped geologists unravel the history of Earth's changing surface and predict future changes.

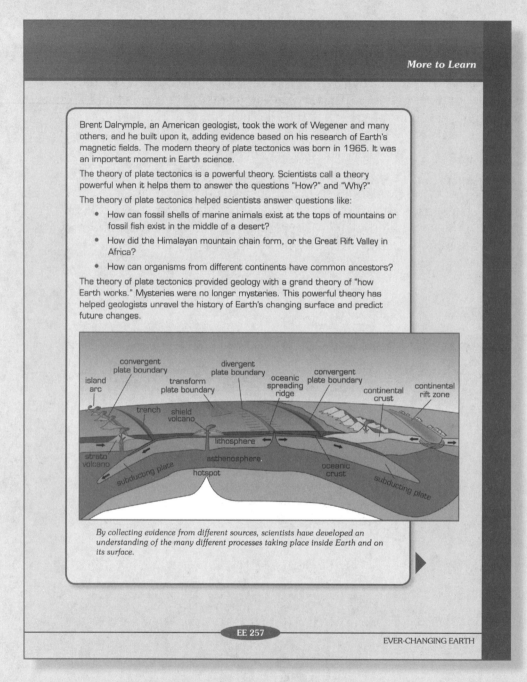

By collecting evidence from different sources, scientists have developed an understanding of the many different processes taking place inside Earth and on its surface.

EE 257

EVER-CHANGING EARTH

Point out the diagram in student text showing plates spreading apart from ridges on the ocean floor and other geologic processes.

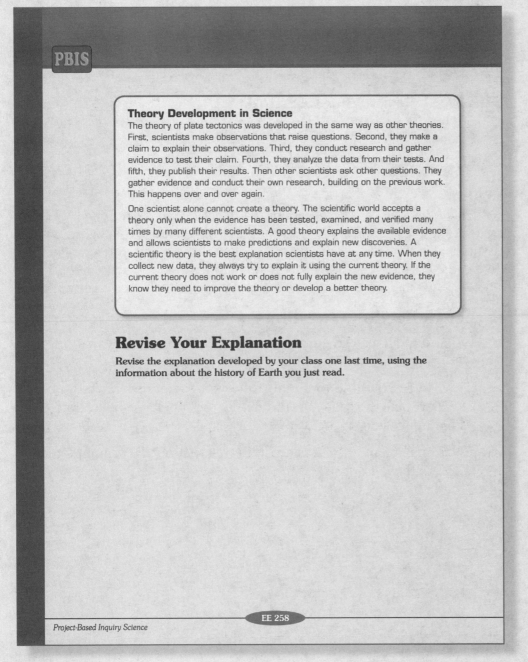

PBIS

Theory Development in Science

The theory of plate tectonics was developed in the same way as other theories. First, scientists make observations that raise questions. Second, they make a claim to explain their observations. Third, they conduct research and gather evidence to test their claim. Fourth, they analyze the data from their tests. And fifth, they publish their results. Then other scientists ask other questions. They gather evidence and conduct their own research, building on the previous work. This happens over and over again.

One scientist alone cannot create a theory. The scientific world accepts a theory only when the evidence has been tested, examined, and verified many times by many different scientists. A good theory explains the available evidence and allows scientists to make predictions and explain new discoveries. A scientific theory is the best explanation scientists have at any time. When they collect new data, they always try to explain it using the current theory. If the current theory does not work or does not fully explain the new evidence, they know they need to improve the theory or develop a better theory.

Revise Your Explanation

Revise the explanation developed by your class one last time, using the information about the history of Earth you just read.

Project-Based Inquiry Science

Theory Development in Science

△ Guide

Discuss how the development of plate tectonic theory shows how scientific theories are developed in general. First, scientists make observations and ask questions. Second, they make claims to explain their observations. Third, they gather evidence to test their claims. Fourth, they analyze the data they gathered. Fifth, they publish their results. After the results are published, other scientists ask questions, gather evidence, and analyze the evidence, building on the work.

Emphasize that creating a theory is a collaborative process. Scientists only accept a theory when the evidence has been tested, examined, and verified by many scientists.

Revise Your Explanation

10 min

The class has a discussion to revise their explanation.

Revise Your Explanation

Revise the explanation developed by your class one last time, using the information about the history of Earth you just read.

△ Guide

Now that students have learned about the development of the theory of plate tectonics, lead a class discussion to revise the class explanation. Ask students if what they just learned helps to resolve any discrepancies between the class explanations or any remaining doubts. What evidence from what they just learned can they use to support their explanation?

Teacher Reflection Questions

- What difficulties did students have revising their explanations and choosing a best explanation?

- How were you able to connect the work scientists have done to develop plate tectonics to the work students have been doing? What might you try next time?

- What management issues arose in this section? How might you address these issues next time?

Ever-Changing Earth Teacher Notes and Suggested Data

Java Trench

Important observations for class conversation from pen pal letters	Physical descriptions from pen pal letters, *My World*, and topographic maps	Earthquake data patterns in *My World*	Volcano data patterns in *My World*	Volcano patterns in relation to earthquake patterns and topography	Depth data pattern in *My World*	Volcano types and patterns from *My World* and pen pal letters
There are active volcanoes in the region.	Deep underwater trench near steep mountains.	Narrow band of earthquakes.	There are a lot of volcanoes in this region that follow the coastline of the islands in a narrow line.	There is a narrow line of volcanoes on the northeast side of a narrow band of earthquakes.	There are deep earthquakes in the east.	Many stratovolcanoes.
The trench, or valley, that runs along the ocean floor is the deepest point in the Indian Ocean.	Next to the trench are about 13,000 islands.	Most earthquakes occur under water off the southern coast of Indonesia.		The narrow band of islands and mountains are volcanic and sit next to a deep ocean trench.	Gradual pattern of deep to shallow earthquakes present.	Three active volcanoes with small eruptions spitting out ash and steam.
There are steep mountains next to trench.		Some earthquakes on the islands.		There is one pattern in the region of this Earth structure.		There have been huge eruptions.
Volcanic eruptions trigger tsunamis.		There is a clear regional pattern.				
New island forming nearby, growing with each volcanic eruption.		The Earth structure is near the plate boundary.				

Ever-Changing Earth Teacher Notes and Suggested Data

Baja Peninsula

Important observations for class conversation from pen pal letters	Physical descriptions from pen pal letters, *My World*, and topographic maps	Earthquake data patterns in *My World*	Volcano data patterns in *My World*	Volcano patterns in relation to earthquake patterns and topography	Depth data pattern in *My World*	Volcano types and patterns from *My World* and pen pal letters
Many volcanoes, a few active; there are some underwater volcanoes.	Different types of mountains.	There is a broad line of earthquakes following the coast of Mexico in the Sea of Cortez on the peninsula.	Scattered volcano pattern.	Near the peninsula there are a few volcanoes scattered on one side of the narrow line of earthquakes.	Very few deep earthquakes.	Quiet eruptions under water.
Earthquakes occur under water.	Most mountains are not jagged, they are rather low and smooth.		There are many volcanoes in this region, but they are scattered.			No real pattern.
Long and narrow peninsula that looks like it is detaching from the coast of Mexico.	Long and narrow peninsula.	Farther north, in California, the earthquakes occur the land and are more scattered.	Some are on land.	In the northern part of the region (California) the volcanoes seem scattered without a clear earthquake pattern.		
Area is mostly flat desert.		There is a different regional pattern in the north than in the south.		Mountains are volcanic but are rather flat and short.		
Mountains are not jagged, they are rather low and smooth.		The Earth structure is near the edge of a plate boundary.				

635

Ever-Changing Earth Teacher Notes and Suggested Data

Hawaiian Islands

Important observations for class conversation from pen pal letters	Physical descriptions from pen pal letters, My World, and topographic maps	Earthquake data patterns in My World	Volcano data patterns in My World	Volcano patterns in relation to earthquake patterns and topography	Depth data pattern in My World	Volcano types and patterns from My World and pen pal letters
Kilauea and Mauna Loa are two of the most active volcanoes in the world.	String of islands in the middle of the ocean.	Clustered in one spot on one island in the center of the region.	Lots of volcanoes in one spot that seem to follow the island chain, but not along their entire length.	A cluster of volcanic activity near the islands, but far away from the plate boundaries.	No deep volcanoes.	Quiet eruptions, which come out quietly or spurt like fountains.
The islands are a chain of active volcanoes.	A lot of land under the sea, with tip of mountain peeking out of the water (island).			Few earthquakes, probably related to volcanic activity.		All shield volcanoes.
Lava can move 35 mi/h.	The Hawaiian Islands are far away from the edges of the plate boundaries.			Volcanic island in the middle of a large plate.		
Hawaiian volcanoes are not dangerous. Lava usually flows slowly.	Low land elevations surrounded by deep water.					
Some vents flow directly into the ocean.						
Fifty acres of new land produced each year.						
Ninety percent of the surface of the Big Island is covered by lava less than 1000 years old.						
The Big Island moves 12 cm (5 in.) per year.						

Ever-Changing Earth Teacher Notes and Suggested Data

Iceland

Important observations for class conversation from pen pal letters	Physical descriptions from pen pal letters, *My World*, and topographic maps	Earthquake data patterns in *My World*	Volcano data patterns in *My World*	Volcano patterns in relation to earthquake patterns and topography	Depth data pattern in *My World*	Volcano types and patterns from *My World* and pen pal letters
Many active volcanoes. Volcanic activity and ice result in mixtures of water, ice, and rocks flowing rapidly. There are also hot springs and geysers. Much of the island is made up of old lava flows. New islands form quickly. Earthquakes occur often and are not always noticed. Volcanic activity makes the land move and settle.	Island sitting in a rift (formed largely by rifting). Not very high in elevation.	There is a curvy, narrow band of earthquakes. Iceland falls on this regional line of earthquakes. There are more earthquakes in the water than on land. Iceland is on the plate boundary.	On the island of Iceland there are a lot of scattered volcanoes. For the rest of the patterns, students should look beyond the Earth structure box. There is a pattern of scattered volcanoes throughout the Mid-Atlantic Ocean.	Volcanoes are clustered on the island. Throughout the rest of the region there is a scattering of few volcanoes on either side of a narrow line of earthquakes. Underwater volcanoes have been described in this region, producing new islands. Iceland is a relatively flat island that gradually grows out of the ocean floor. It sits on a rift on the ocean floor.	Very few deep earthquakes scattered within the earthquake pattern. No gradual pattern of deep to shallow.	Mostly stratovolcanoes. Many active volcanoes.

Ever-Changing Earth Teacher Notes and Suggested Data

Mount Everest

Important observations for class conversation from pen pal letters	Physical descriptions from pen pal letters, *My World*, and topographic maps	Earthquake data patterns in *My World*	Volcano data patterns in *My World*	Volcano patterns in relation to earthquake patterns and topography	Depth data pattern in *My World*	Volcano types and patterns from *My World* and pen pal letters
Many of the world's highest peaks are in the Himalayan Mountain Range (including Mt. Everest).	Many of the world's highest peaks are in the Himalayan Mountain Range.	Earthquakes are scattered throughout a very broad band on land in the middle of a mountain range.	There are very few volcanoes scattered throughout this region.	Few scattered volcanoes in a broad band of earthquakes.	Very few deep earthquakes (all in one or two places).	No pattern. None of the volcanoes fit into any of the three categories selected.
Located in the northern part of India.	Flat plains on either side of the range.	Earthquake patterns tend to go in a northwest-southeast direction.		Mount Everest is part of a large, broad mountain range.		
Top of Mount Everest was once the bottom of an ocean, as shown by fossil evidence.	Large area of very high elevation that slopes quickly.	The Earth structure is near the plate boundary.		Volcanoes and earthquakes happen on the land.		
Earthquakes and avalanches are common.	Wide mountain chain.			Not all the mountains are volcanic.		
Volcanoes are scattered throughout the area.				There seems to be one pattern in the region.		
The mountains are growing upward 3 cm/yr.						
Ground erodes quickly, so much of the range stays the same height.						
India is moving northward.						
The size of the Himalayan Mountains causes different climates and ecosystems.						

Ever-Changing Earth Teacher Notes and Suggested Data

Mount Fuji

Important observations for class conversation from pen pal letters	Physical descriptions from pen pal letters, My World, and topographic maps	Earthquake data patterns in My World	Volcano data patterns in My World	Volcano patterns in relation to earthquake patterns and topography	Depth data pattern in My World	Volcano types and patterns from My World and pen pal letters
Frequent earthquake and volcano activity.	Tall, steep, and rugged volcanic mountains sitting next to a deep trench.	One wide band of earthquakes that branches off in two directions.	There are a lot of volcanoes in this region.	A narrow line of volcanoes runs parallel to and west of a narrow band of earthquakes.	There are deep earthquakes showing a pattern of shallow (in the east) to deep (in the west).	Mostly stratovolcanoes.
Steep underwater mountains with a deep trench nearby.	Not very high elevation.	While there are earthquakes on the island and in the water, there are many more along the southeastern coast of Japan.	The volcanoes seem to follow several narrow lines.	Mount Fuji is part of a narrow chain of steep volcanic islands and mountains that rise from a deep trench.		Dormant volcanoes surround active volcanoes.
Volcanoes can be dormant near active volcanoes.	The depth of the ocean increases close to shore.	The earthquakes patterns fork off in a southern direction into the Pacific Ocean.				
Seismic activity can be devastating here because of the dense population.		The Earth structure is near the plate boundary.				
Seismic activity offshore erodes the land.						

639

Ever-Changing Earth Teacher Notes and Suggested Data

Mount Aconcagua

Important observations for class conversation from pen pal letters	Physical descriptions from pen pal letters, *My World*, and topographic maps	Earthquake data patterns in *My World*	Volcano data patterns in *My World*	Volcano patterns in relation to earthquake patterns and topography	Depth data pattern in *My World*	Volcano types and patterns from *My World* and pen pal letters
A lot of active volcanoes and big and small earthquakes.	Tall, steep, jagged mountains next to a deep trench.	Earthquakes in a narrow band along the western edge of the continent.	There are lots of volcanoes along the western coast of South America that follow the coast in a narrow band.	There is a narrow, dense line of volcanoes to the east, side. parallel to a narrow band of earthquakes.	Deep earthquakes on continental (eastern) side.	Clear north-south pattern of stratovolcanoes.
Largest earthquake ever recorded occured here.	Very high elevation with a steep drop off to the ocean on the western coast.	A broad pattern in the center region; mostly on land, though some occur in the water in a north-south direction.	In the middle of this region there seems to be little or no volcanic activity.	A narrow band of steep mountains rising from a deep ocean trench.	Gradual pattern of deep to shallow earthquakes present.	Explosive, active volcanoes.
Largest mountain range in the world and the highest peak in the Western Hemisphere.		One clear pattern along coast. There is one regional pattern.		There seems to be one pattern along the coast of South America.		
There is a deep trench next to high mountains where they meet the ocean.		The earthquakes happen throughout the Andes Mountain range.				
The Earth structure is responsible for diverse climate, vegetation, and ecosystems.		The Earth structure is near the plate boundary.				
The volcanoes cause mudflows.						

Ever-Changing Earth Teacher Notes and Suggested Data

Mount Popocatépetl

Important observations for class conversation from pen pal letters	Physical descriptions from pen pal letters, My World, and topographic maps	Earthquake data patterns in My World	Volcano data patterns in My World	Volcano patterns in relation to earthquake patterns and topography	Depth data pattern in My World	Volcano types and patterns from My World and pen pal letters
Mount Popo is currently active and erupts steam frequently. The last big eruption was in the ninth century. Only 20 minor eruptions have been recorded since. Activity affects many people in surrounding areas.	A lot of mountains with steep slopes next to a flat plain. Snow-capped mountain, and peak is 5000 m above sea level. Large crater in mountain.	Narrow band of earthquakes in a west to southeast direction over the whole region. Most of the earthquakes in the narrow band are underwater along the coast next to the land. There are several scattered earthquakes radiating from the pattern. Mount Popo is located near the plate boundary.	Near Mt. Popo there seems to be a scattering of volcanoes in an east-west direction. In the southern end of the region there is a narrow line of volcanoes that seem to follow the coast.	In the northern region, there seems to be a scattering of volcanoes parallel, but not right next to, a narrow band of earthquakes. In the south, there is a narrow line of volcanoes to the northeast of a dense, narrow band of earthquakes. There are a lot of steep volcanic mountains next to a flat plain in the north.	Earthquakes show a progression of shallow to deep approaching the continental side.	Many stratovolcanoes along coast. Mount Popo has huge eruptions.

Ever-Changing Earth Teacher Notes and Suggested Data

Mount Kilimanjaro

Important observations for class conversations from pen pal letters	Physical descriptions from pen pal letters, *My World*, and topographic maps	Earthquake data patterns in *My World*	Volcano data patterns in *My World*	Volcano patterns in relation to earthquake patterns and topography	Depth data pattern in *My World*	Volcano types and patterns from *My World* and pen pal letters
Mount Kilimanjaro is a volcanic mountain, but no historical reports of volcanic activity have been reported.	Mount Kilimanjaro is surrounded by plains of earthquakes in the northeast corner of the Earth structure box.	There is a narrow line of earthquakes in the northeast corner of the Earth structure box.	The volcanoes seem to be scattered in a narrow band with a line of volcanic activity running through it.	There is a narrow line of volcanoes with a scattering of earthquakes.	No deep earthquakes.	Small cluster of shield volcanoes.
There are many volcanoes in the African Rift Valley.	Mount Kilimanjaro has a gradual slope and is easy to climb.	There seems to be very few scattered earthquakes in the region of Mount Kilimanjaro.		This narrow line of volcanic mountains is fairly gradual in elevation change and mostly on land.		Subtle chain of stratovolcanoes from north to south.
Earthquakes happen often.	The African Rift Valley is splitting apart and cracking.	The Earth structure is located near the plate boundary.				Many more volcanoes do not fall into one of the three listed types.
The African Rift Valley has a lot of lakes that are warm and salty because of the geologic activity underneath them.	The African Rift Valley is home to a lot of lakes.					No recorded history of Mount Kilimanjaro erupting.

Blackline Masters

Ever-Changing Earth Blackline Masters

* Number indicates Learning Set.section.sequence within section

Name: _____ Date: _____

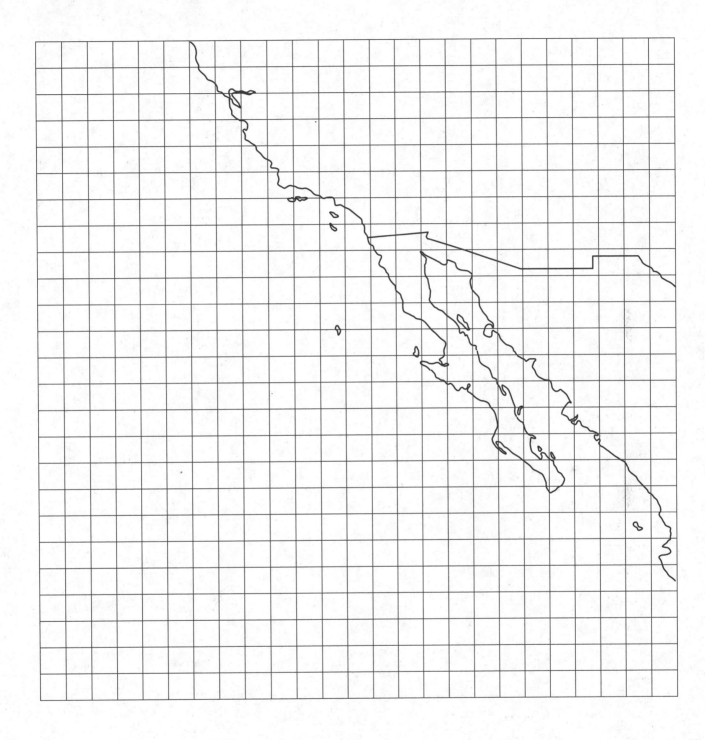

Name: _____ Date: _____

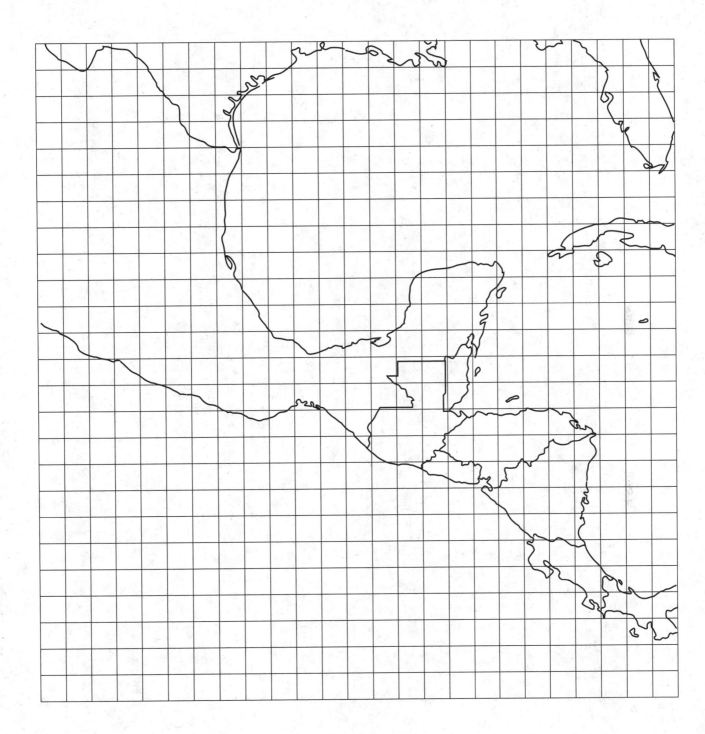

Name: _____   Date: _____

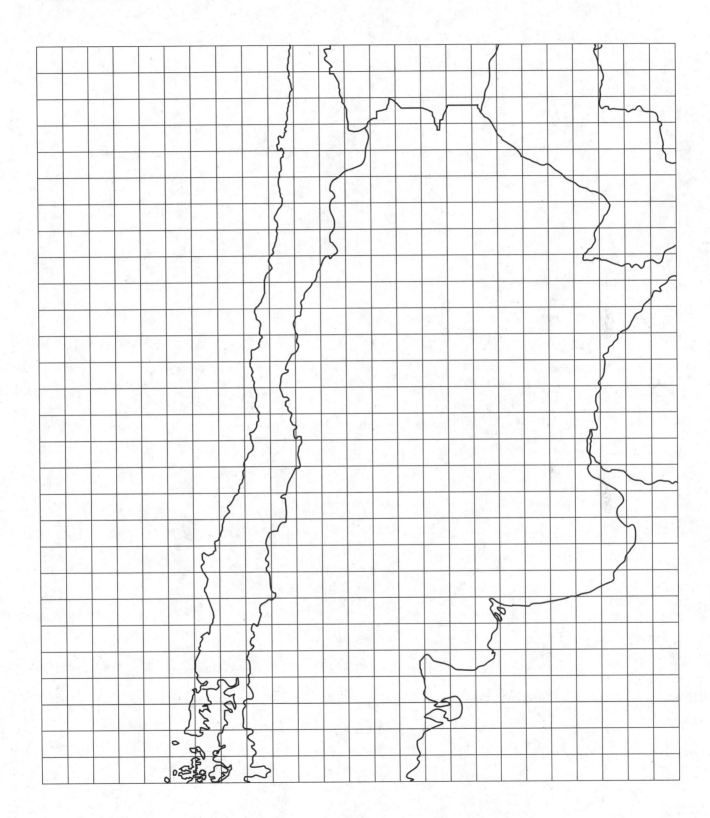

Name: _____   Date: _____

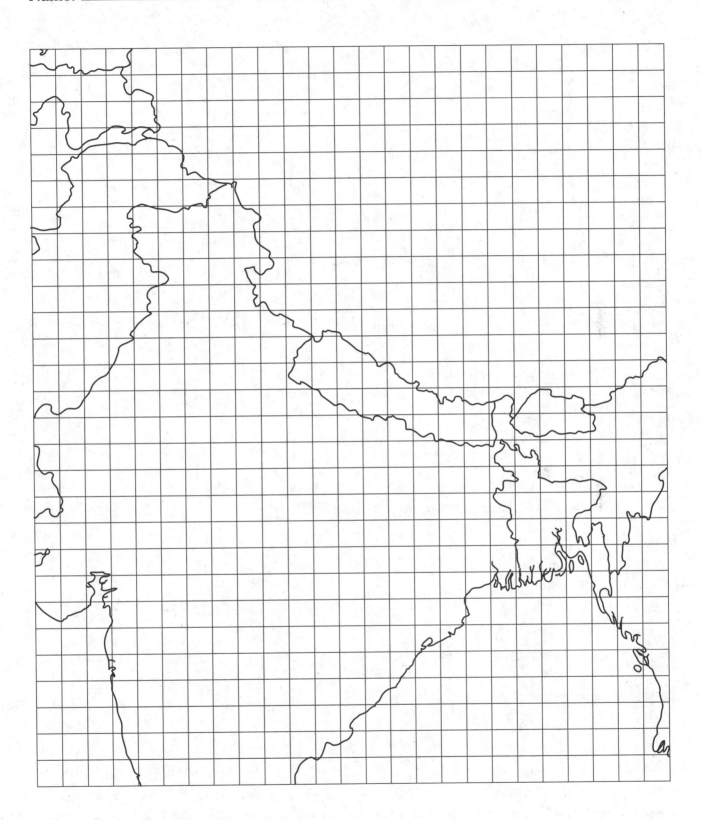

Name: _____ Date: _____

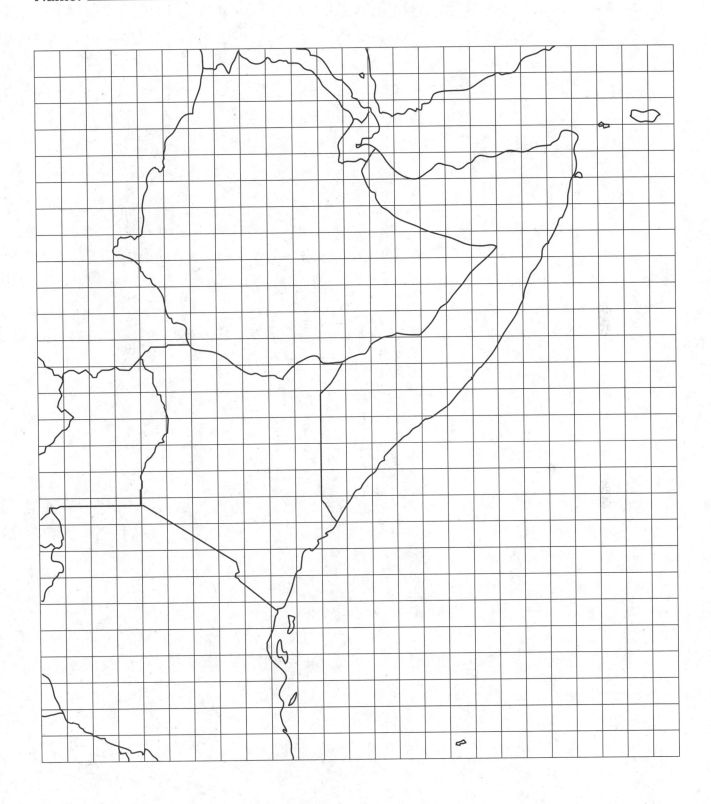

Name: _____ Date: _____

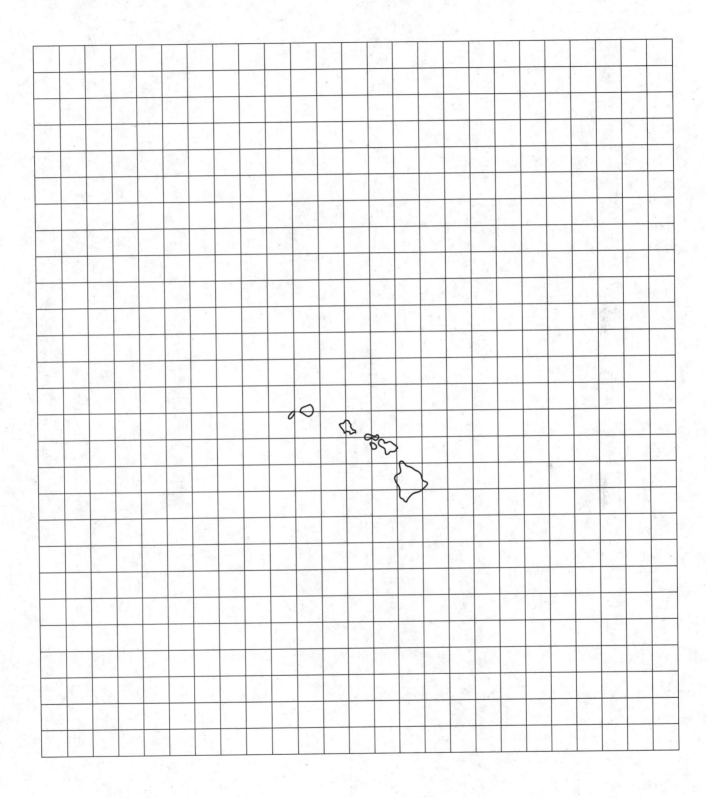

Name: _____   **Date:** _____

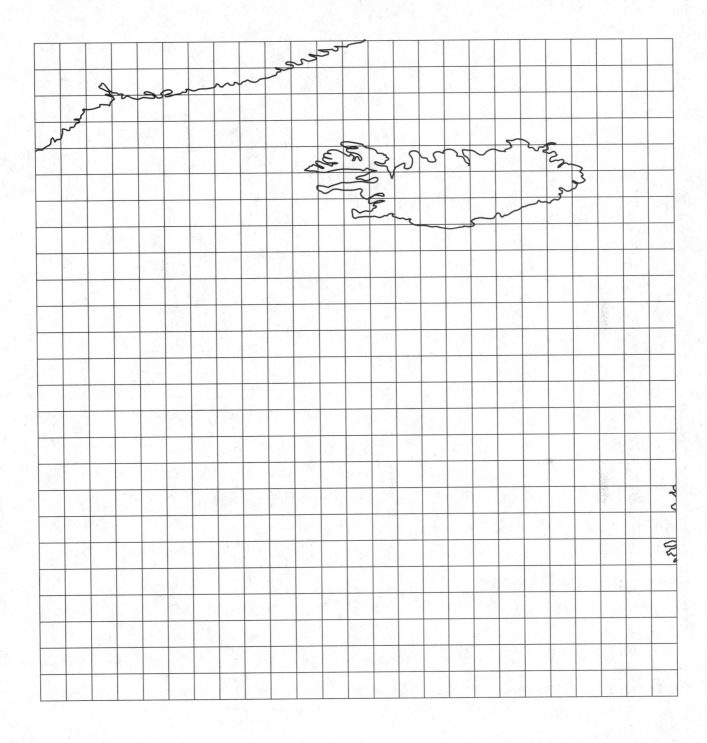

Name: _____   **Date:** _____

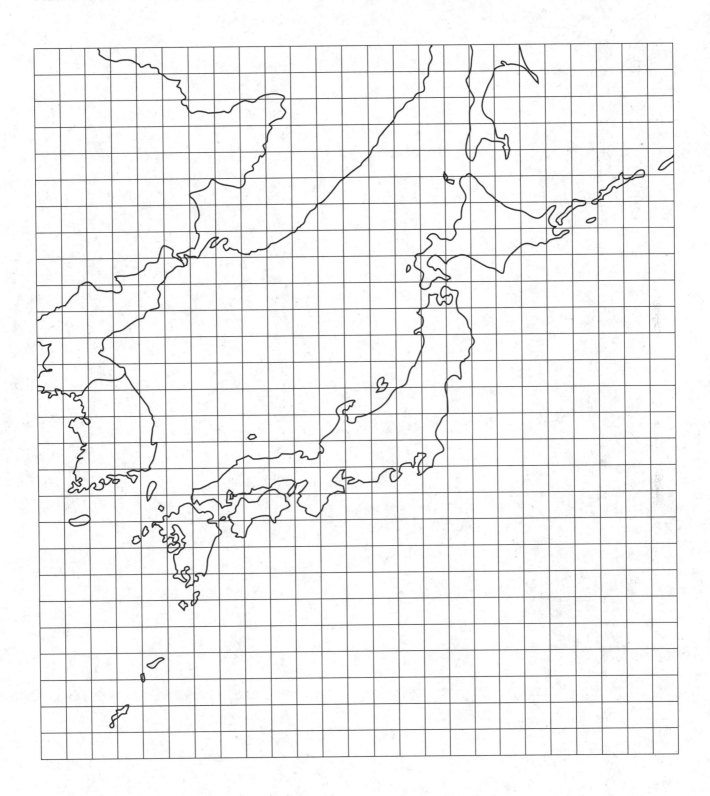

Name: _____   Date: _____

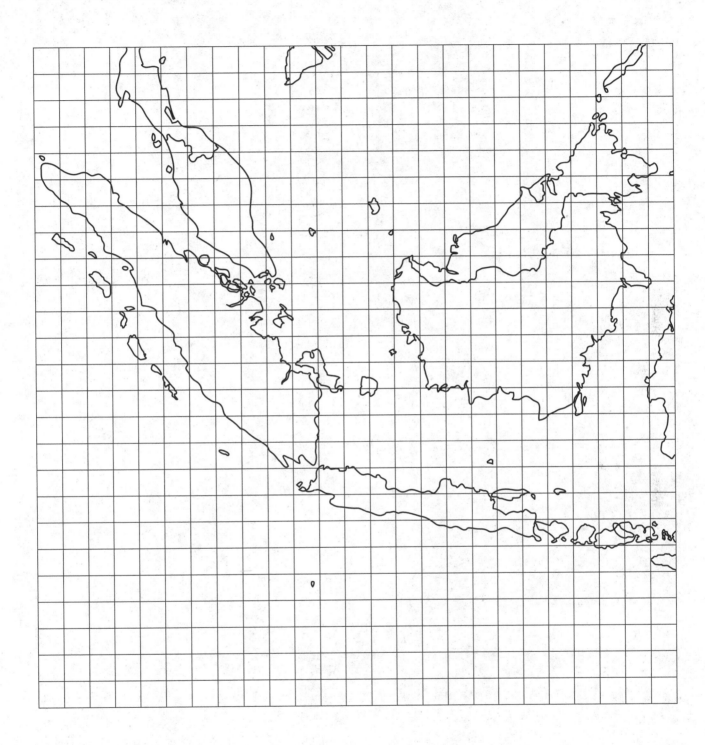

Name: _____ **Date:** _____

Label the horizontal and vertical axes and sketch the profile line in the grid below.

Three-page Map 1

1.2.1/3.5.1/3.6.1/3.7.1
5.1.1/5.4.1/6.3.1

Name: _____ **Date:** _____

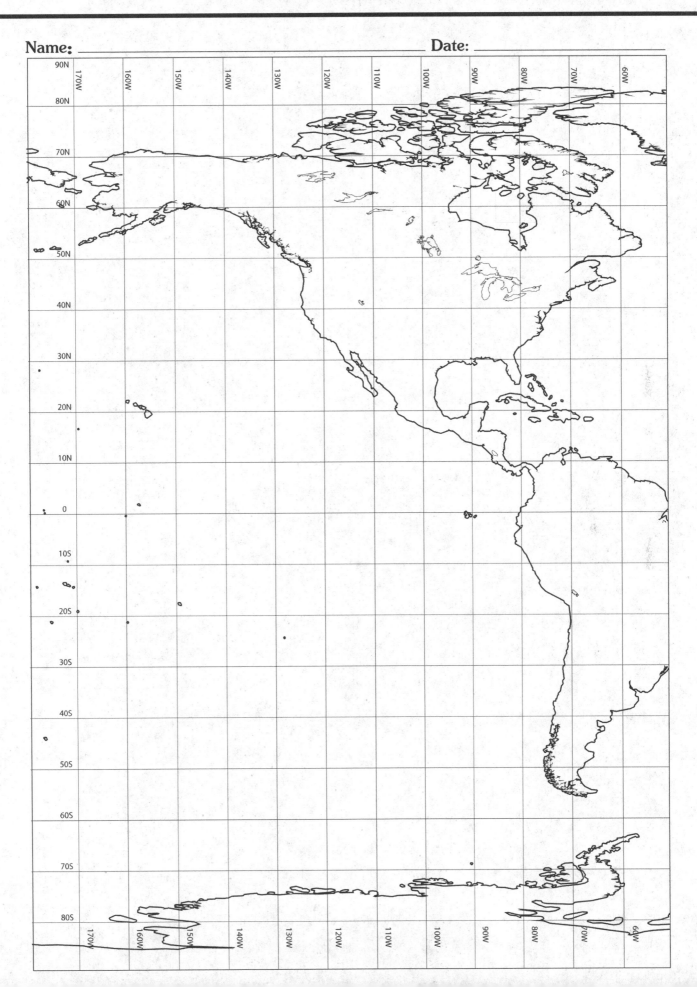

1.2.1/3.5.1/3.6.1/3.7.1
5.1.1/5.4.1/6.3.1

Name: _____ Date: _____

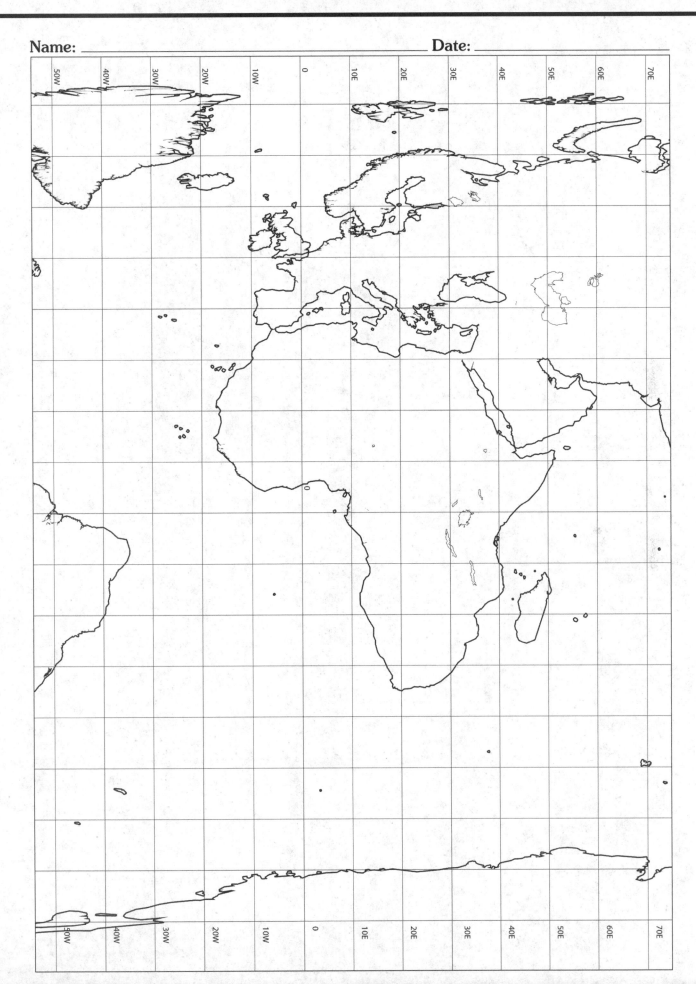

Name: _____ **Date:** _____

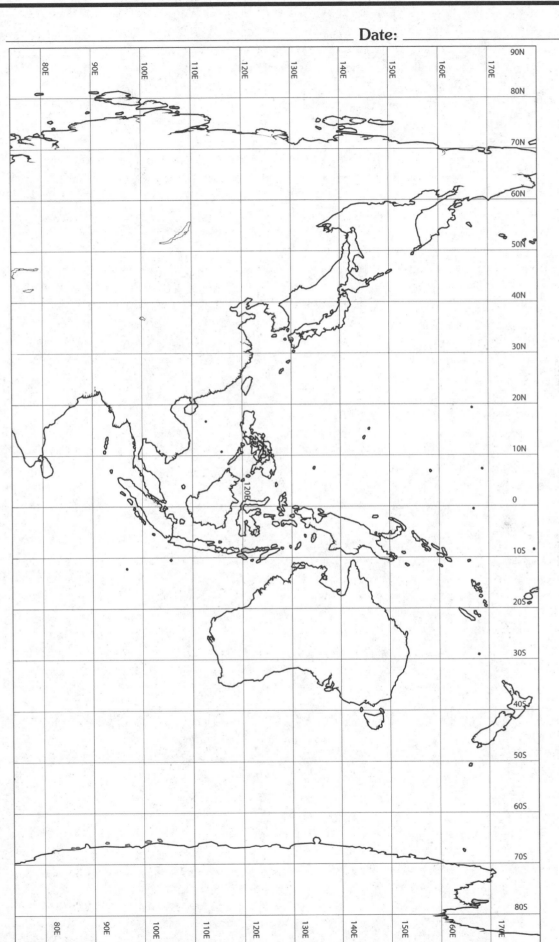

Name: _____   **Date:** _____

Tests	Observations	Inferences

What is inside the box?	Evidence

Methods	Knowledge

Name: _____ **Date:** _____

List the liquids from most dense to least dense:

Draw your predicted order and final order in the columns below.

My predicted order	My group's predicted order	Final order

Name: _____ **Date:** _____

Record your observations from the plate interaction simulation.

Interactions Between Clay Plates	Observations— What happens at the edges of each block when they interact?	Data Analysis— What geologic activity might this interaction represent?	Communicate— What have you learned from others?
Plates move toward each other			
Plates continue moving toward each other			
Plates in contact slide past each other			
One plate is pulled from two sides			
Two plates are pulled away from each other			

Name: _____ **Date:** _____

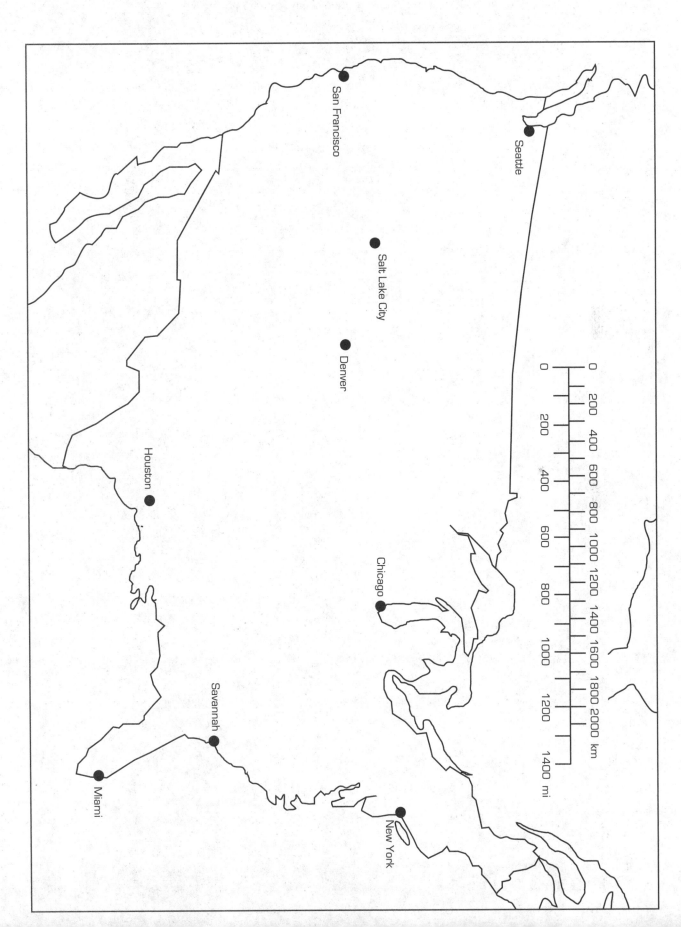

Name: _____ **Date:** _____

Use this page to explain the lesson of your recent investigations.

Write a brief summary of the results from your investigation. You will use this summary to help you write your Explanation.

Claim – a statement of what you understand or a conclusion that you have reached from an investigation or a set of investigations.

Evidence – data collected during investigations and trends in that data.

Science knowledge – knowledge about how things work. You may have learned this through reading, talking to an expert, discussion, or other experiences.

Write your Explanation using the *Claim*, *Evidence*, and *Science knowledge*.

Name: _____ **Date:** _____

Draw a diagram of the movement of water in the small jar and the large jar.

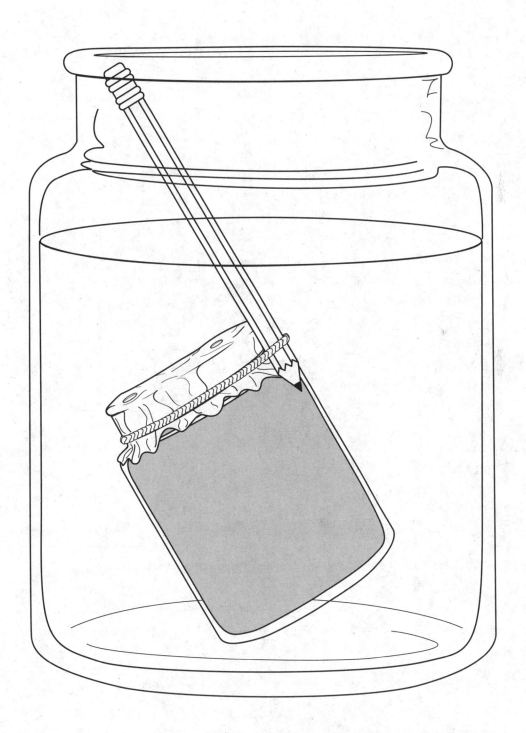

Name: _____ **Date:** _____

Fill in the columns with information about volcano types. Use the last column to fill in information about your region.

	Shield Volcanoes	Stratovolcanoes	Cinder Cone Volcanoes	Volcanoes in my region
Common shape				
Type of eruption				
Materials that are ejected				
How the volcanoes form				
Where the volcanoes form				
Other information				
Location in our region				
Questions				

Name: _____ **Date:** _____

Fill in the chart based on your observations of the animations.

	Animation 1: Plates move apart	Animation 2: Plates come together (continental-continental crust)	Animation 3: Plates come together (oceanic-continental crust)	Animation 4: Plates slide past each other
How the plates move				
Action at the edges				
Type of crust				
How magma reaches the surface				

Name: _____ Date: _____

Cut out the cards and decide the sequence of the animations. Then color, label, and assemble your flip books.

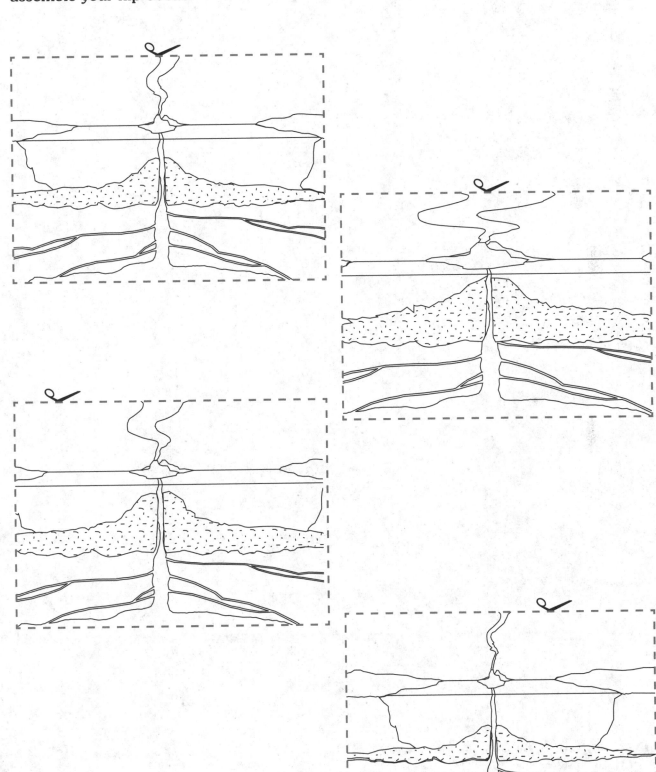

Plate Interaction Flip Book:
Continental-Continental Convergent Plate Boundary

Name: _____ Date: _____

Cut out the cards and decide the sequence of the animations. Then color, label, and assemble your flip books.

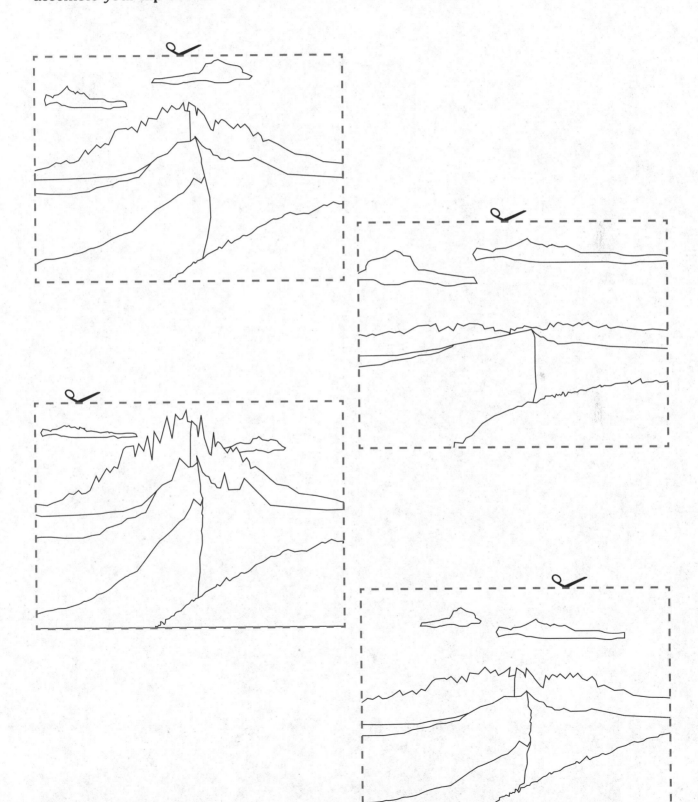

Name: _____ Date: _____

Cut out the cards and decide the sequence of the animations. Then color, label, and assemble your flip books.

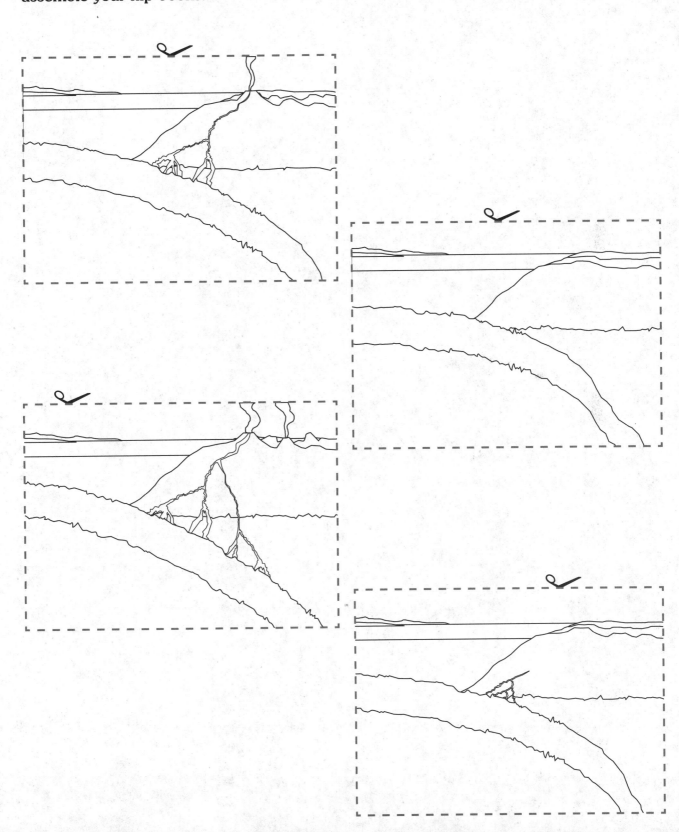

Name: _____   Date: _____

Cut out the cards and decide the sequence of the animations. Then color, label, and
assemble your flip books.

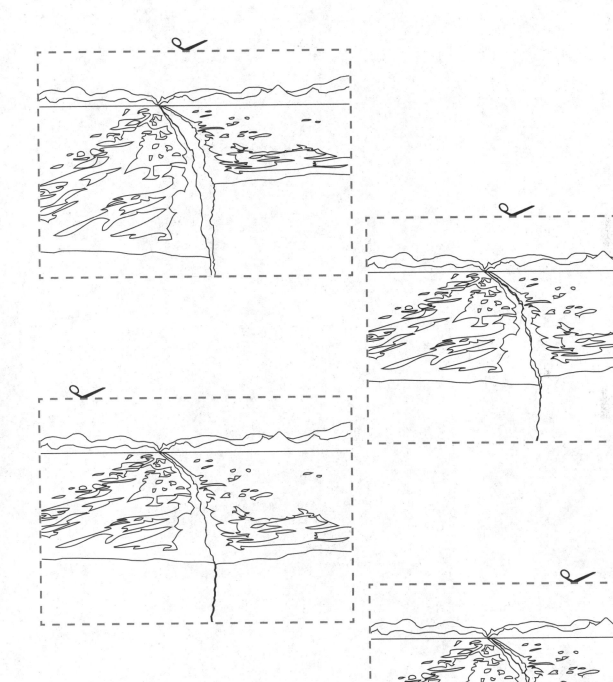

Name: _____ **Date:** _____

Fill in the table below with information from your reading about boundaries and zones.

	Convergent Boundary: Subduction Zone	Convergent Boundary: Buckling Zone	Divergent Boundary: Rift Zone	Transform Boundary
How the plates move				
Typical earthquake and volcano patterns				
Resulting topography				
Regions with plate boundary zones that match these plate movements				

Name: _____ Date: _____

What do I know about my region?				
What do we think we know?	**What do we need to investigate?**	**What are we learning?**	**What is our evidence?**	**What does it mean for the challenge or question?**

Project Board

What do we think we know?	What do we need to investigate?	What are we learning?	What is our evidence?	What does it mean for the challenge or question?

IT'S ABOUT TIME®

HERFF JONES EDUCATION DIVISION

84 Business Park Drive, Armonk, NY 10504
Phone (914) 273-2233 Fax (914) 273-2227
www.its-about-time.com

Publishing Team

President
Tom Laster

Director of Product Development
Barbara Zahm, Ph.D

Managing Editor
Maureen Grassi

Project Development Editor
Ruta Demery

Project Manager
Sarah V. Gruber

Development Editor
Francesca Casella

Assistant Editors, Student Edition
Nomi Schwartz

Assistant Editors, Teacher's Planning Guide
Kelly Crowley
Edward Denecke
Jake Gillis

Creative Director
John Nordland

Production/Studio Manager
Robert Schwalb

Production
Sean Campbell

Illustrator
Dennis Falcon

Technical Art/Photo Research
Sean Campbell
Doreen Flaherty
Roberta Fox
Michael Hortens
Marie Killoran
MaryBeth Schulze
Equipment Kit Developers
Dana Turner
Henry J. Garcia

Safety and Content Reviewers
Edward Robeck

NOTES

NOTES